Foundations
of Optimization

PRENTICE-HALL INTERNATIONAL, INC., *London*
PRENTICE-HALL OF AUSTRALIA, PTY. LTD., *Sydney*
PRENTICE-HALL OF CANADA, LTD., *Toronto*
PRENTICE-HALL OF INDIA PRIVATE LTD., *New Delhi*
PRENTICE-HALL OF JAPAN, INC., *Tokyo*

Foundations
of Optimization

DOUGLASS J. WILDE

Department of Chemical Engineering
Stanford University

CHARLES S. BEIGHTLER

Department of Mechanical Engineering
University of Texas

PRENTICE-HALL, INC.

Englewood Cliffs, N. J.

Printed in the United States of America

To Jane and Pat,
for the next generation

Preface

Scattered bits of isolated knowledge have been organized in this book into a compact, unified theory of optimization. Dealing as it does with achieving the best—maximum gain or minimum loss—in a rational manner, optimization theory naturally holds great interest for the practical professions of engineering, economics, administration, and operations research. Its development over the centuries by architects, physicists, politicians, merchants, astronomers (and astrologers), clerics, and philosophers gives optimization a colorful history and a claim to be considered a branch of mathematics, for most of its contributors are posthumously called *mathematicians*. Yet no one recognized this body of work as "optimization theory" until the middle of the twentieth century, when high-speed computers implemented forgotten procedures of the past and stimulated research on new methods. Spectacular advances followed, producing a massive, jargon-filled literature on "linear, nonlinear, and dynamic programming," as well as on the "maximum principle" and "modern control theory." At first glance, these diverse developments appear to share only their goal of achieving an optimum. But one can, having once mastered their different languages, discern many ideas common to all of them. This book abstracts the concepts underlying the various procedures, constructing from them a definitive theory of optimization. The subject can then take its place among such other theoretical fundamentals of applied science as thermodynamics, mechanics, differential equations, and probability theory. With its foundations identified and its framework strengthened, optimization theory should be able to support even greater achievements in the future.

The authors have accumulated the material in the book during five years of teaching optimization to graduate and advanced undergraduate students of engineering and operations research at Stanford University and the University of Texas. The principal mathematics required is understanding of the differential (not integral) calculus. Matrix algebra is deliberately avoided except where it can be used without confusion for abbreviation. Although, for economy of thought, many abstractions are presented, they are always illustrated with detailed industrial examples based on the authors' experience as practicing engineers and consultants. Clarity and plausibility take precedence over formal logic, although the authors have not hesitated to be rigorous when important fine points are at stake or when an informal treatment would consume too much space. The material takes between three and six semester hours to cover, depending on the preparation and quality of the professor and students. Rather than devote a separate course to optimization, a faculty may prefer to introduce various aspects of it into existing design and analysis courses, using the book for reference rather than as a text.

Readers already expert in optimization will notice several concepts developed here for the first time. The "constrained derivatives" and a novel definition of states and decisions are the key ideas unifying the theory. They lead to improved ways of handling constrained optimum-seeking problems and give novel conditions for nonconvex programming. The generalization of geometric programming, itself a very new topic, has not even appeared in the literature as we go to press. This accomplishment of Passy's, as well as Avriel's block search method, come almost directly from their Ph.D dissertations. In addition to this original material, many results are assembled here for the first time in book form. Among these are several optimum-seeking methods, the use of functional diagrams in nonserial systems, and idealized industrial examples of sensitivity analysis, the decomposition principle, and automatic control.

Besides describing quantitative technical advances, the book tries to distill qualitative guides for making decisions in the sort of ill-defined, hurried situation occurring so often in practice. The authors have also attempted to place the subject in historical perspective in order to help the reader understand the motives and accomplishments of the pioneers of optimization. To this end each chapter has its own bibliography, giving as far as possible the original sources cited in the text.

Over the half decade that the ideas for this book have been germinating and maturing, the authors have been influenced by many colleagues, among them R. Aris, R. J. Buehler, E. D. Crandall, A. Harkins, F. Horn, L. G.

Mitten, G. M. Nemhauser, D. F. Rudd, M. E. Thomas, and C. F. Wood. The U.S. National Science Foundation has supported, not only research upon which some of the results are based, but also a course on optimization theory for chemical engineering professors in August, 1965. The participants were excellent critics for the preliminary edition. To all these people and institutions the authors offer their sincere gratitude.

DOUGLASS J. WILDE
CHARLES S. BEIGHTLER

Contents

4. Polynomial Inequalities : Geometric Programming   99

5. Linear Inequalities and Sensitivity Analysis   134

6. Direct Elimination   215

7. Direct Climbing

8. Partial Optimization of Multistage Systems

9. Optimal Control by Policy Improvement: The Optimum Principle

Optimization and Optimism

1

The aim of princes and philosophers is to improve.

GOTTFRIED WILHELM LEIBNIZ, APRIL, 1702

Man's longing for perfection finds expression in the theory of *optimization*. It studies how to describe and attain what is Best, once one knows how to measure and alter what is Good or Bad. Normally, one wishes the most, or *maximum*, good and the least, or *minimum*, bad. The word *optimum*, meaning "best," is synonymous with "most" or "maximum" in the former case, and with "least" or "minimum" in the latter. *Optimum* has become a technical term connoting quantitative measurement and mathematical analysis, whereas "best" remains a less precise word more suitable for everyday affairs. The technical verb *optimize*, a stronger word than "improve," means to achieve the optimum, and *optimization* refers to the act of optimizing. Thus *optimization theory* encompasses the quantitative study of optima and methods for finding them.

This book is intended to introduce the theory of optimization to students of engineering, economics, and administration, as well as of the physical, mathematical, and social sciences, for many of the "princes and philosophers" of our times will be selected from among them. Since optimization involves finding the best way to do things, it has obvious applications in the practical world of production, trade, and politics, where sometimes small changes in efficiency spell the difference between success and failure.

1

Although many phases of optimization theory have been known to mathematicians for centuries, the tedious and voluminous computations required prevented their practical application. The development of rapid, inexpensive, automatic computers in the middle of the twentieth century has not only made these older methods attractive, but also encouraged much new research on optimization. This book surveys these diverse developments, old and new, and tries to unify them into a single cohesive theory.

There is, however, more to optimization theory than a set of numerical recipes for finding optima. By studying various optimization techniques, each suitable for different quantitative, if idealized, situations, one often discerns fairly general decision rules appropriate to problems not entirely mathematically describable. This can develop decisiveness through skill in recognizing the proper form of an optimal solution even when a problem is not completely formulated in mathematical terms. It can also nurture appreciation of the value of the information needed to describe a system well enough for it to be optimized. Even when the path to the ideal optimum is blocked or obscured, optimization theory often shows how existing conditions can be improved. And this is "the aim of princes and philosophers," or in modern language, of executives and their advisors.

This introductory chapter discusses, in nonmathematical language, the role of optimization theory both in synthesis—design and decision making, and in analysis—understanding how the world behaves. Citing successful applications of optimization to such varied endeavors as city planning, statistics, optics, mechanics, astronomy, economics, and chemistry suggests its possibilities in formulating new decision rules and natural laws. As a matter of historical interest, the mutual influence of optimization and the philosopher-mathematician Leibniz is recounted. In closing the chapter with Voltaire's witty demolition of Leibniz's "philosophical optimism," we expose the limitations of optimization theory while emphasizing its legitimate unrealized potentialities.

1-01 Synthesis: Optimal Design and Decision

Today many important decisions are made by choosing a quantitative measure of effectiveness and then optimizing it. Deciding how to design, build, regulate, or operate a physical or economic system ideally involves three steps: First, one should know, accurately and quantitatively, how the system variables interact. Second, one needs a single measure of system effectiveness expressible in terms of the system variables. Finally, one should choose those values of the system variables yielding optimum effectiveness. Thus optimization and choice are closely related.

The first step, knowledge of the system, is of paramount importance, for it is here that the decision maker brings to bear his professional skill and training as an engineer or operations analyst. There is little point in optimizing a model which does not describe what is truly happening in the system. Hence most of the effort expended on an "optimization" study will in practice be devoted to understanding the system and describing it quantitatively in terms of tables, graphs, computer programs, or mathematical equations. It seems better, therefore, to add optimization theory to professional training in existing disciplines than to develop optimization specialists unable to comprehend the systems to be optimized. Optimization theory must reinforce, rather than supplant, the present professions.

Since the second step, finding a measure of system effectiveness, often involves value judgment, it is usually either trivially simple or practically impossible to accomplish. In many physical and economic systems, the measure is obviously profit, cost, or efficiency, but a social or political system may have such conflicting goals that optimization cannot be carried out at all. Even when the type of measure is clear, it is not always easy to express its quantitative dependence on the system variables. Yet one must try to obtain this information if the fruits of optimization are to be tasted, and one advantage of optimization studies is their way of making economic information valuable enough to be gathered. It is not easy for professionals to agree on a unique measure of effectiveness, but in the words of Confucius, "Those whose courses are different cannot lay plans for one another."

Only upon finishing the first two steps, requiring knowledge and value judgment, can one proceed to apply the theory developed in this book. Relative to the total effort needed to achieve a rational decision, the final optimization step often requires little extra work when properly done. Optimization is decisive because it narrows down the possible choices to one—the best one. Moreover it often yields information about the sensitivity of optimum conditions to fluctuations and uncertainties in the original system description. For these reasons no rational decision-making process is really complete without optimization.

Let us consider examples of the three-step decision-making process just described. The earliest and most poetic is given by Virgil, whose legendary Queen Dido procured for the founding of Carthage the largest area of land that could be surrounded by the hide of a bull. From the hide she made a rope which she arranged in a semicircle with the ends against the sea. Her queenly intuition told her that this half circle had the largest possible area for the perimeter given, a fact conjectured by Archimedes (287–212 B.C.) but not proved for over two millennia. Many ancient cities are in fact circular, probably to minimize the length of the city walls needed to enclose the city's fixed area.

A famous decision problem of the late Renaissance was to design the *brachistochrone* (Greek for "shortest time"), a slide down which a frictionless object would slip in the least possible time. Galileo guessed that it should be a circular arc, but here unaided intuition failed, and Johann Bernoulli eventually proved it to be cycloidal (1694).

More recent examples of using optimization to make decisions involve invention of plausible or mathematically convenient measures of effectiveness. Statisticians fit curves to experimental data by Gauss' "method of least squares" in which one minimizes the sum of the squared deviations between curve and data. Wiener's extension of this idea is used by control engineers to design control systems and electronic filters which minimize the time integral of the squared error. Engineers and economists commonly employ minimum cost or maximum profit as decision-making criteria, and it is to such problems that this book principally addresses itself.

1-02 Philosophical Optimism: The Best of All
Possible Worlds

In 1710 Leibniz coined the word "optimum" in his *Theodicy: Essays on the Goodness of God, the Freedom of Man, and the Origin of Evil.* Although his theological and metaphysical conclusions are not appropriate subjects for discussion here, his line of reasoning illustrates well the role of optimization in both synthesis and analysis. Leibniz, who continually sought philosophical truths through mathematics, speculated on the nature of the world and on its creation, or in our words, its *synthesis.* He writes:

> ... there is an infinitude of possible worlds, among which God must needs have chosen the best, since he does nothing without acting in accordance with supreme wisdom. Now this supreme wisdom, united to a goodness that is no less infinite, cannot but have chosen the best ....
> As in mathematics, when there is no maximum or minimum, everything is done equally or ... nothing at all is done: so it may be said ... that if there were not the best (*optimum*) among all possible worlds, God would not have produced any.

Thus does Leibniz draw his conclusions from his premises, following the three steps given in the preceding section for making rational decisions. For the first step, knowledge, he postulates infinite wisdom; for the second, value judgment, he assumes infinite goodness. The optimization step calls for exhaustive evaluation of all possibilities, a procedure made plausible, if intellectually uninteresting, by the premise of infinite wisdom. Leibniz reduced his analysis of the nature of the world to a study of how it might have been synthesized, a strategy employed, as we shall see, by many later scientists in their studies of nature and man. Notice that he felt it necessary to attempt to prove the existence of an optimum. In modern optimization theory an existence proof is also sometimes essential. We see then in Leibniz's theological speculations the rudiments of decision theory, a description of phenomena in terms of an optimum principle and an existence proof. These patterns will be found throughout this exposition of optimization theory.

The cheerful doctrine that we live in the best of all possible worlds became known as *philosophical optimism*, its adherents being called *Optimists*. They perverted Leibniz's ideas into an excuse for impotent fatalism, since it seemed to them a waste of time to try to improve that which was already optimum. Voltaire, not at all satisfied with the state of the eighteenth-century world, lampooned them so successfully in *Candide* that philosophical optimism did not live to see the French Revolution. But the effect of Leibniz's point of view on the scientists of his day was powerful, as shown in the next section, where it is seen reflected in elegant formulations of natural laws and economic principles.

1-03 Analysis: Optimum Principles

The renowned mathematician Leonhard Euler (1707–1783) appears to have been a philosophical optimist, having written: "Since the fabric of the world is the most perfect and was established by the wisest Creator, nothing happens in this world in which some reason of maximum or minimum would not come to light." Such a sweeping generalization is difficult to accept, even from so great an authority as Euler. Yet this idea has produced many strikingly simple formulations of certain complex laws of nature.

In attempting to use optimization theory for analyzing natural behavior, one reverses the order of the three steps for rational decision making. Knowledge about a system is deduced by assuming it behaves so as to optimize some given measure of effectiveness. Thus the system behavior is completely specified by identifying the criterion of effectiveness and applying optimization theory to it. This approach is known as describing nature in terms of an *optimum principle*.

The earliest optimum principles concerned the behavior of light. Around 100 B.C., Heron of Alexandria asserted that light travels between two points by the shortest path. This minimum distance principle leads to two experimentally verifiable facts: first, that light rays are straight lines unless they are reflected or refracted; second, that rays leave a reflecting surface at the same angle they strike it. The more general principle of Fermat (1657), that light travels between two points in the least time rather than least distance, generates Snell's refraction law without contradicting Heron's principle.

It was in the heyday of philosophical optimism that laws of mechanics were first formulated in terms of minimum principles. Maupertuis' least-action principle, strongly defended by Euler, led Lagrange to invent the "kinetic potential." Even after the demise of Optimism, Gauss (1829) stated a "principle of least restraint" from which could be deduced the equality of internal to external forces in statics.

Light and mechanics were brought together by a single minimum principle conceived by W. R. Hamilton, who was, appropriately, the Astronomer Royal of Ireland (1834,5). From Hamilton's single principle could be obtained, by optimization, all the optical and mechanical laws then known. It remains one of the foundations of wave mechanics (Schrödinger, 1926) and relativity (Einstein, 1916).

Many laws of chemistry and thermodynamics are summarized compactly by saying that a system in equilibrium has minimum "free energy" (Gibbs 1875–78). But efforts to find optimum principles have not been confined entirely to the exact sciences. Adam Smith tried to explain complex economic phenomena of eighteenth-century England in terms of the "economic man," who always acts to maximize his personal profit (1776).

Whether or not it is generally correct, Euler's optimistic view of the world motivated his invention (1744), development, and naming (1766) of that branch of optimization theory known as the *calculus of variations*. He would no doubt be pleased to learn of the recently developed optimum principle, described in Chapters 8 and 9, for solving such variational problems (Bellman; Pontryagin, Boltyanski, Gamkrelidze, and Mischenko). Thus has optimization theory contributed to our understanding, not only of man and nature, but even of optimization theory itself.

1-04 Maxims

From Aesop to George Ade, men have deduced rules for conducting their affairs from fables and parables. These stories, abstractions of the real world, strip away mundane details in order to focus attention on the situation under study. At the end of each fable is a moral, a short summary of the lesson to be learned. Although the moral may not always be valid when taken out of context, recollection of the fable helps one remember the qualifications placed on the conclusions.

In a sense the problems studied in this book are mathematical fables, being simplified abstractions of real situations. Although these problems are principally intended to illustrate optimization techniques, one cannot help drawing more general conclusions from the results. In fact, one reason for studying optimization theory is the insight it gives into how one should react to certain circumstances. It would be pertinent, therefore, to conclude each fable with a moral, or more appropriately, a *maxim*, since this word means "the most important sentence" (Webster).

But the authors, being engineers rather than poets or philosophers, have not always been able to discern the maxims in the text, much less phrase them in suitable language. Since the mathematical variables populating these fables do not lend themselves to imagery as well as Aesop's talking animals, we have been forced to draw on the existing literature for our maxims. This has not always been successful, for the precision and power of mathematics permit analysis of situations far more complicated than is possible by qualitative methods. The reader would be wise then to look for maxims where we may not have noticed them, and to improve upon those we have chosen. Optimization still awaits its Poor Richard.

1-05 Candide : Optimism Lost

Philosophical optimism was so badly distorted by the followers of Leibniz that Voltaire was perhaps merciful when he put it out of its misery in 1759 with his *Candide*, subtitled Optimism. Leibniz meant that people should not despair when confronted by bad luck, but should continue striving for improvement, a point of view which modern "optimists" can accept. Yet the disciples of Leibniz, while parroting his technical terms, missed his main point and settled into gloomy inaction, maintaining that although things were bad, they could not be made better.

A similar fate could overtake modern optimization theory, although for different reasons. As in the eighteenth century, some of its advocates tend not only to bury ideas in impenetrable jargon but also to use knowledge of optimization theory as an excuse for neglecting their professional training and not getting the information needed for the first two steps of the decision process. The remedies are clear: plain speech and hard work. There is, moreover, a tendency toward uncontrolled enthusiasm which leads to exaggerated claims about what particular optimization techniques can do. This, together with the use of incorrect proofs to demonstrate incorrect results, could bring upon optimization theory the same undeserved disrepute that Voltaire hung on Leibniz's philosophical optimism.

On the last page of *Candide*, Dr. Pangloss, Voltaire's caricature of a philosophical optimist, says to Candide:

> There is a chain of events in this best of all possible worlds; for if you had not been turned out of a beautiful mansion at the point of a jackboot for the love of Lady Cunegonde, and if you had not been involved in the Inquisition, and had not wandered over America on foot, and lost all those sheep you brought from Eldorado, you would not be here eating candied fruit and pistachio nuts.
>
> "That's true enough," said Candide; "but we must go and work in the garden."

Let us follow Candide's good advice and get down to cases. Perhaps then we can make some part of this "best of all possible worlds" a little better.

BIBLIOGRAPHY

Ade, George, *Fables in Slang* (Grosset and Dunlap, New York, 1899).

Aesop, *The Fables of Aesop*, by J. Jacobs (Macmillan, London, 1854).

Archimedes, cited in Cajori, p. 370.

Aris, R., *The Optimal Design of Chemical Reactors* (Academic, New York, 1961).

Ball, Walter W. Rouse, *A Short Account of the History of Mathematics* (Macmillan, London, 1888).

Bateman, H., in *A Collection of Papers in Memory of Sir William Rowan Hamilton* (*Scripta Mathematica*, New York, 1945).

Bell, E. T., *The Development of Mathematics* (McGraw-Hill, New York, 1940).

Bellman, Richard, *Dynamic Programming* (Princeton Univ. Press, Princeton, N.J., 1957).

Bernoulli, Johann, quoted in Cajori, p. 217.

Cajori, F., *A History of Mathematics* (Macmillan, New York, 1919).

Confucius, *Analects*, Book XV, chap. 31 (Legge, translator), p. 169.

Davies, Owen L., *The Design and Analysis of Industrial Experiments* (Oliver and Boyd, London, 1956).

Einstein, Albert, *Sitzungber* (Acad. d. Wissenschaften, Berlin) **42** (1916), 1111–16.

Euler, Leonhard, quoted by Polya, p. 121, *Induction and Analogy in Mathematics*.

————, *Methodus inveniendi lineas curvas maximi minimive proprietate gaudentes* (1744) cited in Cajori, p. 232.

————, (1766) cited in Cajori, p. 251.

Fermat, Pierre de, *Oeuvres* (1657) **1**, 170–73; **2**, 354, 457.

Franklin, Benjamin, *Poor Richard's Almanack* (*The Sayings of Poor Richard*) (1733–58), T. H. Russell, ed.

Galileo, *Dialogues* (1630), cited by Bell, p. 351.

Gauss, Carl Friedrich, *Werke*, **4** (Göttingen 1821), cited in Davies, p. 578.

————, (1829), cited in Bell.

Gibbs, J. Willard, "On the equilibrium of heterogenous substances," *Trans. Conn. Acad.* **3** (October, 1875–May, 1876) 108–248; (May, 1877–July, 1878) 343–524.

Hamilton, W. R., *Roy. Soc. London Trans.* (1834) 247–308, cited from Bateman and Bell, p. 348.

————, *Roy. Soc. London Trans.* (1835), pp. 95–144 cited from Bateman and Bell, p. 348.

Heilbroner, Robert L., *The Worldly Philosophers* (Simon and Schuster, New York, 1953).

Lagrange, Joseph Louis, cited by Bell, p. 347.

Legge, J., *The Chinese Classics*, Vol. 1 (Trübner and Co., London, 1861).

Leibniz, G. W., Letter to Father Bouvet (c. Apr. 1702) quoted in Wilhelm, p. 217.

————, *Theodicy: Essays on the Goodness of God, the Freedom of Man and the Origin of Evil* (1710), translated by E.M. Huggard (Yale Univ. Press, New Haven, 1952) p. 128.

Maupertuis, P. L. M., cited in Bell, p. 370.

Polya, G., *Induction and Analogy in Mathematics, I: Of Mathematics and Plausible Reasoning* (Princeton Univ. Press, Princeton, N.J., 1954).

Pontryagin, L. S., V. G. Boltyanski, R. V. Gamkrelidze, and E. F. Mischenko, *The Mathematical Theory of Optimal Processes*, K. N. Trirogoff, translator (Interscience, New York, 1962).

Schrödinger, E., *Annalen Physik* s. 4, **79**, 361–76 (1926) cited by Bateman, p. 52.

Smith, Adam, *The Wealth of Nations* (Modern Library, New York, 1937), see also Heilbroner.

Virgil, *Aeneid* I, 364–68, cited from Aris, p. 2.

Voltaire, *Candide, or Optimism* (1759) translated by John Butt (Penguin Books Ltd., Harmondsworth, Middlesex, 1947).

Wilhelm, Helmut, *Leibniz and the I-ching* (1943), pp. 205–19.

Indirect Methods: The Differential Viewpoint

2

There are many paths to the top of the mountain, but the view there is always the same.

CHINESE MAXIM, QUOTED BY H. L. MENCKEN

The maxim expresses, in allegorical speech, the business of this chapter. For "paths to the top of the mountain," read "optimization methods"; for "view," substitute "mathematics"; for "there," insert "at the optimum." Then the statement becomes, "There are many optimization methods, but the mathematics at the optimum is always the same"—clumsily prosaic, but to the point.

Whatever route a mountain climber takes, he recognizes the peak when he arrives there. Equally important, he can tell when he is not at the top and must therefore continue his climb. These simple facts, intuitively evident where mountains are concerned, have mathematical analogs which provide not only a precise description of an optimum, but also a way to unify the entire subject of optimization theory. For the feature common to almost all optimization techniques is their continual progress by successive betterment. Since a well-conceived method will not overlook any possibilities for improvement, it cannot stop before reaching the optimum, which, by definition, is

10

where further progress is impossible. This point of view exposes a strong resemblance between various methods which may at first glance appear quite different. Its unifying power permits us, in this single volume, to survey optimization in its entirety.

Our zeal for economy of thought must not, however, lead us to over-simplification. Despite strong similarities, the divers optimization schemes have many intriguing differences and special characteristics. After all, differently shaped mountains require different climbing strategies, and one must base his approach not only on the obstacles in his path, but also on the climate surrounding the mountain and on the equipment at hand. Similarly in selecting a specific optimization technique one should take account not only of the mathematical topography, with its computational glaciers, cliffs, and crevasses, but also of the intellectual climate surrounding the problem and the computing facilities available. After this chapter describes the similarities between the methods, the rest of the book will develop the differences.

The technical part of the chapter begins with a simple optimization problem involving a hypothetical manufacturing plant. As far as possible, all general concepts developed are demonstrated in concrete terms by application to this problem. Next, optima are described mathematically and distinctions made between local and global maxima, minima, suprema, and infima. After *feasibility* has been defined, a brief discussion of optimization by total enumeration clears the agenda for a survey of more efficient, and hence more interesting, methods. Ideas dating back over three centuries to Kepler and Fermat are developed for extension in future chapters to problems solved only since World War II. The unifying powers of the concepts of "state," "decision," and "constrained derivative" permit straightforward derivation of most of the optimization methods described in the rest of the book. Thus we find simple mathematical expression for the unchanging view from the mountain top, where all climbers ultimately meet.

2-01 Designing a Hypothetical Manufacturing Plant

The generalities to be developed will, whenever possible, be illustrated by applying them to a particular decision problem involving design of a factory. To prevent our bogging down in technological and computational detail, the hypothetical plant will be oversimplified to the point of fiction. Imagine it intended to produce 10^7 lb per year of a certain chemical, using the five pieces of equipment shown in Fig. 2-1: a main compressor, a chemical reactor, a separator, a recirculating compressor, and a mixer. Raw material gases are brought up to operating pressure x_1 (atmospheres), mixed with reused gas

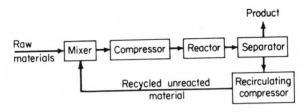

Figure 2-1. A hypothetical chemical plant.

at the same pressure, and passed through a reactor where the gases are partly converted into product. Then a separator removes the product for sale, leaving the unreacted gases to be sent back to the mixer by the recirculating compressor. The fraction converted to product in the reactor relates directly to the ratio of recirculated unreacted gas to raw material entering the process. This second process variable is called the *recycle ratio*, denoted x_2.

Now that the first step of the decision process—acquiring knowledge of the system—has been completed, it remains to develop a measure of effectiveness before optimization is possible. In this case we choose to minimize the total annual cost, including direct operating expenses, such as power cost, as well as capital expenditure amortized over the life of the process. Procedures for doing this are not obvious, and the reader interested in studying them would find Grant and Ireson's book on engineering economics valuable. Here we shall omit these important considerations and merely list, in Table 2-1, the costs as functions of the two operating variables for each piece of equipment. The *objective function*, y, to be minimized will be taken as the sum of all costs which depend on the process variables, x_1 and x_2.

$$y \equiv 1000x_1 + 4 \times 10^9 x_1^{-1} x_2^{-1} + 2.5 \times 10^5 x_2 \qquad (2\text{-}1)$$

Notice that the objective function does not include the cost of the mixer because of its independence of x_1 and x_2. Although this fixed amount of 10^4 affects the total cost, adding this quantity does not influence the optimal pressure x_1 and recycle ratio x_2, which is what we seek.

TABLE 2–1
EQUIPMENT ANNUAL COSTS FOR HYPOTHETICAL PLANT

Equipment	Annual Cost ($)
Main compressor	$1000x_1$
Mixer	10^4
Reactor	$4 \times 10^9 / x_1 x_2$
Separator	$10^5 x_2$
Recirculating compressor	$1.5 \times 10^5 x_2$

2-02 Definitions and Useful Relations

Before proceeding with the optimization, we must define precisely what we mean by it. In general the scalar *objective function*, y, depends on n real scalar *independent variables* $x_1, x_2, \ldots, x_n$, often assembled for abbreviation into an n-component column vector or point $\mathbf{x}$.

$$\mathbf{x} \equiv \begin{pmatrix} x_1 \\ x_2 \\ \cdot \\ \cdot \\ \cdot \\ x_n \end{pmatrix} = (x_1, x_2, \ldots, x_n)^T \qquad (2\text{-}2)$$

In the example, $n = 2$. Vectors are always set in **boldface** type, and the superscript T denotes transposition. When particular numbers are assigned to the components of $\mathbf{x}$ the resulting vector will sometimes be called a *policy* or a *design*. The fact that y is a function depending on $\mathbf{x}$ is expressed by writing $y\langle \mathbf{x} \rangle$. The authors have decided to deviate from standard mathematical notation, which would write $y(\mathbf{x})$ for this functional dependence, because the latter symbol is often confused with that for the *product* of y and $\mathbf{x}$.

In practice many conceivable policies are physically impossible, illegal, unsafe, or known in advance to be uneconomical. In the hypothetical chemical plant, negative values of pressure x_1 and recycle ratio x_2 are not physically possible, and let us assume that safety codes prohibit pressures higher than 2200 atm. Suppose, moreover, that industry practice rules out recycle ratios greater than 8. The remaining points, which satisfy the inequalities

$$0 \le x_1 \le 2200 \qquad (2\text{-}3)$$

$$0 \le x_2 \le 8 \qquad (2\text{-}4)$$

are said collectively to form the problem's *feasible region* $\mathscr{F}$. This terminology is applicable to all problems. When, as in this case, all inequalities also admit the possibility of strict equality, $\mathscr{F}$ is a *closed* region, since it contains all its boundary points (the line segments $(0, x_2)$, $(x_1, 0)$, $(2200, x_2)$, and $(x_1, 8)$ satisfying also Eq. (2–3) and (2–4)). If any of the inequalities are strict, which is really the situation here since absolute zero pressure is not achievable, then parts of the boundary of $\mathscr{F}$ are outside $\mathscr{F}$, and $\mathscr{F}$ is said to be *open*. For reasons that will soon be apparent, problems should be formulated with closed feasible regions whenever possible.

Consider a particular point $\mathbf{x}^{**}$ in $\mathscr{F}$ such that the value of the objective function there is less than at any other point in the region.

$$y\langle \mathbf{x}^{**} \rangle < y\langle \mathbf{x} \rangle \qquad \text{for all } \mathbf{x} \ne \mathbf{x}^{**} \text{ in } \mathscr{F} \qquad (2\text{-}5)$$

Then $y\langle\mathbf{x}^{**}\rangle$, abbreviated y^{**} (read "y-double star"), is the *minimum* of y, and $\mathbf{x}^{**}$, called the *minimizing* (or *minimal*) *policy*, is unique. There is more than one minimal policy, but still only one minimum, when (2–5) is replaced by

$$y\langle\mathbf{x}^{**}\rangle \leq y\langle\mathbf{x}\rangle \qquad \text{for all } \mathbf{x} \neq \mathbf{x}^{**} \text{ in } \mathscr{F} \tag{2-6}$$

and (2–6) may be written

$$y^{**} \equiv \min_{\mathbf{x} \in \mathscr{F}} (y\langle\mathbf{x}\rangle), \tag{2-7}$$

read "y^{**} is defined as the minimum of y for all feasible $\mathbf{x}$ ($\mathbf{x} \in \mathscr{F}$ is read '$\mathbf{x}$ is an element of $\mathscr{F}$')." When $\mathbf{x}^{**}$ is on the boundary of $\mathscr{F}$, y^{**} is called a *boundary minimum;* otherwise, it is an *interior minimum.*

There are fairly ordinary situations in which no minimum exists. For example, suppose one wishes to minimize the value of

$$y\langle x_1\rangle = 2x_1 + 3$$

where $\mathscr{F}$ is the *open* region defined by

$$0 < x_1 \leq 1$$

Then $y\langle 0\rangle < y\langle x_1\rangle$ for all x_1 in $\mathscr{F}$, but 0 itself is not in $\mathscr{F}$. Furthermore, there is no point in $\mathscr{F}$ where y is less than at every other point, for one can always find a better point by moving closer to the origin without actually reaching it.

To handle this situation, consider any point x_1^-, not necessarily in $\mathscr{F}$, which gives a value of y lower than at any point in $\mathscr{F}$.

$$y\langle x_1^-\rangle < y\langle x_1\rangle \qquad \text{for } x_1 \text{ in } \mathscr{F} \tag{2-8}$$

Such a point x_1^- is called a *lower bound* for $y\langle x_1\rangle$; let $\mathscr{F}^-$ be the set of all such lower bounds, in this case all nonpositive real numbers. Now consider the *greatest lower bound* (glb), which is the point x_1^i such that

$$y\langle x_1^i\rangle \geq y\langle x_1^-\rangle \qquad \text{for } x_1^- \text{ in } \mathscr{F}^- \tag{2-9}$$

In this example, $x_1^i = 0$, and in general $y\langle\mathbf{x}^i\rangle$ is called the *infimum* of y, written

$$y\langle\mathbf{x}^i\rangle \equiv \inf_{\mathbf{x} \in \mathscr{F}} (y\langle\mathbf{x}\rangle) \equiv y^i \tag{2-10}$$

An infimum, or greatest lower bound, always exists when y is real, even though a minimum may not (Birkhoff and MacLane, p. 90).

To avoid worry about such fine points, use a closed region, for in this case a theorem of Weierstrass guarantees the existence of a minimum if the region is bounded and the objective function continuous. Thus if $\mathscr{F}$ is closed (strict equality possible), then

$$y^{**} \equiv \min_{\mathbf{x}} (y\langle\mathbf{x}\rangle) = \inf_{\mathbf{x}} (y\langle\mathbf{x}\rangle) \equiv y^i \tag{2-11}$$

Notice that "$\mathbf{x} \in \mathscr{F}$" has been replaced by "$\mathbf{x}$" alone, which will be our practice from now on whenever it is clear that $\mathbf{x}$ must be feasible.

The *maximum* of y and the corresponding *maximizing* (or *maximal*) policy, unique or not, is defined in the same manner, except that all inequalities must be reversed. Asterisks are also used to designate these quantities, since the context of any given problem should make it clear whether maximization or minimization is desired. Thus we shall write

$$y\langle \mathbf{x}^{**} \rangle \equiv y^{**} \equiv \max_{\mathbf{x}} (y\langle \mathbf{x} \rangle)$$

in maximization problems. The *least upper bound* (lub), called the *supremum*, is the maximization analog to the infimum, and Weierstrass's theorem holds for maxima as well as for minima. To cover optimization in general, we shall call y^{**} the *optimum* and $\mathbf{x}^{**}$ the *optimal policy*, writing

$$y\langle \mathbf{x}^{**} \rangle \equiv y^{**} \equiv \operatorname*{opt}_{\mathbf{x}} (y\langle \mathbf{x} \rangle) \tag{2-12}$$

Consider now a feasible point $\mathbf{x}^*$ and the set of points $\mathbf{x}$ in a *feasible neighborhood* of $\mathbf{x}^*$. These are points satisfying not only the inequalities describing $\mathscr{F}$, but also the additional condition

$$0 < |\mathbf{x} - \mathbf{x}^*| < \epsilon \tag{2-13}$$

where

$$|\mathbf{x} - \mathbf{x}^*| \equiv \left[\sum_{j=1}^{n} (x_j - x_j^*)^2 \right]^{1/2} \tag{2-14}$$

Thus ϵ is the radius of an n-dimensional spherical open region centered at $\mathbf{x}^*$ and containing the points $\mathbf{x}$ and $\mathbf{x}^*$. The feasible neighborhood will be denoted $\mathscr{N}$. If there exists a feasible neighborhood containing $\mathbf{x}^*$ such that

$$y\langle \mathbf{x}^* \rangle \leq y \langle \mathbf{x} \rangle \qquad \text{for } x \text{ in } \mathscr{N} \tag{2-15}$$

then $y\langle \mathbf{x}^* \rangle$ is called a *local minimum* and $\mathbf{x}^*$ a *locally minimum policy*. We shall write

$$y^* \equiv y\langle \mathbf{x}^* \rangle \equiv \operatorname*{lmin}_{\mathbf{x}} (y\langle \mathbf{x} \rangle) \tag{2-16}$$

The notation "lmin" means that $\mathbf{x}$ is restricted to a feasible neighborhood of $\mathbf{x}^*$. This new notation is needed to preserve the important distinction between the minimum y^{**}, which is what we usually want, and a local minimum y^*, which by present optimization techniques is what we usually get. A minimum y^{**}, sometimes called the *global* minimum or the *minimum minimorum* (least minimum), is of course always a local minimum, but not vice versa. The concepts of local infimum, maximum, supremum, and optimum are derived in a similar manner, using the notion of feasible neighborhood. When employing existing optimization methods, one must prove (or hopefully assume) in advance that there is only one peak, or at least that one is not climbing the wrong mountain. An objective function with a unique local, and hence global, optimum is said to be *unimodal*.

Certain elementary relations between maxima and minima are of interest. If b is positive, and a arbitrary, then if $\mathbf{x}^{**}$ minimizes $y\langle\mathbf{x}\rangle$, it also minimizes $a + by\langle\mathbf{x}\rangle$, and

$$a + by\langle\mathbf{x}^{**}\rangle = \min_{\mathbf{x}} (a + by\langle\mathbf{x}\rangle) \qquad (2\text{-}17)$$

Moreover, it maximizes $a - by\langle\mathbf{x}\rangle$, and

$$a - by\langle\mathbf{x}^{**}\rangle = \max_{\mathbf{x}} (a - by\langle\mathbf{x}\rangle) \qquad (2\text{-}18)$$

Proofs, which involve manipulation of the defining inequalities, are left as exercises (Exercise 2-1). The mathematical moral is twofold: first, that additive constants and positive factors do not affect the location of the optimum; second, that minimization techniques can be used in maximization problems (and vice versa) simply by changing the sign of the objective function.

2-03 Exhaustive Enumeration

It may be that but a finite number of policies need be considered. Suppose in the hypothetical chemical plant that only designs with pressures in integral numbers of atmospheres 1, 2, . . . , 2199, 2200, and tenths of a recycle ratio 0.1, 0.2, . . . , 7.9, 8.0 are acceptable. Then there are in all (2200)(80) = 176,000 possibilities, a finite, if large, number. The method, if it can be called one, of *exhaustive enumeration*, is simply to evaluate the objective function for every case and pick out the optimum directly. Theoretically simple but practically tedious, this technique, also called informally the *brute force approach*, is appropriate only when the number of cases is small compared to the speed of the computation facilities available. Even with today's high-speed computers, one is justified in asking for better procedures than this.

2-04 The Differential Approach

Fortunately there are methods for finding a peak without mapping the entire mountain. The first inkling that there might be a better way came at the beginning of the seventeenth century, when Johannes Kepler noticed in the midst of his astronomical calculations that differences between successive values of a dependent variable, computed at equally spaced values of the independent variable, tended to vanish near an optimum. A generation later, Pierre de Fermat developed this hint into a method for finding interior optima of continuous functions of a single variable. Since our approach resembles his in some ways, it is instructive to demonstrate its practical strength and logical weakness with a simple example.

Suppose in the hypothetical chemical plant that the recycle ratio x_2 is fixed at unity, defining a new objective function y_1 of a single variable x_1.

$$y_1 \equiv 1000x_1 + 4 \times 10^9 x_1^{-1} + 2.5 \times 10^5$$

Fermat would seek the point x_1^* where the value of the objective function is the same as at a nearby point $x_1^* + \partial x_1$, where ∂x_1 is a small, and for Fermat, ill-defined, quantity known in the seventeenth century as a *virtual displacement* and in the eighteenth as a *differential*. It should be read "differential x." Equating the two values and performing the customary algebraic simplifications gives

$$y\langle x_1^* + \partial x_1 \rangle = y\langle x_1^* \rangle$$

$$1000(x_1^* + \partial x_1) + 4 \times 10^9 (x_1^* + \partial x_1)^{-1} + 2.5 \times 10^5$$

$$= 1000x_1^* + 4 \times 10^9 (x_1^*)^{-1} + 2.5 \times 10^5 \qquad (2\text{-}19)$$

$$1000(x_1^*)^2 \, \partial x_1 + 1000x_1^*(\partial x_1)^2 = 4 \times 10^9 \partial x_1$$

Here Fermat canceled a factor ∂x_1 from each side of (2–19), a permissible operation only as long as ∂x_1 is not zero.

$$1000(x_1^*)^2 + 1000x_1^*(\partial x_1) = 4 \times 10^9 \qquad (2\text{-}20)$$

His next move was completely illogical; he set the differential to zero, obtaining by accident the correct equation for the location of the optimum.

$$1000(x_1^*)^2 = 4 \times 10^9 \qquad (2\text{-}21)$$

whence

$$x_1^* = \pm\, 2000 \qquad (2\text{-}22)$$

In the hypothetical plant only the positive root is feasible, since only positive pressures are physically meaningful.

Before developing the advantages of this approach, namely that it is simple and usually gives correct answers, let us emphasize its logical inconsistencies and show how to avoid them. Fermat's method immediately aroused the suspicions of the clear-thinking Descartes, mainly because of the vagueness of its original description. The logical flaw, which remained concealed when Newton (1669) and Leibniz (1675) used differentials in their invention of the infinitesimal calculus, was finally brought to light by an Irish clergyman-philosopher with a theological ax to grind. George Berkeley, Bishop of Cloyne, was annoyed by mathematicians who had criticized certain contradictions in the religious dogma of the times. His revenge was sweet; in his *Discourse addressed to an infidel mathematician* he exposed the inconsistency in having the differential ∂x_1, assumed nonzero in the beginning of the derivation, vanish conveniently as soon as it gets in the way. Berkeley's taunt drove the eighteenth-century mathematicians to seek a rigorous basis for the calculus, but it wasn't until 1821, when Cauchy defined the concept of limit, that the contradiction was finally removed. The correct way to pass from Eq. (2–20) to Eq. (2–21) is to remark that as the differential ∂x_1 *approaches* zero, the term $1000x_1^*(\partial x_1)$ approaches zero *as a limit*.

$$\lim_{\partial x_1 \to 0} [1000x_1^*(\partial x_1)] = 0 \qquad (2\text{-}23)$$

In any rigorous demonstration this must be proved, not assumed, a task not always as easy as in this simple example.

Despite Bishop Berkeley's rebuke, arguments involving differentials— what we shall call the *differential approach*—were used with great success throughout the eighteenth century. Euler manipulated differentials with no qualms whatever, extending Fermat's method to functions of many variables, while deriving most of the formulae of modern calculus. Later (1799) Lagrange tried to put the calculus on a rigorous basis using series expansions, a project which contributed greatly to optimization theory, even though it did not achieve its original goal. This ancient, although not always honorable, differential approach will, because of its clarity and simplicity, be our guide through the maze of optimization theory. Almost all optimization methods, despite the diverse mathematics of their inventors, can be analyzed successfully from the differential point of view. By using it we decrease the amount of mathematics needed to master the subject and bring optimization theory within the understanding of anyone who has studied the differential (not even integral) calculus. This includes undergraduate students of engineering, economics, and the physical, mathematical, and social sciences, for whom this book is written. But we would be derelict in our duties if we used the differential approach blindly, unaware of its dangers. Therefore we provide references to formal proofs in the literature substantiating any results derived by manipulating differentials. And to instill a sense of caution in the reader, we shall also describe incorrect results derived by differential methods insufficiently tempered with rigor. Not even the great Lagrange was immune to subtle errors of this sort, and they are still being committed today.

2-05 The Classical Indirect Method

Optimization techniques can, for convenience, be divided into two classes: direct and indirect methods (Edelbaum). Direct methods, which start at an arbitrary point and proceed stepwise toward the peak by successive improvement, will be described later, leaving the rest of the chapter for development of the indirect methods. Fermat's classical method is indirect because it ultimately involves solving an equation rather than searching for an optimum. This works because the root of the equation is also the location of the optimum. Because they often pick out an optimum without examining any nonoptimal points, indirect methods are very effective when they can be applied.

Since Fermat's method does not generalize easily to functions of several variables, it behooves us to introduce the more advanced notion of *derivative*. In modern terminology, the *first derivative of y with respect to* x_1, designated $\partial y / \partial x_1$, is defined by

$$\frac{\partial y}{\partial x_1} \equiv \lim_{\partial x_1 \to 0} \left[\frac{y\langle x_1 + \partial x_1\rangle - y\langle x_1\rangle}{\partial x_1} \right] \quad (2\text{-}24)$$

Actually it is more common to write the derivative as dy/dx_1 when there is only one independent variable, the notation $\partial y/\partial x_1$ being reserved for multivariable situations. Here we depart from this tradition, dating back to Leibniz, in order to save the letter d for later use as a mnemonic symbol for a *decision*. In the example the first derivative, interpreted geometrically as the slope of the curve of y versus x_1, depends on x_1 and is given by

$$\frac{\partial y}{\partial x_1} = 1000 - 4 \times 10^9 x_1^{-2} \quad (2\text{-}25)$$

In 1714 the elder Johann Bernoulli remarked that the first derivative vanishes at an optimum

$$(\partial y/\partial x_1)^* = 0 \quad (2\text{-}26)$$

where the asterisk indicates that the derivative is evaluated at $x_1 = x_1^*$. This is, in the notation of the differential calculus, the observation made over a century earlier by Kepler. The reader can verify in the example that combination of Eqs. (2–25) and (2–26) gives $x_1^* = \pm 2000$, confirming Fermat's result.

When there is more than one independent variable the appropriate generalization is the set of *n first partial derivatives* $\partial y/\partial x_j$ $(i = 1, 2, \ldots, n)$, each defined as the function obtained by differentiation with respect to x_j alone, all other independent variables being held constant.

$$\frac{\partial y}{\partial x_j} \equiv \lim_{\partial x_j \to 0} \left[\frac{y\langle x_1, \ldots, x_{j-1}, x_j + \partial x_j, x_{j+1}, \ldots, x_n\rangle - y\langle \mathbf{x}\rangle}{\partial x_j} \right] \quad (2\text{-}27)$$

In the original example involving two independent variables, the first partial derivatives at any point (x_1, x_2) are

$$\frac{\partial y}{\partial x_1} = 1000 - 4 \times 10^9 (x_1)^{-2}(x_2)^{-1} \quad (2\text{-}28)$$

$$\frac{\partial y}{\partial x_2} = 2.5 \times 10^5 - 4 \times 10^9 (x_1)^{-1}(x_2)^{-2} \quad (2\text{-}29)$$

Taylor showed that if $\partial \mathbf{x}$ is a column vector of small displacements

$$\partial \mathbf{x} \equiv (\partial x_1, \ldots, \partial x_n)^T \quad (2\text{-}30)$$

then the difference between $y\langle \mathbf{x} + \partial \mathbf{x}\rangle$ and $y\langle \mathbf{x}\rangle$, abbreviated ∂y, is given at any point $\mathbf{x}$ by the series expansion

$$\partial y \equiv y\langle \mathbf{x} + \partial \mathbf{x}\rangle - y\langle \mathbf{x}\rangle$$

$$= \left(\frac{\partial y}{\partial x_1}\right)\partial x_1 + \cdots + \left(\frac{\partial y}{\partial x_n}\right)\partial x_n + 0(\partial \mathbf{x}^2)$$

$$= \sum_{j=1}^{n} \left(\frac{\partial y}{\partial x_j}\right)\partial x_j + 0\,(\partial \mathbf{x}^2) \quad (2\text{-}31)$$

where $O(\partial \mathbf{x}^2)$ represents an infinity of terms, each involving products of at least two differentials. Lagrange, who was the first to write the remainder as $O(\partial \mathbf{x}^2)$, neglected it in the computations to follow; Euler ignored it entirely. A rigorous proof would need to show that as ∂x_j approaches zero, the ratio $O(\partial \mathbf{x}^2)/\partial x_j$ vanishes in the limit. Let us assume this has been done and consider an analogous expression involving *finite* displacements Δx_j.

$$\Delta y = \sum_{j=1}^{n} \left(\frac{\partial y}{\partial x_j} \right) \Delta x_j \qquad (2\text{-}32)$$

This equation may be written in abbreviated vector (or inner) product form (Phillips) as

$$\Delta y = \nabla y \, \Delta \mathbf{x} \qquad (2\text{-}33)$$

for finite variations, or

$$\partial y = \nabla y \, \partial \mathbf{x} \qquad (2\text{-}34)$$

for infinitesimal ones. Here ∇y is the row vector of first partial derivatives

$$\nabla y \equiv \left(\frac{\partial y}{\partial x_1}, \ldots, \frac{\partial y}{\partial x_n} \right) \qquad (2\text{-}35)$$

called the *gradient of y* for reasons to be made clear in Chapter 7.

Conditions which must hold at an interior local optimum $\mathbf{x}^*$ are derived by combining its definition with the Taylor expansion in any open feasible neighborhood $\mathcal{N}$ containing $\mathbf{x}^*$. Suppose, to be definite, that $\mathbf{x}^*$ is a local *minimum*. Then in the limit

$$\sum_{j=1}^{n} \left(\frac{\partial y}{\partial x_j} \right)^* \partial x_j = \partial y = y\langle \mathbf{x}^* + \partial \mathbf{x} \rangle - y\langle \mathbf{x}^* \rangle \geq 0 \qquad (2\text{-}36)$$

for all possible perturbations ∂x_j. This implies that every partial derivative must vanish

$$\left(\frac{\partial y}{\partial x_j} \right)^* = 0 \; ; \qquad j = 1, \ldots, n \qquad (2\text{-}37)$$

for if on the contrary any $(\partial y/\partial x_j)^* \neq 0$, then any perturbation $\partial x_j'$ with sign opposite from that of $(\partial y/\partial x_j)^*$ would give a negative total change

$$\left(\frac{\partial y}{\partial x_j} \right)^* \partial x_j' < 0.$$

Holding all other perturbations at zero would generate a better point in every feasible neighborhood of y^*, contradicting the assumption that y^* was a local minimum. The same form of argument can be used to prove that Eq. (2-37) must also hold at a local maximum. In summary, a necessary condition that $\mathbf{x}^*$ be optimum is that the gradient vanish there.

$$\nabla y\langle \mathbf{x}^* \rangle \equiv \nabla y^* = \mathbf{0} \qquad (2\text{-}38)$$

where $\mathbf{0}$ is the n-component null vector. In geometric terms, the tangent plane is horizontal at an optimum.

Johann Bernoulli guessed this result while settling a dispute between Huygens and Chevalier Renau (chief marine engineer to Louis XIV) on the best sail angle and tack for ships, given the direction of the wind relative to the course. But in his zeal to show that a landlocked Swiss mathematician could solve sailing problems too subtle for colleagues in seafaring nations, he did not bother to prove his results. The methods described are therefore attributed to Euler, even though the latter's "proof" is marred by his unrigorous casting away of the higher-order differentials.

Euler's classical indirect method, applied to the two-variable example, would be to solve the nonlinear equations resulting when the algebraic expressions for the first partial derivatives are equated to zero.

$$1000 - 4 \times 10^9 (x_1^*)^{-2}(x_2^*)^{-1} = 0 \qquad (2\text{-}39)$$

$$2.5 \times 10^5 - 4 \times 10^9 (x_1^*)^{-1}(x_2^*)^{-2} = 0 \qquad (2\text{-}40)$$

The reader can verify that the only feasible solution is $x_1^* = 1000$, $x_2^* = 4$. Thus the classical indirect method reduces the original optimization problem to the solution of simultaneous equations, usually nonlinear. If the optimum is not interior, or the equations are too difficult to solve, other methods must be employed. Contours of the function are shown in Fig. 2–2.

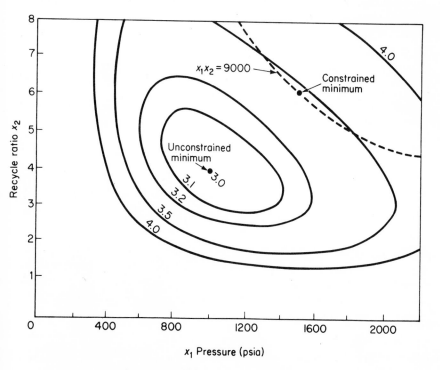

Figure 2-2. Objective function contours.

2-06 Solving Nonlinear Equations

Since the classical indirect method eventually involves solving simultaneous nonlinear equations, let us consider the well-known method conceived by Newton and refined by Raphson for doing just this. Let the first partial derivatives, which are scalar functions of the vector $\mathbf{x}$, be abbreviated by

$$\frac{\partial y}{\partial x_j} \equiv y'_j \langle \mathbf{x} \rangle ; \qquad j = 1, \ldots, n \tag{2-41}$$

so that Eq. (2–38) becomes

$$y'_j \langle \mathbf{x}^* \rangle = 0 \tag{2-42}$$

Let $\mathbf{x}_k$ be a trial point, and let $(\partial y'_j/\partial x_p)_k$ be the n first partial derivatives of the functions y'_j, evaluated at the point $\mathbf{x}_k$. These of course are *second* partial derivatives of the original objective function y, and they can also be abbreviated

$$\left(\frac{\partial y'_j}{\partial x_p}\right)_k \equiv \left(\frac{\partial^2 y}{\partial x_j \partial x_p}\right)_k \equiv y''_{jp} \langle \mathbf{x}_k \rangle \tag{2-43}$$

For the hypothetical chemical plant, the second partial derivatives are, at $\mathbf{x}^*$,

$$\frac{\partial^2 y}{\partial x_1^2} \equiv y''_{11} = 8 \times 10^9 (x_1^*)^{-3}(x_2^*)^{-1} = 2$$

$$\frac{\partial^2 y}{\partial x_1 \partial x_2} = y''_{12} = y''_{21} = 4 \times 10^9 (x_1^* x_2^*)^{-2} = 250$$

$$\frac{\partial^2 y}{\partial x_2^2} = y''_{22} = 8 \times 10^9 (x_1^*)^{-1}(x_2^*)^{-3} = 125{,}000$$

The Newton-Raphson method uses these second derivatives to estimate the values of the first derivatives in the neighborhood of $\mathbf{x}_k$. Then the new point $\mathbf{x}_{k+1}$ where the predicted values all vanish is selected as a better approximation to $\mathbf{x}^*$. The procedure is iterated until all y'_j become acceptably small. Expansion of the y'_j in Taylor series about $\mathbf{x}_k$ gives $\mathbf{x}_{k+1}$ as the solution to

$$y'_j \langle \mathbf{x}_{k+1} \rangle = 0 = y'_j \langle \mathbf{x}_k \rangle + \sum_{p=1}^{n} y''_{jp} \langle \mathbf{x}_k \rangle (x_{p,\,k+1} - x_{pk}) \tag{2-44}$$

Since the $y'_j \langle \mathbf{x}_k \rangle$ and $y''_{jp} \langle \mathbf{x}_k \rangle$ are all known, these n linear equations have only the n coordinates $x_{p,k+1}$ of $\mathbf{x}_{k+1}$ as unknowns.

It is convenient to express all this in matrix notation, which is introduced here formally without any theoretical justification (see Birkhoff and MacLane, Chaps. 7–10, for a deeper treatment of matrices). Let the n^2 second partial derivatives be arranged in an array with n rows and n columns called the *Hessian matrix* $\mathbf{H}$.

$$H\langle x_k \rangle \equiv H_k \equiv \begin{pmatrix} y_{11}'' & y_{12}'' & \cdots & y_{1n}'' \\ y_{21}'' & y_{22}'' & \cdots & y_{2n}'' \\ \cdot & \cdot & & \cdot \\ \cdot & \cdot & & \cdot \\ \cdot & \cdot & & \cdot \\ y_{n1}'' & y_{n2}'' & \cdots & y_{nn}'' \end{pmatrix} \tag{2-45}$$

By the rules of matrix multiplication, Eq. (2–44) can be written, after transposition of terms involving x_{k+1} to the left and changing signs,

$$H_k x_{k+1} = H_k x_k - (\nabla y_k)^T \tag{2-46}$$

where $\nabla y_k \equiv \nabla y \langle x_k \rangle$ is the gradient computed at x_k. If the n linear equations in the n unknown components of x_{k+1} are linearly independent, then the solution to Eq. (2–44) is unique and can be represented formally by

$$x_{k+1} = x_k - H_k^{-1}(\nabla y_k)^T \tag{2-47}$$

Here H_k^{-1} is the unique n by n *inverse matrix*, which has the property that

$$H_k^{-1} H_k = H_k H_k^{-1} = I \tag{2-48}$$

where I is the unit diagonal matrix having diagonal elements unity and all others zero. Equation(2–47) is obtained by multiplying all vectors in Eq. (2–46) on the left by H_k^{-1} and using Eq. (2–48) for simplification. The significance of all this is not yet clear; suffice it to say that it will be useful in the future to have the matrices H_k and H_k^{-1}, which we have seen must be calculated anyway when the Newton-Raphson method is employed.

The Newton-Raphson method, when it converges at all, may not find the proper root. Consider Fig. 2–3, which plots y_1' as a function of the single

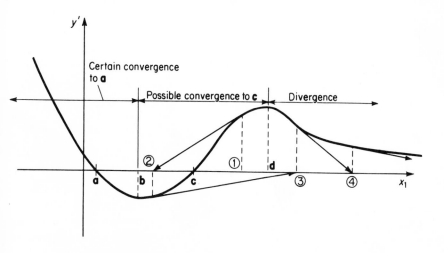

Figure 2-3. Newton-Raphson procedure.

variable x_1. The Hessian "matrix" is in this case a single number equal to the slope y_{11}'' of the curve; its "inverse" is $1/y_{11}''$. The set of points 1, 2, 3, 4, demonstrates how the method works, or, for this unfortunate start, doesn't work. The reader may verify that any search starting to the left of **b** will always converge to the root at **a**. Starts to the right of **d** never converge, while between **b** and **d** a search either converges to **c** or not at all.

2-07 Stationary Points

The vanishing of the first derivatives is a necessary, but by no means sufficient condition for a point to be a local minimum, for the tangent is also horizontal at a maximum and at an inflection point or a flat place. Any point where the gradient vanishes, Eq. (2–38), is called a *stationary point*, and we shall now define the various kinds so that minima can be distinguished among them.

Figure 2–4 displays a minimum of a function of one or two variables; by changing the sign of the objective y the points become maxima. A set of adjacent local minima (maxima) shown in Fig. 2–5, forms a *valley* (*ridge*), a situation which arises when the equality sign in Eq. (2–17) is satisfied for some $\mathbf{x} \neq \mathbf{x}^*$ in the neighborhood of $\mathbf{x}^*$. Figure 2–6 shows *saddle points* $\mathbf{x}^0$ where Eq. (2–17) is violated for some points $\mathbf{x}$ in every feasible neighborhood of the stationary point $\mathbf{x}^0$. Henceforth any stationary point will be denoted $\mathbf{x}^0$ until it has been definitely proved to be an optimum, when it can be positively identified by $\mathbf{x}^*$. We seek then *sufficient* conditions for a minimum.

Maclaurin first gave rules for distinguishing between various kinds of stationary points in one dimension, and Lagrange extended his ideas to the multidimensional case. Let $y\langle \mathbf{x}\rangle$ be expanded about $\mathbf{x}^0$ in a Taylor series exhibiting the second-order terms explicitly.

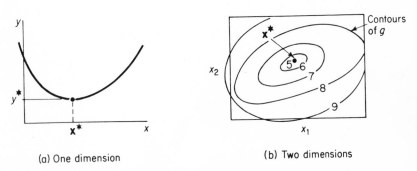

(a) One dimension   (b) Two dimensions

Figure 2-4. Minima.

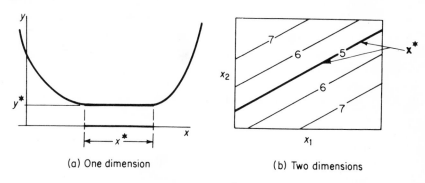

(a) One dimension   (b) Two dimensions

Figure 2-5. Valleys.

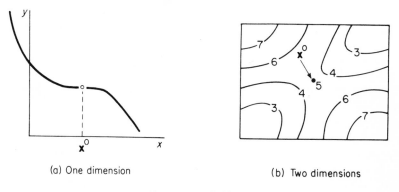

(a) One dimension   (b) Two dimensions

Figure 2-6. Saddlepoints.

$$y^0 \equiv y\langle \mathbf{x}^0 + \partial\mathbf{x}\rangle - y\langle \mathbf{x}^0\rangle$$

$$= \sum_{j=1}^{n} \left(\frac{\partial y}{\partial x_j}\right)^0 + \frac{1}{2}\sum_{j=1}^{n}\sum_{k=1}^{n}\left(\frac{\partial^2 y}{\partial x_j \partial x_k}\right)^0 \partial x_j\, \partial x_k + 0(\partial x^3) \tag{2-49}$$

or more compactly in terms of the gradient vector ∇y and Hessian matrix $\mathbf{H}$,

$$\partial y^0 = \nabla y^0\,(\partial\mathbf{x}) + \tfrac{1}{2}\,(\partial\mathbf{x})^T \mathbf{H}^0(\partial\mathbf{x}) + 0(\partial x^3) \tag{2-50}$$

Here the superscript zero reminds us that all quantities are evaluated at the stationary point, and $0(\partial x^3)$ represents terms in the expansion of degree three and higher. For all $\partial\mathbf{x}$ such that

$$(\partial\mathbf{x})^T\, \mathbf{H}^0(\partial\mathbf{x}) \neq 0 \tag{2-51}$$

it is true that

$$\lim_{\partial x \to 0}\left[\frac{0(\partial x^3)}{(\partial\mathbf{x})^T\, \mathbf{H}^0(\partial\mathbf{x})}\right] = 0 \tag{2-52}$$

so that $O(\partial x^3)$ will be neglected in subsequent argument when Eq. (2–51) holds. By Eq. (2–38) the gradient vanishes, and Eq. (2–50) simplifies to

$$\partial y^0 = \tfrac{1}{2} (\partial \mathbf{x})^T \mathbf{H}^0 (\partial \mathbf{x}) \qquad (2\text{-}53)$$

Combination of this with previous definitions involving ∂y gives the conditions for identifying the various kinds of stationary points in terms of calculable properties of the Hessian matrix $\mathbf{H}^0$, which in the example is given by

$$\mathbf{H}\langle \mathbf{x}^0 \rangle = \begin{pmatrix} 2 & 250 \\ 250 & 125{,}000 \end{pmatrix} \qquad (2\text{-}54)$$

The scalar $(\partial \mathbf{x})^T \mathbf{H}^0 (\partial \mathbf{x})$ is called a *differential quadratic form*, and it may be written in terms of the second partial derivatives of y as

$$(\partial \mathbf{x})^T \mathbf{H} (\partial \mathbf{x}) = \sum_{j=1}^{n} \sum_{k=1}^{n} y''_{jk} \, \partial x_j \, \partial x_k \qquad (2\text{-}55)$$

In the example

$$\partial y^0 = (\partial x_1)^2 + 250(\partial x_1)(\partial x_2) + 62{,}500(\partial x_2)^2 \qquad (2\text{-}56)$$

If this quadratic form is positive for all possible $\partial \mathbf{x}(\neq \mathbf{0})$ then the form (and $\mathbf{H}$) is said to be *positive-definite;* this is the sufficient condition for $\mathbf{x}^0$ to be a local minimum. At local maxima $\mathbf{H}$ is *negative-definite*. In valleys (ridges) the form is nonnegative (nonpositive), vanishing for $\partial \mathbf{x}$ along the valley (ridge), in which case $\mathbf{H}$ is said to be *semidefinite*. At saddlepoints, the quadratic form can be positive, negative, or zero, depending on the value of $\partial \mathbf{x}$ chosen; $\mathbf{H}^0$ is called *indefinite* under these circumstances. It remains only to show how to find perturbations $\partial \mathbf{x}$ which improve y near $\mathbf{x}^0$. If there are none, the point is an optimum.

In the example this can be done most easily by Lagrange's method of completing the square (1759). Thus, by adding and subtracting $(125 \, \partial x_2)^2$ to Eq. (2–56) and rearranging, one obtains a sum of two perfect squares.

$$\begin{aligned} \partial y^0 &= [(\partial x_1)^2 + 250(\partial x_1)(\partial x_2) + 15{,}625(\partial x_2)^2] \\ &\quad + (62{,}500 - 15{,}625)(\partial x_2)^2 \qquad (2\text{-}57) \\ &= (\partial x_1 + 125\partial x_2)^2 + 46{,}875(\partial x_2)^2 \end{aligned}$$

Since this must be positive for every value of $\partial \mathbf{x} \neq \mathbf{0}$, we are assured that the point is a local minimum. If the signs of the squares had all been negative, the point would have been identified as a maximum. Similarly if any signs are different, $\mathbf{x}^0$ is a saddle. For instance, if $\partial y^0 = (\partial x_1 + 125\partial x_2)^2 - 46{,}875(\partial x_2)^2$, then $\partial y^0 > 0$ as long as $\partial x_2 = 0$, and $\partial y^0 < 0$ whenever $\partial x_1 = -125\partial x_2$. In Chapter 3 this technique is demonstrated on a saddle point. Although the method of completing the square is fairly easy to carry out, it is complicated to explain for a general number of variables. Hence the details are deferred to Chapter 3, where a simple and systematic way of carrying out Lagrange's transformation is developed.

If any of the coefficients of the squares vanish, more powerful methods are needed to test the character of the stationary point. Suppose for example that $\partial y^0 = (\partial x_1 + 125\partial x_2)^2 + 0(\partial x_2)^2$. Then for any $\partial x_2 \neq 0$ and $\partial x_1 = -125\partial x_2, \partial y^0 = 0$. Since for any other choice of ∂x_1, ∂y^0 is strictly positive, one might jump to the conclusion that x^0 is in a valley. Although $\mathbf{H}$ must be semidefinite whenever x^0 is in a valley, the converse is not always true, since the valley itself may curve up or down. The vanishing of the second-order terms in these directions means that the third- and higher-order terms cannot be neglected, for if Eq. (2–51) does not hold, the limit in Eq. (2–52) may not be zero. Hence the theory developed so far does not give positive identification of a stationary point when the Hessian matrix is semidefinite.

Things are simple when there is but one independent variable, for if the second derivative $\partial^2 y/\partial x_1^2$ (the one-dimensional Hessian) vanishes, the third derivative must also be zero if x^0 is an optimum. This leaves the fourth derivative; if positive, x^0 is a minimum; if negative, x^0 is a maximum; if zero, the question is still unsettled and one must examine the fifth derivative, etc. Thus Maclaurin (1742) could assert with truth that x^0 is a minimum (maximum) if and only if the lowest order nonvanishing derivative is positive (negative) and of even order. In 1797 Lagrange propounded an analogous principle for multivariable functions; namely that if the lowest-order nonvanishing differentials are positive (negative)-definite and of even order, then x^0 is a minimum (maximum). This myth was not exploded for almost a century, when Peano (in Genocchi and Peano) exhibited an elementary counterexample (see Exercise 2–4) having a *curved* valley. Lagrange's spurious principle, based on an improper discarding of high-order differentials, died hard because of its plausibility, but a rigorous and more difficult theory due to Scheefer and Stolz has finally replaced it. (Since such anomalous situations do not arise enough in practice to justify exposition of the Scheefer-Stolz theory here, the interested reader should consult Hancock's book for a complete discussion.) Let us take Lagrange's error as a warning of the dangers lurking in nonlinear problems, especially when there are several independent variables.

2-08 Geometric Programming

The second indirect method is so indirect that it appears almost magical to the uninitiated. Called *geometric programming* by its inventors Clarence Zener and Richard Duffin, it sometimes locates optima by simple inspection of the exponents in the objective function. Although not as widely applicable as the classical method, geometric programming is strikingly effective when it can be used. Chapter 4 treats geometric programming and its extensions in depth; the brief description here shows its relation to other methods only from the differential point of view. Instead of seeking the optimal values of the independent variables first, geometric programming finds the optimal way to distribute the total cost among the various terms of the objective function. Once these optimal allocations are obtained, often by inspection of simple linear equations, the optimal cost can be found by routine calculation. If this cost is suitably attractive, one can then find the policy that will attain it. Although these last computations may involve solving some nonlinear equations, they are rarely as complicated as those encountered in the classic approach of Euler. Ferron proposed a related approach.

Duffin's development of this technique relies heavily on a certain inequality relating the arithmetic mean of the set of positive numbers to its geometric mean, which is why Duffin and Zener call the method *geometric programming*. The derivation here (Wilde, August, 1965) uses a different approach, for few are acquainted with the geometric mean inequality. The present derivation establishes only the necessity of the conditions, while the Duffin-Zener proof shows their sufficiency as well.

Consider then any objective function which is a sum of T terms $c_j p_j \langle \mathbf{x} \rangle$, where the c_j are positive constants and the $p_j \langle \mathbf{x} \rangle$ are products of powers of the x_i.

$$y = \sum_{j=1}^{T} c_j p_j \langle \mathbf{x} \rangle \qquad (2\text{-}58)$$

The product function p_j is defined by

$$p_j \langle \mathbf{x} \rangle \equiv \prod_{i=1}^{N} x_i^{a_{ij}} \qquad (2\text{-}59)$$

Equation (2–1) has this form, with $c_1 = 1000$, $c_2 = 4 \times 10^9$, $c_3 = 2.5 \times 10^5$, $p_1 = x_1$, $p_2 = (x_1 x_2)^{-1}$, $p_3 = x_2$, $a_{11} = 1$, $a_{21} = 0$, $a_{12} = a_{22} = -1$, $a_{13} = 0$, and $a_{23} = 1$.

At a minimum, the first derivatives must vanish.

$$\left(\frac{\partial y}{\partial x_k} \right)^* = \sum_j c_j a_{kj} (x_k^*)_{a_{kj}-1} \prod_{i \neq k} (x_i^*)^{a_{ij}}$$

$$= \frac{1}{x_k^*} \sum_j a_{kj} c_j p_j \langle \mathbf{x}^* \rangle = 0; \quad k = 1, \ldots, N \qquad (2\text{-}60)$$

But instead of solving these nonlinear equations for the minimizing values x_i^*, Duffin and Zener suggest finding the optimal distribution of the minimum cost y^* among the terms.

Define the optimal weights, w_j, by

$$w_j \equiv \frac{c_j p_j \langle \mathbf{x}^* \rangle}{y^*} \qquad (2\text{-}61)$$

Clearly the weights must sum to unity

$$\sum_j w_j = 1 \tag{2-62}$$

Equations (2–60) and (2–61) give

$$\frac{1}{y^*} \sum_j a_{kj} c_j p_j \langle \mathbf{x}^* \rangle = \sum_j a_{kj} w_j = 0 \; ; \quad k = 1, \ldots, N \tag{2-63}$$

Equations (2–62) and (2–63), being linear, are easy to solve for the w_j. In the example, these equations are

$$w_1 + w_2 + w_3 = 1$$

$$w_1 - w_2 \qquad = 0$$

$$-w_2 + w_3 = 0$$

Simple inspection gives the solution as

$$w_1 = w_2 = w_3 = \tfrac{1}{3} \tag{2-64}$$

Thus, before knowing the optimal pressure and recycle ratio, we can assert that the optimal policy must equalize the compressor cost, the reactor cost, and the combined separator and recirculation cost. More remarkable, the distribution is totally unaffected by changes in the cost coefficients c_j of Eq. (2–58). This separation of technological effects, as reflected by the exponents a_{ij}, from the economic effects, as measured by the coefficients c_j, is one of the attractive features of this approach.

We can now find the minimum cost, still without knowing the optimal policy. Because the weights sum to unity,

$$y^* = \prod_j (y^*)^{w_j} = \prod_j \left(\frac{c_j p_j \langle \mathbf{x}^* \rangle}{w_j} \right)^{w_j} = \prod_j \left(\frac{c_j}{w_j} \right)^{w_j} \prod_j [p_j \langle \mathbf{x}^* \rangle]^{w_j} \tag{2-65}$$

But by Eqs. (2–59) and (2–63) the right-hand product is unity.

$$\prod_j [p_j \langle \mathbf{x}^* \rangle]^{w_j} = \prod_j \prod_i (x_i^*)^{a_{ij} w_j} = \prod_i (x_i^*)^{\sum a_{ij} w_j} = \prod_i (x_i^*)^0 = 1 \tag{2-66}$$

Therefore, the minimum cost can be calculated from the coefficients c_j and the weights w_j.

$$y^* = \prod_j \left(\frac{c_j}{w_j} \right)^{w_j} \tag{2-67}$$

In the example

$$y^* = \left(\frac{1000}{1/3} \right)^{1/3} \left(\frac{4 \times 10^9}{1/3} \right)^{1/3} \left(\frac{2.5 \times 10^5}{1/3} \right)^{1/3}$$

$$= (27 \times 10^{18})^{1/3} = 3 \times 10^6$$

which confirms the result obtained by classical methods.

The minimum total cost and the optimal weights now can be used to find the optimal policy $\mathbf{x}^*$. In the example, it is now clear that compressor cost ($1000 x_1$) must be \$$10^6$, so $x_1^* = 1000$ atm. Similarly, because the separation-recirculation system cost ($2.5 \times 10^5 x_2$) must also be 10^6, it follows that $x_2^* = 4$. At no time during the geometric programming analysis of this particular problem has it been necessary to solve any nonlinear equations. Although in more general circumstances nonlinearities may be encountered, they are usually easier to handle by geometric programming than by Eulerian methods.

The example is special in that there is exactly one more term than variable. Anytime this is true ($T = N + 1$) there will be exactly as many linear equations, Eqs. (2–62) and (2–63), as there are variables, w_j, so there will be a unique set of weights to satisfy the orthogonality and normality conditions. But when $T > N + 1$, further steps must be taken to find the optimum weights from among all those satisfying Eqs. (2–62) and (2–63).

2-09 Equality Constraints—Elimination

When the objective function must satisfy side conditions given as equations relating the independent variables, the optimum necessarily lies on a boundary of the feasible region $\mathscr{F}$. Indirect methods are valid only for interior optima, but equality constrained problems can often be transformed into new ones having the optimum inside the feasible region. The next five sections give two classical ways of accomplishing this transformation and a new method based on classical ideas. At the same time the important distinction between "decision" variables and "state" variables will be introduced. In this section we consider the *elimination* method for handling equality constraints, best described by example.

Suppose in the hypothetical design problem that instead of allowing any positive pressure and recycle ratio, we must for technical reasons consider only those satisfying the following equality constraint.

$$x_1 x_2 = 9000 \tag{2-68}$$

The points satisfying this equation lie on the dashed line of Fig. 2–3. The simplest way to handle this is to use Eq. (2–68) to eliminate one variable, say x_2, from the objective function in Eq. (2–1).

$$y = 1000x_1 + 4 \times \frac{10^9}{9000} + (2.5 \times 10^5)\left(\frac{9000}{x_1}\right)$$
$$= 1000x_1 + 2.25 \times 10^9 x_1^{-1} + 4.44 \times 10^5 \tag{2-69}$$

The minimum of this function of x_1 alone is found by the classical technique described already. The result is $x_1' = 1500$ psia, which, when substituted into Eq. (2–1), gives the constrained minimum cost as $y' = \$3.44 \times 10^6$. Substitution into the constraint gives the optimal recycle ratio as $x_2' = 6$. This constrained optimum is shown in Fig. 2–2 on the dashed line. The minimum cost has gone up because the unconstrained minimum has been forbidden by the constraints.

Elimination, when it can be used, is effective because it reduces the number of independent variables and, consequently, the number of derivative equations which must be solved. It does require, however, the initial solution of the constraint equations in closed form, often an impossible task.

2-10 State and Decision Variables

The remaining indirect ways to solve equality constrained optimization problems involve working with the linear terms of Taylor expansions, not only of the objective function, but also of each constraint. This approach leads us to partition the independent variables into two groups, called *decision variables* and *state variables* for reasons to be made clear in this section. Then the linear equations are solved for the state differentials as linear functions of the decision differentials. The coefficients of these linear expansions, which will be known as *decision derivatives*, are important in developing the generalizations in optimization theory which fill the rest of the book. Of comparable future value will be the concepts of state and decision. Thus the ideas of this section are powerful enough to help solve systems much more complicated than the simple equality constrained case. Although the derivation here involves neglecting second- and higher-order differentials, a rigorous proof based on the implicit function theorem has been given by Wilde (September, 1965).

Let there be M differentiable constraints

$$f_m\langle \mathbf{x} \rangle = 0 \; ; \qquad m = 1, \ldots, M \qquad (2\text{-}70)$$

The feasible region $\mathscr{F}$ now consists of all points $\mathbf{x}$ satisfying Eq. (2–70). Since every point of this region is a boundary point, there are no interior points at all, much less an interior optimum. In every neighborhood of a feasible point $\mathbf{x}$ there are both infeasible points where some of the differentials $\partial f_m \neq 0$, and feasible points where all $\partial f_m = 0$. For points in the feasible neighborhood $\mathscr{N}$, the differentials $\partial \mathbf{x}$ must satisfy, to a first order approximation, the M linear equations

$$0 = \partial f_k = \sum_{n=1}^{N} \left(\frac{\partial f_k}{\partial x_n} \right) \partial x_n = \nabla f_k \cdot \partial \mathbf{x} \qquad (2\text{-}71)$$

Recall that a similar expansion for the objective function gives, with ∂y not necessarily zero,

$$\partial y = \sum_{n=1}^{N} \left(\frac{\partial y}{\partial x_n} \right) \partial x_n = \nabla y \cdot \partial \mathbf{x} \qquad (2\text{-}72)$$

Since at $\mathbf{x}$ the partial derivatives are presumed to be known constants, Eqs. (2–70) and (2–71) constitute $M + 1$ linear equations in $N + 1$ unknown differentials: ∂y and the N components of the feasible differential vector $\partial\mathbf{x}$. Let us assume that the equations are linearly independent (Birkhoff and MacLane, p. 167); if they are not, then take the largest number that form an independent set and discard the rest as redundant. This automatically rules out the case where there are more equations than unknowns ($M > N$), and the case where $M = N$ is of no interest because then the only solution to Eq. (2–71) would be $\partial\mathbf{x} = 0$, meaning there is no feasible neighborhood at all. Therefore assume from now on that $M < N$.

Rearrange Eqs. (2–71) and (2–72), placing on the left terms involving ∂y and the first M components of $\partial\mathbf{x}$.

$$-\partial y + \sum_{n=1}^{M} \left(\frac{\partial y}{\partial x_n}\right)\partial x_n = -\sum_{n=M+1}^{N} \left(\frac{\partial y}{\partial x_n}\right)\partial x_n \qquad (2\text{–}73)$$

$$\sum_{n=1}^{M} \left(\frac{\partial f_k}{\partial x_n}\right)\partial x_n = -\sum_{n=M+1}^{N} \left(\frac{\partial f_k}{\partial x_n}\right)\partial x_n \qquad (2\text{–}74)$$

Actually any M among the N independent variables could have been chosen; the first M were selected for convenience and without sacrificing generality. There is, however, one restriction; the left members of the M equations (2–74) must be linearly independent. That Eqs. (2–71) are independent assures us of the existence of such an independent subset.

To emphasize the distinction between the differentials on the right and those on the left, we introduce new notation and terminology. Let

$$s_m \equiv x_n ; \qquad m, n = 1, \dots, M \qquad (2\text{–}75)$$

be called the *state variables* of the problem. The difference

$$P \equiv N - M \qquad (2\text{–}76)$$

is known as the *number of degrees of freedom*, and a new set of indices $p = 1, \dots, P$ is given by

$$p \equiv n - M ; \qquad n = M + 1, \dots, N \qquad (2\text{–}77)$$

The variables with these indices are called *decision variables* d_p.

$$d_p = x_p \qquad (2\text{–}78)$$

In this terminology Eqs. (2–73) and (2–74) become

$$-\partial y + \sum_{m=1}^{M} \left(\frac{\partial y}{\partial s_m}\right)\partial s_m = -\sum_{p=1}^{P} \left(\frac{\partial y}{\partial d_p}\right)\partial d_p \qquad (2\text{–}79)$$

$$\sum_{m=1}^{M} \left(\frac{\partial f_k}{\partial s_m}\right)\partial s_m = -\sum_{p=1}^{P} \left(\frac{\partial f_k}{\partial d_p}\right)\partial d_p ; \qquad k = 1, \dots, M \quad (2\text{–}80)$$

There must be exactly M state and P decision variables, but in the problem at hand, it doesn't matter which of the original $M + P$ independent variables is placed in these categories as long as linear independence is preserved. In more complicated situations, it may be clear which are to be the decision variables. However they happen to be chosen, any arbitrary specification of the decision differentials permits calculation of numerical values for the right members of Eqs. (2–79) and (2–80). Then Eqs. (2–80) can be solved for the unique values of the state differentials ∂s which keep the new point $x + \partial x$ inside the feasible region. The resulting change ∂y in the objective function, calculated from Eq. (2–79), can then be used to see if the perturbation was an improvement.

Decision variables can be manipulated freely, while state variables adjust to keep the new point feasible. Arbitrary adjustment of more than P variables would move $x + \partial x$ out of the feasible region; specification of fewer than P variables would leave too many unknown quantities, making it impossible to locate the new point. Since P is the exact number of decisions that can be made with no regard for feasibility, it measures the number of "degrees of freedom" in the system. Each additional constraint cuts down the number of degrees of freedom, and by reducing the number of decision variables, actually makes the optimization problem easier. The dimension of the feasible region $\mathscr{F}$ is not the total number of "independent" variables, but the number of degrees of freedom. An optimization problem in a million and one variables with a million equality constraints can in principle be reduced to an unconstrained problem in a single variable.

2-11 Constrained Derivatives

The dependence of the states on the decisions is made even clearer by solving Eqs. (2–79) and (2–80), using Cramer's rule for determinants. This will lead to the useful concept of *constrained derivative*. Some notational preliminaries (Courant) are needed before the solutions can be written down explicitly. The M by M matrix of the coefficients of the state variables is called a *Jacobian matrix* $\mathbf{J}$.

$$\mathbf{J} \equiv \begin{pmatrix} \partial f_1/\partial s_1 & \cdots & \partial f_1/\partial s_M \\ \cdot & & \cdot \\ \cdot & & \cdot \\ \cdot & & \cdot \\ \partial f_M/\partial s_1 & \cdots & \partial f_M/\partial s_M \end{pmatrix} \equiv \frac{\partial \mathbf{f}}{\partial \mathbf{s}} \tag{2-81}$$

The determinant of $\mathbf{J}$, written alternatively $|\mathbf{J}|$ or $\partial(f_1, \ldots, f_M)/\partial(s_1, \ldots, s_M)$, is called a *functional determinant* (Jacobi) or *Jacobian*.

$$\frac{\partial(f_1, \ldots, \partial f_M)}{\partial(s_1, \ldots, s_M)} \equiv |\mathbf{J}| \tag{2-82}$$

Another M Jacobians needed for the solution are obtained by formally replacing f_k ($k = 1, \ldots, M$) by y everywhere it appears.

$$\frac{\partial(f_1, \ldots, f_{k-1}, y, f_{k+1}, \ldots, f_M)}{\partial(s_1, \ldots, s_M)} \equiv \begin{vmatrix} \partial f_1/\partial s_1 & \ldots & \partial f_1/\partial s_M \\ \cdot & & \cdot \\ \cdot & & \cdot \\ \cdot & & \cdot \\ \partial f_{k-1}/\partial s_1 & \ldots & \partial f_{k-1}\partial s_M \\ \partial y/\partial s_1 & \ldots & \partial y/\partial s_M \\ \partial f_{k+1}/\partial s_1 & \ldots & \partial f_{k+1}/\partial s_M \\ \cdot & & \cdot \\ \cdot & & \cdot \\ \cdot & & \cdot \\ \partial f_M/\partial s_1 & \ldots & \partial f_M/\partial s_M \end{vmatrix} ; \quad k = 1, \ldots, M$$

(2-83)

Finally, P more determinants of order $M + 1$ are obtained by adding to $|\mathbf{J}|$ a row and column involving the objective y and a decision d_p.

$$\frac{\partial(y, f_1, \ldots, f_M)}{\partial(d_p, s_1, \ldots, s_M)} \equiv \begin{vmatrix} \partial y/\partial d_p, & \partial y/\partial s_1, & \ldots, & \partial y/\partial s_M \\ \partial f_1/\partial d_p, & \partial f_1/\partial s_1, & \ldots, & \partial f_1/\partial s_M \\ \cdot & \cdot & & \cdot \\ \cdot & \cdot & & \cdot \\ \cdot & \cdot & & \cdot \\ \partial f_M/\partial d_p, & \partial f_M/\partial s_1, & \ldots, & \partial f_M/\partial s_M \end{vmatrix} ; \quad p = 1, \ldots, P \quad (2\text{-}84)$$

In the example, $N = 2$ and $M = P = 1$. Let x_1 be the state variable s_1, and x_2 the decision variable d_1. The single constraint Eq. (2–68) can be written in the form of Eq. (2–70) as

$$f_1\langle s_1, d_1 \rangle \equiv s_1 d_1 - 9000 = 0 \tag{2-85}$$

The Jacobians corresponding to Eqs. (2–82), (2–83), and (2–84) are

$$\frac{\partial f_1}{\partial s_1} = d_1 \tag{2-86}$$

$$\frac{\partial y}{\partial s_1} = 1000 - 4 \times 10^9 (s_1)^{-2}(d_1)^{-1} \tag{2-87}$$

$$\frac{\partial(y, f_1)}{\partial(d_1, s_1)} = \begin{vmatrix} [2.5 \times 10^5 - 4 \times 10^9 (s_1)^{-1}(d_1)^{-2}][1000 - 4 \times 10^9 (s_1)^{-2}(d_1)^{-1}] \\ s_1 \qquad\qquad\qquad\qquad d_1 \end{vmatrix}$$

$$= 2.5 \times 10^5 d_1 - 1000 s_1 \tag{2-88}$$

Returning now to the general case, let us apply Cramer's rule to obtain, after certain elementary determinant manipulations (Exercise 2–5a),

$$\partial y = \sum_{p=1}^{P} \frac{\partial(y, f_1, \ldots, f_M)/\partial(d_p, s_1, \ldots, s_M)}{\partial(f_1, \ldots, f_M)/\partial(s_1, \ldots, s_M)} \partial d_p \tag{2-89}$$

Now differentiate this expression partially with respect to a typical decision variable d_p while holding the other $P - 1$ decision variables constant. The result is the rate of change of the objective resulting from *feasible* (not arbitrary) perturbations in the pth decision variable, which will cause the state variables to readjust. This partial derivative is given the special symbol $\delta y/\delta d_p$ to distinguish it from $\partial y/\partial d_p$, which is obtained for nonfeasible perturbations with all the states held constant.

$$\frac{\delta y}{\delta d_p} = \frac{\partial(y, f_1, \ldots, f_M)/\partial(d_p, s_1, \ldots, s_M)}{\partial(f_1, \ldots, f_M)/\partial(s_1, \ldots, s_M)} \tag{2-90}$$

The quantity $\delta y/\delta d_p$ will be called "the *constrained* derivative of y with respect to d_p," or more simply, the pth *decision derivative*. In the example, Eqs. (2–86), (2–88), and (2–90) give

$$\frac{\delta y}{\delta d_1} = 2.5 \times 10^5 - 1000 \frac{s_1}{d_1} \tag{2-91}$$

Since the decision differentials can be arbitrary without causing $\mathbf{x} + \partial\mathbf{x}$ to leave the P-dimensional feasible neighborhood $\mathscr{P}$, $\mathbf{x}$ is now *interior* to $\mathscr{P}$, even though it is on the boundary of the feasible region $\mathscr{F}$ imbedded in the N-dimensional space of the original "independent" variables $x_1, \ldots, x_N$. Figure 2–2 shows this, for any point on the dashed constraint line $\mathscr{F}$ is a boundary point when both x_1 and x_2 can change arbitrarily in two dimensions, but it is interior when only movement along the unidimensional feasible line is permitted. Hence when decision derivatives are used, the classical theory for *interior* optima applies. Therefore at a feasible optimum it is necessary that the decision derivatives vanish.

$$\left(\frac{\delta y}{\delta d_p}\right)^* = 0 \; ; \qquad p = 1, \ldots, P \tag{2-92}$$

In the example this gives, in view of Eq. (2–91)

$$2.5 \times 10^5 - 1000 \frac{s_1^*}{d_1^*} = 0$$

which, together with the constraint Eq. (2–68),

$$s_1^* d_1^* = 9000$$

permits the constrained solution to be identified as $s_1^*(\equiv x_1^*) = 1500$; d_1^* $(\equiv x_2^*) = 6$, confirming the result obtained by direct elimination. This technique is called the *Jacobian method*.

A vector formulation of this condition is obtained by defining the *gradient projection* ∇y as the row vector of the P decision derivatives. This can be interpreted geometrically as the projection of the N-dimensional gradient ∇y into the P-dimensional feasible region generated by the P decision variables. The necessary condition for a constrained optimum is that the gradient projection vanish there.

$$\nabla y \equiv \left(\frac{\delta y}{\delta d_1}, \ldots, \frac{\delta y}{\delta d_P}\right) = \mathbf{0} \tag{2-93}$$

The same results can be formulated simply in matrix terminology. Define the *state gradient*

$$\nabla_s y \equiv \left(\frac{\partial y}{\partial s_1}, \ldots, \frac{\partial y}{\partial s_M} \right) \qquad (2\text{-}94)$$

The *decision gradient*

$$\nabla_d y \equiv \left(\frac{\partial y}{\partial d_1}, \ldots, \frac{\partial y}{\partial d_P} \right) \qquad (2\text{-}95)$$

and the *control matrix*

$$\mathbf{C} \equiv \begin{pmatrix} \partial f_1/\partial d_1 & \ldots & \partial f_1/\partial d_P \\ \vdots & & \vdots \\ \partial f_M/\partial d_1 & \ldots & \partial f_M/\partial d_P \end{pmatrix} \equiv \frac{\partial \mathbf{f}}{\partial \mathbf{d}} \qquad (2\text{-}96)$$

Then Eqs. (2–79) and (2–80) become, respectively,

$$-\partial y + \nabla_s y \cdot \partial \mathbf{s} = -\nabla_d y \cdot \partial \mathbf{d} \qquad (2\text{-}97)$$

$$\mathbf{J} \, \partial \mathbf{s} = -\mathbf{C} \, \partial \mathbf{d} \qquad (2\text{-}98)$$

Since $\mathbf{J}$ is nonsingular by the way it was constructed, it has an inverse $\mathbf{J}^{-1}$, whence, by Eq. (2–98),

$$\partial \mathbf{s} = -\mathbf{J}^{-1} \mathbf{C} \partial \mathbf{d} \qquad (2\text{-}99)$$

which, when substituted into Eq. (2–97), gives

$$\partial y = (\nabla_d y - \nabla_s y \mathbf{J}^{-1} \mathbf{C}) \, \partial \mathbf{d} \qquad (2\text{-}100)$$

Equation (2–99) shows how the states adjust in response to perturbations of the decisions. If each component of $\partial \mathbf{s}$ is differentiated partially with respect to a typical decision d_p, there results an M by P matrix:

$$\frac{\partial \mathbf{s}}{\partial \mathbf{d}} = -\mathbf{J}^{-1}\mathbf{C} \qquad (2\text{-}101)$$

The element in the mth row and pth column is $\delta s_m/\delta d_p$, written with the special boldface differentiation sign δ to avoid confusing it with $\partial s_m/\partial d_p (=0)$ for unconstrained perturbations. The full name for $\delta s_m/\delta d_p$ is "the *constrained derivative of s_m with respect to d_p.*" It can also be computed from the following Jacobian formula [Exercise 2–5(b)]

$$\frac{\delta s_m}{\delta d_p} = -\frac{\partial(f_1, \ldots, f_M)/\partial(s_1, \ldots, s_{m-1}, d_p, s_{m+1}, \ldots, s_M)}{\partial(f_1, \ldots, f_M)/\partial(s_1, \ldots, s_M)} \qquad (2\text{-}102)$$

The Jacobian technique expands the decision derivatives $\delta y/\delta \mathbf{d}$ as functions of the independent variables and sets them to zero. Ultimately N nonlinear simultaneous equations must be solved—M from the constraints and $N - M$ from the decision derivatives. Since unconstrained problems also require solving N equations, the constraints do not really increase the computational difficulty when the Jacobian method is used. This illustrates the power of the differential approach, coupled with the concepts of state, decision, degrees of freedom, and constrained derivative. These ideas will reappear in different roles throughout the book.

2-12 Sensitivity Analysis

Rarely does one know the constraint functions f_m with absolute precision. As in the example, the constraint often has a term which, although nominally a constant because of its independence of the problem variables, may really change with fluctuating sales, raw material quality, or other uncontrollable factors. Design problems have many constant terms which, being related to actual performance, cannot be predicted before operations begin. Before going ahead with an enterprise, a decision maker wants to estimate the impact of all these uncertainties upon the optimum he has calculated. Determining the rate of change of the optimum value with respect to perturbations in the constraint functions is called *sensitivity analysis*.

To perform a sensitivity analysis, we make the constraint functions infinitesimally different from zero and find the new optimum. Let f_k be the numerical value of the constraint function $f_k\langle \mathbf{x}\rangle$. Keep clearly in mind the distinction between f_k, a scalar, and $f_k\langle \mathbf{x}\rangle$, a function of $\mathbf{x}$. In the example, $f_1\langle \mathbf{x}\rangle$ was always $(x_1 x_2 - 9000)$, whereas f_1 was the number zero. From now on $f_k\langle \mathbf{x}\rangle$ will retain its original character, but the f_k should be considered as M new variables which can assume arbitrary values. Let the f_k be assembled into a column M-vector $\mathbf{f}$, and let it be understood that $\partial f_k/\partial x_n$ is an abbreviation for $\partial f_k\langle \mathbf{x}\rangle/\partial x_n$.

Let $\mathbf{x}^*$ be a feasible optimum where $\mathbf{f} = \mathbf{0}$, and let $\partial \mathbf{f}$ be a vector of perturbations of $\mathbf{f}$ resulting from perturbations $\partial \mathbf{s}$ and $\partial \mathbf{d}$. Eq. (2–71) must be replaced by

$$\partial \mathbf{f} = \frac{\partial \mathbf{f}}{\partial \mathbf{s}}\, \partial \mathbf{s} + \frac{\partial \mathbf{f}}{\partial \mathbf{d}}\, \partial \mathbf{d} = \mathbf{J}\, \partial \mathbf{s} + \mathbf{C}\, \partial \mathbf{d} \qquad (2\text{-}103)$$

The left member was always zero in the previous section, and the matrices $\mathbf{J}$ and $\mathbf{C}$ have been defined in Eqs. (2–81) and (2–96). Multiplication of all vectors on the left by $\mathbf{J}^{-1}$ and rearrangement gives

$$\partial \mathbf{s} = \mathbf{J}^{-1}\, \partial \mathbf{f} - \mathbf{J}^{-1}\mathbf{C}\, \partial \mathbf{d} \qquad (2\text{-}104)$$

which can be substituted into Eq. (2–97) to give

$$\partial y = \nabla_s y \mathbf{J}^{-1}\, \partial \mathbf{f} + (\nabla_d y - \nabla_s y \mathbf{J}^{-1}\mathbf{C})\, \partial \mathbf{d}$$

or, in terms of the gradient projection (Eq. 2-100),

$$\partial y = \nabla_s y \mathbf{J}^{-1}\, \partial \mathbf{f} + \nabla y\, \partial \mathbf{d} \qquad (2\text{-}105)$$

But since $\mathbf{x}^*$ is a local optimum, the gradient projection ∇y must vanish there [Eq. (2–93)], so

$$\partial y^* = \nabla_s y \mathbf{J}^{-1}\, \partial \mathbf{f} \qquad (2\text{-}106)$$

which, upon partial differentiation, gives

$$\frac{\delta y^*}{\delta \mathbf{f}} = \nabla_s y \mathbf{J}^{-1} \qquad (2\text{-}107)$$

The elements of this row M-vector are partial derivatives of y^*, the *optimum* value, with respect to perturbations $\mathbf{f}$ in the constraint functions. Because of this they will be called *sensitivity coefficients*. They can be calculated individually from the following Jacobian formula (Exercise 2–5c):

$$\frac{\delta y^*}{\delta f_k} = \frac{\partial(f_1, \ldots, f_{k-1}, y, f_{k+1}, \ldots, f_M)/\partial(s_1, \ldots, s_M)}{\partial(f_1, \ldots, f_M)/\partial(s_1, \ldots, s_M)} \qquad (2\text{-}108)$$

In the example, this would give

$$\frac{\delta y^*}{\delta f_1} = \frac{\partial y/\partial s_1}{\partial f_1/\partial s_1} = \frac{1000 - 4 \times 10^9 (s_1^*)^{-2}(d_1^*)^{-1}}{d_1^*} = \$117.30/\text{atm} \quad (2\text{-}109)$$

Here $s_1^* = x_1^* = 1500$ and $d_1^* = x_2^* = 6$, since $\mathbf{x}^*$ is the *constrained* minimum. Equation (2–109) means that if f_1 were made 1 instead of 0, the minimum cost at the new optimum satisfying the new constraint $x_1 x_2 = 9001$ would be approximately \$117.30 higher than at the old minimum where $x_1 x_2 = 9000$. Keep in mind that this is an approximation, good only near the point $\mathbf{x}^*$ where the derivatives were evaluated.

The values of the Jacobians in Eq. (2–108) depend on which variables were chosen to be the states. One would at first suppose that there could therefore be a different value of the sensitivity coefficient $\delta y^*/\delta f_k$ for every possible set of states. In Section 2–13 it will be shown that each sensitivity coefficient is in fact unique, and one set of states is as good as any other for calculating the $\delta y^*/\delta f_k$.

2-13 Lagrange's Undetermined Multipliers

The final indirect method covered can be considered "classical" since it goes back to Lagrange (1760–61). It is, in fact, often the only method mentioned when optimization theory is under discussion. Briefly it introduces the M sensitivity coefficients $\delta y^*/\delta f_k$ into the solution, treating them as unknowns, designated λ_k for abbreviation.

$$\frac{\delta y^*}{\delta f_k} \equiv \lambda_k \qquad (2\text{-}110)$$

This ultimately reduces the problem to solving $M + N$ simultaneous equations in the $M + N$ unknowns (the N x_n and M λ_k). Although this may seem harder than merely solving the N equations required by the Jacobian method, and it often is, there are times when the $M + N$ equations resulting are easier to solve. Moreover, Lagrange's method gives the sensitivity coefficients as by-products of the computations.

Although the results derived here are the same as Lagrange's, the development is entirely different. Lagrange did not view the λ_k as derivatives, but merely as "undetermined multipliers"—arbitrary constants introduced for no other purpose than mathematical convenience. Let us proceed now with the demonstration.

In view of how the sensitivity coefficients were defined in the preceding section, Eq. (2–106) can be written

$$\partial y^* = \left(\frac{\delta y^*}{\delta \mathbf{f}}\right)\partial \mathbf{f} = \boldsymbol{\lambda}\, \partial \mathbf{f} \qquad (2\text{-}111)$$

where $\boldsymbol{\lambda}$ is the row M-vector of sensitivity coefficients, for which the conventional terminology is *undetermined multipliers* or *Lagrange multipliers*. Differentiation with respect to any of the N independent variables x_n and subsequent rearrangement gives

$$\frac{\partial y^*}{\partial x_n} - \boldsymbol{\lambda}\left(\frac{\partial \mathbf{f}}{\partial x_n}\right) = 0$$
$$= \frac{\partial}{\partial x_n}(y - \boldsymbol{\lambda}\mathbf{f}) \qquad (2\text{-}112)$$

The quantity inside the parentheses is called the *Lagrangian* (function) L.

$$L\langle \mathbf{x}, \boldsymbol{\lambda}\rangle \equiv y\langle \mathbf{x}\rangle - \boldsymbol{\lambda}\mathbf{f}\langle \mathbf{x}\rangle \qquad (2\text{-}113)$$

Its derivatives with respect to the $\boldsymbol{\lambda}$ are the constraint functions, which by Eq. (2–70) must be zero at a feasible point

$$\frac{\partial L}{\partial \boldsymbol{\lambda}} = -\mathbf{f}\langle \mathbf{x}\rangle = 0 \qquad (2\text{-}114)$$

Equations (2–112) and (2–114) establish that any feasible local optimum $\mathbf{x}^*$ is a stationary point for the Lagrangian function. Jointly they furnish $M + N$ equations in the M unknown λ_k, and N unknown x_n, which in principle can be solved for $\mathbf{x}^*$ and $\boldsymbol{\lambda}$.

There being exactly as many equations as unknowns, any local optimum $\mathbf{x}^*$ has a unique set of sensitivity coefficients $\boldsymbol{\lambda}$ associated with it, provided that Eqs. (2–112) and (2–114) are independent in the neighborhood of $\mathbf{x}^*$. Therefore no matter what set of variables are designated *states* in defining the $\boldsymbol{\lambda}$ of Eq. (2–111), $\boldsymbol{\lambda}$ will be the same. Basically this comes about because the gradient projection ∇y vanishes at the optimum, making the term $\nabla y\, \partial \mathbf{d}$ vanish in Eq. (2–105). With it disappears any dependence of the sensitivity coefficients on the choice of the set of states. This settles the point raised in the preceding section.

The lack of distinction between decision and state variables in the Lagrangian formulation makes it useful in theoretical work where numerical computations need not be performed and where, as in the example, there is no basis for singling out particular variables as "decisions." And even when the $M + N$ equations must be solved, the symmetric Lagrange formulation sometimes exposes an advantageous order of solution which may not show up in the Jacobian method.

In the example the Lagrangian is

$$L \equiv 1000x_1 + 4 \times 10^9(x_1x_2)^{-1} + 2.5 \times 10^5x_2 - \lambda_1(x_1x_2 - 9000) \quad (2\text{-}115)$$

Setting the partial derivatives with respect to x_1, x_2, and λ_1 to zero gives

$$1000 - 4 \times 10^9(x_1^*)^{-2}(x_2^*)^{-1} - \lambda_1 = 0 \quad (2\text{-}116)$$

$$2.5 \times 10^5 - 4 \times 10^9(x_1^*)^{-1}(x_2^*)^{-2} - \lambda_1 = 0 \quad (2\text{-}117)$$

$$-x_1^*x_2^* + 9000 = 0 \quad (2\text{-}118)$$

The reader can verify that the values of x_1^*, x_2^*, and λ_1 found by the other methods also satisfy these equations (Exercise 2–6). In this case the more widely known Lagrange method has no advantages over direct elimination or the Jacobian method, taking more effort than either of them (Exercise 2–7). Lagrange's method will prove its worth later in more complicated situations.

2-14 Summary

Despite this chapter's opening allegorical allusion to "paths to the top of the mountain" the mathematical treatment confined itself entirely to describing peaks, not paths. Knowledge of the mathematical topography of summits leads to indirect methods which, when applicable, find peaks by a procedure resembling a parachute jump straight to the peak more than a mountaineer's climbing ascent. The theory depends heavily on a differential approach which will, in fact, be the key unifying idea throughout the book.

After a warning about careful employment of differentials, they were manipulated to give necessary and sufficient conditions for an optimum. Stationary points other than optima were described, and it was shown how to identify them by completing the square on second-order terms of a Taylor expansion. After completing the development of the classical indirect method for finding interior optima, we derived the modern, and radically different, approach of geometric programming which, for a more restricted class of objective functions, gives quick, elegant solutions.

In adapting the classical methods for finding interior optima to handle equality constraints, the concepts of decision, state, and degrees of freedom were defined. They in turn generated the decision derivatives needed to transform boundary optimization problems into interior ones capable of solution by easy extensions of classical techniques. Similar developments lead to sensitivity coefficients for analyzing the effects on the value of the optimum of changing constraints.

This is the present state of knowledge about indirect methods that proceed straight to the peak without touching the mountainsides. In future chapters, obscured visibility will force us to proceed more cautiously, taking shorter steps and keeping to the trails.

BIBLIOGRAPHY

Bell, E. T., *The Development of Mathematics* (McGraw-Hill, New York, 1940).

Berkeley, G. Bishop, *The Analyst; or, a Discourse Addressed to an Infidel Mathematican.*

Bernoulli, Johann, *Essai d'une Nouvelle Théorie de la Manoeuvre des Vaisseaux* (J. G. König, Basle, 1714), pp. 32, 36.

Birkhoff, G., and S. MacLane, *A Survey of Modern Algebra* (Macmillan, New York, 1941).

Cajori, F., *A History of Mathematics* (Macmillan, New York, 1919).

Cauchy, Auguste L., *Cours d'analyse* (Paris, 1821).

Courant, R., and D. Hilbert, *Methods of Mathematical Physics, I* (Interscience, New York, 1953).

Cramer, Gabriel (for Cramer's rule, see Rosenbach and Whitman, Chap. 18).

Descartes, Réné, cited in Bell, p. 127.

Duffin, R. J., "Cost minimization problems treated by geometric means," *Opns. Res.* **10** (1962), 668–75.

————, "Dual programs and minimum cost," *Jour. Soc. Ind. Appl. Math.* **10** (1962) 119–23.

Edelbaum, T. N., "Theory of maxima and minima," in Leitman, p. 16.

Euler, L., *Calc. diff.* (1755), cited in Hancock, p. 18.

Fermat, Pierre de, "Methodus disquirendum maximam et minimam" (1638) *Oeuvres* **1** (Gauthier-Villars, Paris, 1841), 133–36, cited by Bell, p. 128.

————, "De maximus et minimus," *Oeuvres* **1** (Gauthier-Villars, Paris, 1841), 147–50, cited by Cajori, p. 164.

Gauss, Carl Friedrich, *Disquisitiones Arithmeticae* (Leipzig, 1801) p. 1278, cited in Hancock, p. 86.

Genocchi, A., and G. Peano, *Calcolo Differenziale e principii di Calcolo Integrale* (1884), prob. 133–36, cited by Hancock, p. 33 *et seq.*

Hancock, Harris, *Theory of Maxima and Minima (1917)* (Dover, New York, 1960).

Huygens, Christian, *Bibliothèque Universelle et Historique* (September, 1693).

Jacobi, C. G. J., cited by Bell, p. 400.

Kepler, Johannes, cited by Cajori, p. 163.

Lagrange, Comte Joseph Louis, "Recherches sur la méthode de maximis et mini-mis," *Miscellanea Taurinensia* (1759), *Oeuvres* **1**, 3–20, cited in Hancock, p. 86.

———, "Essai d'une nouvelle méthode pour détérminer les maxima et les minima," *Miscellanea Taurinensia*, **2** (1760–61) *Oeuvres*, **1**, pp. 356–57, 360.

———, *Théorie des Fonctions Analytiques* (1797), p. 290, cited by Hancock, p. 33.

———, *Calcul des fonctions* (1799), cited by Bell p. 267.

———, *Oeuvres de Lagrange* (Gauthier-Villars, Paris, 1867).

Leibniz, Gottfried Wilhelm, *The Early Mathematical Manuscripts of Leibniz*, trans-lated from Latin texts published by Carl Immanuel Gerhardt by J. M. Child (The Open Court Publishing Co., London, 1920).

Leitman, G., *Optimization Techniques with Applications to Aerospace Systems* (New York, Academic Press, 1962).

Maclaurin, Colin, *A Treatise on Fluxions* (1742), pp. 238, 857, cited by Cajori, p. 229.

Mencken, H. L., *A New Dictionary of Quotations* (Alfred A. Knopf, New York, 1942).

Newton, Sir Isaac, cited in Bell, p. 203.

Phillips, H. B., *Vector Analysis* (Wiley, New York, 1933), p. 35 *et seq.*

Raphson, Joseph, *Analysis aequationem universalis*, cited in Cajori, p. 203.

Renau, Chevalier, *Théorie de la Manoeuvre des Vaisseaux* (Paris, 1689).

Rosenbach, J. B., and E. A. Whitman, *College Algebra* (Ginn and Co., Boston, 1939, rev.).

Scheefer, Ludwig, "Über die Bedeutung der Begriffe Maximum und Minimum in der Variationsrechnung," *Math. Ann.*, **26** (1886), 197–208, cited in Hancock, Ch. 4.

———, "Theorie der Maxima und Minima einer Function von zwei Variabeln," *Math. Ann.*, **35** (1890), 541–76, cited in Hancock, chap. 4.

Stolz, O., cited in Hancock, chap. 4, pp. 39–42.

Taylor, Brook, *Methodus incrementorum directa et inversa* (1715–17), cited by Cajori, p. 226.

Weierstrass, K., cited in Courant and Hilbert, p. 164.

Wilde, D. J., "A unified approach to multivariable optimization theory," *Ind. Engng. Chem.* **57**, 8 (August, 1965), 18–30.

———, "Jacobians in constrained nonlinear optimization," *Opns. Res.* **13**, 5 (September, 1965), 248–56.

Zener, C., "A mathematical aid in optimizing engineering designs," *Proc. Nat. Acad. Sci.*, **47** (1961), 537–39.

EXERCISES

2-1. Prove Eqs. (2-17) and (2-18).

2-2. Perform two iterations of the Newton-Raphson method to find the positive root of Eqs. (2-39) and (2-40), starting at (a) $x = (800, 3)$; (b) $x = (1000, 5)$; (c) $x = (800, 4)$.

2-3. Prove Maclaurin's principle that a stationary point is a minimum if and only if the lowest-order nonvanishing derivative present is positive and of even order.

2-4. (Genocchi and Peano's counterexample) Let $y = (x_1 - a_1^2 x_2^2)(x_1 - a_2^2 x_2^2)$, with a_1 and a_2 constants.
   a. Show that Lagrange's criterion indicates a minimum for y at the origin.
   b. Show that y is maximum at the origin for all points on the curve $x_1 = (a_1^2 + a_2^2)x_2^2/2$.

2-5. Prove
   a. Eq. (2-89)
   b. Eq. (2-102) (see Wilde, September, 1965 for proof outline).

2-6. Verify Eqs. (2-116), (2-117), and (2-118).

2-7. Solve Eqs. (2-116), (2-117), and (2-118) algebraically.

Inequality Constraints

3

> *The dragon exceeds the proper limits;
> there will be occasion for repentance.*
>
> THE BOOK OF CHANGES (CHINA, C. 1200 B.C.,
> TRANSLATED BY J. LEGGE)

The ancient Book of Changes (*Yî King* in Cantonese; *I Ching* in Mandarin) is a manual for divining the future from tortoise shells and the stalks of a sacred flower. Its cryptic and ambiguous fortune-telling recipes were refined by Confucius and his disciples into proverbs, an example being the quotation beginning this chapter. With oriental subtlety this maxim reminds us that most human endeavors have bounds which are dangerous or impossible to violate. Policies and designs, like dragons, must not exceed the proper limits, lest later there be "occasion for repentance." To be useful, optimization theory must recognize such bounds and show how to handle them.

In Chapter 2, the question of finding an optimum in a feasible region defined by equations and inequalities was raised, but only partly settled. When there are no equations, but only strict inequalities, satisfied at the optimum, it can be found by setting first derivatives to zero. When a known set of equations, but no inequalities, constrain the optimum, it can be located by a similar indirect approach involving decision derivatives. More generally, however, one cannot predict which inequality constraints will be "tight" (satisfied as strict equalities) and which "loose" (satisfied as strict inequalities) at the optimum. Optimization problems of this sort, which have come to be called *mathematical programming* problems, will appear throughout the rest of the book, especially in Chapters 3, 4, and 5. Chapter 3 shows what can be done when all functions are nonlinear; the next exploits nonlinearities of a special kind; and Chapter 5 discusses the fully linear case. This order of procedure is unconventional, for other books on mathematical programming start with the linear case. Unfortunately the standard ideas and terminology of linear programming are rarely directly applicable to nonlinear situations; hence we find it saves time in the long run to develop the general concepts first. This makes the going rough in the beginning, but once the general ideas have been mastered, linear programming is readily grasped as a special case.

Solving a mathematical programming problem is like looking for the high point inside a fenced-in field on the *side* of a mountain. The peak could in principle be found by classical methods, but it lies outside the fence. If the mountain is unimodal, as in Fig. 3–1, the high point in the field is up against a fence, perhaps even in a corner where two fences meet. Thus an explorer climbs upwards until he strikes the fence and then continues along the fence in a rising direction until he reaches a local optimum, as for the path **abc**. A more fortunate track starts at **d**, hits a fence at **e**, leaves it again at **f**, encounters a new one at **g**, and follows it to the true maximum at **h**. Notice that strictly

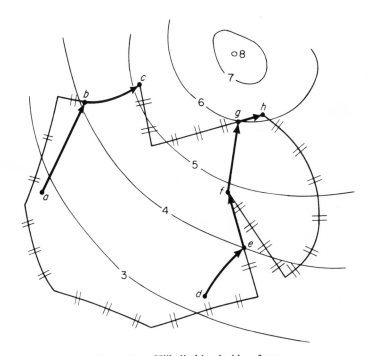

Figure 3-1. Hill-climbing inside a fence.

rising paths do not always lead to the true maximum in a constrained region, even when the objective function is unimodal.

Not knowing against which segments of the boundary the optimum lies forces one to proceed from one trial point to another in several jumps instead of one. But for each step the critical constraints can usually be identified, which permits indirect methods to be used, at least after some modification. Thus many mathematical programming procedures consist of a sequence of indirect optimizations in subregions of the feasible domain, guided by some master strategy for estimating new directions in which to proceed and the constraints most likely to be encountered. This chapter extends the indirect methods for use in these semidirect techniques. The key idea is to develop new constrained derivatives by manipulating differentials as in the preceding chapter.

After posing the nonlinear programming problem in mathematical terms, necessary conditions for a local optimum, under these new conditions, are derived informally by the differential approach. Circumstances under which these same *Kuhn-Tucker* conditions are also sufficient are discussed, as well as the question of unimodality in a constrained region. A new set of useful constrained derivatives, together with Jacobian formulas for computing them, are then developed and applied to construction of an optimization procedure known as the *differential algorithm*. This technique takes a particularly simple form when the objective function is quadratic and the constraint inequalities linear; hence it is described in complete detail for this case and demonstrated with a numerical example. It is shown how Lagrange's transformation (completing the square), an idea introduced in the preceding chapter, can simplify such computations. Not only are Lagrange's transformation and its inverse developed in detail, but the calculations are shown to be identical with "Gauss elimination," a simple and widely known procedure for solving linear simultaneous equations. The chapter ends by surveying the many other nonlinear programming techniques now in existence for keeping the dragon within proper limits.

3-01 Slack Variables and Slack Derivatives

We wish to minimize a differentiable objective function $y \langle \mathbf{x} \rangle$, where $\mathbf{x}$ must lie within or on the boundary of the closed region $\mathscr{F}$ defined by the *nonnegativity conditions*

$$x_n \geq 0 ; \qquad n = 1, \ldots, N \tag{3-1}$$

and the *inequality constraints*

$$f_k \langle \mathbf{x} \rangle \geq 0 ; \qquad k = 1, \ldots, K \tag{3-2}$$

An equivalent way of describing the region is to introduce K *slack variables* f_k which measure the difference between the value of the function $f_k\langle\mathbf{x}\rangle$ and zero. Thus, the K inequalities (3-2) are replaced by K equations

$$f_k\langle\mathbf{x}\rangle - f_k = 0 \tag{3-3}$$

and K nonnegativity conditions

$$f_k \geq 0 \tag{3-4}$$

This problem will be called the *inequality constrained optimization problem* here; it is also called the *linear programming* problem when all the functions are linear, and *nonlinear programming* otherwise (Hadley).

As an example, let the allowable set of pressures x_1 and recycle ratios x_2 in the hypothetical chemical plant be constrained to satisfy the inequality

$$x_1 x_2 \geq 9000 \tag{3-5}$$

To get this into the proper form, let

$$f_1\langle x_1, x_2\rangle = x_1 x_2 - 9000 \geq 0 \tag{3-6}$$

This corresponds to Eq. (3-2). The alternate form involves introducing a nonnegative slack variable f_1 satisfying

$$f_1\langle x_1, x_2\rangle - f_1 = x_1 x_2 - 9000 - f_1 = 0 \tag{3-7}$$

$$f_1 \geq 0 \tag{3-8}$$

which corresponds to Eqs. (3-3) and (3-4). Points satisfying these relations lie above and to the right of the dashed line of Fig. 2-3, the line itself being composed of points where equality holds.

Consider any feasible point $\mathbf{x}$ in $\mathscr{F}$, and let exactly M of the K slack variables f_k be zero there. No generality is lost in numbering the slack variables so that the first M are zero, and they will be given the running index $m = 1, \ldots, M$ to be consistent with the notation of Chapter 2.

$$f_m = 0 \; ; \qquad m = 1, \ldots, M \tag{3-9}$$

$$f_k > 0 \; ; \qquad k = M + 1, \ldots, K \tag{3-10}$$

We shall say informally that the first M constraints are "tight"

$$f_m\langle\mathbf{x}\rangle = 0 \tag{3-11}$$

and the others "loose"

$$f_k\langle\mathbf{x}\rangle > 0 \; ; \qquad k = M + 1, \ldots, K \tag{3-12}$$

For the time being we can forget about the loose constraints, since they will not be violated in any suitably small neighborhood of $\mathbf{x}$. As for the tight ones, only nonnegative perturbations of the f_m are feasible.

The situation now resembles that in Chapter 2 when the feasible region was defined only by M *equality* constraints. The principal difference is that now the M tight variables f_m must be considered as independent variables, in addition to the original N variables x_n. This is so because the f_m no longer must remain zero; they may now take on positive values as well. Since for every tight variable f_m, there is a constraint equation,

$$f_m\langle\mathbf{x}\rangle - f_m = 0 \qquad (3\text{-}13)$$

there are $N (= (M + N) - M)$ degrees of freedom and, of course, N decision variables to be selected from among the $M f_m$ and $N x_n$.

This time there is a better basis for singling out the decision variables than there was in Chapter 2, where the distinction was arbitrary. The state variables vary uncontrollably when the decisions are perturbed and may therefore increase or decrease, but no variable is permitted to become negative. Therefore, it is unwise to designate a variable as a state if its value at $\mathbf{x}$ is already zero, for it might go negative when the decisions are adjusted. It follows that any variable having the value zero at $\mathbf{x}$ must be treated as a decision and never decreased. When $M \leq N$, this rule automatically forces all tight variables f_m to be treated as decisions, leaving $N - M$ more decisions to be selected from the $N x_n$. If on the other hand $M > N$, then the rule cannot be observed strictly, for $M - N$ tight variables must be made states, even though they are zero at $\mathbf{x}$. A similarly embarrassing situation arises when $M \leq N$ but more than $N - M$ of the x_n are already zero. In this case some of the state variables will have to be zero in violation of the rule. Whenever any of the state variables are zero at $\mathbf{x}$, the point is said to be *degenerate* and special measures must be taken. Therefore let the rule for selecting decision variables be weakened to a warning to avoid degeneracy whenever possible. Remedies for degeneracy will be discussed in Section 5–03 after the simpler and more commonly occurring nondegenerate case has been developed.

Suppose then that $M \leq N$ and that $N - M$ variables x_n (not necessarily zero) have been selected as decision variables, redesignated $d_1, \ldots, d_R$ with $R \equiv N - M$ as in Chapter 2. Assume further that the remaining M state variables s_m are all positive.

$$s_m > 0 ; \qquad m = 1, \ldots, M \qquad (3\text{-}14)$$

There are in all $M + R (= N)$ decision variables, of which the $M f_t$ are zero

$$f_t = 0 ; \qquad t = 1, \ldots, M \qquad (3\text{-}15)$$

and the $R d_r$ nonnegative.

$$d_r \geq 0 ; \qquad r = 1, \ldots, R \qquad (3\text{-}16)$$

For abbreviation let vectors $\mathbf{s}$, $\mathbf{f}$, and $\mathbf{d}$ be formed in the usual manner from the variables s_m, f_t, and d_r, and consider the effects of small perturbations $\partial\mathbf{s}$ and $\partial\mathbf{d}$ upon the objective function $y\langle\mathbf{s}, \mathbf{d}\rangle$ and the tight constraint functions $f_t\langle\mathbf{s}, \mathbf{d}\rangle$ ($t = 1, \ldots, M$). The first-order terms of the Taylor expansions give

$$\partial y = \left(\frac{\partial y}{\partial \mathbf{s}}\right) \partial \mathbf{s} + \left(\frac{\partial y}{\partial \mathbf{d}}\right) \partial \mathbf{d} \tag{3-17}$$

$$\partial \mathbf{f} = \left(\frac{\partial \mathbf{f}}{\partial \mathbf{s}}\right) \partial \mathbf{s} + \left(\frac{\partial \mathbf{f}}{\partial \mathbf{d}}\right) \partial \mathbf{d} \tag{3-18}$$

Although the arguments here involve neglecting higher-order differentials, a rigorous proof based on the implicit function theorem is given elsewhere (Wilde, 1965).

Rearrange Eqs. (3–17) and (3–18) as in Chapter 2 to read

$$- \partial y + \left(\frac{\partial y}{\partial \mathbf{s}}\right) \partial \mathbf{s} = - \left(\frac{\partial y}{\partial \mathbf{d}}\right) \partial \mathbf{d} \tag{3-19}$$

$$\left(\frac{\partial \mathbf{f}}{\partial \mathbf{s}}\right) \partial \mathbf{s} = - \left(\frac{\partial \mathbf{f}}{\partial \mathbf{d}}\right) \partial \mathbf{d} + \partial \mathbf{f} \tag{3-20}$$

This gives $M + 1$ linear equations which can be solved for the $M + 1$ variables ∂y and $\partial \mathbf{s}$, provided that the equations are linearly independent. If they are not, the remedies of Chapter 2 can be applied; let us assume this independence, which implies that the Jacobian $|\partial \mathbf{f}/\partial \mathbf{s}|$ is not zero.

$$|\mathbf{J}| = \left|\frac{\partial \mathbf{f}}{\partial \mathbf{s}}\right| = \frac{\partial (f, \ldots, f_M)}{\partial (s, \ldots, s_M)} \neq 0 \tag{3-21}$$

The solutions can be written

$$\partial y = \frac{\delta y}{\delta \mathbf{d}} \partial \mathbf{d} + \frac{\delta y}{\delta \mathbf{f}} \partial \mathbf{f} \tag{3-22}$$

and

$$\partial \mathbf{s} = \frac{\delta \mathbf{s}}{\delta \mathbf{d}} \partial \mathbf{d} + \frac{\delta \mathbf{s}}{\delta \mathbf{f}} \partial \mathbf{f} \tag{3-23}$$

where the decision derivatives $\delta y/\delta \mathbf{d}$ and $\delta \mathbf{s}/\delta \mathbf{d}$ have already been derived in Chapter 2. The $\delta y/\delta \mathbf{f}$ and $\delta \mathbf{s}/\delta \mathbf{f}$ are vectors of *slack derivatives* (note the special symbol δ). They are readily found by the matrix methods of Chapter 2.

Rewrite Eq. (3–20) in the matrix notation of Chapter 2.

$$\mathbf{J} \partial \mathbf{s} = -\mathbf{C} \partial \mathbf{d} + \partial \mathbf{f} \tag{3-24}$$

Multiplying on the left by $\mathbf{J}^{-1}$ gives

$$\partial \mathbf{s} = - \mathbf{J}^{-1}\mathbf{C} \partial \mathbf{d} + \mathbf{J}^{-1} \partial \mathbf{f} \tag{3-25}$$

This may be substituted into Eq. (3–19), rewritten in terms of the state and decision gradients of Chapter 2.

$$-\partial y + \nabla_s y[-\mathbf{J}^{-1}\mathbf{C} \partial \mathbf{d} + \mathbf{J}^{-1}\partial \mathbf{f}] = -\nabla_d y \partial \mathbf{d}$$

or

$$\partial y = [\nabla_d y - \nabla_s y \mathbf{J}^{-1}\mathbf{C}]\partial \mathbf{d} + \nabla_s y \mathbf{J}^{-1} \partial \mathbf{f} \tag{3-26}$$

$$= \nabla y \partial \mathbf{d} + \nabla_s y \mathbf{J}^{-1} \partial \mathbf{f} \tag{3-27}$$

The proper identification of corresponding coefficients gives the new vectors of slack derivatives

$$\frac{\delta s}{\delta f} \equiv J^{-1} \equiv \left(\frac{\partial f}{\partial s}\right)^{-1} \tag{3-28}$$

$$\frac{\delta y}{\delta f} \equiv \nabla_s y J^{-1} \equiv \left(\frac{\partial y}{\partial s}\right)\left(\frac{\partial f}{\partial s}\right)^{-1} \equiv \left(\frac{\partial y}{\partial s}\right)\left(\frac{\delta s}{\delta f}\right) \tag{3-29}$$

Individual slack derivatives can be computed from the Jacobian formulas,

$$\frac{\delta s_m}{\delta f_t} = \frac{\partial(f_{t+1}, \ldots, f_M, f_1, \ldots, f_{t-1})/\partial(s_{m+1}, \ldots, s_M, s_1, \ldots, s_{m-1})}{\partial(f_1, \ldots, f_M)/\partial(s_1, \ldots, s_M)} \tag{3-30}$$

$$\frac{\delta y}{\delta f_t} = \frac{\partial(f_1, \ldots, f_{t-1}, y, f_{t+1}, \ldots, f_M)/\partial(s_1, \ldots, s_M)}{\partial(f_1, \ldots, f_M)/\partial(s_1, \ldots, s_M)} \tag{3-31}$$

Notice that if x is a local optimum x^*, then the right member of Eq. (3-31) is identical with that given in Chapter 2 for the sensitivity coefficients $\delta y^*/\delta f_t$.

$$\left(\frac{\delta y}{\delta f_t}\right)^* = \frac{\delta y^*}{\delta f_t} \tag{3-32}$$

There is, however, a difference in function between the sensitivity coefficient $\delta y^*/\delta f_t$, defined only at a local optimum, and the slack derivative $\delta y/\delta f_t$, defined at every point in the feasible region. The value of the former quantity does not depend upon the set of variables chosen to be the states, as does the value of the second. The slack derivative measures the rate of change of y with respect to changes in f_t, with all decisions and other tight constraints held constant. Except at an optimum, its value depends on which variables are states.

3-02 Necessary Conditions

Once the concepts of slack derivative and decision derivative are understood, it is not difficult to derive the conditions that must hold at a local minimum x^*. At such a point all small perturbations in the decisions or tight constraints cannot decrease y^*, and so

$$0 \leq \partial y = \left(\frac{\delta y}{\delta d}\right)^* \partial d + \left(\frac{\delta y}{\delta f}\right)^* \partial f \tag{3-33}$$

by Eq. (3–22). Since x^* has been assumed nondegenerate, small perturbations will not make any state variables negative. Consider any individual decision variable, say d^0, which happens to be zero.

$$d^0 = 0 \tag{3-34}$$

For such a variable, only nonnegative perturbations can be permitted

$$\partial d^0 \geq 0 \tag{3-35}$$

Thus the corresponding decision derivative must be nonnegative, for otherwise the product $(\delta y/\delta d^0)^* \, \partial d^0$ would be negative and one could decrease y^*, contradicting the hypothesis that $\mathbf{x}^*$ is a local minimum. Hence,

$$(\delta y/\delta d^0)^* \geq 0 \tag{3-36}$$

There may also be a decision variable, say d^+, which is strictly positive at $\mathbf{x}^*$.

$$d^+ > 0 \tag{3-37}$$

For such a variable, small perturbations ∂d^+ can be either positive or negative without making d^+ negative. Hence $(\delta y/\delta d^+)^*$ must vanish, for otherwise one could decrease y^* by making the sign of ∂d^+ opposite to that of the decision derivative. Therefore

$$\left(\frac{\delta y}{\delta d^+}\right)^* = 0 \tag{3-38}$$

Both Eqs. (3–36) and (3–38) can be combined into the single statement that at $\mathbf{x}^*$ it is necessary to have the decision derivatives all nonnegative.

$$\left(\frac{\delta y}{\delta \mathbf{d}}\right)^* \geq \mathbf{0} \tag{3-39}$$

A similar line of reasoning can be used to prove the same result for the slack derivatives.

$$\left(\frac{\delta y}{\delta \mathbf{f}}\right)^* \geq \mathbf{0} \tag{3-40}$$

The latter proof is slightly more direct because no tight constraints are positive. Equations (3–39) and (3–40) are often called the *nonnegativity conditions*.

Since for every decision either Eq. (3–34) or Eq. (3–38) must hold, a decision and its decision derivative cannot simultaneously be nonzero. Hence the product is always zero.

$$\left(\frac{\delta y}{\delta d_r}\right)^* d_r^* = 0 \; ; \qquad r = 1, \ldots, R \tag{3-41}$$

A similar result is trivially true for the tight constraints, since $\mathbf{f} = \mathbf{0}$.

$$\left(\frac{\delta y}{\delta f_t}\right)^* f_t^* = 0 \; ; \qquad t = 1, \ldots, M \tag{3-42}$$

Equations (3–41) and (3–42) are known as the *complementary slackness conditions*. They can be expressed in geometric terms by saying that at a local optimum the decision derivative vector is orthogonal to the decision vector and the slack derivative vector is orthogonal to the slack vector.

$$\left(\frac{\delta y}{\delta \mathbf{d}}\right)^* \mathbf{d}^* = 0 = \left(\frac{\delta y}{\delta \mathbf{f}}\right)^* \mathbf{f}^* \tag{3-43}$$

A third condition of interest is obtained by differentiating Eq. (3–33) partially with respect to any decision d_r, holding all other decision and *state* variables constant but permitting the constraints and objective function to vary.

$$\left(\frac{\partial y}{\partial d_r}\right)^* = \left(\frac{\delta y}{\delta d_r}\right)^* + \left(\frac{\delta y}{\delta \mathbf{f}}\right)^* \left(\frac{\partial \mathbf{f}}{\partial d_r}\right)^* ; \qquad r = 1, \ldots, R \qquad (3\text{-}44)$$

Notice that the left member is the usual partial derivative obtained by differentiating the objective function directly, ignoring the constraints completely. The derivatives $(\partial f_i / \partial d_r)^*$ are also found by direct differentiation of the $f_i \langle \mathbf{s}, \mathbf{d} \rangle$. Rearrangement of Eq. (3–44) gives the decision derivative vector in terms of the unconstrained gradient and a correction for keeping the constraints tight.

$$\left(\frac{\delta y}{\delta \mathbf{d}}\right)^* = \left(\frac{\partial y}{\partial \mathbf{d}}\right)^* - \left(\frac{\delta y}{\delta \mathbf{f}}\right)^* \left(\frac{\partial \mathbf{f}}{\partial \mathbf{d}}\right)^* \qquad (3\text{-}45)$$

In different notation and by Eq. (3–29), this shows the gradient projection vector in terms of state and decision gradients.

$$\nabla^* y = \nabla_d^* y - \nabla_s^* y \left(\frac{\delta \mathbf{s}}{\delta \mathbf{f}}\right)^* \left(\frac{\partial \mathbf{f}}{\partial \mathbf{d}}\right)^* \qquad (3\text{-}46)$$

The nonnegativity conditions of Eqs. (3–39) and (3–40), the complementary slackness conditions (3–41) and (3–42), together with the decision derivative Eq. (3–45), are called the Kuhn-Tucker conditions after the mathematicians who first proved them necessary at a local optimum. Their formulation was different, involving a Lagrangian function instead of constrained derivatives. The original demonstration also places fewer restrictions on the point $\mathbf{x}^*$. Here we require it to be nonsingular (nonzero Jacobian) and nondegenerate (all state variables positive).

3-03 Sufficiency

The nonnegativity and complementary slackness necessary conditions are easy to check at any nonsingular, nondegenerate point. A point where they are violated cannot be an optimum, and we shall see in the rest of the chapter how better points can be sought out under these circumstances. This section develops sufficient conditions which, if satisfied, guarantee that a point is a local optimum. There are several sets of sufficient conditions to be considered, each appropriate in different circumstances.

To establish sufficiency we must reconsider the second- and higher-order terms which were neglected in the original Taylor expansions considered. Had they been included in the original expansions (3–17) and (3–18), they would ultimately have lead to higher-order terms in Eq. (3–33), rewritten correctly as follows (and derived in some detail later in the section):

$$\partial y = \left(\frac{\delta y}{\delta \mathbf{d}}\right) \partial \mathbf{d} + \left(\frac{\delta y}{\delta \mathbf{f}}\right) \partial \mathbf{f} + O_2 \qquad (3\text{-}47)$$

The symbol O_2 represents the nonlinear remainder, composed of products of differentials $\partial d_r \, \partial f_t, \, \partial d_r^2, \, \partial f_t^2$, etc.

One set of sufficient conditions is complementary slackness, Eqs. (3-41) and (3-42), together with positivity of all the decision and slack derivatives.

$$\left(\frac{\delta y}{\delta \mathbf{d}}\right)^* > 0 \tag{3-48}$$

$$\left(\frac{\delta y}{\delta \mathbf{f}}\right)^* > 0 \tag{3-49}$$

Consider a perturbation ∂d_r in a particular decision, all other decisions and constraints being held constant. Then the remainder depends only on ∂d_r.

$$O_2 = 0(\partial d_r^2)$$

In the limit as ∂d_r approaches zero, the ratio of this remainder to $(\delta y / \delta d_r)^* \partial d_r$ must vanish.

$$\lim_{\partial d_r \to 0} \frac{0(\partial d_r^2)}{(\delta y / \delta d_r)^* \partial d_r} = \frac{0(\partial d_r)}{(\delta y / \delta d_r)^*} = 0 \tag{3-50}$$

This passing to the limit is permissible because the derivative in the denominator is not zero. Repeating this argument for all decisions and tight constraints, we see that the remainder is truly dominated by the linear terms and can be neglected. Complementary slackness, together with the positivity assumption, implies that $\mathbf{d}^* = \mathbf{0} = \mathbf{f}^*$, so only positive perturbations are feasible. Hence $\partial y > 0$ in a suitably small feasible neighborhood of $\mathbf{x}^*$, which implies that the point is a local minimum. Positivity and complementary slackness are therefore sufficient, as well as necessary, conditions for a local minimum at a nonsingular, nondegenerate point.

If any derivatives vanish, then Eq. (3-50) is not valid, and the higher-order terms cannot be ignored. Consider then the full Taylor expansion of the objective function y, with the quadratic terms written explicitly using the Hessian matrix $\mathbf{H}$ of second partial derivatives $\partial^2 y / \partial x_j \, \partial x_k$ (see Chapter 2), and with the third- and higher-order terms written as O_3.

$$\partial y = \left(\frac{\partial y}{\partial \mathbf{x}}\right) \partial \mathbf{x} + \frac{1}{2} \partial \mathbf{x}' \mathbf{H} \, \partial \mathbf{x} + O_3 \tag{3-51}$$

Similar expansions for the constraint functions are

$$\partial f_m = \frac{\partial f_m}{\partial \mathbf{x}} \partial \mathbf{x} + \frac{1}{2} \partial \mathbf{x}' \mathbf{H}_m \, \partial \mathbf{x} + O_3 \tag{3-52}$$

Let each of these constraint perturbations be multiplied by the constrained derivative $\delta y / \delta f_m$ (abbreviated as λ_m, the mth Lagrange multiplier) and subtracted from Eq. (3-51) to give

$$\partial y = \frac{\partial}{\partial \mathbf{x}} \left(y - \sum_{m=1}^{M} \lambda_m f_m \right) \partial \mathbf{x} + \frac{1}{2} \partial \mathbf{x}' \left(\mathbf{H} - \sum_{m=1}^{M} \lambda_m \mathbf{H}_m \right) \partial \mathbf{x} + O_3$$

If the perturbation is taken about a constrained stationary point $\mathbf{x}^0$, then the linear terms must vanish, since they are the first derivatives of the Lagrangian function. Let the matrix of the quadratic form be abbreviated

$$\mathbf{P} \equiv \mathbf{H} - \sum_{m=1}^{M} \lambda_m \mathbf{H}_m \tag{3-53}$$

Then the change ∂y^0 is

$$\partial y^0 = \frac{1}{2} \partial \mathbf{x}' \mathbf{P} \partial \mathbf{x} + O_3 \tag{3-54}$$

where it is understood that the $\partial \mathbf{x}$ satisfy

$$\partial \mathbf{f} = \frac{\partial \mathbf{f}}{\partial \mathbf{x}} \partial \mathbf{x} = \mathbf{0}, \tag{3-55}$$

in order that the constraints be tight.

If the matrix $\mathbf{P}$ is such that $\partial y^0 > 0$ for all $\partial \mathbf{x}$ satisfying Eq. (3–55), then $\mathbf{x}^0$ must be a local minimum, a theorem proved first by Carathéodory and subsequently by Phipps and by Burger. Phipps applied a result of Mann concerning quadratic functions subjected to linear constraints to obtain a more convenient test for local minimality. Let r be an index running from M to N, and form the r^2 matrix $\mathbf{P}_r$ from the first r rows and columns of $\mathbf{P}$. Also construct the M by r matrix $\mathbf{D}_r$ from the first derivatives of the f_m with respect to the first r independent variables.

$$\mathbf{D}_r \equiv \begin{pmatrix} \partial f_1/\partial x_1 & \cdots & \partial f_1/\partial x_r \\ \cdot & & \cdot \\ \cdot & & \cdot \\ \cdot & & \cdot \\ \partial f_M/\partial x_1 & \cdots & \partial f_M/\partial x_r \end{pmatrix} \tag{3-56}$$

Then Phipps' sufficient condition for a minimum is that all the following $N - M$ determinants of order $M + r$ be positive.

$$(-1)^M \begin{vmatrix} \mathbf{0} & \mathbf{D}_r \\ \mathbf{D}'_r & \mathbf{P}_r \end{vmatrix} > 0 \; ; \qquad r = M, \ldots, N \tag{3-57}$$

Rather than prove this condition here, we prefer to develop a test based on the concept of constrained *second* derivatives.

To do this, first partition the vector $\mathbf{x}$ into a decision vector $\mathbf{d}$ and a state vector $\mathbf{s}$ as in preceding sections. The Carathéodory-Phipps matrix $\mathbf{P}$ is partitioned similarly so that

$$\partial \mathbf{x}' \mathbf{P} \partial \mathbf{x} = (\partial \mathbf{d}', \partial \mathbf{s}') \begin{pmatrix} \mathbf{P}_{dd} & \mathbf{P}_{ds} \\ \mathbf{P}'_{ds} & \mathbf{P}_{ss} \end{pmatrix} \begin{pmatrix} \partial \mathbf{d} \\ \partial \mathbf{s} \end{pmatrix} \tag{3-58}$$

$$= \partial \mathbf{d}' \mathbf{P}_{dd} \, \partial \mathbf{d} + \partial \mathbf{d}' \mathbf{P}_{ds} \, \partial \mathbf{s}$$

$$+ \partial \mathbf{s}' \mathbf{P}'_{ds} \, \partial \mathbf{d} + \partial \mathbf{s}' \mathbf{P}_{ss} \, \partial \mathbf{s}$$

Eq. (3–25) is now applied to express the state variables in terms of the decisions **d** and slack variables **f**. The final result can be summarized after defining the following matrices:

$$S_{dd} \equiv P_{dd} - P_{ds}J^{-1}C - (P_{ds}J^{-1}C)' + (J^{-1}C)'P_{ss}J^{-1}C \qquad (3\text{-}59)$$

$$S_{df} \equiv P_{ds}J^{-1} - (J^{-1}C)'P_{ss}J^{-1} \equiv S'_{fd} \qquad (3\text{-}60)$$

$$S_{ff} \equiv (J^{-1})'P_{ss}J^{-1} \qquad (3\text{-}61)$$

$$S \equiv \begin{pmatrix} S_{dd} & S_{df} \\ S'_{df} & S_{ff} \end{pmatrix} \qquad (3\text{-}62)$$

Recall that **J**, the Jacobian matrix, and **C**, the control matrix, are simply collections of first derivatives in the constraint expansions ($\partial f = J\,\partial s + C\,\partial d$). The *constrained* change δy^0 can now be written

$$\delta y^0 = \frac{1}{2}(\partial d', \partial f')\begin{pmatrix} S_{dd} & S_{df} \\ S'_{df} & S_{ff} \end{pmatrix}\begin{pmatrix} \partial d \\ \partial f \end{pmatrix} + O_3$$

There are no longer any equality side conditions to be satisfied because the constraints of Eq. (3–55) are automatically satisfied. The elements of the matrix **S** are the *constrained second derivatives*.

If all the constraints are equalities

$$f_m = 0$$

as in the previous chapter, then the perturbations ∂f are all identically zero and

$$\delta y^0 = \tfrac{1}{2}\,\partial d' S_{dd}\,\partial d + O_3$$

For x^0 to be a local minimum (maximum) it is therefore sufficient that S_{dd}, the matrix of constrained second derivatives with respect to the decision variables, be positive (negative) definite. This property can be tested by the Gauss elimination version of Lagrange's transformation described in Section 3–17. This test is equivalent to that of Phipps, but more convenient computationally.

A more interesting situation arises when the constraints are inequalities

$$f_m \geq 0$$

in which case positive perturbations ∂f of the slack variables are allowed. There is no longer any need to distinguish between decision and slack variables, so let them be represented by a single vector

$$v' = (d', f')$$

Let the variables of **v** be identified with a superscript either $+$ or 0 as follows

$$v_n \equiv \begin{cases} v_n^+ & \text{if } \dfrac{\delta y}{\delta v_n} = 0 \\[2ex] v_n^0 & \text{if } \dfrac{\delta y}{\delta v_n} > 0 \end{cases}$$

The point x^0 is now presumed to satisfy the Kuhn-Tucker *necessary* conditions for an inequality constrained minimum, so none of the constrained first derivatives can be negative—Eqs. (3–39) and (3–40). The Taylor expansion for the change in y resulting from nonnegative perturbations in the v can be written, to second order,

$$\delta y^0 = \frac{\delta y}{\delta v} \partial v + \frac{1}{2} \partial v' S \partial v + O_3$$

But by definition the first-order terms for v^+ must vanish. Then if S is partitioned to correspond to v^+ and v^0, the expansion becomes

$$\delta y^0 = \left(\frac{\delta y}{\delta v^0} \right) \partial v^0 + \frac{1}{2} (\partial v^+)' S^{++} \partial v^+ + O_2 + O_3$$

$$O_2 = (\partial v^+)' S^{+0} \partial v^0 + \tfrac{1}{2} (\partial v^0)' S^{00} \partial v^0$$

Since the linear terms for ∂v^0 do not vanish, the quadratic remainder O_2 can be made negligible by making ∂v^+ and ∂v^0 suitably small. Similarly, the third- and higher-order terms can be neglected, provided that S^{++} is definite. Hence for x^0 to be a local minimum, it is sufficient that S^{++} be positive-definite. If S^{++} is indefinite, or negative-definite, the point is not a local minimum, and better feasible points can be found in the neighborhood of x^0 by setting $\partial v^0 = 0$ and choosing ∂v^+ making $(\partial v^+)' S^{++} \partial v^+ < 0$. When S^{++} is positive semidefinite, the point cannot be identified without further analysis of the Scheefer-Stolz variety.

3-04 Convexity

Weaker sufficient conditions for a local minimum can be derived if the objective function is known to be strictly convex, that is, never underestimated by a linear interpolation between any two points, say x_1 and x_2. That is, for every number α satisfying

$$0 < \alpha < 1 \qquad\qquad (3\text{-}63)$$

it is true that

$$y \langle \alpha x_1 + (1 - \alpha) x_2 \rangle < \alpha y \langle x_1 \rangle + (1 - \alpha) y \langle x_2 \rangle \qquad (3\text{-}64)$$

The adjective "strictly" is omitted if the function is ever exactly equal to a linear interpolation between two points. A convex function would have the strict inequality sign in (3–64) replaced by $\leq$. A (strictly) *concave* function is one whose negative is (strictly) *convex*; it is never overestimated by linear interpolation.

For our purposes the important property of a strictly convex function is that at any point where it is twice differentiable, its Hessian matrix is positive-definite (Berge). Hence for *any* perturbations ∂x, and in particular for feasible ones, the quadratic terms in Eq. (3–51) can only increase ∂y. Since complementary slackness and nonnegativity together imply nonnegativity of the linear terms, they are sufficient to insure that such a point is a local minimum when y is a strictly convex function of x, a result first proven by Kuhn and Tucker.

Suppose finally that the feasible region $\mathscr{F}$ is convex. When applied to the region $\mathscr{F}$, convexity means that the straight line between two points x_1 and x_2 in $\mathscr{F}$ lies entirely within $\mathscr{F}$. Thus every point x satisfying

$$x = \alpha x_1 + (1 - \alpha)x_2 \qquad (3\text{-}65)$$

for feasible x_1, x_2 in $\mathscr{F}$ and

$$0 \leq \alpha \leq 1 \qquad (3\text{-}66)$$

is also a feasible point in $\mathscr{F}$. The important result is that if y is strictly convex in the convex region $\mathscr{F}$, then y is unimodal; that is, there is only one local minimum in $\mathscr{F}$, making it, of course, the global minimum.

$$x^* = x^{**} \qquad (3\text{-}67)$$

Figure 3–2 shows contours of a strictly convex function in a convex region. To see why the local minimum is unique in this case, consider any point x ($\neq x^{**}$) in $\mathscr{F}$ and consider the straight line connecting it with the global minimum x^{**}, assuming that one exists, as when $\mathscr{F}$ is closed and bounded.

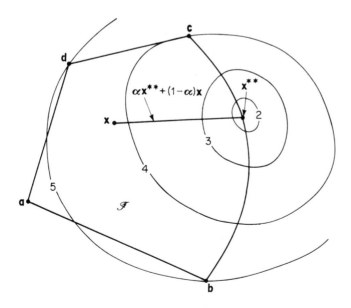

Figure 3-2. A strictly convex function in a convex region.

Since $\mathscr{F}$ is convex, all points $\alpha\mathbf{x}^{**} + (1 - \alpha)\mathbf{x}$ on this line are also in $\mathscr{F}$, including those in an arbitrarily small neighborhood of $\mathbf{x}$. Moreover, the convexity of y implies that along this same line

$$y\langle\alpha\mathbf{x}^{**} + (1 - \alpha)\mathbf{x}\rangle < \alpha y\langle\mathbf{x}^{**}\rangle + (1 - \alpha)y\langle\mathbf{x}\rangle$$
$$= y\langle\mathbf{x}\rangle + \alpha\,(y\langle\mathbf{x}^{**}\rangle - y\langle\mathbf{x}\rangle) < y\langle\mathbf{x}\rangle \qquad (3\text{-}68)$$

The last inequality follows because $\alpha(y\langle\mathbf{x}^{**}\rangle - y\langle\mathbf{x}\rangle)$ can only be negative, since $\alpha > 0$ and $\mathbf{x}^{**}$ is the *global* minimum. It follows that all points on the line are better than $\mathbf{x}$, so $\mathbf{x}$ cannot be a local minimum. Hence if y is strictly convex and $\mathscr{F}$ convex, the complementary slackness and nonnegativity conditions are both necessary and sufficient for a *global* minimum at a nonsingular, nondegenerate point.

Everything would be lost if in this case we wanted to maximize rather than minimize y. Notice in Fig. 3–2 that all four points **a**, **b**, **c**, and **d** are local maxima, **a** also being the global maximum.

3-05 Differential Algorithms

At any feasible, nonsingular, nondegenerate point, the decision and slack derivatives can be evaluated by the Jacobian or matrix equations. Then their signs can be checked to see whether they satisfy the nonnegativity condition. If any, say $\delta y/\delta d_m$ (or $\delta y/\delta f_t$), do not, then y can be decreased by increasing d_m (or f_t). If all derivatives are nonnegative, then the values of all variables are examined to see whether any complementary slackness conditions are violated. This can happen only if a variable d_m (or f_t) and its corresponding derivative $\delta y/\delta d_m$ (or $\delta y/\delta f_t$) are simultaneously positive. In this situation y can be improved by decreasing d_m (or f_t), an allowable move as long as negativity is avoided. If both positivity and complementary slackness conditions are satisfied, the point is a local minimum, since these conditions are sufficient as well as necessary. If only nonnegativity and complementary slackness conditions hold, the second-order analysis described in Section 3–03 may be needed. Of course, convexity makes things easy when it can be assumed.

If any of these conditions do not hold, directions in which improvement is possible are indicated. In making the move, however, one must be careful to avoid leaving the feasible region. Keeping the decisions and tight constraints nonnegative is easy, since they can be manipulated at will, but the states or slack variables could go negative if the step taken is too large. To avoid this, one can examine the vector of *state* derivatives $\delta\mathbf{s}/\delta\mathbf{d}$ and $\delta\mathbf{s}/\delta\mathbf{f}$ to see, at least to a first approximation, how sensitive the states are to changes in the decisions and tight constraints. One also needs derivatives measuring the sensitivity of the *loose* constraints f_k (for $k = M + 1, \ldots, K$) to these perturbations. These *loose constraint derivatives* $\delta f_k/\delta d_m$ and $\delta f_k/\delta f_t$ are derived simply by noticing that the loose constraint functions $f_k\langle \mathbf{s}, \mathbf{d}\rangle$ can be expanded in exactly the same way as the objective function $y\langle \mathbf{s}, \mathbf{d}\rangle$. Let a superscript $+$ denote loose constraints; let a vector $\mathbf{f}^+$ be made up from the f_k^+; their first-order Taylor expansions may be written in matrix-vector form as

$$\partial \mathbf{f}^+ = \left(\frac{\partial \mathbf{f}^+}{\partial \mathbf{s}}\right) \partial \mathbf{s} + \left(\frac{\partial \mathbf{f}^+}{\partial \mathbf{d}}\right) \partial \mathbf{d}$$

$$= \nabla_s \mathbf{f}^+ \partial \mathbf{s} + \nabla_d \mathbf{f}^+ \partial \mathbf{d} \tag{3-69}$$

Combination of this with Eq. (3–25) gives

$$\partial \mathbf{f}^+ = [\nabla_d \mathbf{f}^+ - \nabla_s \mathbf{f}^+ \mathbf{J}^{-1}\mathbf{C}]\, \partial \mathbf{d} + \nabla_s \mathbf{f}^+ \mathbf{J}^{-1}\, \partial \mathbf{f} \tag{3-70}$$

This resembles Eq. (3–26), and the loose constraint derivative vectors can be written, with the usual abbreviations,

$$\frac{\delta \mathbf{f}^+}{\delta \mathbf{d}} \equiv \nabla_d \mathbf{f}^+ - \nabla_s \mathbf{f}^+ \mathbf{J}^{-1}\mathbf{C} \equiv \left(\frac{\partial \mathbf{f}^+}{\partial \mathbf{d}}\right) - \left(\frac{\partial \mathbf{f}^+}{\partial \mathbf{s}}\right)\left(\frac{\delta \mathbf{s}}{\delta \mathbf{d}}\right) \tag{3-71}$$

$$\frac{\delta \mathbf{f}^+}{\delta \mathbf{f}} = \nabla_s \mathbf{f}^+ \mathbf{J}^{-1} \equiv \left(\frac{\partial \mathbf{f}^+}{\partial \mathbf{s}}\right)\left(\frac{\partial \mathbf{f}}{\partial \mathbf{s}}\right)^{-1} \equiv \left(\frac{\partial \mathbf{f}^+}{\partial \mathbf{s}}\right)\left(\frac{\delta \mathbf{s}}{\delta \mathbf{f}}\right) \tag{3-72}$$

The Jacobian formulas for the individual components are, for $k = M + 1, \ldots, K$,

$$\frac{\delta f_k}{\delta d_m} = \frac{\partial(f_k, f_1, \ldots, f_M)/\partial(d_m, s_1, \ldots, s_M)}{\partial(f_1, \ldots, f_M)/\partial(s_1, \ldots, s_M)} \tag{3-73}$$

and

$$\frac{\delta f_k}{\delta f_t} = \frac{\partial(f_1, \ldots, f_{t-1}, f_k, f_{t+1}, \ldots, f_M)/\partial(s_1, \ldots, s_M)}{\partial(f_1, \ldots, f_M)/\partial(s_1, \ldots, s_M)} \tag{3-74}$$

These derivatives, which resemble the decision and tight constraint derivatives previously developed, complete the set needed for developing what we shall call *differential algorithms* to solve constrained nonlinear optimization problems.

A brief numerical example from Wilde (1965) shows how a differential algorithm advances to the minimum by successive improvement, using the various constrained derivatives. Consider the problem of minimizing

$$y \equiv -\exp[(x_1 - 1)^2 + (x_2 - 2)^2] \tag{3-75}$$

subject to

$$x_1, x_2 \geq 0 \tag{3-76}$$

and

$$f_1\langle x_1, x_2\rangle = x_1 - x_2^2 \geq 0 \tag{3-77}$$

$$f_2\langle x_1, x_2\rangle = -e^{-x_1} + x_2 \geq 0 \tag{3-78}$$

$$f_3\langle x_1, x_2\rangle = -2(x_1 - 1)^2 + x_2 \geq 0 \tag{3-79}$$

The search begins at any feasible point, say $x_1 = x_2 = 1$, where $f_1 = 0$, $f_2 = e^{-1} + 1 > 0$, and $f_3 = 1 > 0$, Hence there is exactly *one* tight constraint ($M = 1$), and since there are *two* independent variables ($N = 2$), *one* of them ($N - M$) must be made a decision and the other a state variable. Neither being zero, the choice is arbitrary, so we designate x_1 as the decision d_1 and let x_2 be the state s_1. The decision derivative is obtained from Jacobian Eq. (2–90), with the partial derivatives evaluated at $s_1 = d_1 = 1$.

$$\frac{\delta y}{\delta d_1} = \frac{\partial(y, f_1)/\partial(d_1, s_1)}{\partial f_1/\partial s_1}$$

$$= \begin{vmatrix} \partial y/\partial d_1 & \partial y/\partial s_1 \\ \partial f_1/\partial d_1 & \partial f_1/\partial s_1 \end{vmatrix} / (\partial f_1/\partial s_1) \qquad (3\text{-}80)$$

$$= \begin{vmatrix} 0 & -2y \\ 1 & -2 \end{vmatrix} / -2 = -y = e > 0$$

Hence the nonnegativity, but not the complementary slackness condition, is satisfied for d_1, which could therefore be decreased to improve y.

Let us also examine the slack derivative, given by Eq. (3–31).

$$\frac{\delta y}{\delta f_1} = \frac{\partial y/\partial s_1}{\partial f_1/\partial s_1} = \frac{-2y}{-2} = y = -e < 0 \qquad (3\text{-}81)$$

It violates the nonnegativity condition, so y can be improved by making f_1 positive, that is, by letting the first constraint go loose. This leads to easier computations than would decreasing d_1, since no constraints need be considered at all. Hence the first move would be guided by the unconstrained derivatives $\partial y/\partial x_1 (= 0)$ and $\partial y/\partial x_2 (= 2e)$. We choose to move along the gradient $(0, 2e)$ by holding x_1 constant and changing x_2. Since we want f_1 to increase, we check the value of $\partial f_1/\partial x_2$ at $(1, 1)$. The derivative being negative, a decrease in x_2 will not only decrease y, but increase f_1 as desired. The minimum feasible point on the line $x_1 = 1$ is attained at $x_2 = e^{-1}$ where $f_2 = 0$. In practice, finding such a point would require some nonlinear numerical work, such as the Newton-Raphson method described in Chapter 2, but this would not be difficult because all the derivatives needed have already been computed.

The second trial point is then $(1, e^{-1})$, and again $M = 1$. At this point $\mathbf{x}_2, y\langle \mathbf{x}_2 \rangle = -14.30$, a considerable improvement over $y\langle \mathbf{x}_1 \rangle = -2.72$ at the starting point. This time f_2 is the tight constraint and as before let $x_1 = d_1$ and $x_2 = s_1$. The decision and constraint derivatives are

$$\frac{\delta y}{\delta d_1} = \frac{\partial(y, f_2)/\partial(d_1, s_1)}{\partial f_2/\partial s_1} = \begin{vmatrix} 0 & 2(e^{-1} - 2)y \\ e^{-1} & 1 \end{vmatrix} / 1 \qquad (3\text{-}82)$$

$$= -2e^{-1}(e^{-1} - 2)y < 0$$

and

$$\frac{\delta y}{\delta f_2} = \frac{\partial y/\partial s_1}{\partial f_2/\partial s_1} = \frac{2(e^{-1} - 2)y}{1} > 0 \qquad (3\text{-}83)$$

The first relation violates nonnegativity so y can be decreased further by increasing d_1, with f_2 held at zero. The constrained derivatives of the other constraints and of the dependent variable can now be computed to permit estimation of how far to go along the constraint—[see Eq. (3–73) and Eq. (2–102)].

$$\frac{\delta f_1}{\delta d_1} = \frac{\delta f_1}{\delta x_1} = \frac{\partial(f_1, f_2)/\partial(d_1, s_1)}{\partial f_2/\partial s_1} = 1 + 2e^{-2} > 0 \tag{3-84}$$

$$\frac{\delta f_3}{\delta d_1} = \frac{\delta f_3}{\delta x_1} = \frac{\partial(f_3, f_2)/\partial(d_1, s_1)}{\partial f_2/\partial s_1} = -e^{-1} < 0 \tag{3-85}$$

$$\frac{\delta s_1}{\delta d_1} = \frac{\delta x_2}{\delta x_1} = -\frac{\partial f_2/\partial d_1}{\partial f_2/\partial s_1} = -e^{-1} < 0 \tag{3-86}$$

They show that if one moves in the direction tangent to $f_2 = 0$ in which x_1 is increasing, the first constraint loosens, the third tightens, and x_2 decreases. Given that $f_3\langle \mathbf{x}_2 \rangle = x_2 = e^{-1}$ at $\mathbf{x}_2$, one would expect an encounter with a constraint somewhere around $x_1 = 2$. Although the nonlinearity of the constraints forces this linear estimate to be high, it is not bad as a first guess to be improved by numerical methods.

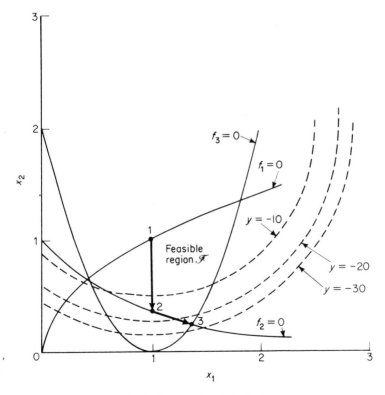

Figure 3-3. Differential algorithm.

Actually the constraint $f_3 = 0$ is reached at $\mathbf{x}_3 = (1.3586, 0.2571)$. Here there are two binding constraints f_2 and f_3, so that $M = 2$ and both x_1 and x_2 must be treated as state variables s_1 and s_2. The two slack derivatives are, from Eq. (3–31),

$$\frac{\delta y}{\delta f_2} = \frac{\partial(y, f_3)/\partial(s_1, s_2)}{\partial(f_2, f_3)/\partial(s_1, s_2)} = \frac{-4.29y}{1.69} > 0 \qquad (3\text{-}87)$$

$$\frac{\delta y}{\delta f_3} = \frac{\partial(f_2, y)/\partial(s_1, s_2)}{\partial(f_2, f_3)/\partial(s_1, s_2)} = \frac{-1.625y}{1.69} > 0 \qquad (3\text{-}88)$$

Not only are the complementary slackness conditions satisfied, but also the slack derivatives are all *positive* (not just nonnegative). These are necessary and sufficient conditions for a local minimum, and so $y^* = y\langle 1.3586, 0.2571 \rangle = -23.8$.

Figure 3–3 shows the feasible region $\mathscr{F}$, contours of the objective function, and the path taken by the algorithm. Although $\mathscr{F}$ is convex, $y\langle \mathbf{x} \rangle$ is not, and so one cannot assume that $\mathbf{x}^*$ is the only local optimum, although this happens to be the case here. Notice that the path would have been simpler if the constraints had been linear, for in that case the tangent lines would have been straight lines. Simplifications brought about by linearities in the constraints are exploited in the next section.

3-06 Linear Constraints

Differential algorithms are particularly attractive when the constraint functions are linear, for then one can predict exactly where a given path of improvement will leave the feasible region. Consider then the problem of minimizing a nonlinear function $y = y\langle \mathbf{x} \rangle$ subject to nonnegativity conditions

$$x_n \geq 0 ; \qquad n = 1, \ldots, N \qquad (3\text{-}89)$$

and the *linear* constraints

$$\sum_{n=1}^{N} a_{kn} x_n \geq b_k ; \qquad k = 1, \ldots, K \qquad (3\text{-}90)$$

where the a_{kn} and the b_k are known constants. In this case the constraint functions are linear.

$$f_k = \sum_{n=1}^{N} a_{kn} x_n - b_k \geq 0 \qquad (3\text{-}91)$$

Their most important property is that all first partial derivatives of the constraints are constant and independent of $\mathbf{x}$.

$$\frac{\partial f_k}{\partial x_n} = a_{kn} \qquad (3\text{-}92)$$

This implies that for any choice of tight constraints and decision variables, the constrained derivatives $\delta s/\delta d$, $\delta s/\delta f$, $\delta f^+/\delta d$, and $\delta f^+/\delta f$ do not change as one moves away from the point $\mathbf{x}$ where the decision and tight constraint derivatives were evaluated. Thus it can be predicted with certainty just where any straight-line path will leave the feasible region.

Suppose, for example, that one wishes to adjust d_1, letting all other decisions and tight constraints alone. The changes in any state variable s_m and in any loose constraint f_i^+ are given, respectively, by

$$\Delta s_m \equiv (\delta s_m/\delta d_1)\, \Delta d_1 \qquad (3\text{-}93)$$

$$\Delta f_i^+ = (\delta f_i^+/\delta d_1)\, \Delta d_1 \qquad (3\text{-}94)$$

where Δd_1 is the adjustment in d_1. Let $s_m\langle\mathbf{x}\rangle$ and $f_i^+\langle\mathbf{x}\rangle$ be the numerical values of the states and loose constraints at the original point $\mathbf{x}$. Then Δd_1 produces a feasible change only so long as

$$s_m + \Delta s_m \geq 0 \qquad (3\text{-}95)$$

and

$$f_i^+ + \Delta f_i^+ \geq 0 \qquad (3\text{-}96)$$

This is no problem for any variable having its corresponding derivative nonnegative, but negative derivatives place an upper bound on Δd_1. Thus

$$\Delta d_1^* = \min\left\{ \frac{-s_m\langle\mathbf{x}\rangle}{(\delta s_m/\delta d_1)},\ \frac{-f_i^+\langle\mathbf{x}\rangle}{\delta f_i^+/\delta d_1} \right\} \qquad (3\text{-}97)$$

where it is understood that only negative derivatives are considered. Similar relations can be derived for other decisions as well as for the tight constraints. Moreover, all decision and tight constraint variables can be adjusted simultaneously along a straight line with a parametric equation

$$(\Delta\mathbf{d}', \Delta\mathbf{f}') = \mu(\mathbf{k}_a', \mathbf{k}_f')$$

where μ is a single parameter and $\mathbf{k}_a'$ and $\mathbf{k}_f'$ are vectors of constants. The resulting changes in $\mathbf{s}$ and $\mathbf{f}^+$ being linear in the $\Delta\mathbf{d}'$ and $\Delta\mathbf{f}'$, one can readily compute the maximum feasible change.

If the variable driven to zero by the maximum change is a state, then it should be made a decision at the new point; if it is a constraint, it will, of course, be considered tight rather than loose. Each move may necessitate a realignment of states, decisions, and tight constraints, but the new constrained derivatives can easily be calculated from the old ones if only one variable was adjusted to begin with. This sort of computation is demonstrated by numerical example in Section 3–07, where all these ideas will be made concrete and incorporated into a specific detailed computation procedure.

3-07 A Differential Algorithm for Linear Constraints

When all constraints are linear, it is convenient to suppress the distinctions between the original variables $x_1, \ldots, x_N$ and the constraint variables $f_1, \ldots, f_K$

to work entirely with equality constraints as in Eq. (3–3). The constraint variables f_k are relabeled x_{N+k}

$$x_{N+k} \equiv f_k \, ; \qquad k = 1, \ldots, K \tag{3-98}$$

and the problem is to minimize $y\langle \mathbf{x} \rangle$, where now $\mathbf{x} = (x_1, \ldots, x_N, x_{N+1}, \ldots, x_{N+K})$, subject to the K perpetually tight equality constraints

$$\sum_{n=1}^{N} a_{kn} x_n - x_{N+k} = b_k \tag{3-99}$$

and the $N + K$ nonnegativity constraints represented by

$$\mathbf{x} \geq 0 \tag{3-100}$$

There being K linearly independent equations, K state variables and N decisions can be selected. The states can always be expressed as linear functions of the decisions

$$s_k = \beta_k - \sum_{n=1}^{N} \alpha_{kn} d_n \tag{3-101}$$

where the α_{kn} and β_k are unique constants, calculable from the matrix and Jacobian equations already derived. Notice that the K state variables chosen must have coefficients a_{kn} which form a nonsingular Jacobian matrix $\mathbf{J}$. This restriction causes no real difficulty in practice, since if worse comes to worst, one can always select the former constraints $x_{N+1}, \ldots, x_{N+K}$ as states, in which case $\beta_k = b_k$ and $\alpha_{kn} = a_{kn}$. The algorithm will always generate a unique set of constants α_{kn} and β_k.

To begin, the algorithm sets all the decisions to zero and therefore requires that for our initial choice of the s_k, the corresponding β_k be nonnegative. In the terminology of linear programming, such a solution to the constraints is called a *basic feasible solution*, and it is usually simplest to start the differential algorithm with this type of solution, for there are well-known methods (Gass) for finding one.

Using Eq. (3–101) we can express $y\langle \mathbf{x} \rangle$ uniquely in terms of the decision variables. This substituted objective function can then be differentiated partially with respect to each of the decision variables, the other *constrained* variables being held constant. The resulting *constrained* derivatives will be designated as $\delta y / \delta d_m$, abbreviated v_m, and it is understood that whereas all other decision variables are held constant in computing one of these partials, the state variables are permitted to adjust in value so that the constraints (3–99) remain satisfied.

Accordingly, there are two results of a perturbation in a decision variable d_m: its direct effect upon the objective function, and its indirect effect produced by the corresponding changes required in each state variable:

$$\begin{aligned}
v_m = \frac{\delta y}{\delta d_m} &= \frac{\partial y}{\partial d_m} + \sum_{k=1}^{K} \frac{\partial y}{\partial s_k} \frac{\delta s_k}{\delta d_m} \\
&= \frac{\partial y}{\partial d_m} - \sum_{k=1}^{K} \alpha_{km} \frac{\partial y}{\partial s_k} \, ; \qquad m = 1, \ldots, N
\end{aligned} \tag{3-102}$$

The partial derivative v_m is called the mth *decision derivative* relative to the current set of state variables, since it indicates whether an increase (or decrease) in the value of the corresponding decision variable d_m would be desirable. For if v_m is negative, then *increasing* d_m (while holding all other decision variables constant) will decrease the value of the objective function; if v_m is positive, then *decreasing* d_m will decrease this function. This latter change, of course, is possible only if d_m is positive, since all variables must remain nonnegative. Unlike most solution methods, the differential algorithm permits the decision variables to take on positive values except at the beginning of the process, when a basic feasible solution is required.

Beginning with the initial solution, the algorithm proceeds iteratively, reducing the value of the objective function at each step, while maintaining a *feasible* solution satisfying the constraints (3–99). The objective function is decreased by adjusting one decision variable at a time, holding all other decision variables constant. This adjustment must terminate at that value beyond which either a state variable would be driven negative, or the objective function would begin to increase rather than decrease. In the former case, the resulting solution would no longer be feasible; in the latter, it would no longer be optimal. In addition, of course, the adjusted decision variable cannot be reduced below zero.

When a state variable s_k has been driven to zero by the change in a decision variable d_m, the kth constraint equation (3–101) is solved for s_k and then used to eliminate this variable from all the other constraints and the objective function. This process is called a *simplex operation*, or just *simplexing*, and it effectively interchanges the roles of s_k and d_m, the former becoming a decision variable, and the latter a state variable. Such interchanges are always made in this manner, and thus always involve just one pair of variables. Furthermore, changes in the values of the variables are always accomplished by adjusting one decision variable, holding all other decision variables constant.

Formal rules may now be set down for carrying out the steps of the algorithm. Let v_i be the smallest negative decision derivative and v_h the largest positive decision derivative for which the corresponding decision variable d_h is positive. If there are no negative v_m, set v_i to zero; if all positive v_m have corresponding decision variables which are zero, set v_h equal to zero. Notice that any positive v_h would violate the complementary slackness conditions for an optimum.

If v_i and v_h are both zero, an optimal solution to the mathematical programming problem has been found.

If v_i and v_h are not both zero, compute

$$V = v_i + v_h \tag{3-103}$$

If V is $\begin{pmatrix} \text{nonpositive} \\ \text{positive} \end{pmatrix}$, then $\begin{pmatrix} \text{increase } d_i \\ \text{decrease } d_h \end{pmatrix}$, holding all other decision variables constant, until

I. Some state variable, say s_p, becomes zero, or

II. v_r becomes zero; where $r = h$ if V is positive, and $r = i$ if V is non-positive, or

III. d_h becomes zero.

We shall call the decision variable to be adjusted d_r and its associated sensitivity coefficient v_r, regardless of the sign of V.

In case (I), d_r replaces s_p in the set of state variables; in the other two cases, no change is made in this set, and d_r remains a decision variable. Clearly, for any such change, ∂d_r, the value of the objective function y always decreases, since the change in this variable is given by

$$\Delta y = \int v_r \, \partial d_r \qquad (3\text{-}104)$$

When v_r is negative, ∂d_r is positive, and when v_r is positive, ∂d_r is negative. In both cases, the integrand is negative over the range of integration, which implies that $\Delta y < 0$.

3-08 A Cubic Example

In order to illustrate the general procedure, let us use the differential algorithm to solve the following programming problem:

$$\text{minimize } y = 6x_1^3 - 12x_1x_2 + 3x_2^2 - 6x_1 + 7x_2 \qquad (3\text{-}105)$$

subject to the constraints

$$3x_1 + 4x_2 \leq 2$$
$$x_1, x_2 \geq 0 \qquad (3\text{-}106)$$

The necessary calculations are simplified if the constraints (3–106) are kept in terms of their *original* numbering throughout the solution procedure. We will also write the constraints in tabular form as shown in Fig. 3–4(a). This form is similar to the simplex tableau used in the linear programming calculations described in Chapter 5. The double vertical line represents an equality sign, so that the constraint is read as $3x_1 + 4x_2 + x_3 = 2$, where x_3 is the slack variable for this constraint. The bottom row gives the value of the decision derivative associated with the variable in its column heading. These coefficients are defined only for decision variables, and the entries in the columns corresponding to state variables are zero. Here we have $v_1 = 18x_1^2 - 12x_2 - 6$, and $v_2 = -12x_1 + 6x_2 + 7$, yielding the values -6 and 7 respectively, when evaluated at the initial basic feasible solution $x_1 = x_2 = 0$, $x_3 = 2$. The number in the bottom row to the right of the double lines gives the current value of the objective function, zero in this first tableau because both x_1 and x_2 are zero.

x_1	x_2	x_3	
3	4	1	2
-6	7	0	0

(a) Initial tableau

0.577

x_1	x_2	x_3	
3	4	1	0.269
0	0.076	0	-2.308

(b) Final tableau

Figure 3-4. Tableaux for cubic problem.

Since the only positive decision derivative v_2 has a corresponding decision variable x_2 which is zero, we set v_h to zero. Then we have $v_i = v_1 = -6$, so that V is negative, and x_1 is the variable d_r to be adjusted. From the tableau, we see that x_1 may be increased by $\frac{2}{3}$ before driving the lone state variable x_3 to zero. From the expression for v_1 in terms of the decision variables, it can, however, be seen that x_1 may only be increased by $1/\sqrt{3} = 0.577$, since beyond that value the objective function would begin to increase. Notice that regardless of the number of decision variables which might have been involved in this problem, we would still have needed only the two terms, $18x_1^2$, and -6, in order to make this calculation.

When x_1 is increased to 0.577, x_3 decreases to a value of 0.269, as calculated from the relation $x_3 = 2 - 3x_1$, since x_2 is held constant while adjusting x_1. Regardless of the number of decision variables involved in a problem, the relation which determines how large an adjustment may be made in a decision variable d_r will always be of the form:

$$s_k = \bar{s}_k - \alpha_{kr}d_r ; \qquad k = 1, \ldots, K \qquad (3\text{-}107)$$

where $\bar{s}_k$ is the current *numerical value* of s_k, obtained by substituting the numerical values of the decision variables into Eq. (3–101). Thus, if v_r is negative (so that d_r is to be *increased*), the first state variable s_ℓ to be driven to zero is found by computing

$$\frac{\bar{s}_\ell}{\alpha_{\ell r}} = \min_{\alpha_{kr}>0} \left(\frac{\bar{s}_k}{\alpha_{kr}}\right) \tag{3-108}$$

Notice that nonpositive α_{kr} are excluded in this calculation, since in equations where this coefficient is nonpositive, an increase in d_r will never decrease the state variable s_k, and therefore can never drive it to zero. When v_r is positive (which implies that d_r is also positive, and will now be decreased), the equations having negative α_{kr} are the only ones in which the associated state variable will be decreased by the adjustment in d_r. Thus, the first state variable s_ℓ to be driven to zero by this adjustment is computed from

$$\frac{\bar{s}_\ell}{\alpha_{\ell r}} = \min_{\alpha_{kr}<0} \left(\frac{\bar{s}_k}{-\alpha_{kr}}\right) \tag{3-109}$$

If the adjustment Δd_r given by Eq. (3–108) or (3–109) (whichever is applicable) does not first drive v_r to zero, then $s_\ell \equiv s_p$ is replaced in the set of state variables by d_r. This interchange of the roles of d_r and s_p is accomplished by replacing d_r in each constraint equation of the tableau, and in the bottom row expression of the objective function in terms of the decision variables, by its value given by Eq. (3–107) (solved, of course, for d_r).

If, however, as in the present problem, this adjustment first drives v_r (v_1 in this problem) to zero, then d_r remains a decision variable. The value of each state variable is then adjusted according to the value given by Eq. (3–107), and each decision derivative is adjusted from the relation

$$\Delta v_m = v_m \langle \Delta d_r \rangle; \qquad m = 1, \ldots, N \tag{3-110}$$

expressing v_m in terms of the decision variables. In the present problem we have $\Delta v_2 = -12\,\Delta x_1 = -12(0.577) = -6.924$, so that the new value of v_2 becomes 0.076, as shown in Fig. 3–4(b). The decision derivative v_1 of course is zero, and the objective function changes (from zero) by the amount $6(\Delta x_1)^3 - 6(\Delta x_1) = -2.308$, which is also shown in the figure. The numerical value of the positive decision variable x_1 is placed just above the variable name in the tableau; the values of all state variables, of course, appear in the right-hand column. Since v_1 is now zero, and there are no other negative v_m, we set v_i to zero; although v_2 is positive, its associated decision variable x_2 is zero, and so we set v_h to zero, as there are no other positive v_m. Thus we have arrived at a locally optimal solution to this problem: $x_1^* = 0.577$, $x_2^* = 0$, yielding the value, $y^* = -2.308$.

Now that the necessary conditions for a local minimum have been checked, sufficiency must be verified. The constraint being loose, it can be ignored, and since $v_1 = 0$ and $v_2 > 0$, one need only observe that $\partial^2 y/\partial x_1^2 = 36x_1 > 0$ to establish the point as a local minimum. Since y is not convex, one cannot be sure immediately that $\mathbf{x}^*$ is also the global minimum, although this does happen to be true in this case.

3-09 Quadratic Programming

When the objective function is quadratic

$$y = \sum_{n=1}^{N} c_n x_n + \frac{1}{2} \sum_{n=1}^{N} \sum_{p=1}^{N} x_n q_{np} x_p \quad (c_n, q_{np} \text{ constants}) \qquad (3\text{-}111)$$

and the constraints linear, an optimization problem is said to involve *quadratic programming*. In this case, the decision derivatives v_m are linear functions of the decision variables.

$$v_m = w_m + \sum_{n=1}^{N} t_{mn} d_n \quad (w_m, t_{mn} \text{ constants}) \qquad (3\text{-}112)$$

Candler and Townsley, and independently, Beightler, Crawford, and Wilde, have developed a differential algorithm exploiting this special characteristic of quadratic programming. The linearity of the derivatives permits a complete description of the quadratic differential algorithm here which furnishes a good introduction to the sort of computations arising in Chapter 5 on linear programming. It also forms a standard against which other quadratic programming procedures can be compared at the end of this chapter. If the details become boring, the reader may wish to skip to the next chapter and return to this subject when he is ready for specific computations.

The numerical values of the v_m must be known at all times, since they determine which decision variable d_r is to be adjusted. Once this variable has been selected, the value of the coefficient t_{rr} must be computed in order to calculate how much of an adjustment in d_r can be tolerated before v_r is driven to zero:

$$\Delta v_r = t_{rr} \Delta d_r \qquad (3\text{-}113)$$

If this change does not drive any state variable negative, then the remaining v_m must be adjusted in value by the relations

$$\Delta v_m = t_{mr} \Delta d_r \; ; \qquad m = 1, \ldots, N \qquad (3\text{-}114)$$

Thus, we need the values of at most only N of the coefficients t_{mr} at any one iteration, and we will describe how these coefficients may be calculated whenever needed from the simplex tableau. This is an important feature of the differential algorithm, since it saves N^2 storage locations (either on paper or in a computer). The numerical values of the w_m are never needed, of course, since if v_m is known, the *change* Δv_m can be computed from Eq. (3–114). In a subsequent section, we shall show how to compute the change in each decision derivative caused by a change in the set of decision variables. This latter change takes place when the adjusted decision variable,

d_r, replaces the state variable, s_p, in the state set. (Recall that this interchange occurs when the adjustment in d_r drives s_p to zero before it drives v_r or d_r to zero.)

3-10 Differentiating the Objective Function

If for a given set of state variables, we substitute expression (3–101) into (3–111), then the objective function will be written only in terms of the decision variables. If this substituted objective function is now differentiated partially with respect to some d_t (holding all other decision variables constant), the result is the decision derivative v_t, expressed as a function of all the decision variables. If this expression is in turn differentiated partially with respect to another decision variable, d_u, then by definition, we have the coefficient, t_{tu}

$$t_{tu} = \frac{\boldsymbol{\delta}^2 y}{\boldsymbol{\delta} d_u \boldsymbol{\delta} d_t} \qquad (3\text{-}115)$$

where the boldface $\boldsymbol{\delta}$ indicates partial differentiation while holding all other decision variables constant [but allowing the state variables to adjust so as to maintain the equality conditions (3–99)].

Since at all times we have available the original coefficients, q_{kn}, of y, and the coefficients α_{kn} of Eqs. (3–101) (from the current tableau), it is possible to compute the t_{tu} from these values by carrying out the substitutions and partial differentiations just described. This is a straightforward process, but its mathematical description can be confusing because of the relabeling and rearrangement problems involved. These problems arise because we have renumbered both original and constraint variables from their original designations, depending upon what role they play as state and decision variables. If the substitutions and differentiations are carried out, keeping the various relabelings in mind, the expressions for the coefficients are

$$t_{tu} = q_{tu} - \sum_{k=1}^{K} q_{tk}\alpha_{ku} - \sum_{k=1}^{K} q_{uk}\alpha_{kt} + \sum_{k=1}^{K}\sum_{j=1}^{K} \alpha_{kt}q_{kj}\alpha_{ju} \qquad (3\text{-}116)$$

where the summations are taken only over the indices of the *state* variables. That is, k and j are subscripts corresponding to state variables; t and u are subscripts corresponding to decision variables; and the q_{kj} have been renumbered from their original designations. Thus, for example, if either s_k or s_j was originally a constraint variable, then $q_{kj} \equiv 0$.

We may now use Eq. (3–116) to compute any t_{tu} coefficient needed by the differential algorithm, using information available from the original objective function and the current tableau. Therefore, these coefficients need not be stored, but can be generated only when needed. Accordingly, we need store only the q_{km}, c_m, α_{km}, and v_m, which amounts to the original

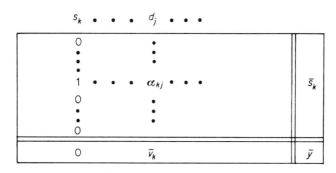

Figure 3-5. Tableau for differential algorithm.

function to be minimized plus $K + 1$ equations in the N decision variables. These equations constitute the tableau used by the differential algorithm, as shown in Fig. 3–5. In this figure, s_k is the state variable in the kth equation; d_j is a typical decision variable; $\bar{y}$ is the current value of the objective function; $\bar{v}_j$ is the numerical value of v_j; $\bar{s}_k$ is the numerical value of s_k.

3-11 Changing the State Set

Let $\bar{d}_r$ be the numerical value of the decision variable d_r at some stage of the calculations, just before an impending change in the set of state variables (that is, replacement of the state variable s_p by d_r). The numerical values of each state variable s_k and each decision derivative v_n depend upon $\bar{d}_r$ as defined by Eqs. (3–101) and (3–112). Let $\hat{s}_k$ and $\hat{v}_n$ be the numerical values of s_k and v_n *after* the change in the state set, before which change the numerical values were $\bar{s}_k$ and $\bar{v}_n$.

When there is a change in the state set, the differential algorithm holds all the decision variables constant except for d_r, the one entering the state set. Thus, by Eq. (3–101), the change in any variable s_k in the old state set is given by

$$\hat{s}_k - \bar{s}_k = -\alpha_{kr}(\hat{d}_r - \bar{d}_r) \qquad (3\text{-}117)$$

After the change in the state set, the variable s_p leaving this set will be zero; therefore:

$$\hat{d}_r = \frac{\bar{s}_p}{\alpha_{pr}} + \bar{d}_r \qquad (3\text{-}118)$$

This value replaces $\bar{s}_p$ in the state set. In *linear programming*, all decision variables are held at zero, so that application of the simplex method would have yielded only the term $\bar{s}_p/\alpha_{pr}$. Substituting Eq. (3–118) into Eq. (3–117) gives the new values for the remaining state variables:

$$\hat{s}_k = \bar{s}_k - \left(\frac{\alpha_{kr}}{\alpha_{pr}}\right)\bar{s}_p \; ; \qquad k \neq r \tag{3-119}$$

Again it may be pointed out that this is exactly the expression which would have been obtained by applying the simplex method of linear programming to these constraints. Indeed, the only significant difference between the differential and simplex algorithms lies in the treatment of the decision derivatives, which are *not* functions of the decision variables when the objective function is a *linear* expression.

Computation of the new values of the decision derivatives is complicated slightly by their dependence upon the decision variables. Equation (3–118) gives the change in d_r as

$$\Delta d_r = \hat{d}_r - \bar{d}_r = \frac{\bar{s}_p}{\alpha_{pr}} \tag{3-120}$$

Equations (3–120) and (3–112), together give the values $v_{\bar{n}}$ associated with the decision variables after the change in d_r as follows:

$$v_{\bar{n}} = \bar{v}_n + t_{nr}\,\Delta d_r = \bar{v}_n + t_{nr}\frac{\bar{s}_p}{\alpha_{pr}} \tag{3-121}$$

If all the numerical values $\hat{s}_k$ and $\hat{d}_n$ of the new state and decision variables are now held constant, the $v_{\bar{n}}$ are the sensitivities relative to the *old* decision set, and we may write the total differential for $\bar{y}$ as

$$\Delta\bar{y} = \sum_{n=K+1}^{K+N} v_{\bar{n}}\,\Delta d_n \tag{3-122}$$

where the summation is understood to be over the indices of those variables in the *old decision* set. Now by Eq. (3–101):

$$v_{\bar{r}}\,\Delta d_r = \left(\frac{v_{\bar{r}}}{\alpha_{pr}}\right)\left[-\Delta s_p - \sum_{n\neq r}\alpha_{pn}\,\Delta d_n\right] \tag{3-123}$$

whence $$\Delta\bar{y} = -\left(\frac{v_{\bar{r}}}{\alpha_{pr}}\right)\Delta s_p + \sum_{n\neq r}\left[v_{\bar{n}} - \left(\frac{\alpha_{pn}}{\alpha_{pr}}\right)v_{\bar{r}}\right]\Delta d_n \tag{3-124}$$

where the summations in Eqs. (3–123) and (3–124) are taken over the indices of all the variables in the old decision set, except for d_r (or, equivalently, over the indices of all the variables in the *new* decision set, except for s_p). The coefficients in Eq. (3–124) are the sensitivities relative to the *new* state set, and so

$$\hat{v}_p = -\left(\frac{v_{\bar{r}}}{\alpha_{pr}}\right)$$

$$= -\left(\frac{1}{\alpha_{pr}}\right)(\bar{v}_r + t_{rr}\bar{s}_p/\alpha_{pr}) \tag{3-125}$$

and for $n \neq p$

$$\hat{v}_n = v_n^- - \left(\frac{\alpha_{pn}}{\alpha_{pr}}\right) v_r^-$$

$$= \bar{v}_n - \left(\frac{\alpha_{pn}}{\alpha_{pr}}\right) \bar{v}_r + \left(\frac{\bar{s}_p}{\alpha_{pr}}\right) \left[t_{nr} - \left(\frac{\alpha_{pn}}{\alpha_{pr}}\right) t_{rr}\right] \tag{3-126}$$

The numerical values in Eqs. (3-125) and (3-126) can thus be computed by first applying the simplex method of linear programming to the $\bar{v}_n$, obtaining the first term in Eq. (3-126), and then adding the second term in that equation as a correction term. Since the second term can be obtained by simplexing the t_{nr}, the process for computing the new sensitivity coefficients after a change in the decision set may be looked upon as a *double-simplexing* operation. Here we see again that only N of the t_{nr} coefficients are needed at a given iteration of the algorithm, just as was the case when the adjusted variable d_r remained a decision variable and there was no change in the decision set.

3-12 Numerical Examples

To illustrate the computations required in the differential algorithm when a change takes place in the state set, first consider the following example given by Beale and repeated by Dorn:

Find nonnegative x_1, x_2, which minimize

$$y = 2x_1^2 - 2x_1 x_2 + 2x_2^2 - 6x_1 + 6$$

and which satisfy the constraint

$$x_1 + x_2 \leq 2$$

The initial tableau is shown in Fig. 3-6(a) where, for illustration, we have written out the entire expressions for v_1 and v_2. This is unnecessary in practice, of course, since the coefficients in these expressions may be computed as desired from Eq. (3-116), and only the numerical values, -6 and 0 (which are circled in the figure), are required.

Proceeding as before, we find that $v_i = v_1 = -6$, and $v_h = 0$, so that x_1 is the decision d_r to be adjusted (increased). The initial rate of change of the objective function with respect to an increase in x_1 is -6, but this value increases linearly as x_1 is increased, reaching a value of zero when x_1 equals $\frac{3}{2}$. On the other hand, it can be seen from the constraint that x_1 could be increased to a value of 2 before driving the state variable x_3 to zero. Therefore, x_1 is increased (from zero) by $\frac{3}{2}$, causing no change in the decision set, although, of course, it does change the numerical values of x_3, v_1, v_2, and y, as shown in Fig. 3-6(b). This adjustment in x_1 corresponds to a move from the origin to point **a** in Fig. 3-7.

x_1	x_2	x_3	
1	1	1	2
$4x_1-2x_2-6$ $\ominus$	$-2x_1+4x_2$ $\odot$	0	6

(a) Initial tableau

3/2

x_1	x_2	x_3	
1	1	1	1/2
$4x_1-2x_2-6$ $\odot$	$-2x_1+4x_2$ $\ominus$	0	3/2

(b) Results of adjustment in x_1

3/2

x_1	x_2	x_3	
1	1	1	1/2
$12x_1+6x_3-18$ $\odot$	0	$6x_1+4x_3-8$ $①$	1/2

(c) Final tableau

Figure 3-6. Tableaux for first quadratic example.

With v_2 now negative, y can be further decreased by increasing x_2; formally, $v_h = 0$, $v_i = v_2 = -3$, so that V is negative. The size of the increase in x_2 which is desirable is the smaller of the two ratios, $-v_2/t_{22}$ and $\bar{x}_3/\alpha_{23}$, which have the numerical values $\frac{3}{4}$ and $\frac{1}{2}$, respectively. Accordingly, x_2 is increased from zero by a value of $\frac{1}{2}$, driving x_3 to zero, and thus causing a change in the decision set. Since x_2 will now be the state variable, the constraint must be solved for this variable, and used to eliminate x_2 from the expressions for the decision derivatives v_1 and v_3 corresponding to the new decision variables. Again, this work is carried out here only for illustration,

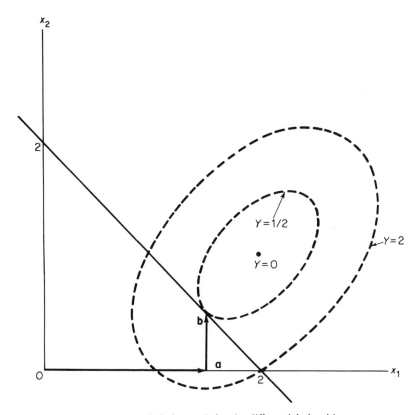

Figure 3-7. Solution path for the differential algorithm.

as the expressions for the v_n in terms of the decision variables are never calculated in practice, the coefficients t_{tu} in these expressions being readily obtainable from Eq. (3–116) when, and if, they are needed.

The coefficient v_2 is made identically zero (which is required of all v_n corresponding to state variables) by multiplying the constraint by $2x_1 - 4x_2$ and adding it to the bottom row. This produces the expressions $v_1 = 6x_1 - 6x_2 - 6$, $v_3 = 2x_1 - 4x_2$, from which x_2 must be eliminated through the constraint relation $x_2 = \frac{1}{2} - (x_1 - \frac{3}{2}) - x_3$, to yield the expressions for v_1 and v_3 as shown in Fig. 3–6(c). (These expressions may be obtained directly, of course, by computing the partial derivatives of the substituted objective function with respect to x_1 and x_3.) From this tableau, we find $v_h = v_i = 0$, so that the optimal solution to this problem is $x_1^* = \frac{3}{2}$, $x_2^* = \frac{1}{2}$, corresponding to point **b** in Fig. 3–7, and producing the minimum value $y^* = \frac{1}{2}$.

Next consider a problem which illustrates all the possible numerical operations required in carrying out the steps of the differential algorithm. In this example we also introduce an abbreviated form of the tableau which reduces the amount of work necessary to solve a given problem.

Find nonnegative x_1, x_2, which minimize

$$y = 2x_1^2 - 2x_1x_2 + 2x_2^2 - 6x_1$$

and which satisfy

$$3x_1 + 4x_2 \leq 6$$
$$-x_1 + 4x_2 \leq 2$$

The initial tableau in Fig. 3–8 omits the columns for the state variables, since those columns always consist of all zeros, save for the lone 1 in the only

	x_1	x_2	
x_3	3	4	6
x_4	-1	4	2
	-6	0	0

(a) Initial tableau

3/2

	x_1	x_3	
x_2	3/4	1/4	3/8
x_4	-4	-1	2
	3/8	3/8	-171/32

(b) Tableau resulting from change in decision set

54/37

	x_1	x_3	
x_2	3/4	1/4	15/37
x_4	-4	-1	68/37
	0	12/37	-198/37

(c) Final tableau

Figure 3-8. Tableaux for second quadratic example.

constraint row in which the variable appears. These columns contain no useful information, and when they are deleted, it is sufficient to keep a record of the state variable associated with each row. In Fig. 3–8(a), the state variables x_3 and x_4 are the slack variables corresponding to the first and second constraints, respectively, as shown in the column at the left. Here, as in the previous example, we find $v_1 = -6$, $v_2 = 0$, and upon increasing x_1, the sensitivity coefficient v_1 is driven to zero without precipitating a change in the state set. This takes place when x_1 reaches a value of $\frac{3}{2}$, producing the new values $x_3 = \frac{3}{2}$, $x_4 = \frac{7}{2}$, $y = -\frac{9}{2}$, and $v_2 = -3$, with the body of the tableau, of course, left unchanged. Notice that in order to compute the new values of v_1 and v_2 it was necessary to calculate only the coefficients $t_{11} = 4$ and $t_{21} = -2$.

Since v_2 is now negative, it pays to increase x_2, and we see that x_2 would have to be increased by $\frac{3}{4}$ in order to reduce v_2 to zero, whereas an increase of only $\frac{3}{8}$ in the value of this variable will drive x_3 to zero. Thus, by increasing x_2 we have encountered a constraint before reaching the line (in general, the hyperplane) $v_2 = 0$, and this necessitates a change in the decision set.

The first constraint, in which x_3 was the state variable, is solved for x_2 and used to eliminate x_2 from the other constraint. The column for x_2 is now dropped and replaced by the x_3 column which formerly consisted of zeros save for the 1 in the first row. In general, if x_j replaces x_i in the state set, the elements in the new column i are computed as follows: the element $\hat{\alpha}_{ji}$ in the row in which x_i was formerly the state variable (and in which x_j is now the state variable) is given by $1/\alpha_{ij}$, the reciprocal of the element which stood in the x_j column of this row in the previous tableau; the remaining elements $\hat{\alpha}_{ki}$ of column i are given by $-\alpha_{kj}/\alpha_{ij}$, where α_{kj} is the element which was in the kth constraint row of the old x_j column. Recall that we designate as the kth constraint that row of the tableau in which x_k is the state variable. The reader can verify that the expressions just given for the elements in column i are exactly what would have been obtained by performing the standard simplex operations on a tableau which retained all the columns for the state variables. The decision derivatives v_1 and v_3, of course, are computed from Eqs. (3–112) and (3–113).

The results of this change in the state set are given in the tableau of Fig. 3–8(b), which shows that the value of the objective function has been reduced to $-\frac{171}{32}$. Since both the decision derivatives are positive, it pays to decrease both x_1 and x_3, but only x_1 can actually be decreased, as x_3 has a value of zero. Upon computing $t_{11} = \frac{37}{4}$ from Eq. (3–116), we see that decreasing x_1 will decrease v_1, and when x_1 has been decreased by an amount $\frac{3}{8} / \frac{37}{4} = \frac{3}{74}$, v_1 will have been driven to zero.

It now remains to determine the effects on the state variables of a decrease in x_1. From the tableau, it can be seen that x_2 will be *increased* by decreasing

x_1, whereas x_4 will be *decreased* by decreasing x_1. In general, if a decision variable d_r is to be increased, it is sufficient to consider its effects on those state variables having positive entries in the d_r column; that is, consider only the state variables s_k such that α_{kr} is positive. Conversely, if d_r is to be decreased, it is sufficient to consider the effects of this decrease on just those state variables having negative entries in the d_r column. Then the first state variable to be driven to zero by the adjustment in d_r is given by Eq. (3–108) or (3–109). From Fig. 3–8(b), it can be seen that a reduction of $\frac{1}{2}$ in the value of x_1 would be required to decrease x_4 to zero; accordingly, x_1 is decreased by $\frac{3}{74}$ to a value of $\frac{54}{37}$, driving v_1 to zero and producing the new values $v_3 = \frac{12}{37}$, $x_2 = \frac{15}{37}$, $x_4 = \frac{68}{37}$, and $y^* = -\frac{198}{37}$, as shown in Fig. 3–8(c). Since both v_h and v_i are zero, the optimal solution to this problem has been reached.

3-13 Oscillation

Since each iteration of the differential algorithm gives a value of the objective function which is lower than any previous one, the optimal solution to a quadratic programming problem will eventually be reached. The algorithm approaches the desired solution arbitrarily closely in relatively few steps, but in general there is no guarantee that this process will converge in a finite number of steps. In fact, the authors have been able to construct problems for which the algorithm moves in steps of decreasing size between several hyperplanes defined by the equations $v_n = 0$, in such a way as to preclude finite convergence. We refer to this phenomenon as *oscillation;* the following problem illustrates the oscillating path which the algorithm may possibly follow:

Find nonnegative x_1, x_2, which minimize

$$y = 2x_1^2 - 4x_1x_2 + 4x_2^2 + x_1 - 3x_2$$

and which satisfy

$$x_1 + x_2 \leq 1$$

The algorithm begins with the basic feasible solution $x_1 = x_2 = 0$, $x_3 = 1$, where the state variable x_3 is the slack variable for the sole constraint. For illustration it is helpful to write out the complete expressions for the decision derivatives: $v_1 = 4x_1 - 4x_2 + 1$, and $v_2 = -4x_1 + 8x_2 - 3$. The numerical values, of course, are 1 and -3, respectively, so that $v_i = -3$, $v_h = 0$, and x_2 is increased to a value of $\frac{3}{8}$, driving v_2 to zero. This adjustment makes v_1 negative, necessitating an increase of $\frac{1}{8}$ in x_1, which returns v_1 to zero but forces v_2 negative once again. This in turn requires a change $\Delta x_2 = \frac{1}{16}$ to bring v_2 back to zero, once more producing a negative value for the decision derivative v_1, and the reader can see that this process will never reach the exact optimum, even though it will get very close in a few more steps. As shown in Fig. 3–9, the successive points calculated by the algorithm form a decreasing stair-step locus, **abcdef** ... , between the lines $v_1 = 0$ and $v_2 = 0$, which approaches the intersection of these lines at the point $(\frac{1}{4}, \frac{1}{2})$. In most problems, even if the solution path should begin to oscillate, it will often be intercepted by a constraint and thus terminate in a finite number of steps. In this problem, however, the sole constraint lies outside the unconstrained optimum, and the oscillating path continues uninterrupted. In Section 3–14, we develop an acceleration technique which may be used when the rate of convergence slows down and which guarantees convergence in a finite number of iterations.

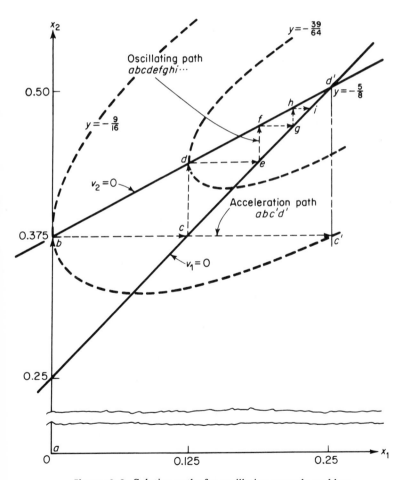

Figure 3-9. Solution paths for oscillating example problem.

3-14 Acceleration

Oscillation can be prevented by imposing side conditions of the form $v_j = 0$ on the adjustment of the decision variables between changes in the state set. Thus, case II of the continuation rule given in Section 3-07 must be replaced by IIa and IIb, as follows:

IIa. v_r becomes zero, and case I applied on the previous iteration.

IIb. v_r becomes zero, and case IIa or IIb applied on the previous iteration, say for the variable d_u ($u \neq r$). Under these circumstances, v_u must be prevented from becoming nonzero because of the subsequent change Δd_r. To accomplish this, eliminate d_u from the expression for v_r, using the side condition $v_u = 0$. Now make the adjustment Δd_r, causing v_r to become zero; in general, this will make $v_u \neq 0$. Fix d_r and readjust d_u to make v_u zero; since v_r is independent of d_u, v_r will remain zero.

When a decision variable d_r is to be adjusted, case IIb may have applied several times since the last change in the state set; let τ be the number of consecutive times IIb has occurred, including the present time. Let U be the set of indices for which $v_u = 0$, where u is in U, and $u \neq r$. No generality is lost in referring to the uth variable to enter U as d_u, $u = 1, 2, \ldots, \tau$. The uth expression, v_u, is independent of d_s for all $s < u$, but at the moment, $\Delta v_r = \Delta v_r \langle \Delta d_1, \ldots, \Delta d_\tau; \Delta d_r \rangle$.

We eventually shall want Δv_r to depend only on Δd_r. To achieve this in τ steps, eliminate, in the order $u = 1, 2, \ldots, \tau$, Δd_u from $\Delta v_r \langle \Delta d_u, \Delta d_{u+1}, \ldots, \Delta d_\tau; \Delta d_r \rangle$ by using the relation $\Delta v_u \langle \Delta d_u, \Delta d_{u+1}, \ldots, \Delta d_\tau; \Delta d_r \rangle = 0$. No generality is lost by suppposing that $r = \tau + 1$. Adjust Δd_u, where $u = \tau + 1, \tau, \tau - 1, \ldots, 1$ (that is, reverse order) according to the sign of v_u. This change will lead to either case I or II. When I holds, IIb is no longer applicable, but if II holds, then v_u will vanish. Since the v_z, for $z > u$, were made independent of Δd_u, this change will not affect the v_z, and therefore $v_z = 0$. This process terminates when finally $v_u = 0$ for all $u = 1, 2, \ldots, \tau + 1$.

In the example just used to illustrate oscillation, case IIb occurs when x_1 is to be adjusted for the first time to make v_1 vanish. The side condition $v_2 = 0$, when solved for x_2, results in $x_2 = \frac{3}{8} + \frac{1}{2}x_1$; this expression is then substituted for x_2 in v_1, with the result: $v_1 = -\frac{1}{2} + 2x_1$. In order to drive v_1 to zero, we make the change $\Delta x_1 = \frac{1}{4}$, causing v_2 to become -1. Then, the required adjustment in x_2 is $\Delta x_2 = \frac{1}{8}$, which returns v_2 to zero, and does not affect v_1, because of the elimination of x_2 from this expression. The decision variables x_1 and x_2 then have the values $\frac{1}{4}$ and $\frac{1}{2}$, respectively, which happens to be the optimal solution to this particular problem, since both v_h and v_i, as previously defined, are zero. Thus acceleration causes the differential algorithm to follow the path **abc'd'** in Fig. 3-9.

3-15 Diagonalization

Consider the quadratic form:

$$q \equiv \mathbf{x'Qx} = \sum_{j=1}^{N} \sum_{n=1}^{N} x_j q_{jn} x_n \qquad (3\text{-}127)$$

where **x** is an N element vector, and $\mathbf{Q} \equiv (q_{jn})$ is an N by N symmetric nonsingular matrix. There exist nonsingular linear transformations (Birkhoff and MacLane, pp. 248–50) such that, in terms of the N variables z_h, the quadratic form

$$\hat{q} = \sum_{h=1}^{N} d_{hh} z_h^2 \qquad (3\text{-}128)$$

becomes a sum of perfect squares. Let **T** be the N by N matrix of such a transformation, and let **D** be the N by N matrix associated with the new quadratic form $\hat{q}$. Then

$$\mathbf{z} = \mathbf{Tx} \qquad (3\text{-}129)$$

and since **T** is nonsingular,

$$\mathbf{x} = \mathbf{T^{-1}z} \qquad (3\text{-}130)$$

Equations (3–127) and (3–130) together with the definition of **D** give

$$\hat{q} = \mathbf{z'(T^{-1})'QT^{-1}z} = \mathbf{z'Dz} \qquad (3\text{-}131)$$

Since $\hat{q}$ is a sum of perfect squares, it follows that **D** is a *diagonal* matrix of elements d_{hh}, and therefore this transformation process is called the *diagonalization* of the coefficient matrix **Q**.

Diagonalization is widely used by operations analysts to simplify systems arising in optimization, control, and statistics problems. The standard diagonalization technique consists of finding the eigenvalues and eigenvectors of **Q**, reducing it to canonical form (Birkhoff and MacLane, pp. 266–68). This *congruence* transformation is appealing theoretically because of its uniqueness and orthogonality, but finding it requires factoring an Nth-degree polynomial followed by solving N *sets* of N linear equations in N unknowns. All this labor is necessary in certain important problems in vibrations, fluid mechanics, and quantum theory where only the congruence transformation is physically meaningful. But most operations analysis problems can be diagonalized with much less effort by using a *similarity* rather than a congruence transformation.

Lagrange's transformation, which involves completing the square, is described in many algebra texts (Birkhoff and MacLane, p. 270); less familiar is the knowledge that this transformation can be obtained by the standard *Gauss elimination* procedure for solving linear equations (Beightler and Wilde). First we describe Lagrange's method constructively and then show that the operations involved are exactly the same as those used in Gaussian elimination. Then we present an algorithm for inverting the transformation, and show that it is possible to diagonalize any quadratic form systematically, using a standard computation routine which takes even less effort than solving a *single* set of N linear equations in N variables.

3-16 Completing the Square (Lagrange's Transformation)

Consider the quadratic form

$$q = x_1^2 + 2x_1x_2 + 4x_1x_3 + 3x_2^2 + 2x_2x_3 + 5x_3^2 \qquad (3\text{-}132)$$

We begin the process of completing the square by expressing as a perfect square all terms containing x_1 as a factor:

$$q = (x_1 + x_2 + 2x_3)^2 + 2x_2^2 - 2x_2x_3 + x_3^2 \qquad (3\text{-}133)$$

The next step consists of writing as a perfect square all terms containing x_2 as a factor:

$$q = (x_1 + x_2 + 2x_3)^2 + 2(x_2 - \tfrac{1}{2}x_3)^2 + \tfrac{1}{2}x_3^2 \qquad (3\text{-}134)$$

For a quadratic form consisting of N variables, completing the square involves a repetition of the foregoing process for $x_1, x_2, \ldots, x_{N-1}$. Since here $N = 3$, we have finished. From the form of Eq. (3–134), we are led to make the following changes of variable:

$$z_1 = x_1 + x_2 + 2x_3, \qquad z_2 = x_2 - \tfrac{1}{2}x_3, \qquad z_3 = x_3 \qquad (3\text{-}135)$$

so that Eq. (3–132) may now be written as

$$\hat{q} = z_1^2 + 2z_2^2 + \tfrac{1}{2}z_3^2 \qquad (3\text{-}136)$$

The foregoing procedure may now be generalized; let N be the order of $\mathbf{Q}$, and let the constants $q_{jn}^{(h)}$ be generated recursively from the q_{jn} as follows:

$$q_{jn}^{(0)} \equiv q_{jn} ; \qquad j, n = 1, \ldots, N \qquad (3\text{-}137)$$

$$q_{hn}^{(h)} \equiv \frac{q_{hn}^{(h-1)}}{q_{hh}^{(h-1)}} ; \qquad n = 1, \ldots, N \qquad (3\text{-}138)$$

$$q_{jn}^{(h)} \equiv q_{jn}^{(h-1)} - q_{jh}^{(h-1)} q_{hn}^{(h)} ; \qquad j = h+1, \ldots, N ; \qquad n = h, \ldots, N \qquad (3\text{-}139)$$

$$q_{jn}^{(h)} \equiv q_{jn}^{(h-1)} ; \qquad j = 1, \ldots, h-1 ; \qquad n = 1, \ldots, N \qquad (3\text{-}140)$$

$$q_{jn}^{(h)} \equiv 0 ; \qquad j = h, \ldots, N ; \qquad n = 1, \ldots, h-1 \qquad (3\text{-}141)$$

If any $q_{hh}^{(h-1)}$ is zero, but some other diagonal element $q_{jj}^{(h-1)}$ is nonzero, then renumber the variables so as to interchange the indices h and j. Let m

be the smallest number for which $q_{jj}^{(m)} = 0$ for all $j = m + 1, \ldots, N$. Define the linear change of variable:

$$z_h = x_h + \sum_{n=h+1}^{N} q_{hn}^{(h)} x_n ; \qquad h = 1, \ldots, m \qquad (3\text{-}142)$$

Then

$$\sum_{j=1}^{N} \sum_{n=1}^{N} x_j q_{jn}^{(h-1)} x_n = q_{hh}^{(h-1)} z_h^2 + \sum_{j=h+1}^{N} \sum_{n=h+1}^{N} x_j q_{jn}^{(h)} x_n ; \qquad h = 1, \ldots, m$$

$$(3\text{-}143)$$

Equation (3-142) may be used inductively to prove that

$$q\langle z_1, \ldots, z_m, x_{m+1}, \ldots, x_N \rangle = \sum_{h=1}^{m} q_{hh}^{(h-1)} z_h^2 + \sum_{j=m+1}^{N} \sum_{n=m+1}^{N} x_j q_{jn}^{(m)} x_n$$

$$(3\text{-}144)$$

If $m = N$, then comparison of Eqs. (3-128) and (3-143) shows that the $q_{hh}^{(h-1)}$ are the elements of the diagonal matrix $\mathbf{D}$:

$$d_{hh} = q_{hh}^{(h-1)} \qquad (3\text{-}145)$$

Moreover, the elements t_{jn} of the corresponding transformation matrix $\mathbf{T}$ are, by Eqs. (3-129) and (3-142),

$$t_{jn} = q_{jn}^{(j)}, \text{ for } j = 1, \ldots, n - 1 \qquad (3\text{-}146\,\text{a})$$

$$t_{jn} = 1, \quad \text{for } j = n \qquad (3\text{-}146\,\text{b})$$

$$t_{jn} = 0, \quad \text{for } j = n + 1, \ldots, N \qquad (3\text{-}146\,\text{c})$$

From Eqs. (3-127), (3-129), (3-131), (3-145), and (3-146), we have

$$q = \mathbf{x'Qx} = \mathbf{z'Dz} = \mathbf{x'T'DTx} \qquad (3\text{-}147)$$

whence $$\mathbf{Q} = \mathbf{T'DT} \qquad (3\text{-}148)$$

If $m < N$, and the $q_{jn}^{(m)}$ all vanish for $j, n, > m$, then m is the rank of $\mathbf{Q}$, evidently a singular matrix. In this case, set $d_{hh} \equiv 0$ and $t_{jn} \equiv 0$ for all h, $j = m + 1, \ldots, N$. Then Eqs. (3-147) and (3-148) still hold even though $\mathbf{T}$ is singular. If $m < N$ but there is a nonvanishing $q_{jn}^{(m)}$ for some $j, n > m$, then it can be shown (Beightler and Wilde) that $\mathbf{Q}$ is an indefinite matrix. As a consequence of this fact, if $\mathbf{Q}$ is definite, or semidefinite, then $q_{jn}^{(m)} = 0$ for all $j, n > m$, and m is the rank of $\mathbf{Q}$. Therefore, in such cases, the process described in Eqs. (3-137) through (3-148) will always accomplish the diagonalization of $\mathbf{Q}$.

3-17 Gaussian Elimination

We now show that Lagrange's diagonalization algorithm may be expressed compactly in the format of the widely known Gauss elimination technique for solving linear equations. Consider the application of this method to the hypothetical set of equations represented by

$$\mathbf{Q}\mathbf{x} = \mathbf{0} \tag{3-149}$$

where $\mathbf{0}$ (zero) is a null column vector of N elements. To begin, the elements q_{1n} of the first row of $\mathbf{Q}$ are divided by q_{11}, the *first pivot*, which is equivalent to solving the first equation for x_1. This result is then used to eliminate x_1 from the remaining $N - 1$ equations. When this is done, the coefficient matrix $\mathbf{Q}^{(1)}$ for the new equations has for elements the $q_{jn}^{(1)}$ of Eqs. (3–138), (3–139), (3–140), and (3–141), specialized for $h = 1$. Notice that

$$q_{11}^{(1)} = 1 \quad \text{and} \quad q_{j1}^{(1)} = 0, \quad \text{for} \quad j = 2, 3, \ldots, N$$

Repeating this cycle of operations, that is, eliminating x_2, gives a new coefficient matrix $\mathbf{Q}^{(2)}$ in which the elements are the $q_{jn}^{(2)}$ of Eqs. (3–138), (3–139), (3–140), and (3–141), for $h = 2$. The second pivot is $q_{22}^{(1)}$, which by Eq. (3–145) is d_{22}, the second diagonal element of $\mathbf{D}$. After N iterations, the unit upper triangular matrix $\mathbf{Q}^{(N)}$ is obtained, and this is identical with the desired transformation matrix $\mathbf{T}$. The N pivots $q_{hh}^{(h-1)}$ must be recorded, since they form $\mathbf{D}$, but otherwise the diagonalization procedure involves only the ordinary elimination phase of the Gauss reduction. Alternatively one may use the Crout reduction (Kunz, pp. 220, 226) a compact version of the Gauss elimination which avoids writing down the intermediate matrices $\mathbf{Q}^{(1)}$ through $\mathbf{Q}^{(N-1)}$.

The coefficient matrix for the quadratic form (3–132), Section 3–15 is

$$\mathbf{Q} = \begin{pmatrix} 1 & 1 & 2 \\ 1 & 3 & 1 \\ 2 & 1 & 5 \end{pmatrix} \tag{3-150}$$

Using Gauss elimination, we find the successive matrices:

$$\mathbf{Q}^{(1)} = \begin{pmatrix} 1 & 1 & 2 \\ 0 & 2 & -1 \\ 0 & -1 & 1 \end{pmatrix}$$

$$\mathbf{Q}^{(2)} = \begin{pmatrix} 1 & 1 & 2 \\ 0 & 1 & -\frac{1}{2} \\ 0 & 0 & \frac{1}{2} \end{pmatrix}$$

$$\mathbf{Q}^{(3)} \equiv \mathbf{T} = \begin{pmatrix} 1 & 1 & 2 \\ 0 & 1 & -\frac{1}{2} \\ 0 & 0 & 1 \end{pmatrix} \tag{3-151}$$

$$\mathbf{D} = \begin{pmatrix} 1 & 0 & 0 \\ 0 & 2 & 0 \\ 0 & 0 & \frac{1}{2} \end{pmatrix} \tag{3-152}$$

Using the foregoing transformation matrix $\mathbf{T}$ in Eq. (3–129) produces the Eq. (3–135) change of variable needed in Lagrange's transformation; the preceding diagonal matrix $\mathbf{D}$, when used in Eq. (3–131), yields the value of $\hat{q}$ given by Eq. (3–136). Since the diagonal elements of $\mathbf{D}$ are all positive, we know that $\mathbf{Q}$ is positive-definite.

3-18 Inversion

The unit upper triangular structure of $\mathbf{T}$ makes it very easy to invert, and it turns out that $\mathbf{T}^{-1}$ is also unit upper triangular. Let $\bar{t}_{jn}$ be a typical element of $\mathbf{T}^{-1}$; then the product of the jth row of $\mathbf{T}^{-1}$ and the $j + i$th column of $\mathbf{T}$ yields

$$\bar{t}_{j,j+i} = - \sum_{k=0}^{i-1} \bar{t}_{j,j+k} t_{j+k,j+i} ; \qquad j = 1, \ldots, N ; \qquad i = 1, \ldots, N - j$$

(3–153)

which describes the elements above the diagonal of $\mathbf{T}^{-1}$. Although Eq. (3–153) contains some of the elements of $\mathbf{T}^{-1}$, the upper triangle of $\mathbf{T}^{-1}$ nevertheless can be computed by calculating the elements in such an order that only previously computed elements appear in the sum. One begins with the super-diagonal elements $\bar{t}_{j,j+1}$, since for $i = 1$ the right members of Eq. (3–153) collapse to $-t_{j,j+1}$, the negatives of the superdiagonal elements of $\mathbf{T}$. Next let $i = 2$ and calculate the second superdiagonal, $\bar{t}_{j,j+2}$. This is possible because the $\bar{t}_{j,j+1}$ are now known. The process is continued until $\mathbf{T}^{-1}$ is complete.

As an application of diagonalization and inversion, consider the problem of finding the vector $\mathbf{x}$ which minimizes

$$y = \mathbf{x}'\mathbf{Q}\mathbf{x} + \mathbf{c}'\mathbf{x}$$

where $\mathbf{Q}$ is given by Eq. (3–150), and $\mathbf{c}'$ is the row vector $\mathbf{c}' = (4, -2, 3)$. Making the change of variable, $\mathbf{z} = \mathbf{T}\mathbf{x}$, we have

$$\hat{y} = \mathbf{z}'\mathbf{D}\mathbf{z} + \mathbf{c}'\mathbf{T}^{-1}\mathbf{z}$$

where $\mathbf{T}$ and $\mathbf{D}$ are given by Eqs. (3–151) and (3–152), respectively; thus,

$$\hat{y} = z_1^2 + 2z_2^2 + \tfrac{1}{2}z_3^2 + 4z_1 - 6z_2 - 8z_3$$

Upon computing the partial derivatives of $\hat{y}$, we find: $2z_1 + 4 = 0$, $4z_2 - 6 = 0$, and $z_3 - 8 = 0$, so that $\hat{y}$ has its minimum at the point $z_1^* = -2$, $z_2^* = \tfrac{3}{2}$, $z_3^* = 8$. From Eq. (3–153), we found

$$\mathbf{T}^{-1} = \begin{pmatrix} 1 & -1 & -\tfrac{5}{2} \\ 0 & 1 & \tfrac{1}{2} \\ 0 & 0 & 1 \end{pmatrix}$$

and hence from Eq. (3–130), $x_1^* = -23.5$, $x_2^* = 5.5$, and $x_3^* = 8$. The (global) minimum for both y and $\hat{y}$ is found to be -40.5.

For this simple problem, only three cross-product terms were present, so that diagonalization was not particularly advantageous. A quadratic form of N variables will in general contain $\frac{1}{2}(N^2 - N)$ cross-product terms, and when these are removed by diagonalization, the transformed expression can be optimized by inspection since its solution is given by N equations of the form $2d_{jj}z_j - k_j = 0$, where k_j is the coefficient of the linear z_j term in $\hat{y}$. Without diagonalization, the optimization would require the solution of N equations in N unknowns, with no assurance that the quadratic form was not indefinite.

In order to illustrate the use of diagonalization when there are linear inequality constraints, we shall write the quadratic programming problem as that of finding nonnegative vectors $\mathbf{x}_q$ and $\mathbf{x}_n$ which minimize

$$y = \mathbf{x}_q' \mathbf{Q} \mathbf{x}_q + \mathbf{c}_q' \mathbf{x}_q + \mathbf{c}_n' \mathbf{x}_n \qquad (3\text{-}154)$$

and which satisfy the constraints:

$$\mathbf{A}_q \mathbf{x}_q + \mathbf{A}_n \mathbf{x}_n + \mathbf{x}_s = \mathbf{b} \qquad (3\text{-}155)$$

where $\mathbf{x}_q$ is the q element vector of variables in the quadratic term, $\mathbf{x}_n$ is the $N - q$ element vector of variables whose effect is purely linear, $\mathbf{x}_s$ is a K element vector of slack variables, and $\mathbf{b}$ is a given K element vector of constants.

Most of the algorithms available for solving this problem require that $\mathbf{Q}$ be positive semidefinite to guarantee convergence to the global minimum. Before solving a quadratic programming problem it would be wise then to verify that $\mathbf{Q}$ is positive semidefinite, and Gauss elimination is the simplest way to do this. Gauss elimination will always succeed when $\mathbf{Q}$ is semidefinite, and failure of the procedure immediately shows that $\mathbf{Q}$ is indefinite. Hence in order to check $\mathbf{Q}$, one must find $\mathbf{D}$ and $\mathbf{T}$, which can then be used to simplify the problem before attempting to solve it.

Let

$$\mathbf{z} = \mathbf{T} \mathbf{x}_q \qquad (3\text{-}156)$$

By combining Eqs. (3–154), (3–155), and (3–156), we obtain the equivalent problem: minimize $\hat{y} = \mathbf{z}' \mathbf{D} \mathbf{z} + \mathbf{c}_q' \mathbf{T}^{-1} \mathbf{z} + \mathbf{c}_n' \mathbf{x}_n$ subject to the original constraints (3–155) and the q additional constraints

$$\mathbf{T} \mathbf{x}_q - \mathbf{z} = 0 \qquad (3\text{-}157)$$

with the understanding that $\mathbf{x}_q$, $\mathbf{x}_n$, and $\mathbf{x}_s$ be nonnegative, but that $\mathbf{z}$ be unrestricted in sign. Since $\mathbf{D}$ is already known, $\mathbf{c}_q' \mathbf{T}^{-1}$ is the only vector to be calculated.

Thus by adding q more variables $\mathbf{z}$, and q more constraints (3–157), we have a problem whose quadratic form is diagonal and whose solution is the same as that of the original problem. Notice that any starting solution feasible for the original constraints (3–155) will also be feasible for the new constraints (3–157), since the dummy quadratic variables $\mathbf{z}$ are unrestricted in sign. The $\mathbf{z}$ would in fact remain formally in the state set throughout the calculations. The final numerical value of $\mathbf{z}$ is irrelevant, since the solution to this modified problem will give the optimal values $\mathbf{x}_q$ and $\mathbf{x}_n$ explicitly, no inversions being necessary.

In the following sections, we discuss briefly some of the other algorithms for solving mathematical programming problems. Some of these methods apply only to quadratic programming problems; some are approximation techniques; still others provide exact solutions to certain classes of problems. We shall not attempt to cover all algorithms which have been proposed, and in particular, we shall postpone discussion of the simplex method of linear programming to Chapter 5. For a comparison of performances of various methods, see Zoutendijk (1966).

3-19 Wolfe's Algorithm

This technique, developed by Wolfe, solves the quadratic programming problem by transforming it into a linear programming problem solvable by the standard simplex method. Specifically, the Kuhn-Tucker conditions for an optimal solution to the problem of finding nonnegative x_n which minimize (3-111) subject to the constraints (3-99) are

$$\sum_{p=1}^{N} q_{np}x_p + c_n - \sum_{k=1}^{K} \lambda_k a_{kn} - v_n = 0 ; \qquad n = 1, \ldots, N \qquad (3\text{-}158)$$

$$\sum_{n=1}^{N} a_{kn}x_n - x_{n+k} = b_k ; \qquad k = 1, \ldots, K \qquad (3\text{-}99)$$

$$v_n \geq 0 ; \qquad n = 1, \ldots, N \qquad (3\text{-}159)$$

$$x_n v_n = 0 ; \qquad n = 1, \ldots, N \qquad (3\text{-}160)$$

$$x_{n+k} \lambda_k = 0 ; \qquad k = 1, \ldots, K \qquad (3\text{-}161)$$

$$\lambda_k \geq 0 ; \qquad k = 1, \ldots, K \qquad (3\text{-}162)$$

$$x_n \geq 0 ; \qquad n = 1, \ldots, N + K \qquad (3\text{-}100)$$

where λ_k is the Lagrange multiplier associated with the kth constraint. These are necessary and sufficient conditions for solving the quadratic programming problem, provided $\mathbf{Q}$ is positive definite. Wolfe first finds a basic feasible solution to the constraints (3-99). (Recall that this consists in solving the equations for K state variables in terms of the remaining N decision variables, the latter then being set to zero.) This solution must be such that the resulting values of the state variables are all nonnegative, and a systematic way to find such a solution is to solve a linear programming problem which formulates the sufficient conditions for the existence of the solution. One adds an artificial variable y_k to each constraint equation (3-99) to obtain a basic feasible solution, $y_k = b_k$, with all x_n, $n = 1, \ldots, M + K$, set equal to zero. Then one minimizes the linear expression, $\sum_{k=1}^{K} y_k$, subject to nonnegativity constraints on the y_k and x_n. If a solution to conditions (3–99) and (3–100) exists, the minimum value of $\sum_{k=1}^{K} y_k$ will be zero, producing the desired basic feasible solution.

Wolfe now sets the v_n and λ_k to zero, so that conditions (3–99), (3–100), and (3–159) through (3–162) are satisfied. His algorithm then uses the simplex method of linear programming to minimize the linear form:

$$f = \sum_{n=1}^{N} \sum_{p=1}^{N} (q_{np}x_p + c_n) \tag{3-163}$$

subject to the constraints (3–99), (3–100), and (3–159) through (3–162) and the additional constraint:

$$\sum_{p=1}^{N} q_{np}x_p + c_n \geq 0 ; \qquad n = 1, \ldots, N \tag{3-164}$$

In order to solve this problem, the simplex method must be modified so that the nonlinear constraints (3–160) and (3–161) are satisfied. This is accomplished by requiring a v_n to remain a decision variable if the corresponding x_n is a state variable, and vice versa. Notice that this linear programming problem is much larger than the original quadratic problem, as it consists of $2(N + K)$ variables and $(N + K)$ constraints, plus the $N + K$ complementary slackness conditions.

3-20 Beale's Method

Another algorithm for solving quadratic programming problems, due to Beale, works more closely with the original K constraints in $N + K$ variables (including K constraint variables), as well as with the original objective function. The algorithm begins with the same tableau as that used by the differential algorithm, but from time to time additional "free" variables and equations must be added to the tableau. The free variables are proportional to the decision derivatives v_n of the differential algorithm, whereas the additional equations are expressions of these free variables in terms of the decision variables. Thus, during the course of the calculations, it may be necessary to add up to N variables and N constraints to the original tableau. Beale still works with a tableau roughly half the size of Wolfe's, however, and his algorithm has significant advantages for *weakly* quadratic problems; that is, those where only a small fraction of the variables appear in the quadratic portion of the objective function. Beale's method for choosing the decision variable to be adjusted, as well as the amount by which it is adjusted, is similar to that described earlier for the differential algorithm. His method for changing the state set is also much the same as the method employed in the differential algorithm, except that he must continually recalculate the coefficients in the expressions for the free variables. The differential algorithm does not recalculate all of these numbers, but instead generates only those coefficients it needs at the time it needs them.

3-21 Theil and van de Panne's Quadratic Algorithm

Theil and van de Panne use a different approach for the solution of the quadratic programming problem. They start at the unconstrained optimum and successively add constraints until the constrained optimum is found. That is, they first find the x_n which minimize the objective function, ignoring the constraints. These x_n define a point in N-dimensional space which will be finite and unique, since the objective function is assumed to be convex. Then, at each iteration, they determine on which side of the constraints the solution lies, and then move (in N space) in the direction of an unsatisfied constraint. Constraints are added one at a time in this manner until the solution is found which satisfies all the constraints.

Thus, Theil and van de Panne do not have a feasible solution until the last step; they move from one optimal solution to another until they find an optimal solution which is also a feasible solution. Contrast this with the methods of Wolfe and Beale, which move from one feasible solution to another until they find a feasible solution which is also an optimal solution.

3-22 Lemke's Algorithm

Another method for solving quadratic programming problems by starting at the unconstrained optimum has been developed by Lemke. His method differs from that of Theil and van de Panne, however, since he transforms the original problem into an equivalent one which is unconstrained except for nonnegativity requirements on the variables. Specifically, Lemke works with the Kuhn-Tucker conditions (3-158), (3-99), and (3-159) through (3-162). If Eq. (3-158) is solved for x_n in terms of λ_k and v_n, the resulting expression may be used to eliminate x_n from the original constraints. These transformed constraints, together with (3-159) through (3-162), produce a new set of Kuhn-Tucker conditions for a problem which is entirely equivalent to the original problem.

Lemke then finds that quadratic programming problem which corresponds to these Kuhn-Tucker conditions, and it turns out that this derived problem is of the following exceedingly simple form:

Find nonnegative z_k which minimize

$$f = \tfrac{1}{2} \sum_{k=1}^{N+K} \sum_{\ell=1}^{N+K} p_{k\ell} z_k z_\ell + \sum_{k=1}^{N+K} D_k z_k \qquad (3\text{-}165)$$

where the $p_{k\ell}$ and D_k are constants derived from the original q_{np}, c_n, a_{kn}, and b_k. A first feasible solution is immediately available: $z_k \equiv 0$, and this derived problem is then solved using an algorithm similar to Beale's.

The methods of Lemke and of Theil and van de Panne have the advantage that there is no need to seek out a first feasible solution as is required by the algorithms of Wolfe and Beale. Both procedures would appear most useful for *strongly* quadratic problems. In fact, if none of the constraints are binding (an unconstrained minimum), both methods converge in one step. On the other hand, Lemke's algorithm requires solving the N Eqs. (3–158) for the x_n, which is not necessary in the methods of Wolfe and Beale. The total amount of computation required to solve a given problem using one of these algorithms depends a great deal upon the structure of the problem, and a precise comparison of the computational advantages of the various methods can be made only with reference to a specific problem.

3-23 Zoutendijk's Method of Feasible Directions

The four algorithms just described are designed to solve programming problems for which the objective function is quadratic and the constraints are linear. Zoutendijk has developed a method for solving a more general nonlinear programming problem in which both the objective function and the constraints are convex.

The algorithm begins with a point in the feasible region; that is, any feasible solution to the constraints (3–1) and (3–2). In this method, it is not necessary that the initial point be a basic feasible solution. Next, a feasible direction of movement is determined. The best possible direction to move is along the gradient evaluated at the point, since this produces the greatest decrease in the value of the objective function. By *feasible direction* is meant one along which a small step can be taken without violating any of the constraints, and in general, the gradient will not be a feasible direction. Zoutendijk chooses to move in that feasible direction which makes the smallest possible angle with the gradient. This direction is found as the solution of a linear programming problem in which the decrease in the objective function is maximized, subject to constraints which insure feasibility. A step is then taken in this direction to a new point, at which a new feasible direction is computed. This step is of a size which either causes a constraint to be reached, or is such that any further movement in this direction will cause the objective function to begin to increase rather than decrease. Thus, at every step a linear programming problem is solved in order to determine the direction of the next step. Zoutendijk has shown that this iterative process will converge, although possibly not in a finite number of steps.

3-24 Rosen's Gradient-Projection Method

Another method for the solution of mathematical programming problems is due to Rosen. This method works best when the constraints are linear, but it can also be used to solve problems having nonlinear constraints. Instead of computing the direction which yields the *greatest* decrease in the objective function, Rosen simply chooses a direction which decreases this function and which also insures that he can move without immediately striking a constraint. For linear constraints, this direction is the projection of the gradient onto the constraint set defined by those constraints (3–15) which hold as strict equalities at the feasible solution point where the gradient is evaluated. Thus the direction of each step can be determined without solving a linear programming problem, and feasibility is always maintained since the solution path never moves outside the boundary. The length of the steps is computed much in the manner of Zoutendijk's method, and after each step, the gradient is recomputed and a new direction is calculated.

For nonlinear constraints, the gradient is projected onto the planes tangent to those constraints which hold as equalities at each successive point, and a step is taken along this projection. Unlike the case of linear constraints, this step moves to a point outside the constraint set, and an iterative procedure is necessary to move the solution to a nearby point on the constraint surfaces. This procedure produces a feasible point at which the objective function takes on a smaller value than that which it had at the last solution point. Then the gradient is again calculated and the process repeated until an optimal solution has been found.

3-25 Kelley's Cutting Plane Method

Kelley has presented a somewhat different technique for solving mathematical programming problems. His algorithm is designed to solve those problems in which *all* the nonlinearities occur in the *constraints;* specifically, his method applies to the problem of minimizing a *linear* expression subject to convex inequality constraints. He replaces the nonlinear constraints by linear constraints in such a way that the resulting linear convex set completely encloses the original constraint set. This approximation produces a linear programming problem which is then solved by the simplex method. A cutting plane (in general, a multidimensional hyperplane) is then passed between this solution point and the nonlinear constraint set. This cutting plane is then added to the other linear constraints, and the linear objective function is minimized with respect to this new constraint set (another linear programming problem). This produces a new solution point, a new cutting plane is introduced, and the process is repeated, each iteration requiring the solution of a linear programming problem. Kelley has shown that these iterations converge to a limit, although an infinite number of iterations may be needed. Wolfe has devised an acceleration scheme which speeds up the rate of convergence, and just as in the case of the differential algorithm, Kelley's method approaches the exact solution quite rapidly. Thus, the iterative process need be continued only until one reaches a solution which is sufficiently near the optimum.

3-26 Wilson's Solver Routine

An algorithm for solving concave programming problems has been devised by Wilson, who has also written a FORTRAN computer routine called SOLVER which carries out the steps of his algorithm. The technique applies to problems concerned with maximizing a concave function subject to convex constraints (note that this is equivalent to minimizing a convex function subject to convex constraints). The objective function and each of the constraint functions must be twice differentiable within a neighborhood of the solution, although this requirement can be relaxed somewhat by artificially smoothing discontinuous second derivatives.

As in the case of most mathematical programming methods, Wilson's technique is based upon the Kuhn-Tucker conditions; for problems of higher than second order, it becomes exceedingly difficult to solve these equations. SOLVER avoids this difficulty by approximating the Lagrangian function by a quadratic function. Then, a succession of approximating quadratic programming problems are solved which converge to the solution of the original problem within any desired degree of accuracy. Wilson states that his program as presently written will handle problems with up to 70 variables and constraints, using 17,000 computer core locations.

3-27 Fiacco and McCormick's SUMT Method

An algorithm developed by Fiacco and McCormick for solving constrained optimization problems is based on an approach quite different from those previously described. In order to minimize an objective function, $y\langle \mathbf{x} \rangle$, on the constraint set (3–2), this method seeks the *unconstrained* minimum of a new function,

$$P\langle \mathbf{x}, r \rangle = y\langle \mathbf{x} \rangle + r \sum_{k=1}^{K} \frac{1}{f_k\langle \mathbf{x} \rangle}$$

over a strictly monotonic decreasing sequence of r values, $\{r_i\}$. Under certain restrictions, there exists a sequence of feasible points, $\{x\langle r_i\rangle\}$, that respectively minimize $\{P\langle x, r_i\rangle\}$. Consequently, as r_i approaches zero ($i \to \infty$), the solutions $x\langle r_i\rangle$ approach x^*, the optimal solution to the original constrained problem. The important restrictions required by this algorithm are that $y\langle x\rangle$ and each of the $f_k\langle x\rangle$ be continuously twice differentiable, and that for every positive value of r, the function $P\langle x, r\rangle$ be strictly convex.

This method, then, is based on transforming a constrained minimization problem into a sequence of unconstrained minimization problems. The algorithm develops both primal-feasible and dual-feasible points, so that the dual solution vector is generated explicitly. The primal objective function, $y\langle x\rangle$, is monotonically decreased as r decreases, and a subproblem of the original problem is solved with each unconstrained minimization. This subproblem provides information for estimating the limiting (solution) values of the problem variables as well as the x which minimizes P for some smaller value of r.

Fiacco and McCormick give a rationale for computing the initial value of r consistent with attempting to reduce the effort of minimizing $P\langle x, r\rangle$; the initial value, r_1, is selected so as to minimize the magnitude of the gradient of $P\langle x, r\rangle$, evaluated at the starting point, x_0. This leads to an analytic determination of r_1 which the authors state has worked well in practice.

The major computational effort required in this algorithm is concerned with obtaining the sequence of feasible points that minimize the P function for various values of r. First-order (steepest ascent) gradient methods have generally converged too slowly to be adequate for minimizing P, and a second-order optimum gradient method has proved to be much more reliable and efficient. In this second-order method, a point, x_{j+1}, is obtained from the previous point, x_j, by descending the mapped gradient of P evaluated at x_j. The mapping is obtained by premultiplying the gradient of P by the inverse of the matrix of second partial derivatives of P. The point x_{j+1} is found by approximating the point where P is minimized on the mapped gradient vector. This becomes the next point in the iteration, and the process is then repeated until the minimum is approached. The authors give criteria for terminating convergence toward the minimum as well as for selecting the rate of reduction of the parameter r. Also given are a theoretical basis for developing the trajectory of minima of P as a function of r, and a detailed computer solution of a numerical problem which illustrates the convergence characteristics of the algorithm.

3-28 Special Topics

Mathematical programming covers an extensive field, composed of a great variety of problems, and numerous methods have been developed for solving particular classes of problems. Here we mention briefly only two of these in order to give an idea of the scope of the subject.

One important class of problems are those in which the objective function and each of the constraints consist of *separable* functions. This means that the problem is of the form:

$$\text{minimize } C = \sum_{j=1}^{N} c_j \langle x_j \rangle \tag{3-166}$$

subject to constraints of the form:

$$\sum_{j=1}^{N} g_{ij} \langle x_j \rangle \geq b_i ; \qquad i = 1, \ldots, K \tag{3-167}$$

$$x_j \geq 0 ; \qquad j = 1, \ldots, N \tag{3-168}$$

Such problems can be solved by iterative techniques which replace the functions $c_j \langle x_j \rangle$ and $g_{ij} \langle x_j \rangle$ with polygonal approximations; that is, each function is approximated by straight-line segments between selected points. The resulting approximation problem can then be solved by a slight modification of the simplex method of linear programming (Miller).

This approximation is often achieved only at the expense of a considerable increase in dimensionality in the derived problem. Also, the solution obtained by this technique is usually a local minimum, and in general the procedure gives no information as to how far this solution is from the global minimum. Nevertheless, this method has proved quite useful for many practical problems which are not readily solvable by other means. Problems which are not originally in the separable form of Eq. (3–166) and (3–167) can sometimes be converted to such a form by a suitable transformation of variables (Hadley, pp. 119–123).

Another special class of optimization problems are those having infinitely many constraints. Depending upon the structure of the particular problem at hand, some efficient computational techniques are available for obtaining a solution (Saaty and Bram, pp. 168–170). Indeed, for certain problems, these methods are sufficiently attractive to justify transforming an ordinary problem with a finite number of constraints into an equivalent problem with an infinite number. Such a transformation may always be accomplished by introducing continuous parameters as Saaty and Bram describe. Again, unless the original problem has the proper convexity and concavity properties, the solution obtained by this procedure will not necessarily yield the global optimum, but rather may converge to one of several local optima. Duffin and Karlovitz have also warned of a "duality gap" phenomenon which can occur in infinite programming.

3-29 Concluding Summary

By introducing slack variables we can extend the indirect methods of Chapter 2 to optimization problems involving inequality constraints. At a given point one can identify feasible directions improving the objective function, but as soon as any constraint tightens or loosens in response to a move, all the constrained derivatives guiding the search must be recomputed. It is therefore rare to locate even a local optimum without making many changes in direction. This chapter has discussed features and problems common to all procedures for supervising these moves.

A differential approach using constrained first derivatives was used to derive the Kuhn-Tucker necessary conditions for a local constrained minimum. Then constrained second derivatives were defined for stating new sufficient conditions holding even when the objective function and feasible region are not convex. Construction and operation of a differential algorithm based on these conditions was then demonstrated in complete computational detail for a quadratic function subject to linear constraints. The fully linear case of Chapter 5 is merely a special case of this, and the terminology here is applicable to any nonlinear optimization problem.

Verifying that a point is a local optimum involves checking a matrix of second derivatives for definiteness. This can be done by completing the square, a much easier procedure than the more widely used method of finding the eigenvalues. We show that Gauss' simple method for solving linear equations is equivalent to completing the square. This gives not only a compact, rapid method for checking the sufficiency conditions for a local optimum, but a way of simplifying the optimization of weakly quadratic functions.

The chapter closed with brief reviews of the most popular algorithms for nonlinear "programming" (optimization) problems, especially those with convex and quadratic objectives. More powerful methods can be used on problems with special structure, as demonstrated in Chapter 4 concerning generalized polynomials, and in Chapter 5 regarding the fully linear case. This chapter on the general nonlinear case provides the foundation for these later chapters and shows in general what must be done to keep the "dragon" from exceeding "the proper limits."

BIBLIOGRAPHY

Arrow, K. J., L. Hurwicz, and H. Uzawa, *Studies in Linear and Nonlinear Programming*, (Stanford U. Press, 1958).

Beale, E. M. L., "On quadratic programming," *Naval Res. Log. Quart.*, 6 (September, 1959), 227–44.

Beightler, C. S., and D. J. Wilde, "Diagonalization of quadratic forms by Gauss elimination," *Man. Sci.*, 12 (January, 1966), 371–79.

Birkhoff, G., and S. MacLane, *A Survey of Modern Algebra*, (Macmillan, New York, 1953).

Candler, C., and R. J. Townsley, "The maximization of a quadratic function of variables subject to linear inequalities," *Man. Sci.*, 10 (April, 1964), 515–23.

Charnes, A., W. W. Cooper, and K. Kortanek, "Duality in semi-infinite programs and some works of Haar and Carathéodory," *Man. Sci.*, **9** (January, 1963), 209–228.

Crawford, J. D., *A Differential Algorithm for Quadratic Programming Problems*, Unpublished Master's thesis, University of Texas, January, 1963.

Dennis, J. B., *Mathematical Programming and Electrical Networks* (M.I.T. Press, New York, 1959).

Dorn, W. S., "Non-linear programming—a survey," *Man. Sci.*, **9** (January, 1963) 171–208.

Duffin, R. J., and L. A. Karlovitz, "An infinite linear program with a duality gap," *Man. Sci.*, **12** (Sept. 1965), 122–34.

Fiacco, A. V., and G. P. McCormick, "Computational algorithm for the sequential unconstrained minimization technique for nonlinear programming," *Man. Sci.*, **10** (1964), 601–617.

Gass, S. I., *Linear Programming*, 2nd ed. (McGraw-Hill, New York, 1964).

Hadley, G., *Nonlinear and Dynamic Programming* (Addison-Wesley, Reading, Mass., 1964).

Kelley, J. E., Jr. "The cutting plane method for solving convex programs," *J. Soc. Ind. Appl. Math.*, **8** (December, 1960), 703–712.

Kuhn, H. W., and A. W. Tucker, "Nonlinear programming," *Proc. Second Berkeley Symp. Math. Statistics and Probability*, J. Neyman, ed. (Univ. California Press, 1951).

Kunz, K. S., *Numerical Analysis* (McGraw-Hill, New York, 1957).

Künzi, H. P., and W. Krelle, *Nichtlineare Programmierung* (Springer-Verlag, Berlin, 1962).

Lemke, C. E., "A method of solution for quadratic programs," *Man. Sci.*, **8** (July, 1962), 442–53.

Miller, C., "The simplex method for local separable programming," in *Recent Advances in Mathematical Programming*, R. Graves and P. Wolfe, eds. (McGraw-Hill, New York, 1963).

Rosen, J. B., "The gradient projection method for nonlinear programming, Part I. Linear constraints," *J. Soc. Ind. Appl. Math.*, **8** (March, 1960), 181–217.
———, "The gradient projection method for nonlinear programming, Part II. Nonlinear constraints," *J. Soc. Ind. Appl. Math.*, **9** (December, 1961), 514–32

Saaty, T. L., and J. Bram, *Nonlinear Mathematics* (McGraw-Hill, New York, 1964), 168–70.

Theil, H., and C. van de Panne, "Quadratic programming as an extension of classical quadratic maximization," *Man. Sci.*, **7** (October, 1960), 1–20.

Wilde, D. J., "Differential calculus in nonlinear programming," *Opns. Res.*, **10** (November, 1962), 764–73.
———, "Jacobians in constrained nonlinear optimization," *Opns. Res.*, **13**, 5 (September, 1965) 848–56.

Wilson, R. B., *A Simplicial Algorithm for Concave Programming*, Doctoral dissertation, Harvard University Graduate School of Business Administration, Boston, 1963.

Wolfe, P., "The simplex method for quadratic programming," *Econometrica*, **27** (1959), 382–98.

——, "Accelerating the cutting plane method for nonlinear programming," *J. Soc. Ind. Appl. Math.*, **9** (September, 1961), 481–88.

Zoutendijk, G., *Methods of Feasible Directions* (Elsevier Publishing Co., Amsterdam, 1960).

——, "Nonlinear programming: a numerical survey," *J. SIAM Control*, **4**, 1 (1966), 194–210.

EXERCISES

3-1. Find x_1, x_2, x_3, which minimize

$$y = x_1^2 + 2x_1x_2 + 4x_1x_3 + 3x_2^2 + 2x_2x_3 + 5x_3^2 + 4x_1 - 2x_2 + 3x_3$$

without diagonalizing y. Check your answer against the answer given in the text, which was obtained by first diagonalizing y.

3-2. Find values of the x_j which minimize

$$y = 5x_1^2 + 12x_1x_2 - 16x_1x_3 + 10x_2^2 - 26x_2x_3 + 17x_3^2 - 2x_1 - 4x_2 - 6x_3$$

by first diagonalizing this expression.

3-3. By diagonalization, show that the quadratic form

$$q = x_1^2 - 4x_1x_2 + 6x_1x_3 + 5x_2^2 - 10x_2x_3 + 8x_3^2$$

is indefinite. For what values of the x_j can q be made arbitrarily small?

3-4. Find nonnegative numbers x_1 and x_2 which minimize

$$y = x_1^3 - 3x_1x_2$$

and which satisfy

$$5x_1 + 2x_2 \geq 20$$
$$-2x_1 + x_2 = 5$$

Use the differential algorithm and begin with the basic feasible solution $x_1 = \frac{10}{9}$, $x_2 = \frac{65}{9}$.

3-5. A company manufactures two products, each of which uses the same two raw materials. Each unit of product 1 requires 8 lb of raw material A and 7 lb of raw material B; each unit of product 2 requires 3 lb of raw material A and 6 lb of raw material B. The maximum amount of raw material A available per week is 1200 lb, and the maximum amount of raw material B available per week is 2100 lb. The company can sell as many units as they can make, but the selling price of each product is dependent upon how many units of both products have been sold. The unit profit for product 1 is $800 - x_1 - x_2$, and the unit profit for product 2 is $2000 - x_1 - 3x_2$, where x_1 and x_2 are the weekly production of products 1 and 2 respectively.

Find the optimal quantities of the two products to produce each week to maximize the weekly profit.

3-6. Use the differential algorithm to solve the following quadratic programming problem:

$$\text{minimize } y = 2x_1^2 - 6x_1x_2 + 9x_2^2 - 18x_1 + 9x_2$$

subject to the constraints:

$$x_1 + 2x_2 \leq 10$$
$$4x_1 - 3x_2 \leq 20$$
$$x_1 \geq 0$$
$$x_2 \geq 0$$

3-7. Solve the following problem by the differential algorithm, as modified by the acceleration algorithm: Find nonnegative x_1, x_2, x_3, which minimize

$$y = x_1^2 - 2x_1x_2 - 2x_1x_3 + 5x_2^2 + 6x_2x_3 + 6x_3^2 - 6x_1 - 2x_2$$

and which satisfy the constraints:

$$16x_1 + 8x_2 + 4x_3 \leq 75$$
$$x_1 + x_2 + x_3 \leq 6$$

3-8. (a) Solve the following problem, using Wolfe's algorithm:

$$\text{minimize } y = x_1^2 - 7x_1x_2 + 5x_1x_3 + 8x_1x_4 + 2x_2^2 - 10x_2x_3 + 17x_2x_4$$
$$+ 3x_3^2 + 12x_3x_4 + x_4^2 - 3x_1 + 11x_2 - 13x_3 - 19x_4$$

subject to

$$x_1 + x_2 + x_3 + x_4 \leq 5$$
$$2x_1 + 3x_2 - 2x_3 + 5x_4 \leq 7$$
$$6x_1 + 2x_2 - 9x_3 + 8x_4 \leq 4$$
$$x_1, x_2, x_3, x_4 \geq 0$$

(b) Use Gaussian elimination to diagonalize the foregoing objective function, and thus show that y is not convex. How does this result affect the solution found in Exercise 3-8(a)?

Polynomial Inequalities: Geometric Programming

4

Which of you, intending to build a tower, sitteth not down first and counteth the cost, whether he have sufficient to finish it?

LUKE XIV, 28, C. 75

This biblical question to potential converts also happens to be good advice to project managers, and it is not difficult to follow after all the plans have been drawn. This chapter shows how to find the cost *before* the dimensions are known, by a remarkable technique known as *geometric programming*. Then, if the minimum cost appears reasonable, one can proceed with detailed plans. This finding the optimum value without knowing the corresponding policy can, in principle, be accomplished whenever the objective function and any constraints are polynomials in the independent variables. And when the number of terms exceeds the number of variables by only a small amount, the computations are much simpler than the highly nonlinear character of the problem would lead one to expect.

Geometric programming, one of the most refreshing developments in optimization theory since the invention of the calculus, has a short history because it is so new. In 1961 Clarence Zener, Director of Science at Westinghouse, observed that a sum of component costs sometimes may be minimized

99

almost by inspection when each cost depends on products of the design variables, each raised to arbitrary but known powers. An example of such a function, given in Chapter 2, is

$$y = 1000x_1 + 4 \times 10^9 x_1^{-1} x_2^{-1} + 2.5 \times 10^5 x_2$$

This is not a polynomial because the exponents are not restricted to the positive integers—any real exponents, positive or negative, will do. Since the coefficients of the terms must be positive, Zener and his co-workers Duffin and Peterson call such functions *posynomials* in their book. Zener's technique, justified roughly in Chapter 2, is to form the *dual* function by dividing each term by a weight w_1, w_2, etc., raising each term to the power given by the weight, and multiplying the results together. In the example, this function is

$$d \equiv \left(\frac{1000x_1}{w_1}\right)^{w_1} \left(\frac{4 \times 10^9}{w_2 x_1 x_2}\right)^{w_2} \left(\frac{2.5 \times 10^5 x_2}{w_3}\right)^{w_3}$$

One next chooses weights which make this expression dimensionless with respect to the original variables x_1 and x_2. Straightforward dimensional analysis shows that the weights must all be equal in this case, and since they must sum to unity, their common value is $\frac{1}{3}$. When these values are substituted back into the dual function, a pure number is obtained because the independent variables cancel out. Zener noticed that this number is in fact the minimum cost.

$$y^* = \left(\frac{1000}{1/3}\right)^{1/3} \left(\frac{4 \times 10^9}{1/3}\right)^{1/3} \left(\frac{2.5 \times 10^5}{1/3}\right)^{1/3} = 3 \times 10^6$$

(A reader bewildered by these nonintuitive results should review the demonstration given in Chapter 2 before proceeding.)

At the same time Richard Duffin, Professor of Mathematics at Carnegie, was developing a duality theory having applications to nonlinear programming. During one of his consultations at the nearby Westinghouse research laboratory, Duffin learned of Zener's work and immediately (March, 1962) extended it to posynomials having an arbitrary number of terms (Zener's results were limited to exactly one more term than variables). He also saw that if the original "primal" function were considered a weighted arithmetic mean

$$y = w_1\left(\frac{1000x_1}{w_1}\right) + w_2\left(\frac{4 \times 10^9 x_1^{-1} x_2^{-1}}{w_2}\right) + w_3\left(\frac{2.5 \times 10^5 x_2}{w_3}\right)$$

and the dual function a weighted geometric mean of the same quantities

$$d = \left(\frac{1000x_1}{w_1}\right)^{w_1} \left(\frac{4 \times 10^9 x_1^{-1} x_2^{-1}}{w_2}\right)^{w_2} \left(\frac{2.5 \times 10^5 x_2}{w_3}\right)^{w_3}$$

then Cauchy's inequality (see Hardy, Littlewood, and Polya) gives

$$y \geq d$$

with equality only when all quantities in parentheses are equal (September, 1962).

$$\frac{1000x_1}{w_1} = \frac{4 \times 10^9 x_1^{-1} x_2^{-1}}{w_2} = \frac{2.5 \times 10^5 x_2}{w_3}$$

This means that the minimum of the primal y can be found by maximizing the dual d with respect to the weights. Moreover, any choice of weights provides a lower bound on the optimum y^* useful for rough estimation. This key role of the arithmetic-geometric mean inequality led Duffin to dub the procedure *geometric programming*, for in his words, "If you have a baby, you have to give it a name."

They kept in close touch, Zener developing applications (1962, 1964) and Duffin the theory. Elmor Peterson, a student of Duffin's, joined forces with them, collaborating with Zener on an electrical transformer law and with Duffin on an extension of the method to include inequality constraints having posynomials less than, or equal to, unity. Charnes and Cooper had previously shown how to handle single term inequalities. All this work is summarized in the book *Geometric Programming*, which goes much more deeply into the subject than this brief chapter. In addition to rigorous proofs, it contains many useful transformations and approximations for expressing optimization problems in the proper posynomial form for geometric programming.

The positive coefficients of the posynomials are needed because they are raised to fractional powers in the geometric inequality, an operation forbidden to negative numbers. The sense of the posynomial inequalities is restricted by the direction of the geometric inequality. Hence extension of geometric programming to negative coefficients and arbitrary inequalities had to await its divorce from the limitations of Cauchy's inequality. A way to accomplish this by employing Lagrangian methods was demonstrated by Wilde in the case of equality constraints (August, 1965), and his student Ury Passy completed the extension by using the Kuhn-Tucker conditions described in Chapter 3. Geometric programming is now applicable to any problem involving *generalized polynomials* (negative coefficients permitted) in the objective function. Generalized polynomial inequalities of either sense can also be handled. Any reader impatient with our gradual development of this result may wish to glance ahead to Section 4–10, where the solution to the general problem is summarized.

As in the posynomial case, generalized geometric programming gives the optimal cost (or profit) before finding the corresponding design or operating plan. In exceptionally fortunate circumstances like those in Chapter 2, the optimal "weights" can be found by inspection of the exponents in the generalized case. But any deviation from the full posynomial situation invalidates the arithmetic-geometric mean inequality and its useful applications. In the posynomial case with inequalities of the proper sense, one can in principle find the optimal weights by searching directly for an interior maximum of the dual function. On the other hand, the optimal weights occur at stationary points of unspecified character in the general case, and this precludes direct search. Instead one must solve nonlinear equations, a more difficult task. A final loss in passing to the general case is that one no longer has a guarantee that the solution obtained by working with the dual function corresponds to a minimum of the objective. One must therefore check any solution carefully by the methods of Chapters 2 and 3 to be sure it is not a stationary point or even a maximum by mistake.

Despite these disadvantages, geometric programming in the general case still preserves many of the most striking features of the posynomial situation: direct cost estimation and revelation of any interesting invariant quantities. When it works, it succeeds admirably.

The chapter opens by developing Duffin's results on unconstrained posynomials with many more terms than variables. Sufficient conditions are derived using methods which, although different from Duffin's, set the stage for the more general case. A numerical example is worked to show the sort of nonlinear computations that can arise in maximizing the dual function. Next, results for posynomial constraints of arbitrary sense are derived. The Duffin and Peterson equations are shown to be a special case, and their use of the geometric inequality for rapid approximate solutions is illustrated in an example. Then it is proved that, for posynomial inequalities of general sense, the dual function can only be assumed stationary, not maximum, at points where the objective is minimum. This is illustrated with a numerical example.

With Passy's result for inequalities of arbitrary sense established, the problem of negative coefficients is attacked. First it is proved that a generalized polynomial inequality constraint can always be replaced by two posynomial inequalities of opposite sense. Then a way is developed for transforming a problem with a generalized polynomial objective into one having an additional generalized polynomial constraint. This completes the generalization, which is then illustrated with an example. All the results are gathered into a general expression in the final technical summary. The chapter ends by discussing the few applications already achieved during geometric programming's brief history. The method has great potential, most of it as yet unrealized.

4-01 Degrees of Difficulty

Suppose that to the hypothetical chemical process described in Chapter 2 one must add a purifying device at an annual cost of $9000x_1x_2$ dollars, making the objective function

$$y = 1000x_1 + 4 \times 10^9 x_1^{-1} x_2^{-1} + 2.5 \times 10^5 x_2 + 9000 x_1 x_2 \qquad (4\text{-}1)$$

Using geometric programming as developed in Chapter 2, one would introduce the weights $w_1 = 1000x_1/y$, etc, rendering the expression $x_1^{w_1}(x_1^{-1}x_2^{-1})^{w_2}x_2^{w_3}(x_1 x_2)^{w_4}$ dimensionless, that is, equal to unity. This would give the orthogonality conditions Eq. (2–63)

$$w_1 - w_2 \qquad + w_4 = 0 \qquad (4\text{-}2)$$

$$- w_2 + w_3 + w_4 = 0 \qquad (4\text{-}3)$$

which, together with the fact that the weights by definition must sum to unity,

$$w_1 + w_2 + w_3 + w_4 = 1 \qquad (4\text{-}4)$$

give three independent linear equations in the four unknown weights. There are not enough equations to determine the optimal weights, since three equations in four variables have no unique solution. There is, in fact, an infinity of solutions, as one can see by solving for the first three weights in terms of the fourth.

$$w_1 = \tfrac{1}{3}(1 - 2w_4) \qquad (4\text{-}5)$$

$$w_2 = \tfrac{1}{3}(1 + w_4) \qquad (4\text{-}6)$$

$$w_3 = \tfrac{1}{3}(1 - 2w_4) \qquad (4\text{-}7)$$

Any choice of w_4 gives w_1, w_2, and w_3 solving the orthogonality and normality conditions. Our problem is to select the optimal weights from among these infinite possibilities.

The difference between the number of variables and the number of independent linear equations is conventionally called the *number of degrees of freedom*, as we have seen in Chapter 2. In this case there are N orthogonality conditions, one for each variable x_n, a single normality condition, and T weights, one for each term. Hence the equations have $T - (N + 1)$ degrees of freedom. Duffin and Zener suggest calling this quantity the number of degrees of *difficulty*, since they make the problem hard to solve.

Geometric programming is spectacular in its power when, as in Chapter 2, there are no degrees of difficulty, for then the orthogonality and normality conditions are not only necessary, but sufficient as well. When there are degrees of difficulty, however, one must find sufficient conditions to supplement the necessary ones already derived. Recall that whenever the optimal weights $w_1^*, \ldots, w_T^*$ are known, the minimum value of the objective function can be written down immediately.

$$y^* = \prod_{t=1}^{T} \left(\frac{c_t}{w_t^*} \right)^{w_t^*} \qquad (4\text{-}8)$$

Although this equation holds for any number of degrees of difficulty, the minimum cost y^* cannot be computed until the optimal weights are known. Let the solutions of the orthogonality and normality conditions in the example be substituted into Eq. (4–8) to give the minimum cost solely as a function of the optimal weight w_4^*.

$$y^* = \left(\frac{3 \times 1000}{1 - 2w_4^*}\right)^{(1 - 2w_4^*)/3} \times \left(\frac{3 \times 4 \times 10^9}{1 + w_4^*}\right)^{(1 + w_4^*)/3}$$
$$\times \left(\frac{3 \times 2.5 \times 10^5}{1 - 2w_4^*}\right)^{(1 - 2w_4^*)/3} \times \left(\frac{9000}{w_4^*}\right)^{w_4^*} \tag{4-9}$$

In the example this is an unknown constant, since w_4^* is unknown. Consider now the function obtained by using the variable w_4 instead of the unknown constant w_4^*.

$$d\langle w_4 \rangle \equiv \left(\frac{3 \times 1000}{1 - 2w_4}\right)^{(1 - 2w_4)/3} \times \left(\frac{3 \times 4 \times 10^9}{1 + w_4}\right)^{(1 + w_4)/3}$$
$$\times \left(\frac{3 \times 2.5 \times 10^5}{1 - 2w_4}\right)^{(1 - 2w_4)/3} \times \left(\frac{9000}{w_4}\right)^{w_4} \tag{4-10}$$

Duffin has proved that $d\langle w_4 \rangle$, called the *substituted dual function*, is maximized by the optimal weight w_4^*.

$$d\langle w_4^* \rangle = \max_{w_4 \geq 0} d\langle w_4 \rangle = y^* \tag{4-11}$$

In general, he showed that a sufficient condition for y to be minimized is that the *dual function* $d\langle w_1, \ldots, w_T \rangle$ defined by

$$d\langle w_1, \ldots, w_T \rangle \equiv \prod_{t=1}^{T} \left(\frac{c_t}{w_t}\right)^{w_t} \tag{4-12}$$

be maximum with respect to the w_t, subject to the orthogonality and normality conditions. The next section will prove this result, using a proof strategy due to Avriel and Passy which is based on the method of undetermined multipliers developed in Chapter 2. Duffin originally employed the arithmetic-geometric mean inequality (see Hardy, Littlewood, and Polya) to establish the result.

4-02 Sufficiency in the Unconstrained Case

The sufficient conditions are established most easily by applying exponential transformations to the original problem. These transformations act as equality constraints on the original objective function, giving a new constrained problem solvable by Lagrange's method of undetermined multipliers. This yields the usual orthogonality and normality necessary conditions. Rearrangement of the Lagrangian function shows that its solution must occur at a stationary point for the *dual* function. Since the transformed objective function turns out to be convex and the transformed dual function concave, each can have only one stationary point— a minimum in the former case, a maximum in the latter. Hence the original (or *primal*) problem is minimized for the choice of weights maximizing the dual function.

Our derivation is less elegant than Duffin's, but it sets the stage for proving a more general theorem generalizing geometric programming problems with inequality constraints and *negative* cost coefficients c_t. One should regard the present demonstration as introducing notation and points of view useful in understanding the general case.

Let y be a posynomial with T terms and N variables

$$y = \sum_{t=1}^{T} c_t \prod_{n=1}^{N} x_n^{a_{tn}} \tag{4-13}$$

with
$$c_t > 0 \tag{4-14}$$

The exponents a_{tn} are any real numbers. Suppose y has a minimum in the open region $x_n > 0$ and that we wish to find it. For notational convenience let

$$x_0 \equiv y$$

be the *accounting variable*, and make the exponential transformation

$$e^{u_n} \equiv x_n ; \quad n = 0, 1, \ldots, N \tag{4-15}$$

Also make a change of variable introducing the weights w_t.

$$w_t \equiv c_t \prod_{n=1}^{N} x_n^{a_{tn}}/x_0 > 0 \tag{4-16}$$

By taking natural logarithms one obtains

$$-u_0 + \sum_{n=1}^{N} a_{tn} u_n = \ln (w_t/c_t) \tag{4-17}$$

The original problem of minimizing y is now to minimize u_0 subject to the constraints

$$\sum_{t=1}^{T} w_t = 1 \tag{4-18}$$

and
$$-u_0 + \sum_{n=1}^{N} a_{tn} u_n = \ln \frac{w_t}{c_t} ; \quad t = 1, \ldots, T \tag{4-19}$$

where the $u_0, u_1, \ldots, u_N$ are unrestricted in sign, although the w_t must be positive. Since each of the functions e^{u_n} is convex with respect to u_n, the sum $\sum_t c_t \exp (\sum_n a_{tn} u_n)$ is also convex because of the positivity of the c_t. Hence there is only one stationary point for y, and it must be the global minimum.

To find this unique point, let us seek the stationary point of the Lagrangian function

$$L\langle \mathbf{u}, \mathbf{w}, \lambda_0, \boldsymbol{\omega} \rangle \equiv u_0 - \lambda_0 (1 - \sum_t w_t)$$
$$- \sum_t \omega_t \left[\ln\left(\frac{w_t}{c_t}\right) + u_0 - \sum_{n=1}^{N} a_{tn} u_n \right] \tag{4-20}$$

where $\lambda_0, \omega_1, \ldots, \omega_T$ are appropriate Lagrange multipliers for the constraints (4–18) and (4–19). Setting the first derivatives to zero gives

$$\frac{\partial L}{\partial u_0} = 1 - \sum_t \omega_t = 0 \tag{4-21}$$

$$\frac{\partial L}{\partial u_n} = \sum_t \omega_t a_{tn} = 0 ; \qquad n = 1, \ldots, N \tag{4-22}$$

$$\frac{\partial L}{\partial w_t} = \lambda_0 - \frac{\omega_t}{w_t} = 0 ; \qquad t = 1, \ldots, T \tag{4-23}$$

It follows from (4–23) that

$$\omega_t = \lambda_0 w_t$$

and by Eqs. (4–18) and (4–21),

$$\sum_t \omega_t = 1 = \lambda_0 \sum_t w_t = \lambda_0$$

Hence $\lambda_0 = 1$ $\tag{4-24}$

and $\omega_t = w_t$ $\tag{4-25}$

Thus this formulation leads to the remarkable fact that the Lagrange multiplier ω_t for the transformation equation (4–19) defining the weight w_t is exactly equal to the weight w_t itself. Equations (4–21), (4–22), and (4–25) give the usual normality and orthogonality conditions

$$\sum_t w_t = 1 \tag{4-26}$$

$$\sum_t a_{tn} w_t = 0 \tag{4-27}$$

Consider now the result of substituting the values of the Lagrange multipliers given by Eqs. (4–24) and (4–25) into the Lagrangian function of Eq. (4–20).

$$L\langle \mathbf{u}, \mathbf{w} \rangle = - \sum_t w_t \ln\left(\frac{w_t}{c_t}\right) + (u_0 - 1)(1 - \sum_{t=1}^T w_t) + \sum_{n=1}^N u_n \sum_{t=1}^T a_{tn} w_t \tag{4-28}$$

This Lagrangian can be considered as that for another constrained optimization problem by regarding $(u_0 - 1)$ and $u_1, \ldots, u_N$ themselves as undetermined multipliers for the new constraints. For this new problem, the objective function is

$$z\langle \mathbf{w} \rangle \equiv - \sum_{t=1}^T w_t \ln\left(\frac{w_t}{c_t}\right) = \ln\left[\prod_{t=1}^T \left(\frac{c_t}{w_t}\right)^{w_t}\right] \tag{4-29}$$

and the constraints are the normality and orthogonality conditions (4–26) and (4–27). It follows that any weights making the Lagrangian of Eq. (4–28) stationary will automatically give a stationary point for that of Eq. (4–20).

The function $z\langle \mathbf{w} \rangle$ is concave with respect to the weights since it is the negative of a sum of functions which are themselves convex. Hence the function has a unique stationary point — a global maximum. The *dual* problem is therefore to maximize $z\langle \mathbf{w} \rangle$ subject to the normality and orthogonality conditions, with the weights w_t constrained to be positive.

Let us now substitute the optimal weights into the Lagrangian expressions of Eqs. (4–20) and (4–28).

$$L\langle \mathbf{u}^*, \mathbf{w}^*, \lambda_0^*, \boldsymbol{\omega}^* \rangle = u_0^*$$
$$= L\langle \mathbf{u}^*, \mathbf{w}^* \rangle = -\sum_t w_t^* \ln \left(\frac{w_t^*}{c_t}\right) = z^* \tag{4-30}$$

Taking exponentials and using previous transformations (4–12), (4–15), and (4–29) confirms Eq. (4–8), previously derived by different methods in Chapter 2.

$$y^* = \prod_t \left(\frac{c_t}{w_t^*}\right)^{w_t^*} \equiv d^* \tag{4-31}$$

We shall stay in the transformed domain and express this as

$$u_0^* = z^* \tag{4-32}$$

Thus the global minimum for the primal problem equals the global maximum for the dual problem. This is important because the dual problem is often easier to solve.

4-03 Maximizing the Dual Function

Now that sufficient conditions have been established, let us apply them to the example. To find the optimal weights it remains to maximize the function $d\langle w_4 \rangle$ given in Eq. (4–10) with respect to the single variable w_4. It is easier to work with the logarithm

$$z\langle w_4 \rangle \equiv \ln d\langle w_4 \rangle$$
$$= -\left(\frac{1 - 2w_4}{3}\right)\ln \left(\frac{1 - 2w_4}{3000}\right) - \left(\frac{1 + w_4}{3}\right)\ln \left(\frac{1 + w_4}{12 \times 10^9}\right) \tag{4-33}$$
$$- \left(\frac{1 - 2w_4}{3}\right)\ln \left(\frac{1 - 2w_4}{7.5 \times 10^5}\right) - w_4 \ln \left(\frac{w_4}{9000}\right)$$

Set its first derivative to zero

$$\frac{\partial z}{\partial w_4} = 0 = \frac{2}{3}\left[1 + \ln \frac{1 - 2w_4}{3000}\right] - \frac{1}{3}\left[1 + \ln \left(\frac{1 + w_4}{12 \times 10^9}\right)\right]$$
$$+ \frac{2}{3}\left[1 + \ln \left(\frac{1 - 2w_4}{7.5 \times 10^5}\right)\right] - \left[1 + \ln \left(\frac{w_4}{9000}\right)\right]$$
$$= \ln \left[(1 - 2w_4)^{4/3}(1 + w_4)^{-1/3}w_4^{-1}\right] - \ln \left[\frac{(3000)^{2/3}(7.5 \times 10^5)^{2/3}}{(12 \times 10^9)^{1/3}(9000)}\right]$$

Notice that the nonlogarithmic constants cancel each other; this is always true because of the orthogonality and normality conditions. The optimal weight w_4^* must satisfy

$$(1 - 2w_4)^{4/3}(1 + w_4)^{-1/3}w_4^{-1} = \tfrac{1}{12} \tag{4-34}$$

The unique real solution may be found numerically with relative ease, since there is only one variable. The optimal weight is

$$w_4^* = 0.453 \tag{4-35}$$

The other weights are found from Eqs. (4-5), (4-6), and (4-7).

$$w_1^* = w_3^* = \frac{1 - 2w_4^*}{3} = 0.031 \tag{4-36}$$

$$w_2^* = \frac{1 + w_4^*}{3} = 0.484 \tag{4-37}$$

In such a process the reactor (w_2) and the purifier consume the lion's share of the total cost, the compressor and separator becoming relatively minor because of the need for much lower pressure x_1 and recycle x_2. The minimum cost is

$$y^* = \left(\frac{1000}{0.031}\right)^{0.031} \left(\frac{4 \times 10^9}{0.484}\right)^{0.484} \left(\frac{2.5 \times 10^5}{0.031}\right)^{0.031} \left(\frac{9000}{0.453}\right)^{0.453} \tag{4-38}$$

$$= \$12.6 \times 10^6$$

This is considerably higher than the \$3 million required in the original problem without the expensive purifier. The compressor and separator now cost $(0.031)(12.6 \times 10^6) = 0.390 \times 10^6$ apiece, much less than before, but the reactor cost has soared to $(0.484)(12.6 \times 10^6) = 6.08 \times 10^6$. The purifier accounts for the remaining 45.3 per cent. The optimal pressure x_1^* comes from the compressor cost:

$$x_1^* = \frac{0.390 \times 10^6}{1000} = 390 \text{ atm} \tag{4-39}$$

and the recycle ratio is obtained from the separator cost:

$$x_2^* = \frac{0.390 \times 10^6}{2.5 \times 10^5} = 1.56 \tag{4-40}$$

The example demonstrates that the weights are no longer independent of the cost coefficients c_t when there are degrees of difficulty. Thus the invariance property that was so striking with zero degrees of difficulty is lost. One can, however, still obtain bounds on the weights which do not depend on the cost coefficients by recognizing that all weights must be positive. In this case, w_4 is bounded above by $\frac{1}{2}$, since at that value w_1 and w_3 would vanish. It is bounded below by zero, since we have already considered the case without any purifier at all. Hence for *all* cost coefficients,

$$0 \leq w_1 = w_3 \leq \tfrac{1}{3} \tag{4-41}$$

$$\tfrac{1}{3} \leq w_2 \leq \tfrac{1}{2} \tag{4-42}$$

$$0 \leq w_4 \leq \tfrac{1}{2} \tag{4-43}$$

It is interesting, for example, that the reactor cost is never less than one-third nor greater than one-half the total cost for an optimal design.

4-04 Inequality Constraints

Optimization problems having inequality constraints involving posynomials can be treated by similar methods. Let there be defined M posynomials $y_1, \ldots, y_M$ in addition to that for the objective function y_0, now given a subscript 0 to make the generalization easier. The number of terms in each posynomial can vary, and will be designated T_m for each $m = 0, 1, \ldots, M$. The index m must now be appended to every term and exponent to identify the posynomial to which they belong. The typical posynomial y_m is defined by

$$y_m \equiv \sum_{t=1}^{T_m} c_{mt} \prod_{n=1}^{N} x_n^{a_{mtn}} \tag{4-44}$$

with

$$c_{mt} > 0 \tag{4-45}$$

and

$$x_n > 0 \tag{4-46}$$

The exponents a_{mtn} can be any real numbers. It is convenient to introduce *signum functions* σ_m, one for each constraint posynomial, which can be either 1 or -1 depending on how the posynomial constraint is written. The problem is to minimize y_0 subject to the constraints

$$f_m \equiv \sigma_m(1 - y_m) \geq 0 \tag{4-47}$$

The symbol f_m, reminiscent of the constraint functions of Chapters 2 and 3, reminds us that this is a nonlinear programming problem. Our task is to exploit the special form of these constraint functions to obtain an equivalent problem with *linear* constraints which is often easier to solve.

As in the unconstrained case the independent variables x_n are exponentially transformed by Eq. (4–15) and weights w_{0t} are introduced for the terms of the objective function $x_0 \ (\equiv y_0)$.

$$w_{0t} \equiv c_{0t} \prod_{n=1}^{N} \frac{x_n^{a_{0tn}}}{x_0} > 0 \ ; \qquad t = 1, \ldots, T_0 \tag{4-48}$$

The weights for the constraint terms are simply the values of the terms themselves, since, if the constraint (4–47) is tight, the terms must sum to unity.

$$w_{mt} \equiv c_{mt} \prod_{n=1}^{N} x_n^{a_{mtn}} \ ; \qquad m = 1, \ldots, M; t = 1, \ldots, T_m \tag{4-49}$$

By taking natural logarithms, one transforms the original problem into that of minimizing u_0 subject to the equality constraints,

$$-u_0 + \sum_{n=1}^{N} a_{0tn} u_n = \ln\left(\frac{w_{0t}}{c_{0t}}\right) \tag{4-50}$$

$$\sum_{n=1}^{N} a_{mtn} u_n = \ln\left(\frac{w_{mt}}{c_{mt}}\right) \ ; \qquad m = 1, \ldots, M \tag{4-51}$$

$$\sum_{t=1}^{T_0} w_{0t} = 1 \tag{4-52}$$

as well as the inequality constraints,

$$f_m \equiv \sigma_m(1 - \sum_{t=1}^{T_m} w_{mt}) \geq 0 \qquad (4\text{-}53)$$

The weights must all be positive, whereas the variables $u_0, u_1, \ldots, u_N$ are unrestricted in sign.

We wish now to construct a Lagrangian function which can be manipulated in the usual way to yield the optimal conditions. The equality constraints pose no difficulties, but the inequalities (4–53) need special consideration. If a given inequality is tight ($f_m = 0$), then a Lagrange multiplier λ_m representing the constrained slack derivative $\delta u_0/\delta f_m$ can be introduced in the conventional manner. If the inequality is loose ($f_m > 0$), then at an optimum the slack derivative must vanish. Both cases are covered by the Kuhn-Tucker complementary slackness condition:

$$f_m\left(\frac{\delta u_0}{\delta f_m}\right) = f_m \lambda_m = 0 \qquad (4\text{-}54)$$

Hence the terms $\lambda_m f_m$ may be added to the Lagrangian without changing its value, and at an optimum such a Lagrangian must be stationary. The appropriate Lagrangian function for this *primal* problem is

$$
\begin{aligned}
L\langle \mathbf{u}, \mathbf{w}, \boldsymbol{\lambda}, \boldsymbol{\omega} \rangle \equiv\ & u_0 - \lambda_0(1 - \sum_{t=1}^{T_0} w_{0t}) \\
& - \sum_{t=1}^{T_0} \omega_{0t}\left[\ln\left(\frac{w_{0t}}{c_{0t}}\right) + u_0 - \sum_{n=1}^{N} a_{0tn}u_n \right] \\
& - \sum_{m=1}^{M} \sum_{t=1}^{T_m} \omega_{mt}\sigma_m\left[\ln\left(\frac{w_{mt}}{c_{mt}}\right) - \sum_{n=1}^{N} a_{mtn}u_n \right] \\
& - \sum_{m=1}^{M} \lambda_m \sigma_m(1 - \sum_{t=1}^{T_m} w_{mt})
\end{aligned}
\qquad (4\text{-}55)
$$

Let us study first the terms connected with the objective function.

$$\frac{\partial L}{\partial u_0} = 1 - \sum_{t=1}^{T_0} \omega_{0t} = 0 \qquad (4\text{-}56)$$

$$\frac{\partial L}{\partial w_{0t}} = \lambda_0 - \frac{\omega_{0t}}{w_{0t}}; \qquad t = 1, \ldots, T_0 \qquad (4\text{-}57)$$

These two equations have the same form as Eqs. (4–21) and (4–23) for the unconstrained case, and now as then they can be combined to give analogs to Eqs. (4–24) and (4–25); namely,

$$\lambda_0 = 1 \qquad (4\text{-}58)$$

and

$$\omega_{0t} = w_{0t} \qquad (4\text{-}59)$$

As before, the Lagrange multipliers ω_{0t} for the objective function terms turn out to be the corresponding weights.

Next consider the derivatives with respect to the constraint term weights w_{mt} ($m \neq 0$).

$$\frac{\partial L}{\partial w_{mt}} = -\frac{\omega_{mt}\sigma_m}{w_{mt}} + \lambda_m\sigma_m = 0$$

whence

$$\omega_{mt} = \lambda_m w_{mt} \qquad (4\text{-}60)$$

Summing on t, we find that

$$\sum_{t=1}^{T_m} \omega_{mt} = \lambda_m \qquad (4\text{-}61)$$

since the weights sum to unity for each constraint. Therefore, if $\lambda_m \neq 0$

$$w_{mt} = \frac{\omega_{mt}}{\sum\limits_{t=1}^{T_m} \omega_{mt}} \qquad (4\text{-}62)$$

and the weights can be obtained from the Lagrange multipliers for the transformations. The ω_{mt} can be found by differentiating with respect to the u_n ($n \neq 0$).

$$\frac{\partial L}{\partial u_n} = \sum_{m=0}^{M} \sum_{t=1}^{T_m} \omega_{mt}\sigma_m a_{mtn} = 0 \qquad (4\text{-}63)$$

with the convention that

$$\sigma_0 \equiv 1 \qquad (4\text{-}64)$$

These are the orthogonality conditions for the constrained case. Notice that the variables are the Lagrange multipliers ω_{mt} rather than the weights w_{mt}. Also observe the presence of the signum functions σ_m which, together with the exponents a_{mtn}, are known from the statement of the problem. No distinction is made in these orthogonality conditions between objective function and constraint function exponents. On the other hand, the normality conditions of Eq. (4–56) involve only multipliers for the objective function terms, which happen to equal the weights.

There are in all $N + 1$ linear equations in as many variables as there are terms T in all the posynomials.

$$T \equiv \sum_{m=0}^{M} T_m \qquad (4\text{-}65)$$

Hence the number of degrees of difficulty is $T - (N + 1)$, provided that the equations are linearly independent. When there are no degrees of difficulty, the solution is unique, and once the optimal values ω_{mt}^* of the multipliers are known, the optimal weights w_{mt}^* for all terms can be computed from Eq. (4–62) for further use. But when there are degrees of difficulty, more analysis is required to establish sufficiency.

Since the λ_m ($m \neq 0$) are slack derivatives $\delta u_0 / \delta f_m$, and only positive perturbations of the f_m are feasible, they must all be nonnegative.

$$\lambda_m \geq 0 \qquad (4\text{-}66)$$

By Eq. (4–60) this implies that all the other multipliers ω_{mt} are also nonnegative, since the weights cannot be negative.

$$\omega_{mt} \geq 0 \qquad (4\text{-}67)$$

As a matter of fact, the signum functions σ_m were introduced in order to guarantee this nonnegativity, which, together with the complementary slackness conditions, completes the Kuhn-Tucker necessary conditions for a local minimum. Since the objective function y_0 is strictly convex with respect to the transformed variables $\mathbf{u}$, these conditions are also sufficient for identifying a local, although not global, minimum, a fact established in Section 3-04.

The dual problem is discovered by expressing the Lagrangian in terms of the u_n, the ω_{mt}, and the constraint functions f_m.

$$
\begin{aligned}
L\langle \boldsymbol{\omega}, \mathbf{u}, \mathbf{f} \rangle = {} & \sum_{m=0}^{M} \sum_{t=1}^{T_m} \sigma_m \omega_{mt} \ln \left(c_{mt} \omega_{mt}^{-1} \sum_{u=1}^{T_m} \omega_{mu} \right) \\
& + (u_0 - 1)\left(1 - \sum_{t=1}^{T_0} \omega_{0t}\right) \\
& + \sum_{n=1}^{N} u_n \sum_{m=0}^{M} \sum_{t=1}^{T_m} \sigma_m a_{mtn} \omega_{mt} \\
& - \sum_{m=1}^{M} f_m \lambda_m
\end{aligned}
\qquad (4\text{-}68)
$$

As in the unconstrained problem, the variables $(u_0 - 1)$ and $u_1, \cdots, u_N$ may be now regarded as Lagrange multipliers for the normality and orthogonality conditions. A new feature is the presence of the constraint functions f_m, which in this form play the roles of multipliers for the nonnegativity restrictions on the λ_m. The equivalent problem has for its objective function

$$z\langle \boldsymbol{\omega} \rangle \equiv \sum_{m=0}^{M} \sum_{t=1}^{T_m} \sigma_m \omega_{mt} \ln \left(c_{mt} \omega_{mt}^{-1} \sum_{u=1}^{T_m} \omega_{mu} \right) \qquad (4\text{-}69)$$

The independent *dual* variables ω_{mt} are constrained to satisfy normality conditions,

$$\sum_{t=1}^{T_0} \omega_{0t} = 1 \qquad (4\text{-}70)$$

orthogonality conditions for $n = 1, \ldots, N$,

$$\sum_{m=0}^{M} \sum_{t=1}^{T_m} \sigma_m a_{mtn} \omega_{mt} = 0 \qquad (4\text{-}71)$$

and nonnegativity conditions,

$$\lambda_m = \sum_{t=1}^{T_m} \omega_{mt} \geq 0 \qquad (4\text{-}72)$$

The exponential of $z\langle \boldsymbol{\omega} \rangle$ is called the *dual function* $d\langle \boldsymbol{\omega} \rangle$.

$$
\begin{aligned}
d\langle \boldsymbol{\omega} \rangle & \equiv \exp\left[z\langle \boldsymbol{\omega} \rangle \right] \\
& = \prod_{m=0}^{M} \prod_{t=1}^{T_m} \left(c_{mt} \omega_{mt}^{-1} \sum_{u=1}^{T_m} \omega_{mu} \right)^{\sigma_m \omega_{mt}}
\end{aligned}
\qquad (4\text{-}73)
$$

For the moment we defer the complicated question of whether one should maximize, minimize, or find some other special point for the dual function or its logarithm. Right now it can be established that any set of dual variables $\boldsymbol{\omega}^0$ making u_0 a local minimum (with value u_0^0) will also be such that

$$z\langle\boldsymbol{\omega}^0\rangle = u_0^0 \qquad (4\text{-}74)$$

This is true because at the local minimum, u_0^0, all the constraint terms vanish from the Lagrangian, and for the corresponding weights $\boldsymbol{\omega}^0$, the dual constraint terms disappear. When there are no degrees of difficulty, the normality and orthogonality conditions have a unique solution $\boldsymbol{\omega}^0$. In this case one can obtain y_0^0, the stationary value of the objective function, directly from the formula,

$$y_0^0 = d\langle\boldsymbol{\omega}^0\rangle = \prod_{m=0}^{M} \prod_{t=1}^{T_m} \left(c_{mt}(\omega_{mt}^0)^{-1} \sum_{u=1}^{T_m} \omega_{mu}^0 \right)^{\sigma_m \omega_{mt}^0} \qquad (4\text{-}75)$$

This stationary point can be identified as a minimum only if it can be assumed in advance that y has a minimum. In this case $y_0^0 = y_0^{**}$ (the global minimum) since there can be only one stationary point when there are no degrees of difficulty.

4-05 Positive Signum Functions

The questions of sufficiency and uniqueness are settled quickly when all the signum functions are positive, the case developed by Duffin and Peterson. Suppose

$$\sigma_m = 1 ; \qquad m = 0, 1, \ldots, M \qquad (4\text{-}76)$$

We have already pointed out that the objective function y_0 is strictly convex with respect to the transformed variables $\mathbf{u}$. By the same token, all the posynomials are also strictly convex functions of the $\mathbf{u}$. According to Eq. (4–76), all the constraints take the form

$$y_m \leq 1 ; \qquad m = 1, \ldots, M \qquad (4\text{-}77)$$

which forms a convex set with respect to $\mathbf{u}$ (Exercise 4–2). In Section 3–04 it was shown that a strictly convex function defined on a convex set has only one local minimum. Thus the local minimum satisfying the normality and orthogonality conditions must also be the global minimum.

As for the transformed dual function $z\langle\boldsymbol{\omega}\rangle$, it is strictly concave when Eq. (4–76) holds because it is then a positively weighted sum of negative logarithms of the weights $w_{mt} \equiv \omega_{mt}/\sum_{u=1}^{T_m} \omega_{mu}$. Hence it has only one stationary point—a global maximum. As in the unconstrained case, one can therefore find the *minimum* u_0(or y_0) by *maximizing* the dual function $d\langle\boldsymbol{\omega}\rangle$ or its logarithm $z\langle\boldsymbol{\omega}\rangle$, and this condition is sufficient. The dual problem for positive signs σ_m is therefore to maximize $d\langle\boldsymbol{\omega}\rangle$, Eq. (4–73), subject to the normality and orthogonality conditions (4–70) and (4–71), with the ω_{mt} restricted to be nonnegative (Eq. 4–72). This can be written

$$y\langle\mathbf{x}\rangle \geq y^{**} = d^{**} \geq d\langle\boldsymbol{\omega}\rangle \qquad (4\text{-}78)$$

with the double asterisks signifying global optima—a minimum for y_0 and a maximum for the dual function $d\langle\boldsymbol{\omega}\rangle$.

Duffin and Peterson have shown how to use Eq. (4–78) for obtaining quick estimates of the optimal value of the objective function. For example, consider the chemical plant objective function of Eq. (4–1)

$$y = 1000x_1 + 4 \times 10^9(x_1x_2)^{-1} + 2.5 \times 10^5x_2 + 9000x_1x_2 \qquad (4\text{-}1)$$

Having one degree of difficulty, this problem can be solved by maximizing the dual function as described earlier. A fast estimate is obtainable by neglecting one of the terms and solving the resulting zero degree problem for the weights. These weights are then substituted into the dual function to obtain a lower bound on the true optimum cost. The corresponding x_1 and x_2 can be used to construct an upper bound simply by substituting them into the objective function.

Let us, for instance, neglect the purifier cost $9000x_1x_2$, since we already know that in this case (solved in Section 2-08) the proper weights would be $\omega_1 = \omega_2 = \omega_3 = \frac{1}{3}$. The dual function, evaluated for these weights, is

$$d\left\langle\frac{1}{3}, \frac{1}{3}, \frac{1}{3}\right\rangle = \left(\frac{1000}{1/3}\right)^{1/3}\left(\frac{4 \times 10^9}{1/3}\right)^{1/3}\left(\frac{2.5 \times 10^5}{1/3}\right)^{1/3}$$

$$= 3 \times 10^6$$

a result obtained earlier which can be used as a lower bound on y^{**}. The corresponding values $x_1 = 1000$; $x_2 = 4$ can be substituted into Eq. (4–1) to obtain the upper bound

$$y\langle 1000, 4\rangle = 39 \times 10^6$$

which reflects $\$36 \times 10^6$ for the neglected purifier. Of course this is a terrible pair of bounds, meaning that the purifier is an important cost item which shouldn't be ignored. Better bounds are obtained by neglecting the separator cost and setting $\omega_3 = 0$. From Eqs. (4–5), (4–6), and (4–7) it is seen that the normality and orthogonality conditions are satisfied in this case when $\omega_2 = \omega_4 = \frac{1}{2}$ and $\omega_1 = \omega_3 = 0$. The dual function gives a lower bound as

$$d\left\langle 0, \frac{1}{2}, 0, \frac{1}{2}\right\rangle = \left(\frac{4 \times 10^9}{1/2}\right)^{1/2}\left(\frac{9000}{1/2}\right)^{1/2}$$

$$= 12 \times 10^6$$

It is interesting that in this case the corresponding design is not unique, since the equations

$$4 \times 10^9(x_1x_2)^{-1} = 6 \times 10^6 \quad \text{and} \quad 9000x_1x_2 = 6 \times 10^6$$

both give the same equation

$$x_1 x_2 = 667$$

To estimate, let us choose x_1 and x_2 that make the compressor and separator costs equal.

$$1000x_1 = 2.5 \times 10^5 x_2$$

The proper values are $x_1 = 411$ and $x_2 = 1.63$, for which the compressor and separator costs are each 0.411×10^6. This gives a true primal cost of \$12.8 \times 10^6$, a close upper bound on the solution.

$$12.0 \times 10^6 \leq y^* \leq 12.8 \times 10^6$$

The upper bound is in this case within 2 per cent of the true minimum (\$12.6 \times 10^6$) which was obtained in Eq. (4–38) only after considerably more effort.

The preceding example was not entirely satisfying because there were no constraints. Consider the following synthetic problem involving the same numbers for comparison. It is a variant of a problem solved by other methods in Section 2–09, namely, to minimize y_0

$$y_0 \equiv 1000x_1 + 4 \times 10^9 x_1^{-1} x_2^{-1} + 2.5 \times 10^5 x_2 \tag{4-79}$$

subject to

$$x_1 x_2 \geq 9000 \tag{4-80}$$

which may be written in the form of Eq. (4–53) as

$$1 - 9000 x_1^{-1} x_2^{-1} \geq 0 \tag{4-81}$$

Here $\sigma_0 = \sigma_1 = 1$, so the theory of the present section applies. The orthogonality and normality conditions are (notice the sign change on ω_{11} and that the normality condition covers only ω_{01}, ω_{02}, and ω_{03}):

$$\omega_{01} - \omega_{02} \qquad - \omega_{11} = 0 \tag{4-82}$$

$$- \omega_{02} + \omega_{03} - \omega_{11} = 0 \tag{4-83}$$

$$\omega_{01} + \omega_{02} + \omega_{03} \qquad = 1 \tag{4-84}$$

The solutions, in terms of ω_{11}, are

$$\omega_{01} = \omega_{03} = \frac{1 + \omega_{11}}{3} \tag{4-85}$$

$$\omega_{02} = \frac{1 - 2\omega_{11}}{3} \tag{4-86}$$

and the dual function is

$$d \equiv \left(\frac{1000}{\omega_{01}}\right)^{\omega_{01}} \left(\frac{4 \times 10^9}{\omega_{02}}\right)^{\omega_{02}} \left(\frac{2.5 \times 10^5}{\omega_{03}}\right)^{\omega_{03}} \left(\frac{9000\omega_{11}}{\omega_{11}}\right)^{\omega_{11}} \tag{4-87}$$

Rather than solving the problem by maximizing d, let us try to establish tight bounds on the solution with rapid computations. One might be tempted first just to set $\omega_{11} = 0$, since this gives the unconstrained optimum already computed. This is unwise because the solutions obtained are not feasible and the numbers computed are therefore irrelevant to the constrained problem. Instead let us set $\omega_{02} = 0$, that is, neglect the reactor cost. This is clearly absurd because this cost, being of the form $4 \times 10^9 x_1^{-1} x_2^{-1}$, cannot vanish for finite x_1 and x_2. Yet by being a little careful we can allow for this anomaly and quickly come up with the optimal solution (by coincidence). If $\omega_{02} = 0$, then Eqs. (4–85) and (4–86) give $\omega_{01} = \omega_{02} = \omega_{11} = \frac{1}{2}$. One can then compute a cost estimate for these weights by ignoring the second factor in Eq. (4–87)

$$\left(\frac{1000}{1/2}\right)^{1/2} \left(\frac{2.5 \times 10^5}{1/2}\right)^{1/2} (9000)^{1/2} = 3 \times 10^6$$

This is *not* a lower bound because it is not really the dual function, but it can be used to obtain design parameters. For example, x_1 is obtained by setting the compressor cost equal to half of the \$3 $\times$ 10^6 estimate.

$$1000 x_1 = 1.5 \times 10^6$$

whence
$$x_1 = 1500$$

Similarly x_2 is found to be 6. Hence the reactor cost, originally neglected, can be calculated as

$$4 \times 10^9 (1500)^{-1} 6^{-1} = 0.444 \times 10^6$$

Since the other two pieces of equipment together cost \$3 $\times$ 10^6, the total cost for this design is \$3.444 $\times$ 10^6—an upper bound on the minimum cost.

A lower bound can now be computed by finding the true weights for this design. They are

$$\omega_{01} = \omega_{03} = \frac{1.5 \times 10^6}{3.444 \times 10^6} = 0.435$$

$$\omega_{02} = \frac{0.444}{3.444} = 0.130$$

$$\omega_{11} = \omega_{01} - \omega_{02} = 0.305$$

The corresponding dual function is

$$d = \left(\frac{1000}{0.435}\right)^{0.435} \left(\frac{4 \times 10^9}{0.130}\right)^{0.130} \left(\frac{2.5 \times 10^5}{0.435}\right)^{0.435} (9000)^{0.305}$$

$$= 3.444 \times 10^6$$

Since this lower bound turns out to equal the upper bound, we know we have stumbled fortuitously upon the constrained minimum without having to perform any difficult computations. This result verifies the one obtained in Section 2–09.

The examples have shown how useful it is to have the dual function as a lower bound on the minimum cost. Unfortunately, this is a property only of problems in which all of the signum functions are positive, the case treated by Duffin and Petersen. In more general situations the dual function cannot be used in this way, as Section 4–06 will show.

4-06 Mixed Signs

Suppose now that some or all of the signum functions σ_m are negative (excluding σ_0 for the objective function, which was defined formally to be positive). In this case no general statements can be made about the concavity or convexity of the constraint set. Since the objective is bounded below by zero, the objective function, being continuous, must have a minimum, provided that there exist points satisfying the constraints. Let $\mathbf{u}^0$ be a feasible local minimum for the primal problem. In Section 4–04 it was shown that the Lagrangian function for the primal problem, when evaluated at a stationary point or constrained local optimum $\mathbf{u}^0$, is the same as that associated with finding a stationary point or constrained local optimum for the transformed dual function

$$z\langle\boldsymbol{\omega}\rangle \equiv \sum_{m=0}^{M} \sum_{t=1}^{T_m} \sigma_m \omega_{mt} \ln\left(c_{mt}\omega_{mt}^{-1} \sum_{u=1}^{T_m} \omega_{mu}\right) \tag{4-69}$$

with respect to the nonnegative dual variables $\boldsymbol{\omega}$, which are constrained to satisfy normality and orthogonality conditions (4–70) and (4–71). When all signum functions are positive, this point has just been proved to be a local maximum. It remains to describe the character of this point when the signs are mixed, for then $z\langle\boldsymbol{\omega}\rangle$ is not concave.

Consider the unconstrained derivative of $z\langle\boldsymbol{\omega}\rangle$ with respect to any of the duals, say ω_{mv}

$$\begin{aligned}
\frac{\partial z}{\partial \omega_{mv}} &= \sigma_m \frac{\partial}{\partial \omega_{mv}}\left[\omega_{mv} \ln\left(c_{mv}\omega_{mv}^{-1} \sum_{u=1}^{T_m} \omega_{mu}\right) + \sum_{\substack{t=1 \\ t\neq v}}^{T_m} \omega_{mt} \ln\left(c_{mt}\omega_{mt}^{-1} \sum_{u=1}^{T_m} \omega_{mu}\right)\right] \\
&= \sigma_m\left\{\ln\left(c_{mv}\omega_{mv}^{-1} \sum_{u=1}^{T_m} \omega_{mu}\right) + \omega_{mv}\left[-\omega_{mv}^{-1} + \left(\sum_{u=1}^{T_m} \omega_{mu}\right)^{-1}\right] \right. \\
&\qquad\qquad \left. + \sum_{\substack{t=1 \\ t\neq v}}^{T_m} \omega_{mt}\left(\sum_{u=1}^{T_m} \omega_{mu}\right)^{-1}\right\} \\
&= \sigma_m \ln\left(\frac{c_{mv}}{w_{mv}}\right)
\end{aligned} \tag{4-88}$$

This remarkable simplification follows from Eq. (4–62) relating the weights to the duals, and from the fact that the weights must add up to unity. Let us study next the derivative of the dual Lagrangian, Eq. (4–68), with respect to ω_{mv} ($m \neq 0$).

$$\begin{aligned}
\frac{\partial L}{\partial \omega_{mv}} &= \frac{\partial z}{\partial \omega_{mv}} + \sum_{n=1}^{N} \sigma_m a_{mvn}u_n - f_m \\
&= \sigma_m\left[-\ln\left(\frac{w_{mv}}{c_{mv}}\right) + \sum_{n=1}^{N} a_{mvn}u_n\right] - f_m
\end{aligned} \tag{4-89}$$

But by Eq. (4–51), which defined the weights $\mathbf{w}$, the quantity in brackets must vanish, leaving

$$\frac{\partial L}{\partial \omega_{mv}} = -f_m \leq 0 \qquad (4\text{-}90)$$

The inequality comes from the definition of the constraint function f_m, which has a signum function in it to keep it nonnegative, Eq. (4–53). Hence $\partial L/\partial \omega_{mv}$, which is also the constrained derivative $\delta z/\delta \omega_{mv}$, must be nonpositive at $\mathbf{u}^0$.

At $\mathbf{u}^0$ the complementary slackness condition must also hold for f_m and each ω_{mv}.

$$f_m \omega_{mv} = 0 \qquad (4\text{-}91)$$

Since the duals are nonnegative, either f_m or ω_{mv} must be zero. If the mth constraint is loose ($f_m > 0$), then all its corresponding duals ω_{mt} ($t = 1, \ldots, T_m$) will be zero and consequently on the boundary of the set of dual variables satisfying the dual constraints. Therefore z attains a local maximum there with respect to any ω_{mt} whose constrained derivatives do not vanish. On the other hand, if the mth constraint is tight ($f_m = 0$), then the corresponding duals ω_{mt} will be positive, placing the point inside the dual constraint set. Since by Eq. (4–89), the constrained derivatives will vanish, z must be stationary there with respect to the ω_{mt}.

Remember that the primal point $\mathbf{u}^0$ could be a constrained local *maximum* rather than the desired minimum. It could also be a stationary point. Hence one must check any point $\mathbf{u}^0$ obtained by dual manipulations to see that it has the proper character. This is readily done by computing the constrained derivatives $\delta u_0/\delta u_{mt}$ at $\mathbf{u}^0$, using the Jacobian formulas of Chapters 2 and 3. Since u_0 is convex, satisfaction of the Kuhn-Tucker nonnegativity and complementary slackness conditions is sufficient to establish $\mathbf{u}^0$ as a local minimum. Let the superscript 0 be replaced by a superscript i (for "infimum") whenever $\mathbf{u}^0$ has been established as a local minimum $\mathbf{u}^i$. Similarly let the dual point corresponding to $\mathbf{u}^i$ be labeled $\boldsymbol{\omega}^i$ instead of $\boldsymbol{\omega}^0$. Then the solution to the primal minimization problem may be written

$$u_0^* = \min u_0^i = \min_{\mathbf{u}} (\operatorname{lmin} u_0) \qquad (4\text{-}92)$$

In terms of the transformed dual function, this is

$$u_0^* = \min z\langle \boldsymbol{\omega}^i \rangle \qquad (4\text{-}93)$$

One must find the smallest of the local minima, each computed in the dual space by setting derivatives to zero.

This result extends the geometric programming procedure of Duffin, Peterson, and Zener to sets of posynomial constraints of arbitrary sense (that is, mixed signum functions). An important feature of original geometric programming is lost, however, when the signs are mixed. This is the use of the dual solution for quick estimates and successive approximation algorithms. The important inequality (4–78) holds if and *only* if all signum functions are positive.

Dual stationary points can be found indirectly by using the normality and orthogonality conditions to eliminate $N + 1$ duals from z and setting the first derivatives of the function obtained to zero. This would require solving nonlinear equations resembling Eq. (4–34)—as many equations as there are degrees of difficulty $T - (N + 1)$. The numerical difficulties of this approach can make it impractical, especially since one must also estimate which primal constraints are tight at the stationary point. But when it does work, it succeeds admirably, as the example in the next section demonstrates.

4-07 A Mixed Sign Example

Consider a problem due to Passy, namely, to minimize x_0 subject to the constraints:

$$3.18 \times 10^{-4}x_0x_1^{1.1}x_2^{0.6}x_4^{-1} + 114.3x_0x_2^{-1}x_3^{-1}x_4^{-1} + 2.28x_0x_3x_4^{-1} + x_4^{-1} \leq 1 \quad (4\text{-}94)$$

$$3.38x_0x_1^{0.25}x_4^{-1} \geq 1 \quad (4\text{-}95)$$

$$x_n > 0 ; \qquad n = 0, 1, \ldots, 4$$

At the moment, this example seems artificial, without apparent economic or industrial significance, but the result will be used later to solve a more complicated version of the chemical process design problem. For the moment, regard it as a mathematical exercise.

There are six terms and five variables, giving zero degrees of difficulty. Hence the normality and orthogonality conditions have a unique solution, the optimal dual variables $\omega_{01}^*, \omega_{11}^*, \omega_{12}^*, \omega_{13}^*, \omega_{14}^*, \omega_{21}^*$. As the objective function has only one term, the normality conditions give immediately

$$\omega_{01}^* = 1 \quad (4\text{-}96)$$

Since $\sigma_1 = 1$ and $\sigma_2 = -1$, the orthogonality conditions are

$$\omega_{01} + \omega_{11} + \omega_{12} + \omega_{13} \qquad\qquad - \omega_{21} = 0 \quad (4\text{-}97)$$

$$1.1\omega_{11} \qquad\qquad\qquad - 0.25\omega_{21} = 0 \quad (4\text{-}98)$$

$$0.6\omega_{11} - \omega_{12} \qquad\qquad\qquad = 0 \quad (4\text{-}99)$$

$$- \omega_{12} + \omega_{13} \qquad\qquad = 0 \quad (4\text{-}100)$$

$$- \omega_{11} - \omega_{12} - \omega_{13} - \omega_{14} \qquad + \omega_{21} = 0 \quad (4\text{-}101)$$

The solutions are

$$\omega_{11}^* = 0.454 ; \qquad \omega_{12}^* = \omega_{13}^* = 0.273 ; \qquad \omega_{14}^* = 1 ; \qquad \omega_{21}^* = 2 \quad (4\text{-}102)$$

The value of the dual function, and therefore of the objective function x_0, is

$$x_0^* = d^* = \left(\frac{1}{1}\right)^1 \left(\frac{3.18 \times 10^{-4} \times 2}{0.454}\right)^{0.454} \left(\frac{114.3 \times 2}{0.273}\right)^{0.273}$$

$$\times \left(\frac{2.28 \times 2}{0.273}\right)^{0.273} \left(\frac{1}{1}\right)^1 \left(\frac{3.38 \times 2}{2}\right)^{-2} \quad (4\text{-}103)$$

$$= 0.1192$$

The reader can verify that this value is the minimum for x_0 (Exercise 4–4).

Values of the primal variables are readily computed from the individual terms. We know that $x_0^* = 0.1192$. The value of x_4^* comes immediately from the fourth term of the first constraint.

$$(x_4^*)^{-1} = \frac{\omega_{14}^*}{\sum_{t=1}^{4} \omega_{1t}^*} = \frac{1}{2}$$

whence
$$x_4^* = 2 \qquad (4\text{-}104)$$

Next x_1^* is calculated from the second constraint.

$$3.38(x_0^*)(x_1^*)^{0.25}(x_4^*)^{-1} = \tfrac{2}{2} = 1$$
$$= 3.38(0.1192)(x_1^*)^{0.25}(2)^{-1}$$

whence
$$x_1^* = 604 \qquad (4\text{-}105)$$

The third term of the first constraint gives

$$2.28(0.1192)x_3^*(2)^{-1} = \frac{0.273}{2}$$

whence
$$x_3^* = 1.00 \qquad (4\text{-}106)$$

Use of either term remaining yields

$$x_2^* = 49.9 \qquad (4\text{-}107)$$

The simplicity of the computations shows the power of the technique when there are no degrees of difficulty.

4-08 Negative Constraint Coefficients

Until now the development has been confined to posynomials, principally because if any of the c_{mt} were negative, the dual function d could involve fractional powers of negative numbers, which lead to imaginary numbers. This would seriously limit the applicability of the method, since many problems must take account not only of costs but also of income from product sales, which would have to be treated as negative costs. Furthermore, many inequality constraints have negative as well as positive terms. Passy has shown how to take any inequality constrained polynomial problem with coefficients of arbitrary sign and transform it into one which, involving only posynomials, is solvable by the dual techniques just described. Although new variables are introduced by the transformation, an equal number of terms are added which keep the number of degrees of difficulty unchanged.

Consider first how to handle negative terms in the constraints. For abbreviation let

$$\prod_{n=1}^{N} x_n^{a_{mtn}} \equiv p_{mt} \qquad (4\text{-}108)$$

Let there be a known signum function $\sigma_{mt}(\equiv \pm 1)$ for each term so that the mth constraint can be written uniquely as

$$f_m = \sigma_m\left(1 - \sigma_m \sum_{t=1}^{T_m} \sigma_{mt} c_{mt} p_{mt}\right) \geq 0 \tag{4-109}$$

with $c_{mt} > 0$. It is convenient to assume, without loss of generality, that the terms are so ordered that

$$\sigma_{mt} = \begin{cases} \sigma_m \text{ for } t = 1, \ldots, S_m \\ -\sigma_m \text{ for } t = S_m + 1, \ldots, T_m \end{cases} \tag{4-110}$$

where S_m is the number of terms having the same sign as the constraint signum σ_m. For abbreviation write

$$P_m \equiv \sum_{t=1}^{S_m} c_{mt} p_{mt} > 0 \tag{4-111}$$

and

$$N_m \equiv \sum_{t=S_m+1}^{T_m} c_{mt} p_{mt} > 0 \tag{4-112}$$

so that Eq. (4–109) becomes

$$f_m = \sigma_m(1 - P_m + N_m) \geq 0 \tag{4-113}$$

Let x_{m0} be a new positive variable whose value is for the moment unspecified, and consider the two posynomial inequalities

$$\sigma_m(1 - x_{m0}^{-1} P_m) \geq 0 \tag{4-114}$$

and

$$-\sigma_m(1 - x_{m0}^{-1} - x_{m0}^{-1} N_m) \geq 0 \tag{4-115}$$

Adding them term by term gives

$$x_{m0}^{-1} \sigma_m(1 + N_m - P_m) \geq 0$$

which is equivalent to Eq. (4–113) since $x_{m0}^{-1} \geq 0$. We want the two new constraints to be tight simultaneously if and only if $f_m = 0$, which is accomplished by choosing

$$x_{m0} \equiv 1 + N_m \tag{4-116}$$

When $f_m = 0$, this choice forces both new constraints (4–114) and (4–115) to be tight. But when $f_m > 0$, the left member of (4–114) is strictly positive, which signals that both constraints (4–114) and (4–115) can be ignored.

As an example consider the generalized polynomial constraint

$$1 - 3.18 \times 10^{-4} x_0 x_1^{1.1} x_2^{0.6} - 114.3 x_0 x_2^{-1} x_3^{-1} - 2.28 x_0 x_3 + 3.38 x_0 x_1^{0.25} \geq 0$$

This can be replaced by the two posynomial constraints

$$1 - 3.18 \times 10^{-4} x_0 x_1^{1.1} x_2^{0.6} x_{10}^{-1} - 114.3 x_0 x_2^{-1} x_3^{-1} x_{10}^{-1} - 2.28 x_0 x_3 x_{10}^{-1} \geq 0$$

and

$$-(1 - x_{10}^{-1} - 3.38 x_0 x_1^{0.25} x_{10}^{-1}) \geq 0$$

Thus each constraint with negative coefficients (4–113) can be replaced by two posynomial constraints (4–114) and (4–115). This introduces an additional term and one more variable x_{m0}, leaving the number of degrees of difficulty unchanged. Although the resulting problem may be solved by the posynomial dual methods already described, we prefer to find the new dual variable ω_{m0} in terms of the others by studying the orthogonality condition for x_{m0}, which is

$$-\sigma_m \sum_{t=1}^{S_m} \sigma_{mt}\omega_{mt} + \sigma_m\omega_{m0} + \sigma_m \sum_{t=S_m+1}^{T_m} a_{mtn}\omega_{mt} = 0$$

This gives

$$\omega_{m0} = \sigma_m \sum_{t=1}^{T_m} \sigma_{mt}\omega_{mt} \; ; \qquad m = 1, \dots, M \tag{4-117}$$

which means that the ω_{mt} ($t \neq 0$) can be found separately from the orthogonality conditions for the x_n (Eq. 4-71), namely

$$\sum_{m=0}^{M} \sum_{t=1}^{T_m} \sigma_{mt}a_{mtn}\omega_{mt} = 0 \tag{4-118}$$

where the exponents a_{0tn} and dual variables ω_{0t} for the objective function have been included by formally setting $\sigma_0 = \sigma_{0t} \equiv 1$ for $t = 1, \dots, T_0$, a convention to be justified in Section 4-09. Notice that Eq. (4-118) closely resembles the posynomial orthogonality conditions (4-71). The dual variables must all be nonnegative, including ω_{m0}, and since ω_{m0} is to be eliminated from the orthogonality conditions, Eq. (4-117) implies that the duals must also satisfy the M linear constraints

$$\sigma_m \sum_{t=1}^{T_m} \sigma_{mt}\omega_{mt} \geq 0 \; ; \qquad m = 1, \dots, M \tag{4-119}$$

Now the factors in the dual function pertinent to the mth constraint in Eq. (4-73) can be simplified drastically by applying Eq. (4-117).

$$\prod_{t=1}^{S_m} \left[\frac{c_{mt}}{\omega_{mt}}\left(\sum_{t=1}^{S_m} \omega_{mt} \right) \right]^{\sigma_m\omega_{mt}} \prod_{t=S_m+1}^{T_m} \left[\frac{c_{mt}}{\omega_{mt}}\left(\sum_{t=S_m+1}^{T_m} \omega_{mt} + \omega_{m0} \right) \right]^{\sigma_m\omega_{mt}}$$

$$\times \left[\frac{1}{\omega_{m0}}\left(\sum_{t=S_m+1}^{T_m} \omega_{mt} + \omega_{m0} \right) \right]^{-\sigma_m\omega_{m0}}$$

$$= \prod_{t=1}^{T_m} \left[\frac{c_{mt}}{\omega_{mt}}\left(\sum_{t=1}^{S_m} \omega_{mt} \right) \right]^{\sigma_{mt}\omega_{mt}} \prod_{t=1}^{T_m} \left[\frac{1}{\omega_{m0}}\left(\sum_{t=1}^{S_m} \omega_{mt} \right) \right]^{-\sigma_{mt}\omega_{mt}}$$

$$= \prod_{t=1}^{T_m} \left(\frac{c_{mt}\omega_{m0}}{\omega_{mt}} \right)^{\sigma_{mt}\omega_{mt}} \; ; \qquad m = 1, \dots, M$$

Since Section 4-09 will prove that $\omega_{00} = 1$, the dual function can be written compactly as

$$d = \prod_{m=0}^{M} \prod_{t=1}^{T_m} \left(\frac{c_{mt}\omega_{m0}}{\omega_{mt}} \right)^{\sigma_{mt}\omega_{mt}} \tag{4-120}$$

This dual function (whose logarithm may *not* be concave) relates to the primal one in the same way as the dual function for posynomial constraints of mixed sense, the case treated in Section 4-06.

4-09 Profits and Negative Coefficients

Finally suppose that the objective function has negative terms. This situation arises whenever a machine has salvage value or when the market values of products are affected by operating or design conditions. Such cases contribute negative "costs"—revenue in reality—to the objective function being minimized. If in fact one wants to maximize profits, the equivalent "cost" minimization problem will lead to a negative "cost" if the operation makes money.

The proper way to transform such problems into posynomial form depends on whether the optimal cost is positive or negative. Although it is not always possible to predict which case applies, a wrong guess will be exposed in the course of the computation and can be easily corrected. In the notation of Eqs. (4-108) through (4-112) for $m = 0$, the generalized polynomial objective function $y\langle \mathbf{x} \rangle$ can be written as a difference of two posynomials.

$$y \equiv P_0 - N_0 \tag{4-121}$$

Let
$$x_0 \equiv y \tag{4-122}$$

so that at the minimum

$$y^* = P_0\langle \mathbf{x}^* \rangle - N_0\langle \mathbf{x}^* \rangle \leq x_0 \tag{4-123}$$

If one can assume

$$x_0 > 0 \tag{4-124}$$

then Eq. (4-123) becomes

$$1 - x_0^{-1}P_0 + x_0^{-1}N_0 \geq 0 \tag{4-125}$$

which is a generalized polynomial constraint of the form given in Eq. (4-113). It can be replaced in turn by two posynomial constraints [see Eqs. (4-114) and (4-115)].

$$1 - x_{00}^{-1}x_0^{-1}P_0 \geq 0 \tag{4-126}$$

$$-(1 - x_{00}^{-1}x_0^{-1}N_0 - x_{00}^{-1}) \geq 0 \tag{4-127}$$

Here x_{00} is a new variable given at the optimum by

$$x_{00} = 1 + x_0^{-1}N_0 \tag{4-128}$$

These equations are formally the same as Eqs. (4-114)–(4-116) if the convention is adopted that

$$\sigma_0 \equiv 1 \tag{4-129}$$

Hence the original problem of minimizing a generalized polynomial has been replaced by that of minimizing x_0, subject to two posynomial constraints of opposite sense.

Although two new variables x_0 and x_{00} have been introduced, their two corresponding dual variables can be determined immediately. Since the new objective function is simply x_0, the corresponding dual variable ω_0 must be unity by the normality condition.

$$\omega_0 = 1 \qquad (4\text{-}130)$$

Let signum functions σ_{0t} be defined by Eq. (4–110). Then the orthogonality condition for x_0, together with Eq. (4–130), gives

$$\sum_{t=1}^{T_0} \sigma_{0t}\omega_{0t} = 1(= \omega_0) \qquad (4\text{-}131)$$

This looks like a normality condition for the original objective function, with all dual variables corresponding to negative terms being subtracted instead of added. Eq. (4–131) is called the *generalized normality condition*. Next let ω_{00} be the value of the dual variable for the term x_{00}^{-1} in Eq. (4–127). The orthogonality condition for x_{00} gives

$$-\sum_{t=1}^{T_0} \sigma_{0t}\omega_{0t} + \omega_{00} = 0 \qquad (4\text{-}132)$$

whence by Eq. (4–131)

$$\omega_{00} = 1 \qquad (4\text{-}133)$$

Hence Eq. (4–132) need not be written down in practice. One can instead use the generalized normality condition (4–131) and the orthogonality conditions for the original variables $x_1, \ldots, x_N$. The resulting problem has therefore exactly as many equations, dual variables, and degrees of difficulty as a posynomial problem. One must merely be sure to change the signs of the exponents coming from the negative part N_0. The *generalized orthogonality* conditions are exactly the same as those given in Eq. (4–118), and the dual function $d\langle \boldsymbol{\omega} \rangle$ is that of Eq. (4–120).

Suppose now that profit instead of loss is expected so that

$$y^* < 0 \qquad (4\text{-}134)$$

In this case Eq. (4–125) does not follow from Eq. (4–123), so let

$$x_0 \equiv -y^{-1}(> 0) \qquad (4\text{-}135)$$

making

$$(N_0\langle \mathbf{x}^* \rangle - P_0\langle \mathbf{x}^* \rangle)^{-1} \leq x_0 \qquad (4\text{-}136)$$

Upon rearrangement this becomes

$$-(1 + x_0 P_0 - x_0 N_0) \geq 0 \qquad (4\text{-}137)$$

a generalized polynomial constraint replaceable by

$$-(1 - x_{00}^{-1} x_0 N_0) \geq 0 \qquad (4\text{-}138)$$

$$1 - x_{00}^{-1} x_0 P_0 - x_{00}^{-1} \geq 0 \qquad (4\text{-}139)$$

The objective this time is to minimize x_0. Notice that the result is not the minimum cost (or maximum profit in this case). The minimum cost is given by

$$y^* = - (\min x_0)^{-1} = - (x_0^*)^{-1} \tag{4-140}$$

As before, the variables x_0 and x_{00} need not appear in the orthogonality and normality conditions. Analysis similar to that used earlier shows that $\omega_0 = \omega_{00} = 1$ and that the generalized normality condition has signs opposite from those of Eq. (4-131).

$$- \sum_{t=1}^{S_0} \sigma_{0t}\, \omega_{0t} = 1 \tag{4-141}$$

Both cases can be covered in a single formulation by introducing a new signum function σ which is the sign of y^*. Then the generalized normality condition replacing both Eqs. (4-131) and (4-141) is

$$\sum_{t=1}^{T_0} \sigma_{0t}\omega_{0t} = \sigma(= \pm 1) \tag{4-142}$$

This function σ is regarded as a dual variable unknown in advance. Since the orthogonality conditions are homogeneous, changing σ from $+1$ to -1 (or vice versa) simply reverses the signs of all the other dual variables ω_{mt}. Once σ and the dual variables have been determined, one can compute the dual function by

$$d = \sigma \left[\prod_{m=0}^{M} \prod_{t=1}^{T_m} \left(\frac{c_{mt}\omega_{m0}}{\omega_{mt}} \right)^{\sigma_{mt}\omega_{mt}} \right]^{\sigma} \tag{4-143}$$

This dual function relates to the primal, which can now assume negative values, in all the ways developed in Section 4-06. It remains only to summarize and give some numerical examples.

4-10 Technical Summary

The results of this chapter can now be summarized with a few compact formulas. For abbreviation define the product function

$$p_{mt} \equiv \prod_{n=1}^{N} x_n^{a_{mtn}} \tag{4-144}$$

for all $m = 0, 1, \ldots, M$ and $t = 1, \ldots, T_m$. Let a signum function σ_{mt} be associated with every term so that any generalized polynomial $y_m\langle \mathbf{x} \rangle$ may be written

$$y_m \equiv \sum_{t=1}^{T_m} \sigma_{mt} c_{mt} \prod_{n=1}^{N} x_n^{a_{mtn}} ; \qquad m = 0, 1, \ldots, M \tag{4-145}$$

with

$$\sigma_{mt} = \pm 1 \tag{4-146}$$

and

$$c_{mt} > 0 \tag{4-147}$$

The primal problem is to minimize

$$y \equiv y_0 \tag{4-148}$$

subject to

$$y_m \le \sigma_m(\equiv \pm 1) ; \qquad m = 1, \ldots, M \tag{4-149}$$

and
$$x_n > 0 \, ; \qquad n = 1, \ldots, N \tag{4-150}$$

Consider now a signum function σ and a set of T dual variables $\boldsymbol{\omega}$ satisfying a normality condition

$$\sum_{t=1}^{T_0} \sigma_{0t} \omega_{0t} = \sigma \tag{4-151}$$

and N orthogonality conditions

$$\sum_{m=0}^{M} \sum_{t=1}^{T_m} \sigma_{mt} a_{mtn} \omega_{mt} = 0 \tag{4-152}$$

as well as T nonnegativity conditions

$$\omega_{mt} \geq 0 \tag{4-153}$$

M linear inequality constraints

$$\omega_{m0} \equiv \sigma_m \sum_{t=1}^{T_m} \sigma_{mt} \omega_{mt} \geq 0 \, ; \qquad m = 1, \ldots, M \tag{4-154}$$

and the definition

$$\sigma \equiv \pm 1 \tag{4-155}$$

From these variables, the coefficients c_{mt}, and the signum functions σ_{mt} and σ, form the dual function

$$d\langle \boldsymbol{\omega} \rangle \equiv \sigma \left[\prod_{m=0}^{M} \prod_{t=1}^{T_m} \left(\frac{c_{mt} \omega_{m0}}{\omega_{mt}} \right)^{\sigma_{mt} \omega_{mt}} \right]^{\sigma} \tag{4-156}$$

where it is understood formally that

$$\omega_{00} \equiv 1 \tag{4-157}$$

and
$$\lim_{\omega_{mt} \to 0} \left(\frac{c_{mt} \omega_{m0}}{\omega_{mt}} \right)^{\sigma_{mt} \omega_{mt}} = 1 \tag{4-158}$$

Then for every point $\mathbf{x}^0$ where y is locally minimum there exists a set of dual variables $\boldsymbol{\sigma}^0$ and $\boldsymbol{\omega}^0$ satisfying Eqs. (4–151) through (4–155) and such that

$$d\langle \boldsymbol{\omega}^0 \rangle = y\langle \mathbf{x}^0 \rangle \tag{4-159}$$

The dual function is stationary at $\boldsymbol{\omega}^0$ with respect to all $\omega_{mt} > 0$ and locally maximum with respect to all $\omega_{mt} = 0$ whose constrained first derivatives do not vanish. In particular at the global minimum $\mathbf{x}^*$, if it exists, the corresponding dual variables $\boldsymbol{\omega}^*$ are such that

$$d\langle \boldsymbol{\omega}^* \rangle = y\langle \mathbf{x}^* \rangle \tag{4-160}$$

Once the dual variables $\boldsymbol{\omega}$ and $\boldsymbol{\sigma}$ are known, the corresponding values of the primal variables $\mathbf{x}$ are found from the following relations:

$$c_{0t} \prod_{n=1}^{N} x_n^{a_{0tn}} = \omega_{0t} \sigma y^0 \, ; \qquad t = 1, \ldots, T_0 \tag{4-161}$$

and
$$c_{mt} \prod_{n=1}^{N} x_n^{a_{mtn}} = \frac{\omega_{mt}}{\omega_{m0}} \, ; \qquad t = 1, \ldots, T_m \, ; \qquad m = 1, \ldots, M \tag{4-162}$$

Since there are always more terms than variables $\mathbf{x}$, one can find N equations solvable for the N primals. This task is not difficult because each equation, albeit nonlinear, has only one variable term. Consequently, variables can be eliminated easily by raising the equations to various powers and multiplying them together. Equivalently, one can take logarithms and solve the resulting simultaneous equations, linear in $\log x_n$.

$$\sum_{n=1}^{N} a_{0tn}(\log x_n) = \log\left(\frac{\omega_{0t}\sigma y^0}{c_{0t}}\right); \qquad t = 1, \ldots, T_0 \qquad (4\text{-}163)$$

$$\sum_{n=1}^{N} a_{mtn}(\log x_n) = \log\left(\frac{\omega_{mt}}{c_{mt}\omega_{m0}}\right); \qquad t = 1, \ldots, T_m; \qquad m = 1, \ldots, M$$

$$(4\text{-}164)$$

From these logarithms the policy $\mathbf{x}$ is readily obtained.

4-11 Generalized Polynomial Example

To demonstrate how to use the equations of the preceding section, a contrived example is worked below. Suppose we wish to maximize

$$y' = 5x_1^2 - x_2^2 x_3$$

subject to the usual nonnegativity conditions and the inequality

$$-5x_1 x_2^{-1} + 3x_2^{-1}x_3^2 \geq -2$$

To get this into the proper form we must minimize the negative of y' and multiply all terms of the inequality by $-\frac{1}{2}$ in order to reverse its sense. The equivalent problem is to minimize $y \, (\equiv -y')$

$$y = -5x_1^2 + x_2^2 x_3$$

subject to

$$\tfrac{5}{2}x_1 x_2^{-1} - \tfrac{3}{2}x_2^{-1}x_3^2 \leq 1$$

The dual variables must satisfy

$$
\begin{aligned}
-\omega_{01} + \omega_{02} &= \sigma \\
-2\omega_{01} \qquad\quad + \omega_{11} &= 0 \\
2\omega_{02} - \omega_{11} + \omega_{12} &= 0 \\
\omega_{02} \qquad\quad - 2\omega_{12} &= 0
\end{aligned}
$$

The solution is $\sigma = -1$, $\omega_{01} = 5$, $\omega_{02} = 4$, $\omega_{11} = 10$, and $\omega_{12} = 2$. By definition $\omega_{00} \equiv 1$ and

$$\omega_{10} = \sigma_1(\omega_{11} - \omega_{12}) = 8 > 0$$

The value of y at the stationary point $\mathbf{x}^0$ is

$$y^0 = -\left[\left(\frac{5 \cdot 1}{5}\right)^{-5}\left(\frac{1 \cdot 1}{4}\right)^4\left(\frac{5}{2} \cdot \frac{8}{10}\right)^{10}\left(\frac{3}{2} \cdot \frac{8}{2}\right)^{-2}\right]^{-1} = -9$$

To find the optimal policy, start by considering the value of the first term of the objective function

$$5x_1^2 = \omega_{01}\sigma y^0 = 5(-1)(-9)$$

whence $\qquad\qquad\qquad x_1 = 3$

The weight on the first term of the constraint is

$$\frac{\omega_{11}}{\omega_{10}} = \frac{10}{8} = \frac{5}{2} \cdot x_1(x_2)^{-1}$$

which gives

$$x_2 = 6$$

The second term of the objective gives x_3.

$$(x_2)^2 x_3 = (6)^2 x_3 = 4(9)$$

$$x_3 = 1$$

Since these are zero degrees of difficulty, this is the only stationary point. We leave it to the reader to verify that $\mathbf{x}^0$ is a saddlepoint rather than a minimum (Exercise 4–9). For a problem with $\sigma_1 = -1$, see Exercise 4–6.

4-12 A Profitable Operation

The following industrial example involves slight modification of the chemical plant problem previously used. It demonstrates that the economic interpretations of the invariant weights, so striking in the posynomial case, also hold when there are income terms with negative coefficients. Suppose a plant makes a byproduct having some commercial value. Let x_1 be the reactor temperature, x_2 the reactor pressure, x_3 the weight fraction of a catalyst used, and x_4 the weight of the fraction of product leaving the reactor. Table 4–1 gives costs and income for the operation.

TABLE 4–1
COSTS AND INCOME FOR CHEMICAL PLANT EXAMPLE

Item	Cost ($/100 lb material processed)
Reactor	$3.18 \times 10^{-4} x_1^{1.1} x_2^{0.6}$
Separator	$114.3 x_2^{-1} x_3^{-1}$
Catalyst	$2.28 x_3$
Byproduct sales	$-33.8 x_4$

Let the product concentration x_4 be affected directly by the temperature x_1 according to

$$x_4 = 0.100 x_1^{0.25}$$

Then the net cost of the operation can be expressed as a generalized polynomial in x_1, x_2, and x_3 alone.

$$y = 3.18 \times 10^{-4}x_1^{1.1}x_2^{0.6} + 114.3x_2^{-1}x_3^{-1} + 2.28x_3 - 3.38x_1^{0.25} \qquad (4\text{-}165)$$

Assume first that this cost is positive ($\sigma = +1$).

The generalized normality condition is

$$\omega_{01} + \omega_{02} + \omega_{03} - \omega_{04} = 1$$

The orthogonality conditions for x_1, x_2, and x_3 respectively are

$$1.1\omega_{01} \qquad\qquad\qquad - 0.25\omega_{04} = 0$$

$$0.6\omega_{01} - \omega_{02} \qquad\qquad\qquad = 0$$

$$- \omega_{02} + \omega_{03} \qquad\qquad = 0$$

The unique solution is $\omega_{01} = -\frac{5}{11}$, $\omega_{02} = \omega_{03} = -\frac{3}{11}$, $\omega_{04} = -2$. The negativity of the dual variables signals that no stationary point exists for the problem as formulated. This anomaly comes from the false assumption that the optimal cost y^* is positive.

If the problem has a minimum at all, it must therefore represent the profitable situation where

$$y^* < 0$$

Then the dual variables must satisfy

$$-\omega_{01} - \omega_{02} - \omega_{03} + \qquad \omega_{04} = 1 \qquad\qquad (4\text{-}166)$$

$$1.1\omega_{01} \qquad\qquad\qquad - 0.25\omega_{04} = 0 \qquad\qquad (4\text{-}167)$$

$$0.6\omega_{01} - \omega_{02} \qquad\qquad\qquad = 0 \qquad\qquad (4\text{-}168)$$

$$- \omega_{02} + \omega_{03} \qquad\qquad = 0 \qquad\qquad (4\text{-}169)$$

Notice that only the signs in the generalized normality condition are changed; the orthogonality conditions are just as before. Hence the solution is simply the one obtained previously, but with all signs changed to positive.

$$\omega_{01} = \tfrac{5}{11}; \qquad \omega_{02} = \omega_{03} = \tfrac{3}{11}; \qquad \omega_{04} = 2$$

The minimum value of y_0 is obtained from the dual function

$$y^* = d^* = -\left[\left(\frac{3.18 \times 10^{-4}}{0.454}\right)^{0.454}\left(\frac{114.3}{0.273}\right)^{0.273}\left(\frac{2.28}{0.273}\right)^{0.273}\left(\frac{3.38}{2}\right)^{-2}\right]^{-1}$$

$$= -(0.1192)^{-1} = -\$8.38 \text{ per } 100 \text{ lb processed}$$

Income from product sales apparently exceeds the cost of operation, leading to a net profit. Interestingly, in this case with zero degrees of difficulty, the process can never operate at a loss, no matter how much the cost coefficients fluctuate—as long as none of them changes sign—because the dual variables depend only on the exponents and signs, not on the magnitudes of the coefficients.

Study of the invariants $\boldsymbol{\omega}$ gives more insight into the economics of the process. Since $\omega_{04} = 2$, the income from byproduct sales is twice the net profit. Similarly one deduces that total operating costs always equal the net profits in magnitude at the optimum, and that 45.4 per cent of this cost comes from the reactor, 27.3 per cent from the separator, and 27.3 per cent from catalyst consumption. Equations (4–161) and (4–162) together give $x_1^* = 604°$. The other decision variables can be obtained similarly by matching terms; the results are $x_2^* = 49.9$ atm, $x_3^* = 1.00$ per cent; $x_4^* = 0.495$ per cent. Many of the advantages of geometric programming have been preserved, even in the presence of a negative coefficient.

A word of warning is in order. With the negative sign present, neither the transformed primal or dual functions have any convexity properties. Hence one cannot be certain that a solution obtained by geometric programming is a minimum; it could be any kind of stationary point. Therefore the investigator should check the point for minimality by the methods described in Chapters 2 and 3.

4-13 Applications

Geometric programming can now be used wherever a system is described by generalized polynomials. Potential applications abound because the technique is so new that only a few engineers have had time to put it to work. Duffin gave the first practical example—a hypothetical hauling operation—in his March, 1962, article (see Exercise 4–5). Peterson and Zener later showed how to design optimal electrical transformers. Sherwood early saw applications to chemical process design, and more recently Avriel and Wilde have applied geometric programming to the design of vapor condensers (see Exercise 4–8). All these cases involve only posynomials, and except for Passy's example of the preceding section, there have been no applications to truly generalized polynomial systems with negative coefficients and mixed constraints as we go to press.

This is a challenging situation for any reader who has gotten this far into the subject, for most systems can be decomposed into components, each with its own cost or revenue. Component behavior in most engineering systems can usually be expressed as products of powers of the design variables, as is testified by the frequency of logarithmic graphs in the technical literature. The effect of scale of operation is often expressed by such approximations as the "six-tenths" rule, which states that the cost of a piece of equipment varies as the $\frac{6}{10}$ power of its rate capacity. Geometric design problems usually involve integral powers of diameters and other key dimensions. For problems with few degrees of difficulty, geometric programming promises to yield fast, accurate solutions to horribly nonlinear problems. And when there are no degrees of difficulty at all, the method should produce rigorous "rules of thumb" giving optimal component proportions that are completely independent of fluctuating prices and unit charges.

BIBLIOGRAPHY

Avriel, M., and D. J. Wilde, "Optimal condenser design by geometric programming," *Stanford Chemical Engineering Report* (September, 1966).

Charnes, A., and W. W. Cooper, "Optimizing engineering designs under inequality constraints," *Northwestern Univ. ONR Research Memo 64* (August, 1962).

Duffin, R. J., "Dual programs and minimum cost," *J. Soc. Ind. Appl. Math.*, **10**, 1 (March, 1962) 119–23.

———, "Cost minimization problems treated by geometric means," *Opns. Res.*, **10**, 5 (September, 1962) 668–75.

———, and E. L. Peterson, "Constrained minima treated by geometric means," Westinghouse Scientific Paper 64–158–129–P3 (March, 1964).

———, E. L. Peterson, and C. Zener, *Geometric Programming* (Wiley, New York, 1967).

———, "A technique for optimizing engineering designs," *Westinghouse,   R and D Letter*, **7**, 7 (April, 1964).

Passy, U., and D. J. Wilde, "Generalized polynomial optimization," *Stanford Chemical Engineering Report* (August, 1966).

Peterson, E. L., and C. Zener, "The rectangularity law of transformers," *Proc. Natl. Acad. Sci.* (June, 1964).

Sherwood, T. K., *A Course in Process Design* (MIT Press, Cambridge, Mass., 1963).

Wilde, D. J., "A unified approach to multivariable optimization theory," *Ind. Engng. Chem.*, **57** (August, 1965) 18–31.

Zener, C., "A mathematical aid in optimizing engineering designs," *Proc. Natl. Acad. Sci.*, **47**, 4, (April, 1961) 537–9.

———, "A further aid in optimizing engineering designs," *Proc. Natl. Acad. Sci.*, **48** (1962), 518

———, "Minimization of system costs in terms of subsystem costs," *Proc. Natl. Acad. Sci.*, **51** (1964) 162–64.

———, and R. J. Duffin, "Optimization of engineering problems," *Westinghouse Engineer* (September, 1964) 154–60.

EXERCISES

4-1. An insurance company pays a farmer $1000 in compensation for a silo which has burned down. The foundation is undamaged, so the farmer need pay only for the cylindrical sides and flat top of the new tower. He wants it to hold 1000π cu ft. If building costs are \$1.00 per sq ft of surface area, can he afford it? Answer the question *without* finding the tower dimensions first.

4-2. Prove that Eq. (4–77) describes a convex set with respect to **u**.

4-3. Minimize y_0

$$y_0 \equiv 1000x_1 + 4 \times 10^9 x_1^{-1} x_2^{-1}$$

subject to

$$2.5 \times 10^5 x_2 + 9000 x_1^{-1} x_2^{-1} \leq 1$$

$$x_1, x_2 > 0$$

4-4. Prove that $x_0^* = 0.1192$ obtained in Eq. (4–103) is the minimum.

4-5. (Duffin, March, 1962) Suppose that 400 cu yd of building material must be ferried across a river. The material is to be shipped in an open box of length x_1, width x_2, and height x_3. The sides and bottom of the box cost \$10 per sq yd to build; the ends, \$20 per sq yd. Runners cost \$2.50 a yd, and two are required for the box to slide on. Each round trip of the ferry costs \$0.10. Find the minimum cost to within \$5. Give the corresponding dimensions of the box. If the fare were to double, by what factor would the transportation cost increase, provided that the box could be redesigned?

4-6. Minimize y_0

$$y_0 \equiv -5x_1^2 + x_2^2 x_3^4$$

subject to

$$\tfrac{5}{2} x_1^2 x_2^{-2} - \tfrac{3}{2} x_2^{-1} x_3 \leq -1$$

$$x_1, x_2 > 0$$

4-7. A vertical cylindrical tank has a base but no roof. Given that the sides and bottom are made from the same material, but that the bottom is twice as thick as the sides, find the optimal ratio of diameter to height for any given volume.

4-8. (Avriel and Wilde) The following problem arises in the design of horizontal vapor condensers, after some simplifying assumptions. Minimize the variable cost

$$c = \frac{\beta_1}{N^{7/6} D L^{4/3}} + \frac{\beta_2 D^{0.8}}{N^{0.2} L} + \beta_3 N D L + \frac{\beta_4 L}{D^{4.8} N^{1.8}}$$

where $c =$ variable cost, dollars per year
 $N =$ number of tubes
 $D =$ average tube diameter, inches
 $L =$ tube length, feet

and $\beta_1, \beta_2, \beta_3,$ and β_4 are coefficients that vary with the fluids involved and construction costs. The first two terms represent the cost of thermal energy; the third, the fixed charges on the heat exchanger; and the fourth, the cost of pumping the cold liquid through the tubes.

(a) Verify that the optimal cost distribution is, in all circumstances, as follows: 43.3% thermal energy, 53.3% fixed charges, and 3.33% pumping cost. (This case is oversimplified; see the article for a more realistic model.)

(b) Find the minimum cost, in dollars per year, given that, for a certain seawater desalination plant using low pressure steam for heating, $\beta_1 = 1.724 \times 10^5, \beta_2 = 9.779 \times 10^4, \beta_3 = 1.57,$ and $\beta_4 = 3.82 \times 10^{-2}$.

(c) Find the optimal values of the design variables for this desalination plant.

4-9. Verify that the stationary point x^0 found in the generalized polynomial example of section 4-11 is a saddlepoint rather than a minimum.

4-10. Minimize

$$y = 7x_1 x_2 x_3 x_4$$

subject to $x > 0$ and

$$3x_1^2 + 8x_2^2 + 2x_3^2 + 27x_4^2 \geq 1$$

and check the nature of the stationary point.

4-11. Minimize

$$y = 7x_1 x_2 x_3 x_4$$

subject to $x > 0$ and

$$-3x_1^{-2} + 8x_2^2 + 2x_3^2 - 27x_4^{-2} \geq 1$$

and check the nature of the stationary point.

4-12. Maximize $y = 24x - 2x^3$ for nonnegative x.

4-13. Maximize $y = 5x_1 - x_2^2 x_3^4$ subject to $x \geq 0$ and

$$-5x_1 x_2^{-2} + 3x_2^{-1} \geq 2.$$

Prove that the point obtained is the maximum.

4-14. The simplest form of the economic lot size problem may be stated as follows: For a given product, the manufacturer must decide what size lots he will put into stock periodically. The total variable cost associated with the manufacture and storage of this product is given by:

$$y = \frac{Q}{2}I + \frac{R}{Q}S$$

where Q = lot size (pieces per run)
   I = carrying cost per piece per year
   R = annual requirements
   S = setup cost ($ per run)

The first term in this objective function represents the total carrying costs, and the second term gives the total setup costs. The function to be minimized is then of the form

$$y = c_1 Q + c_2 Q^{-1}$$

(a) Find the values of the dual variables by inspection, and hence show that the optimum lot size should always be chosen to make the total carrying and setup costs equal. From this result find Q^* by inspection.

(b) A modification of the above problem may be made to include quantity discounts when the product is being purchased rather than produced. Accordingly, Q would be the number of pieces per order, and S the cost of processing an order. Suppose the vendor charges $P + kQ$ dollars for an order of Q pieces, where P and k are given constants. Then an additional term, $RQ^{-1}(P + kQ)$, must be added to the objective function given in part (a). Show that this new function has the same form as the previous one had, and hence find Q^* by inspection.

Linear Inequalities and Sensitivity Analysis

5

When the Well's dry, they know the Worth of Water.

BENJAMIN FRANKLIN, POOR RICHARD'S ALMANACK (1758)

Poor Richard's maxim raises a subtle question: what is the value of water? To a man dying of thirst, water is worth a great deal, but to a drowning man it has no value at all. The answer often depends on how much water is available, how much is needed, and what it is to be used for.

The availability of a commodity is expressed mathematically by an inequality constraint. If at the optimum this constraint is tight, then its slack variable, which represents unused material, is zero. In this case the slack *derivative* measures the value to the system of having a small amount more of this scarce commodity. For this reason slack derivatives are called *imputed values* by economists. Finding the enhancement of a material's worth due to its scarcity is therefore closely related to optimization theory. The quantitative study of such questions is called *sensitivity analysis* because it involves computing the effects of changes in availability upon the optimum value of the objective.

The impact of constraints on an optimum is especially marked when the objective and constraints are all linear functions of the independent variables. Since in this case it is impossible to have an interior optimum, the optimum is profoundly affected by the constraints and, consequently, by availabilities of scarce commodities. Moreover, the linearity implies that the slack derivatives will remain constant over finite ranges of availability changes, which is not the case in general. This makes possible precise predictions of the economic effects of availability shifts—without extrapolation.

The main topic of this chapter, linear sensitivity analysis, is illustrated in full detail by an example due to Symonds involving a hypothetical petroleum refinery. Changes in availability of raw material or in the demands for products force alterations in the production plan which may at first contradict what one's intuition might suggest. The imputed scarcity values of certain materials fluctuate remarkably as the availabilities of *other* commodities change. When other availabilities are held constant, a commodity's imputed value decreases in jumps as more of it becomes available, until ultimately its worth to the system drops to zero. This illustrates the well-known economic "law of diminishing returns," even though the problem is completely linear. Detailed study of this idealized example gives great insight into the behavior of complicated multivariable systems.

Aside from the ease with which its sensitivity analysis can be performed, the fully linear case has many interesting characteristics described in this chapter. Historically, the linear case was the first inequality constrained optimization problem to be solved, and Dantzig's successful *simplex* algorithm for doing it stimulated the current revived interest in optimization theory. By now there are hundreds of applications of linear programming to subjects ranging from agriculture to zinc smelting (see Dantzig, 1963) and existing computer codes can handle several thousand independent variables and a thousand constraints. The simplex method is effective because all Jacobians remain constant as decision variables are adjusted; hence large improvement steps can be taken without concern for possible infeasibility due to extrapolation errors. Furthermore one need test only points where all decision variables are zero, since in the linear case the optimum must be at such a place. This makes it unnecessary to check the complementary slackness conditions—only nonnegativity need be tested.

The linearity also allows exploitation of the structure of a large problem to permit its decomposition into small problems of manageable size. This *decomposition principle* of Dantzig and Wolfe, illustrated here with a numerical example having intriguing economic interpretations, is a foretaste of the partial optimization and policy improvement approaches of Chapters 8 and 9.

The *transportation problem*, in which one wishes to distribute goods from depots to customers in an optimal fashion, is a special case of the linear programming problem. Its elegant solution algorithm and simple sensitivity analysis justify a brief discussion here. The chapter ends by describing the difficult *integer programming* problem in which the independent variables must be whole numbers. Even for linear functions, the present integer programming algorithms are not sufficiently effective to justify extensive discussion of them here.

5-01 Linear Programming

The linear programming problem is a special case of the quadratic programming problem in which all coefficients of the second-degree terms in the objective function are identically zero. Thus the problem is to find nonnegative x_n minimizing the *linear* form

$$y = \sum_{n=1}^{N} c_n x_n \tag{5-1}$$

subject to the linear constraints,

$$\sum_{n=1}^{N} a_{mn} x_n \geq b_m; \qquad m = 1, \ldots, M \tag{5-2: m}$$

Since this is only a special kind of quadratic programming problem, the differential algorithm can be used to obtain the solution. With $q_{ij} \equiv 0$, for all i, j, the decision derivatives, v_j, are no longer functions of the decision variables, and thus all coefficients t_{tu} in these expressions vanish.

Beginning with a basic feasible solution, all the decision variables will be zero, and so the first d_r to be adjusted can only be *increased*. Furthermore, as this adjustment does not affect the decision derivatives, case I of the differential algorithm must apply, and d_r will replace some state variable s_p in the state set. Thus, each time a decision variable is increased from zero, it becomes a state variable, and each new variable added to the decision set enters with a zero value. From this it is clear that in a linear programming problem, all N decision variables are zero at every step of the solution procedure. Accordingly, we will always have $v_h \equiv 0$, and case I is the only case that need ever be considered.

Setting N of the variables in Eq. (3–99) to zero corresponds to the selection of a point in N-dimensional space, since it designates the intersection of N hyperplanes, each of which is N-dimensional. For example, if $x_{N+k} (\equiv f_k) = 0$, this selects the hyperplane

$$\sum_{n=1}^{N} a_{kn} x_n = b_k \tag{5-3: k}$$

and if $x_n = 0$ $(n = 1, \ldots, N)$, this selects the coordinate hyperplane $x_n = 0$. The intersection point of these hyperplanes is called an *extreme point* of the convex set defined by Eqs. (3–99) and (3–100); for a linear programming problem, each iteration of the differential algorithm will move from one extreme point to another by exchanging one state variable for one decision variable. Wehl first proved that the optimal solution must lie on at least one of the extreme points, which is intuitively clear in two and three dimensions.

For example, consider the problem of finding nonnegative x_1, x_2, which maximize

$$y = 3x_1 + 2x_2 \tag{5-4}$$

and which satisfy the constraints

$$2x_1 + x_2 \leq 8 \tag{5-5}$$

$$x_1 + 3x_2 \leq 15 \tag{5-6}$$

This two-dimensional problem can be solved graphically, as shown in Fig. 5-1. The objective function is a family of parallel straight lines which move

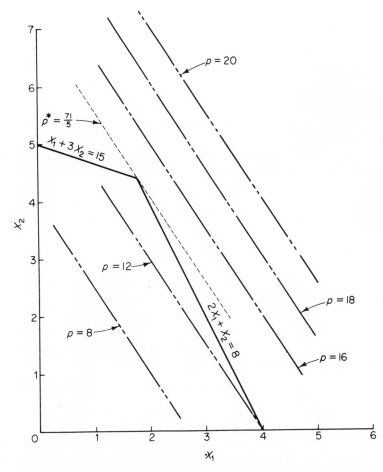

Figure 5-1. Graphical solution of two-dimensional example problem.

further away from the origin as y is increased through positive values. We want to maximize y and at the same time satisfy the constraints. These constraints consist of the nonnegativity conditions plus the inequalities (5–5) and (5–6), and serve to define the convex set bounded by the lines $x_1 = 0$, $x_2 = 0$, $x_1 + 3x_2 = 15$, and $2x_1 + x_2 = 8$. In the general linear programming problem defined by (5–1) and (5–2), the convex set will be bounded by $M + N$ hyperplanes, each of which is N-dimensional, and the objective function will consist of a family of N-dimensional hyperplanes. When $N = 2$, the hyperplanes are lines; when $N = 3$, they are planes. In either case, the extreme value (maximum or minimum) of the objective function will be reached by that member of the family of lines (or planes) which touches the convex set on the boundary, and this must include at least one extreme point. In a two-dimensional problem, the objective hyperplane (line) can touch the convex set at no more than two extreme points. This can occur when the slope of the line is the same as the slope of a constraint; then the optimal solution is achieved at all points on the line joining these extreme points, producing alternate optimal solutions. In a three-dimensional problem, the objective plane may be optimized when it strikes a point (intersection of three constraint planes), a line (intersection of two constraint planes), or a plane (the direction cosines of the objective function coincide with those of a constraint). In an N-dimensional problem the optimal solution may be achieved at up to N different points. In high-dimensional problems, therefore, alternate optima are the rule rather than the exception. For the present problem, the optimum is achieved at the unique point $x_1 = \frac{9}{5}$, $x_2 = \frac{22}{5}$, determined by the intersection of the constraint lines $x_1 + 3x_2 = 15$, and $2x_1 + x_2 = 8$, as shown in Fig. 5–1.

5-02 The Simplex Algorithm

In linear programming problems, the differential algorithm specializes to the simplex method of George Dantzig in a straightforward manner. Equations (3–119) remain unchanged, but since all decision variables have zero values, Eq. (3–118) becomes

$$\hat{s}_r = \frac{\bar{s}_p}{\alpha_{pr}} \tag{5-7}$$

Furthermore, with all t_{tv} coefficients identically zero, Eqs. (3–125) and (3–126) become, respectively,

$$\hat{v}_p = -\frac{1}{\alpha_{pr}} \bar{v}_r \tag{5-8}$$

and

$$\hat{v}_n = \bar{v}_n - \frac{\alpha_{pn}}{\alpha_{pr}} \bar{v}_r; \qquad n \neq p \tag{5-9: n}$$

In addition to these modifications, one notational change is required in the tableau for linear problems. In order to conform to the usual practice in simplex computations, we shall write the v_j in the bottom row of the tableau with their signs *reversed*. That is, the bottom row to the left of the double vertical lines will consist of entries $-v_j$; then, when this entire row is "simplexed" using Eqs. (5–8) and (5–9), the current value of the objective function appearing to the right of the double vertical lines in the bottom row will have the correct sign. At each iteration, the new value $\hat{y}$ of the objective function is obtained from the previous value $\bar{y}$ by means of the simplex operation defined by:

$$\hat{y} = \bar{y} - \frac{\bar{s}_p}{\alpha_{pr}}(-\bar{v}_r) \tag{5-10}$$

As an example of the simplex procedure, consider the analytic solution of the problem given by (5–4), (5–5), and (5–6), which was solved graphically in Fig. 5–1. The initial tableau is shown in Fig. 5–2(a), corresponding to the basic feasible solution $f_1 = 8$, $f_2 = 15$. Here again we retain the columns associated with the state variables only for illustration since, as described in Chapter 3, these columns may always be deleted if a record is kept of the state variable associated with each row. Also, for ready reference, we have circled the *pivot number* is each tableau of the figure. This number lies at the intersection of the column corresponding to the decision variable to be increased and the row corresponding to the state variable which will be driven to zero by this increase. Thus the pivot number indentifies the two , variables which will exchange places in the decision set at the next iteration.

From the initial tableau we see that $v_1 = 3$, $v_2 = 2$, and thus x_1 is the first decision variable to be adjusted, since it has the larger decision derivative. When x_1 is increased to 4, f_1 is driven to zero, and these variables exchange places in the state set, producing the tableau of Fig. 5–2(b). This tableau corresponds to the point $(4, 0)$ in Fig. 5–1, at which point the objective function takes on the value $y = 12$. The state variables and the objective function are now written in terms of the decision variables x_2 and f_1; from the body of the tableau we may read $x_1 = 4 - \frac{1}{2}x_2 - \frac{1}{2}f_1, f_2 = 11 - \frac{5}{2}x_2 + \frac{1}{2}f_1$; and from the bottom row we have $y = 12 + \frac{1}{2}x_2 - \frac{3}{2}f_1$. Notice that, since the decision variables are always zero in a linear programming problem, *every* iteration (tableau) of the simplex method produces a basic feasible solution.

Since the only positive decision derivative is that associated with x_2, this variable is increased until it drives f_2 to zero at a value of 22/5. Rewriting the constraints and the objective function in terms of the new decision variables f_1 and f_2 (by "simplexing" the elements in the previous tableau) results in the final tableau of Fig. 5–2(c). This is the optimal solution since both decision derivatives $(-7/5$ and $-1/5)$ are negative, indicating that if either decision variable f_1 or f_2 were increased, the value of the objective function

x_1	x_2	f_1	f_2	
②	1	1	0	8
1	3	0	1	15
-3	-2	0	0	0

(a) Initial tableau

x_1	x_2	f_1	f_2	
1	1/2	1/2	0	4
0	⑤/2	-1/2	1	11
0	-1/2	3/2	0	12

(b) Results of replacing f_1 with x_1 in
state set

x_1	x_2	f_1	f_2	
1	0	3/5	-1/5	9/5
0	1	-1/5	2/5	22/5
0	0	7/5	1/5	71/5

(c) Final tableau

Figure 5-2. Tableaux for two-dimensional linear problem.

would decrease. Note that this local maximum is also the global maximum since every linear programming problem satisfies the necessary convexity properties described in Chapter 3.

Thus the simplex method, at each iteration, has moved the objective function line parallel to itself and away from the origin ($y = 0$) until a further move in this direction would yield an infeasible solution, as shown in Fig. 5-1. Values such as $y = 16$ correspond to solutions which are optimal (since all the decision derivatives would be negative) but not feasible, whereas solution points anywhere along the lines $y = 8$ or $y = 12$ (and within the convex set) are feasible but not optimal. The line $y = 8$ does not pass through an extreme point of the convex set, and therefore no basic feasible solution would produce this value of the objective function.

The simplex method moves from one basic feasible solution to another and never returns to a previous solution point, because it improves the value of the objective function at each iteration. There being only a finite number of extreme points, each corresponding to a unique basic feasible solution, the simplex method will find the optimal solution to any linear programming problem in a finite number of steps. This algorithm does not usually investigate every extreme point of the convex set, of course, but example problems have been constructed (Goldman and Kleinman) for which the method *does* encounter every extreme point. Consequently, upper bounds on the maximum number of iterations required to solve a general problem containing N variables and M inequality constraints are determined solely by the total number of such points, or vertices (Saaty). This number, of course, is considerably smaller than the number of all intersections of the constraint and coordinate hyperplanes, given by the combinatorial $(M + N)!/M! N!$, which includes such infeasible points, for example, as (0,8) and (15,0) in Fig. 5–1. The expected number of iterations required by the simplex method has been estimated empirically as $2M$, that is, twice the number of inequality constraints (5–2). Both the average and the maximum number of iterations, however, can be decreased by modifying the rule for selecting the order in which decision variables are brought into the state set (Quandt and Kuhn).

Linear programming has been used extensively in business and industry, and its applicability to a wide variety of problems has resulted in numerous computer codes and techniques for handling special formulations of the problem. Although few practical problems are actually linear, the simplex method is so efficient that the approximate solution given by the linear programming model is sometimes the most practical one for very large problems. In a later section, we shall describe briefly some of the algorithms for solving certain special classes of linear programming problems. These are all modifications of the general simplex method previously described, and we shall not attempt a complete listing of them, nor of the numerous applications of linear programming, as these are well documented elsewhere (Dantzig, 1963).

5-03 Degeneracy

Since $\bar{s}_p$, α_{pr}, and $\bar{v}_r$ in Eq. (5–10) will always be positive (in a maximization problem), the objective function will increase with each iteration. The sole exception occurs when $\bar{s}_p$ is zero; when this happens, the current simplex iteration produces no change in the value of the objective function. If at any time during the solution procedure one or more of the state variables take on a value of zero, this condition is referred to as *degeneracy*. Although degeneracy occurs often in linear programming problems, it has never caused any difficulties in the solution of problems arising in practice. If, however, the value of the objective function does not change for several iterations, it is possible for the simplex method to return to a previous solution point, forming an endless *cycle*, and thus never reach the optimal solution (Hoffman). Cycling can always be prevented by recourse to a perturbation method due to Charnes (1952) which resolves degeneracy from the theoretical point of view.

Computationally, however, this method is rarely used; even if degenerate solutions *are* encountered in a problem, the objective function will fail to improve only during those iterations in which a state variable having a zero value is removed from the state set. This has never caused any real-world problem to cycle back to a previous solution point, however, so that degeneracy is nothing to worry about. The following example shows some of the effects produced by degenerate basic feasible solutions:

$$\text{maximize } y = x_1 + 2x_2$$

subject to the constraints:

$$x_1 + 3x_2 \leq 105$$
$$-x_1 + x_2 \leq 15$$
$$2x_1 + 3x_2 \leq 135$$
$$-3x_1 + 2x_2 \leq 15$$
$$x_1, x_2 \geq 0$$

The solution to this problem requires four iterations, as shown in the tableaux of Fig. 5–3; again we have circled the pivot numbers to indicate which variables will enter and leave the state set at the next iteration. Notice that there is no increase in the objective function between the tableaux (c) and (d) in this figure, since f_4 enters the state set with a zero value. This does not prevent the process from reaching the optimal solution on the next step, and indeed, in many problems the value of the objective function may not change for several iterations before once again beginning to improve.

5-04 Finding a First Feasible Solution

When all the b_m in the constraint inequalities (5–2) are negative, a first basic feasible solution, required in the simplex method, is immediately at hand. Simply multiply each constraint through by -1, and set all the x_n variables to zero; then the slack variables will constitute the state set, and the first feasible solution will be given by $f_m = b_m$, $m = 1, \ldots, M$. This procedure fails, however, if any of the b_m are positive, for then the corresponding slack variable would be negative. To take care of this situation, we add an *artificial* (or dummy) variable, u_k, to each such constraint (5–2: k), which thus becomes

$$\sum_{n=1}^{N} a_{kn}x_n - f_k + u_k = b_k; \qquad k = 1, \ldots, \ell \qquad (5\text{-}11\text{:}k)$$

where we have renumbered these constraints from 1 to ℓ with no loss in generality. If any of the constraints (5–2) are *equalities*, rather than inequalities, we add a dummy variable to these constraints also, after first multiplying through by -1 if necessary to make the right-hand side positive. These will

x_1	x_2	f_1	f_2	f_3	f_4	
1	3	1	0	0	0	105
−1	1	0	1	0	0	15
2	3	0	0	1	0	135
−3	②	0	0	0	1	15
−1	−2	0	0	0	0	0

(a) Initial tableau

11/2	0	1	0	0	−3/2	165/2
⑴/2	0	0	1	0	−1/2	15/2
13/2	0	0	0	1	−3/2	225/2
−3/2	1	0	0	0	1/2	15/2
−4	0	0	0	0	1	15

(b) Tableau resulting from x_2 replacing f_4 in state set

0	0	1	−11	0	④	0
1	0	0	2	0	−1	15
0	0	0	−13	1	5	15
0	1	0	3	0	−1	30
0	0	0	8	0	−3	75

(c) Tableau resulting from x_1 replacing f_2 in state set

0	0	1/4	−11/4	0	1	0
1	0	1/4	−3/4	0	0	15
0	0	−5/4	⑶/4	1	0	15
0	1	1/4	1/4	0	0	30
0	0	3/4	−1/4	0	0	75

(d) Tableau resulting from f_4 replacing f_1 in state set

0	0	−13/3	0	11/3	1	55
1	0	−1	0	1	0	30
0	0	−5/3	1	4/3	0	20
0	1	2/3	0	−1/3	0	25
0	0	1/3	0	1/3	0	80

(e) Final tableau

Figure 5-3. Tableaux for problem illustrating degeneracy.

then be of the form of Eqs. (5–11) except that, of course, they will not contain any slack variables. Thus we have generated the *artificial* basic feasible solution: $u_k = b_k$, $k = 1, \ldots, \ell$; $f_m = b_m$, $m = \ell + 1, \ldots, M$. This does not satisfy the original constraints, but we may now use the simplex method to move to another basic feasible solution which does satisfy the constraints. This is accomplished by *minimizing*

$$K = \sum_{k=1}^{\ell} u_k \qquad (5\text{-}12)$$

subject to Eqs. (5–11), the constraints

$$\sum_{n=1}^{N} a_{mn} x_n + f_m = b_m; \qquad m = \ell + 1, \ldots, M \qquad (5\text{-}13)$$

and nonnegativity conditions on all the variables. It can be shown (Hadley, pp. 80–84) that if *any* feasible solution exists to Eqs. (5–2), then a basic feasible solution also exists. Therefore, unless there is no solution to the original constraints, the optimal solution to this auxiliary linear programming problem will be $K = 0$. Since the u_k were required to be nonnegative, their sum can be zero only when each variable is itself zero. We have driven the dummy variables to zero while retaining a basic feasible solution which may now be used as the first feasible solution for the original problem. The dummy variables will be dropped, of course, since they were introduced only in order to obtain a basic feasible solution in terms of the x_n and f_m.

The final tableau of the auxiliary problem can now be used as the initial tableau for the original problem, except for the bottom row, which must now express the *original* objective function in terms of the current decision variables. This is accomplished by replacing all state variables in the original objective function by their expressions in terms of the decision variables, as given by the simplex tableau. Thus, if the original objective function is given by Eq. (5–1), substitution of the expressions (3–101) for the state variables x_m yields the substituted objective function:

$$
\begin{aligned}
y &= \sum_{m=1}^{M} c_m \left[\beta_m - \sum_{n=M+1}^{M+N} \alpha_{mn} x_n \right] + \sum_{n=M+1}^{M+N} c_n x_n \\
&= \sum_{m=1}^{M} c_m \beta_m + \sum_{n=M+1}^{M+N} \left[c_n - \sum_{m=1}^{M} c_m \alpha_{mn} \right] x_n
\end{aligned}
\qquad (5\text{-}14)
$$

where the state variables have been renumbered from 1 to M, as before. The decision derivatives can thus be found from the expressions

$$v_n = c_n - \sum_{m=1}^{M} c_m \alpha_{mn}; \qquad n = M + 1, \ldots, M + N \qquad (5\text{-}15)$$

Equation (5–15) can always be used to find the elements $-v_n$ in the bottom row for any linear programming problem having numbers α_{mn} in the body of the tableau and coefficients c_n in the objective function. This equation is useful in the procedure for finding a first feasible solution, and it will be of fundamental importance in the following section on sensitivity analysis.

As a numerical example of determining a first (basic) feasible solution, consider the problem of finding nonnegative x_1, x_2, x_3, which *minimize*

$$y = 6x_1 + 2x_2 + 3x_3 \qquad (5\text{-}16)$$

and which satisfy the constraints:

$$30x_1 + 20x_2 + 40x_3 \geq 34 \qquad (5\text{-}17)$$

$$x_1 + x_2 + x_3 = 1 \qquad (5\text{-}18)$$

$$10x_1 + 70x_2 \leq 11 \qquad (5\text{-}19)$$

This problem is so simple that a first feasible solution is immediately evident. It will, however, serve to illustrate the systematic method for finding such a solution in much larger problems where this task is almost as difficult as finding the *optimal* solution.

The third constraint (5-19) requires no artificial variable since it is of the form of Eq. (5-13), and the slack variable f_3 may serve as the state variable. We shall add artificial variables to the other two constraints, of course, but Eq. (5-18) will not have a slack variable. The first tableau for the auxiliary problem, shown in Fig. 5-4(a), corresponds to the artificial basic feasible solution $u_1 = 34$, $u_2 = 1$, and $f_3 = 11$. The bottom row may be read as

$$K = u_1 + u_2 = 35 - 31x_1 - 21x_2 - 41x_3 + f_1 \qquad (5\text{-}20)$$

Since this is a minimization problem, x_3 is the first decision variable to be adjusted, and it will replace u_1 in the state set, as indicated by the circled pivot number. Continuing with the simplex method, we arrive (after one more iteration) at the optimal solution to the auxiliary problem given by the tableau of Fig. 5-4(b). The artificial variables have been driven to zero, so that we now have a first basic feasible solution to the original problem; namely, $x_3 = 1$, $f_1 = 6$, and $f_3 = 11$.

This state set produces the initial tableau of Fig. 5-4(c), where the bottom row has been obtained by replacing the state variable x_3 in the objective function (5-16) by the expression $1 - x_1 - x_2$, as given by the first row of the tableau. Alternatively, one may simply use Eq. (5-15) to obtain the numbers in the bottom row. (Recall that these numbers are the *negatives* of the decision derivatives.) Thus, for example, we find:

$$v_1 = 6 - [3(1) + 0(10) + 0(10)] = 3$$

and

$$v_2 = 2 - [3(1) + 0(20) + 0(70)] = -1$$

so that x_2 is increased, driving f_3 out of the state set. This produces the tableau of Fig. 5-4(d), which is the optimal solution to the original problem.

Before leaving the problem of finding a first feasible solution, we think that the reader should be aware of certain dangers in handling equality constraints. One is tempted to solve each such constraint for one of the variables and then use the resulting expression to eliminate this variable from the remaining constraints and the objective function, thereby reducing the

x_1	x_2	x_3	f_1	f_3	u_1	u_2	
30	20	(40)	−1	0	1	0	34
1	1	1	0	0	0	1	1
10	70	0	0	1	0	0	11
31	21	41	−1	0	0	0	35

(a) Initial tableau for auxiliary problem

x_1	x_2	x_3	f_1	f_3	u_1	u_2	
1	1	1	0	0	0	1	1
10	20	0	1	0	−1	40	6
10	70	0	0	1	0	0	11
0	0	0	0	0	−1	−1	0

(b) Final tableau for auxiliary problem

x_1	x_2	x_3	f_1	f_3	
1	1	1	0	0	1
10	20	0	1	0	6
10	(70)	0	0	1	11
−3	1	0	0	0	3

(c) Initial tableau for original problem

x_1	x_2	x_3	f_1	f_3	
0.857	0	1	0	−0.0143	0.843
7.14	0	0	1	−0.286	2.86
0.143	1	0	0	0.0143	0.157
−3.143	0	0	0	−0.0143	2.843

(d) Final tableau for original problem

Figure 5-4. Finding a first feasible solution.

dimension of the problem. That this is an unjustifiable practice is well illustrated by the present example. If the equality constraint (5–18) is solved for
x_1 and then substituted for x_1 in (5–16), (5–17), and (5–19), the reduced
problem becomes one of minimizing

$$y = 6 - 4x_2 - 3x_3 \qquad (5\text{-}21)$$

subject to the usual nonnegativity conditions and the constraints:

$$-5x_2 + 5x_3 \geq 2 \qquad (5\text{-}22)$$
$$60x_2 - 10x_3 \leq 1 \qquad (5\text{-}23)$$

which clearly has an unbounded solution. We may, of course, obtain a reduced problem having an optimal solution which *is* the correct solution to
the original problem by adding the constraint, $x_2 + x_3 \leq 1$, to (5–21), (5–22),

and (5–23). All this work, however, has not reduced the number of constraints, which is the determining factor in the number of iterations needed to solve a problem, and in addition, we still must find a basic feasible solution to the reduced problem. Furthermore, in a large problem, eliminating variables using the equality constraints is not a trivial process, nor is the necessary resubstitution of the solution values of the reduced problem into the equality constraints in order to obtain the optimal values of the deleted variables. In general, then, this procedure should be avoided.

5-05 Sensitivity Analysis

One particularly important feature of linear problems is the ease with which a *sensitivity analysis* can be carried out. This technique analyzes the sensitivity of the optimal solution to changes or uncertainty in the input data, without re-solving the problem for each new value. Such analyses provide insight into the structure of the problem which cannot be gained by examining only the optimal solution. Sensitivity analysis can also be performed on certain non-linear problems (Boot), but the calculations become exceedingly difficult unless an electronic computer is used. For even large linear programming problems, however, the necessary computations for carrying out the analysis are simple enough to be done manually, or occasionally, even by inspection. All the information needed for sensitivity analysis is contained in the final (optimal) tableau, and thus is generated automatically by the simplex method in the course of finding the optimal solution.

Symonds has shown how to use linear programming to find the most profitable plan for processing crude petroleum in a hypothetical refinery. We base our discussion of sensitivity analysis on this example, which is the prototype of certain scheduling problems common to the entire chemical industry. No knowledge of petroleum technology is needed to understand this simple example.

Four different kinds of crude petroleum are available for purchase by an oil company: 100,000 bbl per week each of crudes 1, 2, and 3, and 200,000 bbl per week of crude 4. We shall designate by x_1, x_2, and x_3, the amounts of crudes 1, 2, and 3, respectively, which are purchased (and processed), expressed in thousands of barrels per week. Accordingly, we may write the following constraint equations for these crudes:

$$x_i + f_i = 100; \qquad i = 1, 2, 3 \qquad (5\text{-}24\text{:}\,i)$$

where the f_i are the unpurchased quantities of the respective crudes.

Slightly different handling is required for crude 4 because it can be processed two ways. Let x_4 be the amount of crude 4 processed primarily to make heating oil, and let x_5 be the amount processed mainly to make lubricating oil. Then

$$x_4 + x_5 + f_4 = 200 \qquad (5\text{-}25)$$

where f_4 is the unpurchased crude 4.

Four products—gasoline, heating oil, lubricating oil, and jet fuel—are made from these crudes, as shown schematically in Fig. 5–5. Table 5–1 gives

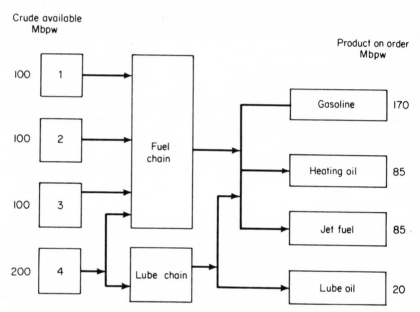

Figure 5-5. Schematic diagram of refinery processing operations.

TABLE 5–1

PROFITS, YIELDS, AND AVAILABILITIES FOR REFINERY PROBLEM

| | | \multicolumn{5}{c|}{Crude} | Product |
| | | 1 | 2 | 3 | \multicolumn{2}{c|}{4} | Product on order barrels/wk |
					Fuel process	Lube process	
Yield, bbl product per bbl crude	Gasoline	0.6	0.5	0.3	0.4	0.4	170,000
	Heating oil	0.2	0.2	0.3	0.3	0.1	85,000
	Lube oil	0	0	0	0	0.2	20,000
	Jet fuel	0.1	0.2	0.3	0.2	0.2	85,000
	Loss	0.1	0.1	0.1	0.1	0.1	
Crude available, bbl/wk		100,000	100,000	100,000	\multicolumn{2}{c	}{200,000}	
Profit, \$/1000 bbl crude processed		100	200	70	150	250	

the amount of each product which can be sold. The bottom row of Table 5-1 shows the profit gained per 1000 bbl of crude processed. These numbers are obtained by adding the market value of the products coming from 1000 bbl of the crude in question and then deducting the costs of production, sales, and the crude itself. The yields (inside the double lines) are fixed by process technology and remain constant throughout the week. On the other hand, the other data—availabilities, orders, and profits—are only estimates and may change between the receipt of the computer solution and the actual crude run.

The gasoline yields in the top row can be used to show that the weekly gasoline production (in thousands of barrels) in terms of the crude consumption is $0.6x_1 + 0.5x_2 + 0.3x_3 + 0.4x_4 + 0.4x_5$. It will be assumed that we are permitted to make *less* product than is ordered, but not more. Thus, letting f_g be the amount by which the gasoline demand is unsatisfied, we may write the following constraint on gasoline production:

$$0.6x_1 + 0.5x_2 + 0.3x_3 + 0.4x_4 + 0.4x_5 + f_g = 170 \qquad (5\text{-}26)$$

Similarly we obtain production constraints on heating oil:

$$0.2x_1 + 0.2x_2 + 0.3x_3 + 0.3x_4 + 0.1x_5 + f_h = 85 \qquad (5\text{-}27)$$

lube oil:

$$0.2x_5 + f_\ell = 20 \qquad (5\text{-}28)$$

and jet fuel:

$$0.1x_1 + 0.2x_2 + 0.3x_3 + 0.2x_4 + 0.2x_5 + f_j = 85 \qquad (5\text{-}29)$$

The bottom line of Table 5-1 enables us to calculate the profit p (in dollars/week) in terms of the quantities of each crude processed:

$$p = 100x_1 + 200x_2 + 70x_3 + 150x_4 + 250x_5 \qquad (5\text{-}30)$$

Naturally, the crude consumptions x_1, x_2, x_3, x_4, x_5, cannot be negative, and from the way the slack variables $f_1, f_2, f_3, f_4, f_g, f_h, f_\ell$, and f_j are defined, they can't be negative either. Thus, this scheduling problem takes the form of a linear programming problem concerned with maximizing the objective function (5-30), subject to the foregoing nonnegativity conditions and the constraints (5-24) through (5-29). The initial tableau is shown in Fig. 5-6, where the slack variables form the state set for this first basic feasible solution. Since every x_n is a decision variable, no raw materials are processed, and all orders go unfilled, so the profit at this beginning point is zero. Five simplex iterations are required to find the optimal solution to this scheduling problem, as shown in Figs. 5-6(a) through 5-6(e) and 5-7. The lines in each of these tableaux define the variables which will enter and leave the state set at the next iteration, and thus they intersect at the pivot number.

The optimal tableau given in Fig. 5-7 shows that for the given inputs, the maximum weekly profit will be $67,833. This profit is achieved by running all available quantities of crudes 2 and 4, but only 37.5 and 58.3 Mbpw

x_1	x_2	x_3	x_4	x_5	f_1	f_2	f_3	f_4	f_g	f_h	f_ℓ	f_j	
1					1								100
	1					1							100
		1					1						100
			1	1				1					200
0.6	0.5	0.3	0.4	0.4					1				170
0.2	0.2	0.3	0.3	0.1						1			85
				0.2							1		20
0.1	0.2	0.3	0.2	0.2								1	85
-100	-200	-70	-150	-250	0	0	0	0	0	0	0	0	0

Figure 5-6 (a). Starting simplex tableau for refinery problem.

x_1	x_2	x_3	x_4	x_5	f_1	f_2	f_3	f_4	f_g	f_h	f_ℓ	f_j	
1					1								100
	1					1							100
		1					1						100
			1					1			-5		100
0.6	0.5	0.3	0.4						1		-2		130
0.2	0.2	0.3	0.3							1	$-\frac{1}{2}$		75
				1							5		100
0.1	0.2	0.3	0.2								-1	1	65
-100	-200	-70	-150	0	0	0	0	0	0	0	1250	0	25,000

Figure 5-6 (b). Results of first iteration.

x_1	x_2	x_3	x_4	x_5	f_1	f_2	f_3	f_4	f_g	f_h	f_ℓ	f_j	
1					1								100
	1					1							100
		1					1						100
			1					1			-5		100
0.6		0.3	0.4			-0.5			1		-2		80
0.2		0.3	0.3			-0.2				1	-0.5		55
				1							5		100
0.1		0.3	0.2			-0.2					-1	1	45
-100	0	-70	-150	0	0	200	0	0	0	0	1250	0	45,000

Figure 5-6 (c). Results of second iteration.

x_1	x_2	x_3	x_4	x_5	f_1	f_2	f_3	f_4	f_g	f_h	f_ℓ	f_j	
1					1								100
	1					1							100
		1					1						100
			1					1			-5		100
0.6		0.3				-0.5		-0.4	1		0		40
0.2		0.3				-0.2		-0.3		1	1		25
				1							5		100
0.1		0.3				-0.2		-0.2			0	1	25
-100	0	-70	0	0	0	200	0	150	0	0	500	0	60,000

Figure 5-6 (d). Results of third iteration.

x_1	x_2	x_3	x_4	x_5	f_1	f_2	f_3	f_4	f_g	f_h	f_ℓ	f_j	
		-0.5			1	$\frac{5}{6}$		$\frac{2}{3}$	$-\frac{5}{3}$				$\frac{100}{3}$
	1					1							100
		1					1						100
			1					1			-5		100
1		0.5				$-\frac{5}{6}$		$-\frac{2}{3}$	$\frac{5}{3}$				$\frac{200}{3}$
		0.2				$-\frac{1}{30}$		$-\frac{1}{6}$	$-\frac{1}{3}$	1	1		$\frac{35}{3}$
			1								5		100
		0.25				$-\frac{7}{60}$		$-\frac{2}{15}$	$-\frac{1}{6}$			1	$\frac{55}{3}$
0	0	-20	0	0	0	$\frac{35}{3}$	0	$\frac{25}{3}$	$\frac{50}{3}$	0	50	0	$\frac{200{,}000}{3}$

Figure 5-6 (e). Results of fourth iteration.

x_1	x_2	x_3	x_4	x_5	f_1	f_2	f_3	f_4	f_g	f_h	f_ℓ	f_j	
					1	$\frac{3}{4}$		$\frac{1}{4}$	$-\frac{5}{2}$	$\frac{5}{2}$	$\frac{5}{2}$		62.5
	1					1							100
						$\frac{1}{6}$	1	$\frac{5}{6}$	$\frac{5}{3}$	-5	-5		41.67
		1						1			-5		100
1						$-\frac{3}{4}$		$-\frac{1}{4}$	$\frac{5}{2}$	$-\frac{5}{2}$	$-\frac{5}{2}$		37.5
		1				$-\frac{1}{6}$		$-\frac{5}{6}$	$-\frac{5}{3}$	5	5		58.33
			1								5		100
						$-\frac{3}{40}$		$\frac{3}{40}$	$\frac{1}{4}$	$-\frac{5}{4}$	$-\frac{5}{4}$	1	3.75
0	0	0	0	0	0	$\frac{340}{3}$	0	$\frac{200}{3}$	$\frac{400}{3}$	100	600	0	$\$67{,}833$

Figure 5-7. Final tableau for refinery problem.

(thousand barrels per week) respectively of crudes 1 and 3; the weekly demands for all products are exactly met except for jet fuel ($f_j = 3.75$). The reader may verify that this optimal state set is made up of x_1 through x_5, supplemented by f_1, f_3, and f_j.

5-06 Availability Charts

It is now of interest to show how the production schedule and the associated maximum profit would change with variations in the availability of the crudes (Beightler and Wilde, 1965). With the methods to be described, we shall be able to construct availability charts similar to Figs. 5–8 and 5–9 which trace the behavior of raw material consumption, product sales, and net profit as a function of the amount of crude 2 available. Before showing how to do this, we shall discuss several interesting properties of the system which, although shown quite clearly on the graphs, would possibly not be evident without sensitivity analysis. Some of these results would even seem to contradict our intuition, which is not always able to weigh properly the effects of complicated interactions.

Notice, for example, that increased availability of crude 2 cuts down

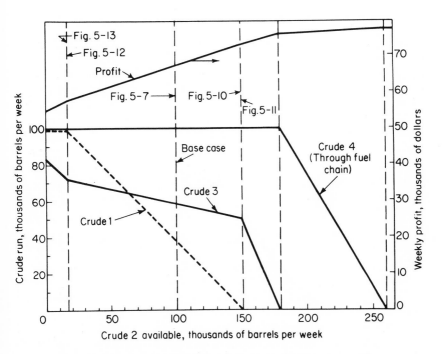

Figure 5-8. Maximum profit and optimal raw material consumption as functions of crude 2 availability.

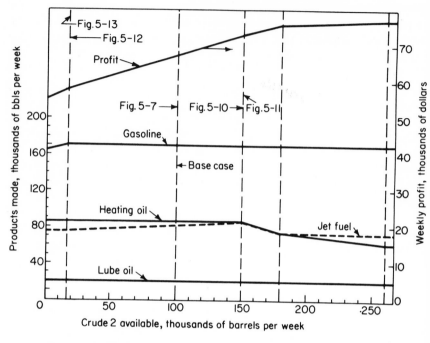

Figure 5-9. Maximum profit and otpimal product sales as functions of crude 2 availability.

the consumption of crude 1 faster than that of crude 3, even though the profit per barrel for crude 3 is 30 per cent less than that for crude 1. This paradox occurs because both crudes 1 and 2 are rich in gasoline, whereas crude 3 contains relatively little gasoline. Thus it is the limit on gasoline sales which forces crude 1 out of the state set (when 150,000 bbl per week of crude 2 are available) before crude 3 (at 180,000 bbl per week of 2).

Another result which may seem surprising is shown in Fig. 5–9. As more crude 2 becomes available, more jet fuel is produced at first. But, when more than 150,000 bbl per week of crude 2 can be run, jet fuel production steadily drops off. Similarly, heating oil production no longer meets the sales demands when large amounts of crude 2 are available.

It is not surprising that the profit climbs steadily as more crude 2 becomes available, for one would expect any loosening of restrictions to increase the profit possibilities. Nevertheless, it may be of some interest to notice that the slope of the profit curve never increases as the restrictions on crude 2 are loosened. This occurs because the slope changes only when a new restriction on some other material is encountered, and these additional limitations always eliminate the most profitable alternatives. To see how this works, let us trace the effects of increasing availability of crude 2. When there is very little crude 2, it is not economical to meet the gasoline requirements, and any additional crude 2 can be run without affecting the consumption of the rather profitable crude 1. The first change in the state set occurs when $x_2 = 16,667$ bbl per week. Since at this point no more gasoline can be produced, it is necessary to reduce the amount of crude 1 run, and the profit does not climb as steeply as before. The profit rate stays constant until $x_2 = 150,000$, when it is no longer feasible to run crude 1. This additional constraint further slows down the rate of profit increase. When $x_2 = 180,000$, the amount of crude 3 run drops to zero, and it becomes necessary to cut down on the crude 4 run through the fuel chain. From this point on, the rate of climb of the profit curve is very small. Since it is not economical to process more than 260,000 bbl per week of crude 2, the profit line becomes horizontal for greater values of x_2.

That the profit line is concave illustrates what economists call the *law of diminishing returns*; that is, increases in availability of crude 2 do not always bring proportional profits. Thus, if one already has 100,000 bbl per week of crude 2 (the base case) one can afford to pay up to $5667 for 50,000 additional bbl and still make a profit. But Fig. 5–8 shows that the next 50,000 bbl will bring in only an additional $2750, and the premium should be set accordingly.

A final fact of general interest is that all the curves are piecewise linear. The slopes change whenever the state set changes. Sensitivity analysis shows exactly at what availabilities these changes take place.

5-07 Small Availability Changes

Having seen some of the advantages of sensitivity analysis, let us now consider how to perform one. First we shall study the effects of changes of availability so small that a change in the state set is not called for. Suppose that the availability of crude 2 changed from the present value of 100 Mbpw by a small amount Δb_2. *This is equivalent to changing the corresponding slack variable f_2 by an amount* $-\Delta b_2$. Thus, the equations of the final tableau in Fig. 5–7 affected by the change become

$$f_1 + \tfrac{3}{4}f_2 - \tfrac{3}{4}\Delta b_2 \quad + \tfrac{1}{4}f_4 - \tfrac{5}{2}f_g + \tfrac{5}{2}f_h + \tfrac{5}{2}f_l \qquad = 62.5$$

$$x_2 + \quad f_2 - \quad \Delta b_2 \qquad\qquad\qquad\qquad\qquad = 100$$

$$\tfrac{1}{6}f_2 - \tfrac{1}{6}\Delta b_2 + f_3 + \tfrac{5}{6}f_4 + \tfrac{5}{3}f_g - 5f_h - 5f_l \quad = 41.7$$

$$x_1 - \tfrac{3}{4}f_2 + \tfrac{3}{4}\Delta b_2 \quad - \tfrac{1}{4}f_4 + \tfrac{5}{2}f_g - \tfrac{5}{2}f_h - \tfrac{5}{2}f_l \quad = 37.5$$

$$x_3 - \tfrac{1}{6}f_2 + \tfrac{1}{6}\Delta b_2 \quad - \tfrac{5}{6}f_4 - \tfrac{5}{3}f_g + 5f_h + 5f_l \quad = 58.3$$

$$- \tfrac{3}{40}f_2 + \tfrac{3}{40}\Delta b_2 \quad + \tfrac{3}{40}f_4 + \tfrac{1}{4}f_g - \tfrac{5}{4}f_h - \tfrac{5}{4}f_l + f_j = 3.75$$

Transposing the terms in Δb_2 to the right-hand side of each equation and noting that the decision variables are zero, we see that none of the state variables becomes negative so long as all the following quantities remain nonnegative:

$$62.5 + \tfrac{3}{4}\Delta b_2, \qquad 100 + \Delta b_2, \qquad 41.7 + \tfrac{1}{6}\Delta b_2,$$

$$37.5 - \tfrac{3}{4}\Delta b_2, \qquad 58.3 - \tfrac{1}{6}\Delta b_2, \qquad 3.8 - \tfrac{3}{40}\Delta b_2$$

Therefore, the present optimal running plan will remain feasible so long as $-83.3 \leq \Delta b_2 \leq 50$, or equivalently, when b_2 lies between 16.7 and 150 Mbpw. Notice that this range can be found directly from the final tableau by dividing each value in the right-hand column by the value on the same line in the f_2 column (unless it is zero), and then selecting the positive and negative quotients that are smallest in absolute value.

Within the foregoing range, the optimal values for the present state variables will change as follows:

$$\Delta f_1 = \tfrac{3}{4}\Delta b_2 \tag{5-31}$$

$$\Delta x_2 = \Delta b_2 \tag{5-32}$$

$$\Delta f_3 = \tfrac{1}{6}\Delta b_2 \tag{5-33}$$

$$\Delta x_1 = -\tfrac{3}{4}\Delta b_2 \tag{5-34}$$

$$\Delta x_3 = -\tfrac{1}{6}\Delta b_2 \tag{5-35}$$

$$\Delta f_j = -\tfrac{3}{40}\Delta b_2 \tag{5-36}$$

and the maximum profit will then change by

$$\Delta p = 100 - \tfrac{3}{4}\Delta b_2 + 200(\Delta b_2) + 70(-\tfrac{1}{6}\Delta b_2) = \tfrac{340}{3}\Delta b_2, \tag{5-37}$$

a result which could have been read directly from Fig. 5-7 as the decision derivative in the f_2 column. Thus, if additional crude 2 were available at the present price plus any premium cost less than \$113 (more precisely, \$340/3 per thousand barrels), it would pay to buy it, run it, and decrease the amounts of crudes 1 and 3 purchased according to Eq. (5-34) and Eq. (5-35). In an optimal, feasible tableau, the decision derivatives are *sensitivity coefficients* for the associated decision variable.

Notice that this change in one of the b_m of Eqs. (5-2) has not affected any of the sensitivity coefficients, and this is how we know that the final tableau will remain *optimal* in the Δb_2 range previously found. In fact, from Eq. (5-15) we see that the sensitivity coefficients are altered only by changes either in the c_n of the original objective function, or in the α_{mn} of the final tableau. Thus, perturbations in the b_m can affect the *feasibility* of the optimal solution to a linear programming problem, but they never destroy the *optimality*.

5-08 A Large Availability Change

If the availability of crude 2 were to increase by more than 50,000 bbl/wk (or decrease by more than 83,300 bbl/wk), then some of the variables would become negative, which, of course, would produce an infeasible solution. Figure 5-10 shows that when Δb_2 reaches 50, both x_1 and f_j are zero. To keep these variables from becoming negative, we must change the variables in the state set in such a way that the associated production schedule will be both feasible and optimal in spite of the altered availability of crude 2. Fortunately, it is not necessary to reshuffle all the variables in the set; we need only replace one of them at a time—the one on the verge of becoming negative. In this case, there are two such variables (x_1 and f_j), but instead of replacing them both simultaneously, we shall find it easier to remove only one and formally keep the other as a state variable with its value equal to zero. The choice being arbitrary so far as the ultimate consequences are concerned, we shall remove x_1.

x_1	x_2	x_3	x_4	x_5	f_1	f_2	f_3	f_4	f_g	f_h	f_ℓ	f_j	
					1	$\frac{3}{4}$		$\frac{1}{4}$	$-\frac{5}{2}$	$\frac{5}{2}$	$\frac{5}{2}$		100
	1					1							150
						$\frac{1}{6}$	1	$\frac{5}{6}$	$\frac{5}{3}$	-5	-5		50
		1						1			-5		100
1						$-\frac{3}{4}$		$-\frac{1}{4}$	$\frac{5}{2}$	$-\frac{5}{2}$	$-\frac{5}{2}$		0
			1			$-\frac{1}{6}$		$-\frac{5}{6}$	$-\frac{5}{3}$	5	5		50
				1						5			100
						$-\frac{3}{40}$		$\frac{3}{40}$	$\frac{1}{4}$	$-\frac{5}{4}$	$-\frac{5}{4}$	1	0
0	0	0	0	0	0	$\frac{340}{3}$	0	$\frac{200}{3}$	$\frac{400}{3}$	100	600	0	$73,500

Figure 5-10. Optimal tableau for $b_2 = 150$.

Next, we must decide which decision variable should replace x_1 in the state set. The new set must be feasible and optimal for the altered availability of crude 2. Finding the change that will do this is straightforward since it actually amounts to one simplex iteration. There is a difference between this operation and the usual simplex procedure, however, since here we first decide which variable is to be removed from the state set, and then select the variable which will replace it, rather than the other way around. Also, only a negative value can be chosen for the pivot number, since a positive pivot would make the f_2 column entry in the x_1 row negative for any further increase in Δb_2, whereas a negative pivot will allow the new variable to increase with Δb_2. Further, the pivot must be chosen in such a way that the optimality of the solution is preserved. Suppose, for example, that f_l were chosen to come into the state set. Then in the next tableau, the bottom row entry for f_h would be

$$100 - \frac{(-\frac{5}{2})(600)}{(-\frac{5}{2})}, \qquad \text{or a value of } -500.$$

Note that this negative value results because the ratio of 600 to $\frac{5}{2}$ is greater than the ratio of 100 to $\frac{5}{2}$.

In general, then, if s_p is to be removed from the state set, we see from Eq. (5–8) that the pivot, α_{pr}, must be a *negative* number, if $\hat{v}_p$ is to be nonpositive. Furthermore, from Eq. (5–9), the necessary condition for each sensitivity coefficient, $\hat{v}_n$, to be nonpositive in the next tableau is

$$\bar{v}_n - \frac{\alpha_{pn}}{\alpha_{pr}} \bar{v}_r \leq 0$$

or

$$\bar{v}_n \leq \frac{\alpha_{pn}}{\alpha_{pr}} \bar{v}_r \qquad (5\text{-}38\text{:}\,n)$$

where $\bar{v}_n$ and $\bar{v}_r$ are nonpositive (since we have an optimal solution in the present tableau), and α_{pr} is negative. It is clear that if α_{pn} is nonnegative, then inequality (5–38: n) is satisfied for *any* negative α_{pr}. If α_{pn} is negative, however, then we see from Eq. (5–38) that optimality can be preserved only by selecting that decision d_r to enter the state set as determined from the relation:

$$\frac{\bar{v}_r}{\alpha_{pr}} \leq \frac{\bar{v}_n}{\alpha_{pn}}; \qquad \text{for all } \alpha_{pn} < 0 \qquad (5\text{-}39)$$

Recall that in the simplex tableau, the bottom row entries are the *negatives* of the sensitivity coefficients. Therefore, to select the variable to come into the state set, compute, for each column having a negative entry in the pivot row, the ratio of the bottom row number in this column to the entry in the pivot row and choose the ratio smallest in *absolute value*. In Fig. 5–10 this smallest ratio will be 100: $\frac{5}{2}$, so that f_h is the variable which replaces x_1, with the results as given in Fig. 5–11.

From the foregoing discussion, it is clear that a linear programming problem may be solved either by the simplex method, which maintains a series of feasible solutions which approach optimality, or by an alternate method which maintains a series of optimal solutions which approach feasibility. This latter method was developed by Lemke, and it is usually referred to as the *dual-simplex* method. The importance of this method has already been seen in connection with sensitivity analysis, and it also plays a significant role in duality and in integer programming, topics to be discussed in sections 5–31 and 5–32.

x_1	x_2	x_3	x_4	x_5	f_1	f_2	f_3	f_4	f_g	f_h	f_ℓ	f_j	
1						1							100
	1					1							150
-2						$\frac{5}{3}$	1		$\frac{4}{3}$	$-\frac{10}{3}$			50
		1							1		-5		100
$-\frac{2}{5}$						$\frac{3}{10}$			$\frac{1}{10}$	-1	1	1	0
2	1					$-\frac{5}{3}$			$-\frac{4}{3}$	$\frac{10}{3}$			50
			1								5		100
$-\frac{1}{2}$						$\frac{3}{10}$			$\frac{1}{5}$	-1		1	0
40	0	0	0	0	0	$\frac{250}{3}$	0	$\frac{170}{3}$	$\frac{700}{3}$	0	500	0	$73,500

Figure 5-11. Results of f_h replacing x_1 in dependent set of Fig. 5-10.

5-09 Further Increases in Availability

With this new state set, increases in the amount of crude 2 run will no longer tend to decrease f_j (which measures the amount by which the weekly production of jet fuel falls short of maximum weekly sales), but will actually cause it to increase. That is, the maximum total profit p can be increased by producing *less* total products. (At $\Delta b_2 = 50$, all maximum weekly sales of products were exactly met). Proceeding as before, it can be seen that further increases in the availability of crude 2 will not cause another change in the state set until the term $50 - \frac{5}{3}\Delta b_2'$ becomes negative, where $\Delta b_2' = \Delta b_2 - 50$.

Therefore, in the range $50 \leq \Delta b_2 \leq 80$, the optimal amount of crude 3 to run decreases at $\frac{5}{3}$ the rate of increase of crude 2 available, so that the best amount to run will be $50 - \frac{5}{3}\Delta b_2'$, or $\frac{400}{3} - \frac{5}{3}\Delta b_2$. In this same range, the amounts of jet fuel and heating oil produced will each continue to decrease at $\frac{3}{10}$ the rate of increase in the amount of crude 2 available, and the profit will increase at a rate of $\frac{250}{3}$ of this same value. Again, all these figures can be read directly from Fig. 5-11.

When $\Delta b_2 = 80$ (which means that 180 Mbpw of crude 2 are available), x_3 is driven to zero, and further increases in Δb_2 would give this variable a negative value were it to remain in the state set. The reader may verify that when x_3 is removed from this set, f_4 must be brought in to replace it, and this new state set will be optimal in the range $80 \leq \Delta b_2 \leq 160$.

At the upper limit of this range ($b_2 = 260$), x_4 reaches zero and must be removed from the state set, to be replaced by f_2. The only effect of further increases in Δb_2 will be to increase the slack variable f_2 (which measures the amount of the available crude 2 which is *unpurchased*), causing no change in the maximum profit, nor in the values of the other state variables. The meaning of this result is now clear; it does not pay to run more than 260 Mbpw of crude 2 so long as there is no change in the availabilities of the other crudes nor in the maximum weekly sales of the products. The reader may verify that when b_2 is greater than 260, the maximum profit will be \$77,000, achieved by running 260 Mbpw of crude 2 and 100 Mbpw of crude 4 (through the lube chain). At these availabilities of crude 2, it does not pay to purchase any of crudes 1 or 3, nor to run any of crude 4 through the fuel chain. Thus, we have reached the upper limit for Δb_2, and it now remains only to investigate the effects on the problem structure of diminished supplies of crude 2.

5-10 Decreased Availability

When the availability of crude 2 decreases, this is equivalent to making Δb_2 negative, so that, for example, the change in the amount of crude 1 run will increase $\frac{3}{4}$ for each unit decrease in crude 2, whereas the amount of jet fuel produced will decrease by $\frac{3}{40}$. These values can be read directly from Fig. 5–7, and are valid until Δb_2 reaches -83.3, below which the state set in that tableau is no longer feasible.

Proceeding as before, we find that f_1 is the first variable to be driven negative (Fig. 5–12), being replaced by f_0 as shown in Fig. 5–13. If the availability of crude 2 continues to decrease below the value of 16.7 Mbpw, we see from Fig. 5–13 that the state set for this tableau will remain feasible so long as $\Delta b_2 \geq -100$.

Since $x_2 - \Delta b_2 = 100$, Δb_2 cannot be less than -100. Thus, the present running plan will be feasible for the remaining range of Δb_2: $-100 \leq \Delta b_2 \leq -83.3$. Within this range, there will be no further changes in the amount of jet fuel produced or in the amount of crude 1 run. The amount of crude 3 run, however, now increases (for *decreasing* availability of crude 2) by a factor of 4 (from $\frac{1}{6}$ to $\frac{2}{3}$), and the maximum total profit decreases more rapidly, to a rate of $\frac{460}{3}$, as compared to the previous rate of $\frac{340}{3}$, which held throughout the range $-83.3 \leq \Delta b_2 \leq 50$. These results are all shown graphically in Figs. 5–8 and 5–9.

Similar analyses, of course, can be made concerning the effects on the optimal solution of changes in the availability of the other crudes and also changes in the maximum amounts of the various products which can be

x_1	x_2	x_3	x_4	x_5	f_1	f_2	f_3	f_4	f_g	f_h	f_ℓ	f_j	
					1	$\frac{3}{4}$		$\frac{1}{4}$	$-\frac{5}{2}$	$\frac{5}{2}$	$\frac{5}{2}$		0
	1						1						16.7
						$\frac{1}{6}$	1	$\frac{5}{6}$	$\frac{5}{3}$	-5	-5		27.8
		1						1			-5		100
1						$-\frac{3}{4}$		$-\frac{1}{4}$	$\frac{5}{2}$	$-\frac{5}{2}$	$-\frac{5}{2}$		100
			1			$-\frac{1}{6}$		$-\frac{5}{6}$	$-\frac{5}{3}$	5	5		72.2
				1							5		100
						$-\frac{3}{40}$		$\frac{3}{40}$	$\frac{1}{4}$	$-\frac{5}{4}$	$-\frac{5}{4}$	1	10
0	0	0	0	0	0	$\frac{340}{3}$	0	$\frac{200}{3}$	$\frac{400}{3}$	100	600	0	$58,389

Figure 5-12. Optimal tableau for $b_2 = 16.7$.

x_1	x_2	x_3	x_4	x_5	f_1	f_2	f_3	f_4	f_g	f_h	f_ℓ	f_j	
					$-\frac{2}{5}$	$-\frac{3}{10}$		$-\frac{1}{10}$	1	-1	-1		0
	1						1						16.7
					$\frac{2}{3}$	$\frac{2}{3}$	1	1		$-\frac{10}{3}$	$-\frac{10}{3}$		27.8
		1						1			-5		100
1						1							100
			1		$-\frac{2}{3}$	$-\frac{2}{3}$		-1		$\frac{10}{3}$	$\frac{10}{3}$		72.2
				1							5		100
					$\frac{1}{10}$			$\frac{1}{10}$		-1	-1	1	10
0	0	0	0	0	$\frac{160}{3}$	$\frac{460}{3}$	0	80	0	$\frac{700}{3}$	$\frac{2200}{3}$	0	$58,389

Figure 5-13. Results of f_g replacing f_1 in dependent set of Fig. 5-12.

sold (that is, perturbations in f_g, f_h, f_ℓ, and f_j). These analyses are carried out in exactly the same manner as that described for crude 2 availability, and are left as an exercise for the reader.

5-11 Simultaneous Availability Changes

The situation in which the availabilities of several of the crudes change during the same time period can be analyzed by a method which is a direct extension of that just described. As a simple example, consider the effects of simultaneous availability changes in crudes 2 and 4, by amounts Δb_2 and Δb_4, respectively. Proceeding as before, we see from Fig. 5–7 that the state variables are affected by these changes in the following manner:

$$f_1 = 62.50 + \tfrac{3}{4}\Delta b_2 + \tfrac{1}{4}\Delta b_4 \qquad (5\text{-}40)$$

$$x_2 = 100 + \Delta b_2 \qquad (5\text{-}41)$$

$$f_3 = 41.67 + \tfrac{1}{6}\Delta b_2 + \tfrac{5}{6}\Delta b_4 \qquad (5\text{-}42)$$

$$x_4 = 100 + \Delta b_4 \qquad (5\text{-}43)$$

$$x_1 = 37.50 - \tfrac{3}{4}\Delta b_2 - \tfrac{1}{4}\Delta b_4 \qquad (5\text{-}44)$$

$$x_3 = 58.33 - \tfrac{1}{6}\Delta b_2 - \tfrac{5}{6}\Delta b_4 \qquad (5\text{-}45)$$

$$f_j = 3.75 - \tfrac{3}{40}\Delta b_2 + \tfrac{3}{40}\Delta b_4 \qquad (5\text{-}46)$$

The optimal solution of Fig. 5–7 will remain feasible as long as the right-hand sides of Eqs. (5–40)–(5–46) remain nonnegative. This nonnegativity restriction changes the foregoing equations into inequalities which define the shaded area of Fig. 5–14. Within this area, the simultaneous changes Δb_2 and Δb_4 result in alteration of the objective function by the amount

$$\Delta p = 100\Delta x_1 + 200\Delta x_2 + 70\Delta x_3 + 150\Delta x_4$$

or, by Eqs. (5–40)–(5–46),

$$\Delta p = 100(-\tfrac{3}{4}\Delta b_2 - \tfrac{1}{4}\Delta b_4) + 200(\Delta b_2) + 70(-\tfrac{1}{6}\Delta b_2 - \tfrac{5}{6}\Delta b_4) + 150\Delta b_4$$

which may be written as

$$\Delta p = \tfrac{340}{3}\Delta b_2 + \tfrac{200}{3}\Delta b_4 \qquad (5\text{-}47)$$

Notice that the coefficients in Eq. (5–47) are the negatives of the sensitivity coefficients corresponding to f_2 and f_4 in Fig. 5–7, so that this expression for Δp could have been obtained directly from the bottom row of the optimal tableau. A similar statement holds for the case in which more than two crude availabilities are changed simultaneously, so that in general we have

$$\Delta p = \sum_i (-v_i)\Delta b_i \qquad (5\text{-}48)$$

where the v_i are the sensitivity coefficients corresponding to the slack variables

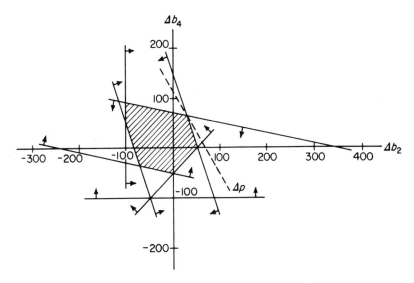

Figure 5-14. Region of feasibility for optimal solution under simultaneous availability changes in crudes 2 and 4.

f_i. If we are able to purchase unlimited quantities of crudes 2 and 4, but do not wish to change the optimal running plan of Fig. 5–7 (that is, do not want to change the state set), it is important to know what quantities of these crudes to purchase so as to maximize the total profit. Clearly, this is equivalent to maximizing (5–47) subject to the inequalities resulting from the nonnegativity restrictions on Eqs. (5–40)–(5–46). This new linear programming problem is solved graphically in Fig. 5–14. The solution is easily found to be $\Delta b_2 = 28.6$, $\Delta b_4 = 64.2$, for an increase in profit of $7520. From Eqs. (5–40)–(5–46) it can be seen that this additional profit is achieved by running 128,600 bbl per week of crude 2; 164,200 bbl per week of crude 4, and none of crudes 1 and 3.

Notice that in this new linear programming problem, we should not limit all the Δb_i to nonnegative values. For example, if the sensitivity coefficients corresponding to f_2 and f_4 had had the values -50 and -300, respectively, then the point $\Delta b_2 = -100$, $\Delta b_4 = 90$, would have resulted in an increase in profit of $22,000, and for these values of the sensitivity coefficients, this would indeed have been the maximum profit attainable.

Thus, the general problem of maximizing (5–48) subject to constraints of the form:

$$K + \sum_i \alpha_{ik} \Delta b_i \geq 0 \qquad (5\text{–}49)$$

cannot be solved by the simplex method (which forces all $\Delta b_i \geq 0$) without some modification. The modification required, however, is quite simple;

we merely express each variable Δb_i as the difference of two nonnegative variables as follows:

$$\Delta b_i = \Delta''b_i - \Delta'b_i \tag{5-50}$$

Each Δb_i is then replaced in (5–48) and (5–49) by the value given in (5–50), and the standard simplex method is used to find the optimal solution to this equivalent problem, where the $\Delta''b_i$ and $\Delta'b_i$ are all required to be non-negative.

5-12 Sensitivity Analysis on the Objective Coefficients

Analyses of the effects on the optimal solution of perturbations in the co-efficients c_n in the objective function (5–1) are performed in much the same manner as were those concerned with the constants b_m in the constraint equations. From Eq. (5–15) it is clear that a change in any of the c_n will affect the value of some of the sensitivity coefficients, v_n, but will leave the state variables unchanged. Thus, such changes can affect the optimality of the final solution to a linear programming problem, but never the feasibility.

For a maximization problem, a solution is optimal so long as the sensitivity coefficients are all nonpositive. *Since the bottom row entries are the negatives of the v_n, these entries must be nonnegative for the corresponding solution to be optimal.* Thus, if an objective coefficient, c_n, corresponding to a decision variable, d_n, is changed by an amount Δc_n, then from Eq. (5–15), the final solution will remain optimal if

$$\Delta c_n \leq - v_n \tag{5-51}$$

In other words, the objective coefficient for a decision variable may *decrease* by any amount without affecting the optimality of the solution, but must not *increase* by more than the value of the bottom row entry for that variable. Thus, such a change affects only the sensitivity coefficient, and its effect can be evaluated by inspection.

Changes in some objective coefficient c_m corresponding to a state variable s_m can, however, affect every sensitivity coefficient. Indeed, we see from Eq. (5–15) that

$$\Delta v_n = -\alpha_{mn}\Delta c_m; \qquad n = M + 1, \ldots, M + N \tag{5-52}$$

and so the solution remains optimal within the range

$$\frac{v_L}{\alpha_{mL}} \leq \Delta c_m \leq \frac{v_{U}}{\alpha_{mU}} \tag{5-53}$$

where

$$\frac{v_{U}}{\alpha_{mU}} = \min_{\alpha_{mn}<0} \left(\frac{v_n}{\alpha_{mn}}\right) \tag{5-54}$$

and
$$\frac{v_L}{\alpha_{mL}} = \max_{\alpha_{mn}>0}\left(\frac{v_n}{\alpha_{mn}}\right) \tag{5-55}$$

since in both Eqs. (5-54) and (5-55), we want to choose the ratio of v_n to α_{mn} which is smallest in absolute value. For *minimization* problems, of course, the sensitivity coefficients must remain *nonnegative*, and Eqs. (5-51) and (5-53) must be adjusted accordingly.

Let us now suppose that in the refinery scheduling problem the *cost* of crude 1 changes by an amount $-\Delta c_1$; this is equivalent to changing the objective coefficient of x_1 from the present value of 100 to a value of 100 $+ \Delta c_1$. Changes in the selling price of the products could also affect the net *profit*, c_1, as could changes in the production and sales costs. For brevity, we shall speak of changes Δc_m without reference to the changes in costs or market values which produced them.

From Fig. 5-7, we see that the *bottom row entries* affected by the change Δc_1 in the profit of crude 1 become:

$$-v_2 = \tfrac{340}{3} - \tfrac{3}{4}\Delta c_1; \quad -v_4 = \tfrac{200}{3} - \tfrac{1}{4}\Delta c_1$$

$$-v_g = \tfrac{400}{3} + \tfrac{5}{2}\Delta c_1$$

$$-v_h = 100 - \tfrac{5}{2}\Delta c_1 \quad \text{and} \quad -v_\ell = 600 - \tfrac{5}{2}\Delta c_1$$

Since the present state set will remain optimal only so long as all of these numbers are nonnegative, no change in this set will be required in the range $-53.33 \leq \Delta c_1 \leq 40$. The values -53.33 and 40, of course, are obtained from Eqs. (5-55) and (5-54), respectively. In this range, the values taken on by the state variables do not change, and therefore, the maximum profit will be given by $p = 67{,}833 + 37.5\,\Delta c_1$, since $x_1 = 37.5$, and no other terms in the objective function will change.

If the profit from running crude 1 were to decrease by more than \$53.33 per 1000 bbl, then some of the sensitivity coefficients would become positive, indicating the the state set which generated them was no longer optimal. Figure 5-15 shows that when Δc_1 reaches -53.33, only the sensitivity coefficient associated with f_g has been driven to zero. All the other coefficients have decreased, because of negative entries for these columns in the x_1 row (that is, the fifth row, in which x_1 is the state variable). Any further decrease in Δc_1 will cause the sensitivity coefficient v_g to become positive, meaning that the total profit can be increased by bringing f_g into the state set.

Using the simplex method, we replace x_1 in the state set with f_g, obtaining the tableau of Fig. 5-16. Here, x_1 and f_j tied as the variable to be removed, so that our arbitrary choice of x_1 has produced a degenerate solution with the state variable f_j having a zero value. Notice that in Fig. 5-16 and Fig. 5-17, we have appended a column on the left containing the objective coefficients, c_m, corresponding to the state variable, s_m, in each row. In addition to this new column, we have written all the objective coefficients in a

c_m	x_1	x_2	x_3	x_4	x_5	f_1	f_2	f_3	f_4	f_g	f_h	f_ℓ	f_j	
						1	$\frac{3}{4}$		$\frac{1}{4}$	$-\frac{5}{2}$	$\frac{5}{2}$	$\frac{5}{2}$		62.5
200		1					1							100
							$\frac{1}{6}$	1	$\frac{5}{6}$	$\frac{5}{3}$	-5	-5		41.67
150				1					1			-5		100
$\frac{140}{3}$	1						$-\frac{3}{4}$		$-\frac{1}{4}$	$\frac{5}{2}$	$-\frac{5}{2}$	$-\frac{5}{2}$		37.5
70			1				$-\frac{1}{6}$		$-\frac{5}{6}$	$-\frac{5}{3}$	5	5		58.3
250					1							5		100
							$-\frac{3}{40}$		$\frac{3}{40}$	$\frac{1}{4}$	$-\frac{5}{4}$	$-\frac{5}{4}$	1	3.75
	0	0	0	0	0	0	$\frac{460}{3}$	0	80	0	$\frac{700}{3}$	$\frac{2200}{3}$	0	$65,833

(The top of the tableau also shows the c_n row: c_n | $\frac{140}{3}$ | 200 | 70 | 150 | 250)

Figure 5-15. Optimal tableau for $c_1 = 46.67$ ($\Delta c_1 = -53.33$)

row at the top of each tableau, just above the variable to which they correspond. This is a convenient means for keeping track of these coefficients, and is sometimes used in preparing linear programming problems for hand computation.

Unlike the case of variation in the availability of crudes, here the change in production schedule is discontinuous and accompanied by substantial changes in the values of many of the state variables. The solutions in Figs. 5–15 and 5–16, however, produce exactly the same profit of $65,833, even though they represent considerable differences in the running plans employed. Since this is a linear programming problem, the decrease in the profit, p, has taken place at a constant rate of $37.50 for each dollar decrease in the net profit of crude 1, for a total decrease between Fig. 5–7 and 5–15 of $37.50 × ($53.33) = $2000.

Figure 5–16, however, shows that this decrease is now at an end, for x_1 has been removed from the state set. Thus we see that when the net profit from running 1000 bbl of crude 1 falls below $46.67, it is no longer profitable to run any of this crude. Although the net profit has been uniformly decreased from the original value of $100 per 1000 bbl to $46.67, no changes in the running plan have been desirable, so that the maximum profit has been

c_n	$\frac{140}{3}$	200	70	150	250									
c_m	x_1	x_2	x_3	x_4	x_5	f_1	f_2	f_3	f_4	f_g	f_h	f_ℓ	f_j	
	1					1								100
200		1					1							100
	$-\frac{2}{3}$						$\frac{2}{3}$	1	1		$-\frac{10}{3}$	$-\frac{10}{3}$		16.67
150			1						1			-5		100
	$\frac{2}{5}$						$-\frac{3}{10}$	$-\frac{1}{10}$	1		-1	-1		15
70	$\frac{2}{3}$						$-\frac{2}{3}$	-1			$\frac{10}{3}$	$\frac{10}{3}$		83.3
250					1							5		100
	$-\frac{1}{10}$							$\frac{1}{10}$			-1	-1	1	0
	0	0	0	0	0	0	$\frac{460}{3}$	0	80	0	$\frac{700}{3}$	$\frac{2200}{3}$	0	\$65,833

Figure 5-16. Results of replacing x_1 with f_g in dependent set of Fig. 5-15.

achieved by continually processing 37,500 bbl per week of crude 1. At the $46.67 figure, however, crude 1 is suddenly dropped out of the running plan altogether, with compensating increases in the amounts of crude 3 processed. Notice that this change in running plan has also reduced the gasoline production, since crude 3 is not as rich in gasoline as is crude 1. (See Table 5-1: this also explains the increase in production of jet fuel.)

The effects of *increased* net profit from running crude 1 are handled in the same manner as were the decreases. Thus, until the unit profit from this crude has increased by more than $40 per 1000 bbl, no change in the state set will occur since all the sensitivity coefficients will remain nonpositive. Unlike the values of the state variables, these coefficients do change continuously with uniform changes in the unit profit for crude 1. For example, the sensitivity coefficient for f_h will be $v_h = \frac{5}{2}\Delta c_1 - 100$, so that it increases linearly to zero as Δc_1 increases to 40. This is the first coefficient to be driven to zero, and the reader may verify that f_h replaces x_3 as a result of the required simplex iteration.

Figures 5–17 and 5–18 summarize the effects of changes in the unit profit c_1; notice that the curves are piecewise linear, and that the three products are affected strongly by the profit of crude 1. Crude 2, not shown in Fig. 5–17,

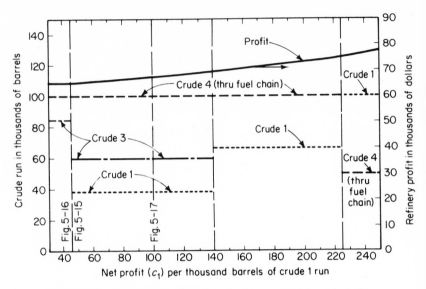

Figure 5-17. Maximum profit and optimal raw material consumption as functions of crude 1 unit profit.

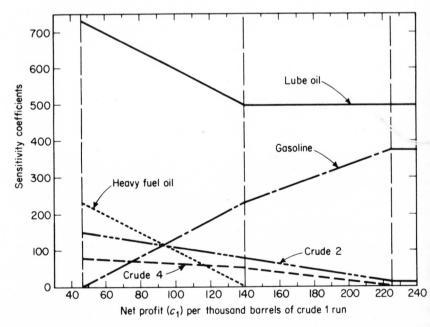

Figure 5-18. Sensitivity coefficients as functions of crude 1 unit profit.

has a constant value of 100 Mbpw throughout the entire range of c_1, even though the per barrel profit on the crude is exceeded by that of crude 1 for $c_1 > 200$. From Fig. 5–18, however, we see that the penalty which would be incurred by reducing the amount of crude 2 steadily declines as crude 1 contributes more and more profit per barrel run.

Simultaneous changes in the objective coefficients are handled in the same manner as were such changes in the constraint constants b_m. For example, if the unit profit from both crudes 1 and 3 were to change by the respective amounts Δc_1 and Δc_3, then the solution of Fig. 5–7 would remain optimal so long as the following inequalities were satisfied:

$$v_2 = \tfrac{3}{4}\Delta c_1 + \tfrac{1}{6}\Delta c_3 - \tfrac{340}{3} \leq 0$$

$$v_4 = \tfrac{1}{4}\Delta c_1 + \tfrac{5}{6}\Delta c_3 - \tfrac{200}{3} \leq 0$$

$$v_g = -\tfrac{5}{2}\Delta c_1 + \tfrac{5}{3}\Delta c_3 - \tfrac{400}{3} \leq 0$$

$$v_h = \tfrac{5}{2}\Delta c_1 - 5\,\Delta c_3 - 100 \leq 0$$

$$v_\ell = \tfrac{5}{2}\Delta c_1 - 5\,\Delta c_3 - 100 \leq 0$$

Within the region defined by the foregoing inequalities, the total refinery profit would then be given by the expression, $p = 37.5\,\Delta c_1 + 58.33\,\Delta c_3$.

5-13 Combined Effects of Profit and Availability Changes

We now turn to a consideration of the effects of simultaneous changes in the unit profit and availability of a crude. It may happen that as larger quantities of a crude become available, the market price will decrease, or alternatively, larger amounts of the crude may be made available by paying a premium to get them. Figure 5–19 summarizes the results obtained from an investigation of all possible combinations of changes in the profits and availabilities of crude 2. In this figure, changes in availability are plotted horizontally; profit changes are plotted vertically. The origin may be taken as the point $\Delta b_2 = 0$, $\Delta c_2 = 0$, which represents the tableau of Fig. 5–7. At this point, $b_2 = 100$ Mbpw, $c_2 = \$200$ per 1000 bbl processed, and the total refinery profit is \$67,833.

The vertical dashed lines represent the values of b_2 at which a change in the state set is required (because some state variable has been driven to zero). The horizontal boundaries of the shaded areas define the values of c_2 at which a change in the state set is necessary (because some sensitivity coefficient has been driven to zero). All these values are computed exactly as described earlier, where changes were made in only one parameter. For example, having obtained the tableau resulting from the change in the state

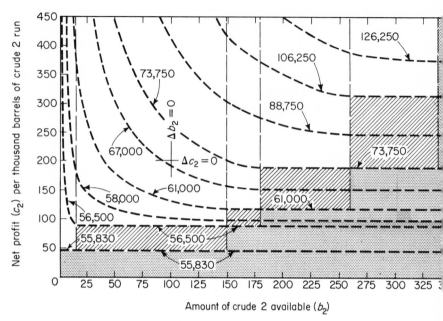

Figure 5-19. Summary of simultaneous changes in unit profit and availability of crude 2.

set required when $\Delta b_2 = 160$, one can now examine changes in c_2, and compute the range $-12.5 \leq \Delta c_2 \leq 112.5$ for which the state set of this tableau is optimal. Thus, this tableau would give the optimal solution to the refinery problem for the combined range $260 \leq b_2 \leq 340$, $187.5 \leq c_2 \leq 312.5$, as shown in Fig. 5-19. The remaining areas in the figure are calculated in a similar manner, and clearly, the results obtained are independent of the order in which the changes Δb_2 and Δc_2 are computed.

An interesting situation occurs at the point $\Delta b_2 = 240$, $\Delta c_2 = \frac{225}{2}$; for these changes, crude 2 has become so profitable, and so much of it is available, that no other crude is being processed. Thus, when the profit from each 1000 bbl of this crude exceeds \$312.50, and at least 340 Mbpw of it are available, the entire refinery should be run on this one crude alone. If more than 340 Mbpw are available, they cannot be run since we have already reached the sales limit on gasoline.

The dashed lines on Fig. 5-19 are constant profit lines; for example, a maximum total refinery profit of \$88,750 will be achieved at $\Delta b_2 = 0$, $\Delta c_2 = 210$; at $\Delta b_2 = 80$, $\Delta c_2 = 75$; and at $\Delta b_2 = 160$, $\Delta c_2 = 45$. The line becomes horizontal to the right of the latter point, indicating that increased availabilities of crude 2 beyond that point cannot be processed. The constant profit lines define areas of profitable change in the quantities of crude 2 purchased. For example, if 50 Mbpw of the crude were now being run at a net profit of $300 per 1000 bbl, Fig. 5-19 shows that the total refinery profit would be $67,000. Any change in b_2 and c_2 which resulted in a point above this line would be profitable. Thus, if unlimited amounts were available at a price increase of less than $150 per 1000 bbl, it would pay to purchase an additional 130 Mbpw, for a total of 180 Mbpw. Beyond this amount, of course, all available quantities are not processed, so that further purchases could not be justified.

5-14 Other Sensitivity Analyses

The sensitivity analyses most frequently required are those concerned with variations either in the constraint constants, b_m, or in the objective coefficients, c_n, as previously described. Changes in the constraint coefficients, a_{mn}, occur less often and are more difficult to analyze, especially when several of them change simultaneously. We shall describe the procedure for analyzing those cases in which one such coefficient changes, after first discussing the important topics of deleted variables and constraints.

For very large problems, computer storage and running time become critical considerations, and the original problem may have to be decreased in size by removing constraints and/or variables. After the reduced problem is solved, the effect of having eliminated a constraint or variable may be computed without re-solving the problem. The procedure for eliminated variables consists in testing the hypothesis that these variables would have been decision variables in the optimal solution and thus would not have affected the solution had they been retained. The analysis for the eliminated constraints consists in checking the implicit assumption that the slack variables for these constraints would have been state variables, indicating that the constraints would not have been binding.

For example, suppose that, in the refinery scheduling problem, it was assumed that a constraint on total refinery capacity would not be exceeded by the optimal solution obtained when this constraint is deleted. Specifically, if the refinery were not able to process more than, say, 350,000 bbl of crude per week, then the eliminated constraint would be

$$x_1 + x_2 + x_3 + x_4 + x_5 + f_r = 350 \tag{5-56}$$

where f_r is the slack variable which measures the unused refinery capacity. Substitution of the optimal solution from Fig. 5-7 into this constraint results in a value of $f_r = -45.83$, assuming f_r to be the state variable in this constraint row in the final tableau. This means that the refinery capacity has been exceeded by 45.83 Mbpw, so that the optimal solution obtained is no longer feasible when this constraint is included.

Since the optimal tableau of Fig. 5–7 expresses the state variables in terms of the decision variables, we may use these expressions to eliminate all state variables in Eq. (5-56) and produce the new constraint row in the optimal tableau:

$$-\tfrac{1}{12}f_2 + \tfrac{1}{12}f_4 - \tfrac{5}{6}f_g - \tfrac{5}{2}f_h - \tfrac{5}{2}f_\ell + f_r = -45.83 \qquad (5\text{-}57)$$

Then the new optimal (but no longer feasible) tableau is as shown in Fig. 5–20, where f_h will replace f_r in the state set on the next iteration, as indicated by the lines on the figure. Notice that the addition of an eliminated constraint never changes the sensitivity coefficients, since it affects only feasibility, not optimality. The reader may verify that two iterations of the dual-simplex method are required to obtain the new optimal feasible solution: $x_1 = 50$, $x_2 = 100$, $x_3 = 100$, $x_4 = 100$, and $x_5 = 100$, which produces a total refinery profit of $65,000.

c_n	100	200	70	150	250										
c_m	x_1	x_2	x_3	x_4	x_5	f_1	f_2	f_3	f_4	f_g	f_h	f_ℓ	f_j	f_r	
							$-\frac{1}{12}$		$\frac{1}{12}$	$-\frac{5}{6}$	$-\frac{5}{2}$	$-\frac{5}{2}$	1		-45.83
						1	$\frac{3}{4}$		$\frac{1}{4}$	$-\frac{5}{2}$	$\frac{5}{2}$	$\frac{5}{2}$			62.5
200		1					1								100
							$\frac{1}{6}$	1	$\frac{5}{6}$	$\frac{5}{3}$	-5	-5			41.67
150				1			1					-5			100
100	1						$-\frac{3}{4}$		$-\frac{1}{4}$	$\frac{5}{2}$	$-\frac{5}{2}$	$-\frac{5}{2}$			37.5
70			1				$-\frac{1}{6}$		$-\frac{5}{6}$	$-\frac{5}{3}$	5	5			58.33
250					1							5			100
							$-\frac{3}{40}$		$\frac{3}{40}$	$\frac{1}{4}$	$-\frac{5}{4}$	$-\frac{5}{4}$		1	3.75
	0	0	0	0	0	0	$\frac{340}{3}$	0	$\frac{200}{3}$	$\frac{400}{3}$	100	600	0	0	$67,833

Figure 5-20. Optimal tableau of Fig. 5-7 with additional constraint, $x_1 + x_2 + x_3 + x_4 + x_5 \le 350$ included.

Again, suppose that a variable, x_e, were eliminated from the original problem, and it was desired to check whether inclusion of this variable would have affected the optimal solution as obtained by ignoring it. If x_e would have been a decision variable in the final tableau, then its coefficient, α_{ie}, in the ith constraint row (the row in which x_i is the state variable) could be calculated from

$$\alpha_{ie} \equiv \frac{\delta x_i}{\delta x_e} = \sum_k \frac{\delta x_i}{\delta x_k} \frac{\partial x_k}{\partial x_e} = \sum_k \alpha_{ik} a_{ke} \qquad (5\text{-}58 : \text{i, e})$$

where the summation is taken over those variables, x_k, which were state variables in the initial tableau and where again the notation δ indicates differentiation in which only decision variables are held constant. (The reader familiar with matrix algebra will recognize that for this set of indices, k, the α_{ik} are the elements of a matrix B^{-1}, ("inverse of the basis") which when postmultiplied by the initial simplex tableau matrix, yields the final (optimal) tableau matrix.) Thus, the first term in the summation is taken from the final tableau, whereas the second term is obtained from the initial tableau. If any x_k is also a state variable in the *final* tableau, then of course the first term vanishes for $i \neq k$, and is equal to unity for $i = k$.

From Eqs. (5–15:e) and (5–58:i,e), the sensitivity coefficient for x_e in the final tableau would be given by:

$$v_e = c_e - \sum_i c_i \sum_k \alpha_{ik} a_{ke}$$
$$= c_e - \sum_k a_{ke}(c_k - v_k) \qquad (5\text{-}59 : \text{e})$$

where again the summation on k is defined as it was for Eq. (5–58). If v_e is negative (for a maximization problem), then the optimal solution would not have been changed by introducing the variable x_e into the problem. If v_e is positive, however, then the solution can be improved by bringing x_e into the state set. This is accomplished by performing a simplex iteration on the final tableau to which the column of elements, α_{ie} and v_e, has been added. (More than one iteration may be required to find the new optimal solution if this first one makes any of the other sensitivity coefficients positive.)

The methods for analyzing the effects of changes in the constraint coefficients, a_{ij}, consist of two separate procedures, depending upon whether the variable x_j is a state or a decision variable in the final tableau (x_i, in our notation, is always a *state* variable in this tableau).

First consider the case in which some x_h is a decision variable in the final tableau. In such a case, changes in an a_{ih} will not affect the elements α_{ik} in Eq. (5–58) which map the initial tableau entries a_{ij} into the final tableau entries α_{ij} (where j is indexed over *all* the variables in both tableaux). Therefore, from Eq. (5–58) we see that a change $\Delta a_{\ell h}$ in the constraint coefficient $a_{\ell h}$ changes the final tableau entries α_{ih} by an amount:

$$\Delta \alpha_{ih} = \alpha_{i\ell} \Delta a_{\ell h}; \qquad i = 1, \ldots, M \qquad (5\text{-}60 : \text{i, h})$$

where ℓ must necessarily be one of the indices over which k was defined in Eqs. (5–58) and (5–59). From Eq. (5–15), this change in each α_{ih} will change the sensitivity coefficient v_h by an amount

$$\Delta v_h = -\sum_i c_i \Delta \alpha_{ih} \qquad (5\text{-}61 : \text{h})$$

so that from Eq. (5-60), the new sensitivity coefficient becomes

$$\hat{v}_h = v_h - \sum_{i=1}^{M} c_i \alpha_{i\ell} \Delta a_{\ell h} \qquad (5\text{-}62\text{:h}, \ell)$$

$$= v_h - \Delta a_{\ell h}(c_\ell - v_\ell)$$

and (for a maximization problem), the change in $a_{\ell h}$ will not affect the optimal solution already found so long as

$$\Delta a_{\ell h}(c_\ell - v_\ell) \geq v_h \qquad (5\text{-}63\text{: h}, \ell)$$

If the magnitude of the change $\Delta a_{\ell h}$ is large enough to cause v_h to exceed the left side of inequality (5–63), then one simply changes v_h and each of the α_{ih} in the final tableau by the amounts calculated from Eqs. (5–61) and (5–60) and proceeds with the simplex method (first bringing in x_h) as in the case of eliminated variables.

A change $\Delta a_{\ell\lambda}$, where x_λ is a state variable in the final tableau, is best analyzed by introducing a new variable, $\hat{x}_\lambda$, having constraint coefficients $\hat{a}_{k\lambda}$ identical with the $a_{k\lambda}$ corresponding to x_λ, except for the one coefficient $\hat{a}_{\ell\lambda}$, which is set equal to $a_{\ell\lambda} + \Delta a_{\ell\lambda}$. Then, using Eq. (5–58: ℓ, λ), the coefficients $\hat{\alpha}_{\ell\lambda}$ in the x_λ column of the final tableau can be calculated, as can the sensitivity coefficient $\hat{v}_\lambda$. One then introduces the new objective coefficient, $\hat{c}_\lambda$, making its value identical with that of the original c_λ, and replaces the original c_λ with a very large negative number (for a maximization problem). This latter operation has the effect of changing the sensitivity coefficients in the final tableau—since c_λ is one of the c_i in Eq. (5–15)—in such a way that subsequent application of the simplex method to this tableau will drive x_λ out of the state set, thus effectively removing it (and therefore $a_{\ell\lambda}$) from the problem.

For some linear programming problems, it is important to know the optimal solution for all values of a particular parameter, usually one of the b_m or c_n. As we have seen in the case of b_2 in the refinery problem, this can be accomplished by solving the problem first for some numerical value of the parameter, and then investigating the effects of changes Δb_2 on this solution. Alternatively, one may proceed by finding the set of optimal solutions corresponding to various ranges of the parameter without introducing a specific numerical value. This procedure is called *parametric programming* (Gass and Saaty), and we illustrate it by parameterizing the objective coefficient c_1 in the following problem:

Find nonnegative x_1, x_2, which maximize

$$y = c_1 x_1 + x_2 \qquad (5\text{-}64)$$

and which satisfy the constraints:

$$2x_1 + x_2 \leq 10 \qquad (5\text{-}65)$$

$$x_1 + x_2 \leq 8 \qquad (5\text{-}66)$$

$$x_1 \leq 3 \qquad (5\text{-}67)$$

$$x_2 \leq 7 \qquad (5\text{-}68)$$

An initial basic feasible solution for this problem is immediately at hand since the state set can be selected to consist of the slack variables f_1–f_4, corresponding to the constraints (5–65)–(5–68), respectively. This produces the tableau of Fig. 5–21(a), which clearly cannot be an optimal solution for any value of c_1, since the decision derivative for x_2 is positive. Therefore, we select x_2 to enter the state set, replacing f_4, with the results shown in Fig. 5–21(b). The state set for this tableau will be optimal so long as c_1 is negative, for then all the sensitivity coefficients will be negative. When c_1 becomes

x_1	x_2	f_1	f_2	f_3	f_4	
2	1	1	0	0	0	10
1	1	0	1	0	0	8
1	0	0	0	1	0	3
0	1	0	0	0	1	7
$-c_1$	−1	0	0	0	0	0

(a) Initial tableau, nonoptimal for all values of c_1

2	0	1	0	0	−1	3
1	0	0	1	0	−1	1
1	0	0	0	1	0	3
0	1	0	0	0	1	7
$-c_1$	0	0	0	0	1	7

(b) Optimal solution for $c_1 < 0$

0	0	1	−2	0	1	1
1	0	0	1	0	−1	1
0	0	0	−1	1	1	2
0	1	0	0	0	1	7
0	0	0	c_1	0	$1-c_1$	$7+c_1$

(c) Optimal solution in the range $0 \leq c_1 \leq 1$

0	0	1	−2	0	1	1
1	0	1	−1	0	0	2
0	0	−1	1	1	0	1
0	1	−1	2	0	0	6
0	0	c_1-1	$2-c_1$	0	1	$6+2c_1$

(d) Optimal solution in the range $1 \leq c_1 \leq 2$

0	0	−1	0	2	1	3
1	0	0	0	1	0	3
0	0	−1	1	1	0	1
0	1	1	0	−2	0	4
0	0	1	0	c_1-2	0	$4+3c_1$

(e) Optimal solution for $c_1 \geq 2$

Figure 5-21. Tableaux for parametric programming problem.

positive, the sensitivity coefficient for x_1 also becomes positive, and the solution can be improved by replacing f_2 with x_1 in the state set, producing the tableau of Fig. 5–21(c). Since now the sensitivity coefficients for f_2 and f_4 will remain nonpositive if c_1 is respectively nonnegative and not greater than 1, the state set for this tableau is optimal in the range $0 \leq c_1 \leq 1$. When c_1 exceeds a value of $+1$, f_4 is made a state variable with the results shown in Fig. 5–21(d). Continuing in this manner, we compute the tableau of Fig. 5–21(e), which remains the optimal solution for all values of c_1 greater than 2.

Although this simple problem can be worked by hand, most parametric programming must be performed on a digital computer, since it requires that numerous simplex iterations be performed on the full tableau.

5-15 The Decomposition Principle

One of the difficulties in certain practical linear programming problems is that the simplex tableau is often so large that it exceeds the storage capacity of the available computer. This is especially true when one is attempting to optimize the operation of a company consisting of several manufacturing plants, for here the number of variables and constraints may run into the thousands. Furthermore, even when storage space is not at a premium, the optimization of an entire super-system, such as a company, may not be efficient, since the time required for the solution of a linear programming problem on a high-speed computer is approximately proportional to the cube of the number of constraints. For these reasons, a method has been developed for decomposing the large problem, representing the super-system, down into smaller problems, representing the component systems (say, plants), and then adjusting the optimal solutions of the smaller problems in such a way that they produce an optimal solution for the super-system.

Dantzig and Wolfe have developed a decomposition principle which imposes on each local system additional constraints that allow the system problems to be optimized individually, ignoring the effects of the solution on the other systems. These artificial restrictions, which reflect the interactions between the systems, are selected by the decomposition principle in such a way that the solutions found for each small problem will also be optimal for the large super-system problem. This principle was developed mainly as a computational device for solving large linear programming problems. This aspect, although certainly of practical value, is not discussed here because of its specialized character. As Dantzig and Wolfe pointed out, the calculation process itself is interesting because it suggests a rational method for reconciling the conflicting requirements of the various systems in a way which is best for the super-system. This feature of the decomposition principle is discussed here.

The numerical example itself is something of a mathematical parable. It concerns two manufacturing plants which must share raw materials and markets. One plant is less effective than the other, say, because it is older and not designed for the materials being processed. If a coordinating board were to allocate raw material based on the profit each plant could make under the most favorable circumstances, it would award all material to the newer plant. This would leave none for the older one, which would presumably be shut down—a situation not uncommon when a strong company absorbs a weaker one in a merger. It happens, though, that it is really much more profitable to the entire company if the better plant uses an inferior material under less advantageous circumstances, for this releases other material to put the older plant into production. The increased profits from operating the older plant outweigh, in the example, the decreased effectiveness of the newer one, to the benefit of the entire company. This demonstrates not only the perils of suboptimization, but also the fruits of cooperation.

The highly simplified numerical example (Wilde, 1963) involves a hypothetical manufacturing firm converting three raw materials (identified by the numbers 1, 2, and 3) into two products. The company has two plants (designated A and B), each located near the source of one of the raw materials— plant A near raw material 1 and plant B near raw material 3. Because of high transportation costs it is uneconomical for plant A to use material 3 or for plant B to use material 1, but material 2 is available to either plant and must be shared by them. Production is limited by the market for the two products. Both plants can sell their output of the principal product anywhere in the company's marketing area, but each secondary product must be sold locally, near the plant producing it. Thus the plants share the market for the primary product but not for the by-product.

In any given month, each plant manager knows two things: the local demand for his by-product and the amount available of his exclusive raw material. Both may know the total demand for the main product as well as the availability of the shared raw material 2, but neither has the authority to determine his own share of the market or of material 2. The president of the company has appointed a coordinator to decide this question. Raw material availability and product demands are given in Table 5–2.

TABLE 5–2

MONTHLY SUPPLIES AND DEMANDS

Supply of raw material, tons			Product demands, tons		
			Main product	By-products	
1	2	3		Plant A	Plant B
80	160	180	180	100	200

Each local manager is, of course, familiar with the economic and technological performance of his plant. Given a production plan telling how much of each raw material to process, each manager can predict the amount of each product made and the corresponding profit. The specific technological and economic information for this problem is summarized in Table 5–3.

TABLE 5–3

LOCAL YIELDS AND PROFITS

	Plant A raw material		Plant B raw material	
	1	2	2	3
Yield of main product	0.40	0.80	0.60	0.20
Yield of by-product	0.60	0.20	0.40	0.80
Profit, $/ton processed	15	22	18	8

From the information in Tables 5–2 and 5–3, we may now write out the linear programming model representing the super-system (company) maximization problem. Let x_{1a} and x_{2a} be respectively the tons of raw materials 1 and 2 consumed per month in plant A only; then the limitations on the availability of material 1 and the sale of by-product from plant A lead to the constraints .

$$x_{1a} + f_1 = 80 \tag{5-69}$$

and
$$0.60x_{1a} + 0.20x_{2a} + f_2 = 100 \tag{5-70}$$

Similarly, if x_{2b} and x_{3b} are, respectively, the monthly consumption of raw materials 2 and 3 by plant B, then,

$$x_{3b} + f_3 = 180 \tag{5-71}$$

and
$$0.40x_{2b} + 0.80x_{3b} + f_4 = 200 \tag{5-72}$$

Equations (5–69) and (5–70) represent the constraints affecting only plant A; Eqs. (5–71) and (5–72), those affecting plant B alone. The limitation on material 2, which is shared by both plants, is

$$x_{2a} + x_{2b} + f_5 = 160 \tag{5-73}$$

Demand for the main product, to be filled by production from both plants, is represented by

$$0.40x_{1a} + 0.80x_{2a} + 0.60x_{2b} + 0.20x_{3b} + f_6 = 180 \tag{5-74}$$

The f_m in Eqs. (5–69)–(5–74) are, of course, the slack variables for these constraints.

The super-system problem then is to find the production plan which maximizes the monthly profit, p, given by

$$p = 15x_{1a} + 22x_{2a} + 18x_{2b} + 8x_{3b} \tag{5-75}$$

and which satisfies the feasibility constraints (5–69)–(5–74). It would be very easy to find the optimal plan by solving this small problem directly, but in order to demonstrate the workings of the decomposition principle, let us assume that the two plants and the coordinating group each has a computer capable of solving linear programming problems having no more than four constraints. We shall in fact allow each plant manager to ignore the presence not only of the common constraints (5–73) and (5–74), but even of the other plant. Thus, manager A is responsible for constraints (5–69) and (5–70); manager B, for (5–71) and (5–72); while the coordinating group is custodian of the shared constraints (5–73) and (5–74). The objective function is split into two parts, one for each plant. The monthly profit p_a from plant A is

$$p_a = 15x_{1a} + 22x_{2a} \tag{5-76}$$

and that from plant B is

$$p_b = 18x_{2b} + 8x_{3b} \tag{5-77}$$

5-16 Locally Optimal Plans

The computations begin with each manager finding the plan which is the most profitable for his plant. In either case this is a linear programming problem involving only two constraints and solvable by direct inspection, for it is clear that each manager would like to use as much of the profitable raw material 2 as he can. Thus the optimal plan for plant A (labeled solution $A1$) is $x_{1a1} = 0$ and $x_{2a1} = 500$, with a profit $p_{a1} = \$11,000$ per month. Notice that the last number of the subscript identifies the number of the plan. The optimal plan for plant B is $x_{2b1} = 500$ and $x_{3b1} = 0$, which would give a profit of $p_{b1} = \$9000$ per month.

When these locally optimal plans are transmitted to the coordinating group the application of the decomposition principle begins. It is clear that the local proposals cannot be applied, for although each plant wants 500 tons of raw material 2, only 160 are available for both plants. Furthermore, the production plans would produce 700 tons of the main product, more than three times as much as the market will bear. Now if each plan is multiplied by a nonnegative weighting factor less than one, the new plans generated will certainly be feasible locally. And if the factors are made small enough, the common constraints (5–73) and (5–74) can be satisfied.

5-17 Weighting Factors

Let λ_{a1} and λ_{b1} be the weighting factors for solutions $A1$ and $B1$ respectively. The variables of the problem can be expressed in terms of these factors as follows:

$$x_{1a} = x_{1a1}\lambda_{a1} = 0$$
$$x_{2a} = x_{2a1}\lambda_{a1} = 500\lambda_{a1}$$
$$x_{2b} = x_{2b1}\lambda_{b1} = 500\lambda_{b1}$$
$$x_{3b} = x_{3b1}\lambda_{b1} = 0$$
$$p_a = p_{a1}\lambda_{a1} = 11{,}000\lambda_{a1}$$
$$p_b = p_{b1}\lambda_{b1} = 9000\lambda_{b1}$$

In terms of the factors λ_{a1} and λ_{b1}, the shared constraints can be written

$$500\lambda_{a1} + 500\lambda_{b1} + f_5 = 160 \qquad (5\text{-}78)$$

for the availability of raw material 2, and

$$400\lambda_{a1} + 300\lambda_{b1} + f_6 = 180 \qquad (5\text{-}79)$$

for the main product demand. The requirement that the factors be between zero and unity imposes two more constraints,

$$\lambda_{a1} + f_a = 1 \qquad (5\text{-}80)$$

for plant A, and

$$\lambda_{b1} + f_b = 1 \qquad (5\text{-}81)$$

for plant B, where f_a and f_b are, of course, nonnegative slack variables.

5-18 First Master Plan

The coordinators now have the problem of maximizing the total profit

$$p = 11{,}000\lambda_{a1} + 9000\lambda_{b1} \qquad (5\text{-}82)$$

subject to the four constraints (5–78)–(5–81). Since the variables λ_{a1} and λ_{b1} cannot be negative, this is a linear programming problem which can be solved by the computation facilities assumed available. The optimal solution, obtainable in this case by inspection, is $\lambda_{a1} = 0.320$, $\lambda_{b1} = 0$, and $p = \$3520$. Thus if only locally optimal solutions are considered, plant A will operate at 32 per cent of its optimal rate and plant B will be shut down. This all-or-nothing aspect is often the way that capital improvement funds are allocated, various plants competing for funds which are given ultimately to the manager who can make the best use of them.

One would suspect, however, that it would be more profitable for the company as a whole to divert some of the raw material and market to plant B, even though this would mean compelling plant A to operate under conditions which, locally at least, would appear not to be optimal. Moreover, it might be possible to use some of the locally available raw materials 1 and 3 to add to the profit without using any of the scarce raw material 2, especially since Eq. (5–79) shows that only $400(0.32) = 128$ tons of the main product are produced—52 tons short of the total demand. In reality the allocation generated is "optimal" only relative to the two production plans submitted. Possibly, a more profitable over-all plan could be found if more local plans were available.

5-19 Generating Profitable Alternatives

Since the number of possible feasible local production plans is literally infinite, a means of picking out the more promising ones is needed. One intriguing feature of the decomposition principle is that the coordinating group actually can guide the local managers in their search for profitable alternatives. It accomplishes this by using the sensitivity coefficients generated by the solution to the coordinating problem. The bottom row of the optimal tableau for this first coordinating problem is found to be

$$p = 3520 - 2000\lambda_{b1} - 22f_5 \tag{5-83}$$

Now consider the effect of adding a new production plan A2 from plant A and giving it a weighting factor of λ_{a2}. Since at the moment the value of λ_{a2} is zero, we can treat it as a decision variable that would appear in Eq. (5–83) as follows

$$p = 3520 - 2000\lambda_{b1} - 22f_5 + v_{a2}\lambda_{a2} \tag{5-84}$$

where v_{a2} is the decision derivative, as yet unknown, of the weight factor λ_{a2}. If we knew the value of v_{a2}, we could decide immediately whether to bring plan A2 into consideration, for the profit can be increased only if v_{a2} is positive. Let p_{a2} be the profit (not yet known) associated with plan A2. We know that

$$p = 11{,}000\lambda_{a1} + 9000\lambda_{b1} + p_{a2}\lambda_{a2} \tag{5-85}$$

An expression for v_{a2} is now obtained by equating (5–84) to (5–85) and differentiating partially with respect to λ_{a2}, holding λ_{a1} and λ_{b1}, but not f_5, constant. Upon rearrangement, we get

$$v_{a2} = p_{a2} + 22\frac{\partial f_5}{\partial \lambda_{a2}} \tag{5-86}$$

It remains to evaluate the partial derivative. To do this, we first write Eq. (5–73) in terms of the weight factors and the still unknown variables x_{1a2} and x_{2a2} of plan A2. Since

$$x_{2a} = 500\lambda_{a1} + x_{2a2}\lambda_{a2}$$

we have
$$500\lambda_{a1} + x_{2a2}\lambda_{a2} + 500\lambda_{b1} + f_5 = 160$$

whence
$$\frac{\partial f_5}{\partial \lambda_{a2}} = -x_{2a2} \tag{5-87}$$

The profit p_{a2} may be written in terms of plan A2 as

$$p_{a2} = 15x_{1a2} + 22x_{2a2} \tag{5-88}$$

Combining Eqs. (5-86)–(5-88), we obtain

$$v_{a2} = 15x_{1a2} \tag{5-89}$$

Thus any plan using raw material 1 will be worthy of consideration.

It would seem attractive to make the coefficient v_{a2} as large as possible, since it is the rate of profit increase with respect to changes in the weight λ_{a2} placed on plan A2. To do this, plant manager A solves a new linear programming problem using the same constraints (5–69) and (5–70) as before, but with the altered profit function

$$p'_{a2} \equiv v_{a2} = 15x_{1a2} \tag{5-90}$$

In comparing this with the original profit function $p_a = 15x_{1a} + 22x_{2a}$, we see that the coordinating committee has effectively reduced the profit rate for raw material 2 to zero in plant A. Manager A is asked to generate the best plan he can, taking this handicap into account. The solution, designated solution A2, is evidently to use as much raw material 1 as possible:

$$x_{1a2} = 80, \quad x_{2a2} = 0, \quad p_{a2} = 15(80) = \$1200$$

In a similar way the coordinating group instructs manager B to find, if he can, a production plant which is locally profitable even when the return from processing raw material 2 is artificially reduced to zero. Manager B simply maximizes

$$p'_{b2} = 8x_{3b2} \tag{91}$$

subject to constraints (5–71) and (5–72), obtaining solution B2: $x_{2b2} = 0$, $x_{3b2} = 180$, $p_{b2} = 8(180) = \$1440$.

5-20 Second Master Plan

The coordinating group now has four local solutions to work with. As before, weighting coefficients λ_{a2} and λ_{b2} are assigned to the new solutions. The two solutions from plant A are combined, so that

$$x_{1a} = x_{1a1}\lambda_{a1} + x_{1a2}\lambda_{a2} = 80\lambda_{a2}$$

$$x_{2a} = x_{2a1}\lambda_{a1} + x_{2a2}\lambda_{a2} = 500\lambda_{a1}$$

and
$$p_a = p_{a1}\lambda_{a1} + p_{a2}\lambda_{a2} = 11,000\lambda_{a1} + 1200\lambda_{a2}$$

These expressions for the plant A production plan will be feasible locally because they represent weighted averages of solutions which are themselves locally feasible. The weighting coefficients for plant A must, of course, be nonnegative and add up to unity or less. Similar expressions can be derived involving the two plans for plant B. When these are combined with those for plant A and substituted into the shared constraints (5–73) and (5–74), the following equations result.

$$500\lambda_{a1} + 500\lambda_{b1} + f_5 = 160 \tag{5-92}$$

$$400\lambda_{a1} + 32\lambda_{a2} + 300\lambda_{b1} + 36\lambda_{b2} + f_6 = 180 \tag{5-93}$$

In addition, the definition of the weights requires that they satisfy

$$\lambda_{a1} + \lambda_{a2} + f_a = 1 \tag{5-94}$$

and

$$\lambda_{b1} + \lambda_{b2} + f_b = 1 \tag{5-95}$$

with f_a and f_b nonnegative. The coordinators wish to find a set of weights which satisfy these four constraints and which also maximize the profit

$$p = 11{,}000\lambda_{a1} + 1200\lambda_{a2} + 9000\lambda_{b1} + 1440\lambda_{b2} \tag{5-96}$$

The solution to this linear programming problem is $\lambda_{a1} = 0.2645$, $\lambda_{a2} = 0.7355$, $\lambda_{b1} = 0.0555$, and $\lambda_{b2} = 0.9445$, giving a monthly profit of $5652 —an increase of over $2000.

This new coordinating plan diverts some of the scarce raw material 2 from plant A to plant B, since manager A can now make money by processing his local raw material 1. Although this increases his monthly profit only slightly (from $3520 to $3792), the released material 2 can now go to work in plant B, which previously was not even operating. Drawing also on some of its local material 3, plant B now makes $1860 a month.

5-21 Penalties

The coordinating group must now check to see whether further improvement is possible. As before, they consider the effects of any new plan A3 submitted by manager A. The new profit equation, whose decision derivatives were generated during the solution of the most recent coordinating linear program, is more complicated than before because all four slack variables are now in it.

$$p = 5652 - 3.75f_5 - 21.55f_6 - 510.8f_a - 664.4f_b + v_{a3}\lambda_{a3} \tag{5-97}$$

The result is differentiated partially with respect to λ_{a3}, holding the other weights constant but allowing the four slack variables to change. Rearranging this we obtain

$$v_{a3} = p_{a3} + 3.75\frac{\partial f_5}{\partial \lambda_{a3}} + 21.55\frac{\partial f_6}{\partial \lambda_{a3}} + 510.8\frac{\partial f_a}{\partial \lambda_{a3}} + 664.4\frac{\partial f_b}{\partial \lambda_{a3}} \tag{5-98}$$

To evaluate $\partial f_5/\partial\lambda_{a3}$ we write Eq. (5–73) in terms of the weight factors and the still unknown variables x_{1a3} and x_{2a3} of plan A3. Since

$$x_{2a} = 500\lambda_{a1} + x_{2a3}\lambda_{a3}$$

we have

$$500\lambda_{a1} + x_{2a3}\lambda_{a3} + 500\lambda_{b1} + f_5 = 160$$

whence

$$\frac{\partial f_5}{\partial\lambda_{a3}} = -x_{2a3} \tag{5-99}$$

Similarly, Eq. (5–74) may be written

$$400\lambda_{a1} + 32\lambda_{a2} + (0.40x_{1a3} + 0.80x_{2a3})\lambda_{a3} + 300\lambda_{b1} + 36\lambda_{b2} + f_6 = 180$$

This gives

$$\frac{\partial f_6}{\partial\lambda_{a3}} = -0.40x_{1a3} - 0.80x_{2a3} \tag{5-100}$$

The definition of the weights requires that

$$\lambda_{a1} + \lambda_{a2} + \lambda_{a3} + f_a = 1$$

from which it follows that

$$\frac{\partial f_a}{\partial\lambda_{a3}} = -1 \tag{5-101}$$

Since f_b is the slack variable for the plant B weights only, it must be true that

$$\frac{\partial f_b}{\partial\lambda_{a3}} = 0 \tag{5-102}$$

The remaining variable p_{a3}, the profit associated with plan A3, is given by

$$p_{a3} = 15x_{1a3} + 22x_{2a3} \tag{5-103}$$

Equations (5–98)–(5–103) give

$$v_{a3} = 6.38x_{1a3} + x_{2a3} - 510.8 \tag{5-104}$$

If manager A can find a plan which makes this expression positive, then the plan will be effective in increasing the system profit. He cannot affect the constant -510.8, but he is able to maximize the pseudo profit

$$p'_{a3} \equiv 6.38x_{1a3} + x_{2a3} \tag{5-105}$$

subject to the plant A constraints. To do this he simply solves a linear programming problem as before, treating the factors 6.38 and 1 as profit decision derivatives. Notice that the availability of plans A1, A2, B1, and B2 has lowered the effective profit on material 1 from \$15 to \$6.38 per ton. On the other hand, the effective profit for the shared raw material 2, which went from its original value of \$22 per ton down to zero after solution A1 was available, is now back up to \$1.00. The coordinating group communicates this information to manager A by asking him if he can find a solution that would make at least \$510.80 a month if his profit were lowered \$8.62 per ton of material 1 and \$21.00 per ton of material 2. Manager A solves the corresponding linear programming problem and reports that if $x_{1a3} = 80$ and $x_{2a3} = 260$, he can make $770.80 a month in spite of the penalties. Thus solution A3, for which the actual profit p_{a3} is $6920 per month, is submitted to the coordinating committee as capable of improving the company-wide profit. It is perhaps interesting that this solution is the first to use all of material 1 and to satisfy the demand for by-product from plant A.

5-22 A General Equation

Until now we have used direct analysis to obtain the penalties to be imposed on the raw materials. We shall now show how to obtain a simple formula for the penalties. Let the decision derivatives of the slack variables f_k generated by the coordinating linear program be denoted by v_k so that, taking into account a potential new solution B3, we would have from the bottom row of the optimal tableau:

$$p = p_0 + \sum_k v_k f_k + v_a f_a + v_b f_b + v_{b3} \lambda_{b3} \tag{5-106}$$

where p_0 is the numerical value of the profit when all the f_j are zero. Equations (5-84) and (5-97) are special cases of this equation written for other solutions. Let the equations for the shared constraints be written

$$\sum_j a_{kj} x_j + f_k = b_k \tag{5-107: k}$$

Using the methods of analysis already described in the numerical cases, one can show that

$$v_{b3} = \sum_j \left(p_j - \sum_k v_k a_{kj} \right) x_{jb3} - v_b \tag{5-108}$$

For abbreviation, let the penalty $\hat{p}_j$ to be assessed against material j in solution B3 be defined by

$$\hat{p}_j = \sum_k v_k a_{kj} \tag{5-109: j}$$

Then

$$v_{b3} = \sum_j (p_j - \hat{p}_j) x_{jb3} - v_b \tag{5-110}$$

In this case the penalties to be transmitted to manager B are

$$\hat{p}_{2b} = 3.75(1) + 21.55(0.6) = 16.68$$

and

$$\hat{p}_{3b} = 3.75(0) + 21.55(0.2) = 4.31$$

Thus manager B will try to find a plan whose penalized profit, calculated from

$$p'_{b3} = 1.32 x_{2b3} + 3.69 x_{3b3}$$

must exceed $v_b (= \$664.40/\text{month})$ to be worth considering by the coordinators. Solving the proper linear program, he generates solution B3, with $x_{2b3} = 140$, $x_{3b3} = 180$, and a penalized profit of $795.00 per month which qualifies it as potentially profitable. Its true profit is $p_{a3} = 140(18) + 180(8)$

= \$3960. This solution uses all of material 3 and satisfies the local demand for by-product.

5-23 Optimal Master Plan

The reader may easily verify that the new coordinating constraints, using all six local solutions, are

$$500\lambda_{a1} \qquad + 260\lambda_{a3} + 500\lambda_{b1} \qquad + 140\lambda_{b3} + f_5 = 160$$
$$400\lambda_{a1} + 32\lambda_{a2} + 240\lambda_{a3} + 300\lambda_{b1} + 36\lambda_{b2} + 120\lambda_{b3} + f_6 = 180$$
$$\lambda_{a1} + \lambda_{a2} + \lambda_{a3} \qquad\qquad\qquad + f_a = 1$$
$$\lambda_{b1} + \lambda_{b2} + \lambda_{b3} + f_b = 1$$

The coordinating group is to find weights satisfying these equations and maximizing the total profit

$$p = 11{,}000\lambda_{a1} + 1200\lambda_{a2} + 6920\lambda_{a3} + 9000\lambda_{b1} + 1440\lambda_{b2} + 3960\lambda_{b3}$$

The solution is $\lambda_{a1} = 0$, $\lambda_{a2} = 0.693$, $\lambda_{a3} = 0.307$, $\lambda_{b1} = 0$, $\lambda_{b2} = 0.427$ and $\lambda_{b3} = 0.573$. This gives a total profit of \$5840 per month, an increase of about 4 per cent over the previous case.

5-24 Termination

We shall see that this allocation is optimal and that we need no longer search for new local solutions. To find this out, we generate penalties as before to guide the local managers in selecting production plans. Given the coefficients $v_5 = 6.22$, $v_6 = 19.6$, $v_a = 572$, and $v_b = 733$, obtained from the coordinating linear program, the reader may use Eq. (5–109) to verify that the penalties in this case are $\hat{p}_{1a} = 7.85$, $\hat{p}_{2a} = 22.00$, $\hat{p}_{2b} = 18.00$, and $\hat{p}_{3b} = 4.07$.

Manager A then tries to generate a solution that will give a penalized profit of more than \$ 572 a month with only a unit profit of \$7.15 allowed on raw material 1 and no profit at all permitted on material 2. He finds he cannot do this, the "new" proposal turning out to be identical to solution A2 already under consideration. With the present penalties, this proposal will bring in only \$572 per month, exactly the threshold specified. Thus, no better solution from plant A is available. It turns out that plant B cannot improve things either, so the coordinator is able to conclude that the allocation problem is at last solved.

The six local plans and the final coordinated plan are shown in Table 5–4. All the restrictions are satisfied except the demands for by-products. It is interesting that the scarce raw material 2 is divided almost equally between the two plants, for if only locally optimal plans were considered,

TABLE 5–4

OPTIMAL ALLOCATION

Proposal	Solution			Solution		
	A1	A2	A3	B1	B2	B3
Consumed:						
1	0	80	80	...	...	...
2	500	0	260	500	0	140
3	...	...	...	0	180	180
Produced:						
Main	400	32	240	300	36	120
By-product	100	48	100	200	144	200
Profit	11,000	1200	6920	9000	1440	3960
Weight	0	0.693	0.307	0	0.427	0.573

Allocation	Plant A Total				Plant B Total				Grand Total
Consumed:									
1	0	55.4	24.6	80	...	...	...	...	80
2	0	0	79.8	79.8	0	0	80.2	80.2	160
3	...	...	...	...	0	76.9	103.1	180	180
Produced:									
Main	0	22.2	73.7	95.9	0	15.4	68.8	84.2	180
By-product	0	33.3	30.7	64.0	0	61.5	114.6	176.1	...
Profit	0	832	2124	2956	0	615	2269	2884	5840

plant A would get it all. Notice also that neither of the locally optimal plans is used; both plans require too much of the scarce material and do not permit any money to be made processing local materials. It may seem strange that plant A actually makes $564 a month *less* with this optimal allocation than it would by operating with its locally optimal plan. This sacrifice is advantageous because it permits plant B to bring in $2884 a month more. Plant B is in fact almost as profitable as plant A in the optimum company-wide plan. Recall that when locally optimal plans were considered alone it did not appear economical to run plant B at all.

Here at least there are no problems of unemployment caused by technological change and corporate merger. The decomposition principle, with its rational rewards and penalties, has shown each manager how to run his plant for the maximum profit of the entire company. Other methods for optimizing interacting systems are developed in Chapters 8 and 9.

5-25 Transportation Problems

An important special case of linear programming is called the *transportation* or *distribution* problem. Such problems are important both because they occur often in practice, and because they can be solved by algorithms which are more efficient for this class of problem than is the simplex method. Many different situations may produce a model having this simple structure, but in general these problems concern the distribution of limited resources to satisfy known demands so as to optimize the distribution cost or profit. The distribution may, for example, involve assignment of facilities to operations, or it may require physical transportation of a homogeneous product from given sources to known destinations. For clarity in the following mathematical presentation, we use the latter concept, although the derivation is general and applies to all distribution problems.

In linear programming terms, let the amount of product available at origin m be given by a_m, the amount required at destination n by b_n, and the cost of shipping one unit from m to n by $c_{(m-1)N+n}$, where $m = 1, \ldots, M$, and $n = 1, \ldots, N$. Hence we wish to determine the amounts $x_{(m-1)N+n}$ to be shipped from each origin m to each destination n so as to minimize the total cost of transportation, while satisfying constraints on availabilities at the origins and requirements at the destinations.

Setting $k \equiv (m-1)N + n$, the problem is to minimize

$$y = \sum_{k=1}^{MN} c_k x_k \qquad (5\text{-}111)$$

subject to the constraints on availabilities at the M origins:

$$\sum_{k=(m-1)N+1}^{mN} x_k = a_m; \qquad m = 1, \ldots, M \qquad (5\text{-}112)$$

and the demands at the N destinations:

$$\sum_{j=0}^{M-1} x_{n+jN} = b_n; \qquad n = 1, \ldots, N \qquad (5\text{-}113)$$

as well as the nonnegativity conditions:

$$x_k \geq 0; \qquad k = 1, \ldots, MN \qquad (5\text{-}114)$$

which state that shipments may not be made from a destination to an origin. From Eqs. (5-111)–(5-114), it can be seen that the transportation problem is a special case of the general linear programming problem defined at the beginning of this chapter. Here, all the a_{mn} are either 0 or 1; furthermore, these constraint coefficients appear in the particular pattern shown in the simplex tableau of Fig. 5–22. Notice the echeloned structure of the first M equations, associated with the origin availabilities, and the diagonal structure of the last N equations, associated with the destination requirements. Each variable appears in exactly two equations (rows), and we would need to add M artificial variables to obtain a first basic feasible solution if this problem were solved by the simplex method. A transportation problem having M

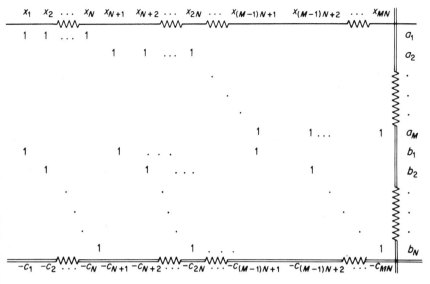

Figure 5-22. Simplex tableau for a transportation problem.

origins and N destinations then requires a *simplex* tableau with $M + N$ rows and $(M + 1)(N + 1)$ columns (including the column for the a_m and b_n constants). Owing to the special structure of this problem, we may modify the simplex method in such a way that we need work with only an M by N table.

5-26 Finding a First Feasible Solution

Each variable appears in exactly one of the first M equations, and also in exactly one of the last N equations, so by summing these two sets of equations, we obtain:

$$\sum_{k=1}^{MN} x_k = \sum_{m=1}^{M} a_m = \sum_{n=1}^{N} b_n \equiv T \qquad (5\text{-}115)$$

Since the sum of the first M rows is equal to the sum of the last N rows, the $M + N$ equations are not linearly independent. In fact, we can demonstrate that any $M + N - 1$ rows are linearly independent and that therefore we need work with only $M + N - 1$ state variables. First, we delete the $M + N$th (last) row, and choose $x_1, x_2, \ldots, x_N, x_{2N}, x_{3N}, \ldots, x_{MN}$, as the state variables, setting the remaining variables to zero. Rearranging these first $M + N - 1$ equations, we may write them in terms of the state variables as:

$$x_N + \qquad\qquad + x_1 + x_2 + \cdots + x_{N-1} = a_1$$
$$x_{2N} \qquad\qquad\qquad = a_2$$
$$x_{3N} \qquad\qquad\qquad = a_3$$
$$\cdot$$
$$\cdot \qquad\qquad \cdot$$
$$\cdot \qquad\qquad\qquad \cdot$$
$$x_{MN} \qquad\qquad = a_M$$
$$x_1 \qquad\qquad = b_1 \qquad (5\text{-}116)$$
$$x_2 \qquad\qquad = b_2$$
$$\cdot \qquad\qquad \cdot$$
$$\cdot \qquad\qquad \cdot$$
$$x_{N-1} = b_{N-1}$$

If each of the last $N - 1$ equations ($x_n = b_n$; $n = 1, \ldots, N - 1$) is now subtracted from the first equation, each state variable will appear in one and only one equation, showing that the $M + N - 1$ equations are linearly independent. Considering that any one of the $M + N$ equations may be written as a linear combination of the remaining $M + N - 1$ equations, it is clear that we have lost no generality in selecting the last equation as the one to be deleted; any other equation could just as well have been selected. Thus we have shown that a basic feasible solution to the constraints (5–112) and (5–113) will contain exactly $M + N - 1$ state variables. Now we shall show that a feasible solution to these constraints can always be found; in fact, an obvious solution may be obtained simply by setting

$$x_{(m-1)N+n} = \frac{a_m b_n}{T}; \qquad m = 1, \ldots, M; \qquad n = 1, \ldots, N \qquad (5\text{-}117)$$

This solution, although feasible, makes each of the MN variables positive; to obtain no more than $M + N - 1$ positive variables, one may use the *northwest corner* rule (Charnes and Cooper, 1954): set $x_1 = \min(a_1, b_1)$; if $a_1 > b_1$, set $x_2 = \min(a_1 - b_1, b_2)$; if $a_1 < b_1$, set $x_{n+1} = \min(b_1 - a_1, a_2)$, etc. In other words, at each step, either an origin or a destination constraint is satisfied, until at the last step, the value of x_{MN} satisfies simultaneously the Mth origin and the Nth destination constraint. So long as none of the other variables selected satisfies both an origin and a destination constraint simultaneously, we will have chosen exactly $M + N - 1$ positive variables; otherwise, we will have less than $M + N - 1$ positive variables.

Hence we can find a basic feasible solution from among the original variables. It will always be possible then to drive the artificial variables to zero; in fact, we shall find that the artificial variables need never be introduced at all.

From the manner in which we solved Eqs. (5–116) for the state variables, it is clear that all the α_{mn} in Eq. (3–101) are either 0, $+1$, or -1. Furthermore, from Eq. (5–7), α_{pr} must be $+1$, so that the decision variable d_r entering the state set will have a positive value, and thus, the ratio α_{ir}/α_{pr} in the "simplex" equation (3–119) will also be 0, $+1$, or -1. Therefore, in transportation problems, it is not necessary to perform the division (simplex) operations of Eq. (3–119), since the value of any state variable can be found by adding and subtracting the values of some subset of the decision variables. If some decision variable, say d_r, is found in terms of the state variables (holding all other decision variables at zero), then in the resulting expression the coefficients of the state variables will also be 0, $+1$, or -1, a fact of considerable importance in the special tableau for solving transportation problems.

We find it convenient to rewrite Eqs. (5–111)–(5–114), using a *double subscript* notation on both the variables and the objective coefficients. Let

$$c_{mn} \equiv c_{(m-1)N+n}, \quad \text{and} \quad x_{mn} \equiv x_{(m-1)N+n}, \quad \text{for all } m \text{ and } n$$

With this notation change, the transportation problem now appears as

Minimize
$$y = \sum_{m=1}^{M} \sum_{n=1}^{N} c_{mn} x_{mn} \tag{5-118}$$

subject to

$$\sum_{n=1}^{N} x_{mn} = a_m; \quad m = 1, \ldots, M \tag{5-119}$$

$$\sum_{m=1}^{M} x_{mn} = b_n; \quad n = 1, \ldots, N \tag{5-120}$$

and
$$x_{mn} \geq 0; \quad m = 1, \ldots, M; \quad n = 1, \ldots, N \tag{5-121}$$

Double subscripts are natural in the formulation of a transportation problem; c_{mn} and x_{mn} are respectively the unit shipping cost and amount shipped from origin m to destination n. Transportation problems are usually solved using the special tableau format shown in Fig. 5–23. Since the decision variables in a linear programming problem are always zero, their values (x_{mn}) would not actually be entered in this form of tableau when working a problem, but would be left blank. Thus, any zeros appearing in the x_{mn} portion of a cell would be those belonging to state variables in a degenerate basis.

From the appearance of the transportation tableau of Fig. 5–23, it is clear why the name "northwest corner rule" is appropriate to the rule previously described for finding a first feasible solution containing no more than $M + N - 1$ positive variables. (Allocations are begun in the northwest (upper left) corner of the tableau, and continued in a path moving south and east.) Modifying this rule to select exactly $M + N - 1$ variables, we may use these as the state variables, even though some of them may occasionally have a zero value. Since all of the α_{ij} are either 0, $+1$, or -1, a great deal of work can be saved by not eliminating each state variable from all but one constraint equation, as required in the simplex method. Thus, in the trans-

Destinations

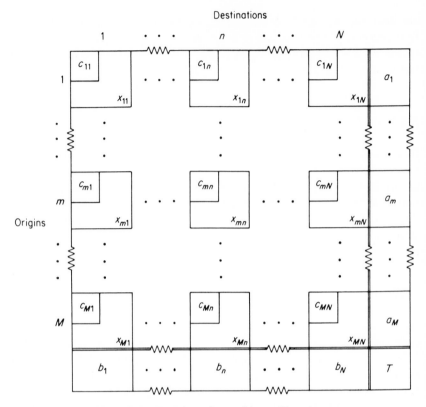

Figure 5-23. Transportation problem tableau format.

portation problem, each constraint equation will contain one *or more* state variables. To handle the problem of degeneracy, the northwest corner rule is modified as follows: When a row (origin) and a column (destination) constraint are both satisfied by the assignment of a value to some variable, increase the requirement for the row by a small amount ϵ, and continue with the northwest corner rule. In general, this means that we perturb the values of the original constants a_m and b_n to produce new constants a'_m and b'_n defined by

$$a'_m = a_m + \epsilon; \qquad m = 1, \ldots, M$$

$$b'_n = b_n; \qquad n = 1, \ldots, N - 1 \qquad (5\text{-}122)$$

$$b'_N = b_N + M\epsilon$$

Notice that these new constants still satisfy Eq. (5–115):

$$\sum_{m=1}^{M} \sum_{n=1}^{N} x_{mn} = \sum_{m=1}^{M} a'_m = \sum_{n=1}^{N} b'_n \equiv T' = T + M\epsilon \qquad (5\text{-}123)$$

Upon completion of the steps of the rule, ϵ is set to zero to provide a degenerate basic feasible solution containing exactly $M + N - 1$ state variables. In practice, of course, it is not actually necessary to introduce the ϵ's, since it is clear where zeros must be added in order to carry out the steps of the modification.

5-27 Evaluating a Solution

By the northwest corner rule, there must be at least one state variable in each equation. Thus, when it is necessary to express some decision variable x_{mn} in terms of the state variables, there will be some state variable x_{ms} in this same (mth) row, and from the pattern produced by the northwest corner rule, there must also then be at least one state variable, x_{ps}, in the column s constraint equation. In fact, it can be shown that any decision variable x_{mn} may be expressed uniquely in terms of the state variables as

$$x_{mn} = x_{ms} - x_{ps} + x_{pt} - \cdots - x_{wr} + x_{wn} \qquad (5\text{-}124)$$

Equation (5–124) shows that the expression of a decision variable in terms of the state variables always contains an odd number of state variables, and also that the plus and minus coefficients of the state variables alternate, beginning and ending with a plus sign. In the transportation tableau of Fig. 5–23, Eq. (5–124) corresponds to the formation of a *path* which begins and ends at the cell containing the decision variable x_{mn}. All other cells in the path are occupied by state variables which form the expression in Eq. (5–124).

This path must be traced out by alternating horizontal and vertical moves, which change direction at the cells containing state variables ("stepping stones") and must also be such that any two adjacent cells in the path lie in the same row or same column. Each horizontal move must be followed by a vertical move, and vice versa; thus no three adjacent cells in the path will lie in the same row or same column. Also, since the representation of a decision variable in terms of the state variables is unique, the required path is also unique. Note that if one could trace out a path of the type just described which, however, contained only state cells (beginning and ending with a state cell), then this would express one of the state variables in terms of some of the others, indicating that the state variables were not linearly independent. Hence, such a "loop" among the state variables should never be possible.

The illustrative problem shown in Fig. 5–24(a) will clarify the foregoing discussion. Here, $c_{11} = 1, c_{12} = 4, c_{13} = 6, c_{21} = 0, c_{22} = 2, c_{23} = 5, c_{31} = 2, c_{32} = 7, c_{33} = 5, a_1 = 5, a_2 = 4, a_3 = 6, b_1 = 3, b_2 = 5, b_3 = 7,$ and $T = 15$. Beginning in the northwest corner (cell (1,1)), we set $x_{11} = \min(a_1, b_1) = \min(5,3) = 3$, which satisfies the first column constraint; then, $x_{12} = \min(a_1 - b_1, b_2) = \min(2,5) = 2$, etc., producing the first feasible solution of Fig. 5–24(b). The evaluation path for cell (3,1) is also shown in this figure, and it

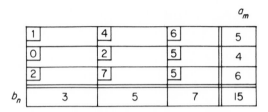

(a) Tableau containing problem statement

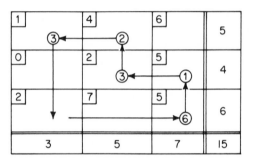

(b) Results of northwest corner rule, showing
evaluation path for cell (3,1)

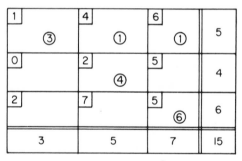

(c) Optimal tableau; $y^* = 51$

Figure 5-24. Tableaux for first transportation problem.

happens to contain all the state cells. This is not usually the case, of course, and in fact all the other decision cells in this tableau can be written in terms of exactly three of the state variables.

If now x_{31} is increased (from zero) by an amount k, then we see that x_{33} must be *decreased* by k in order that the sum of the variables in the third row will remain equal to a_3 (=6). Decreasing x_{33} then requires that x_{23} be increased by k so that the sum of the elements in column 3 will still add up to 7; this is turn requires that x_{22} be decreased by k, etc. Now it can be seen that this evaluation path, or closed loop, will always be such as to leave the row and column totals unchanged; a feasible solution will be maintained at all times. The evaluation of cell (3,1) is obtained by calculating the effect of increasing x_{31} by the amount k. Tracing through the path shows that the total cost would change by $2k - 5k + 5k - 2k + 4k - k = 3k$, or a unit *increase* in y of 3; clearly, it does not pay to increase x_{31}. From this analysis (and from the analogy with the similar process used in the simplex method), it can be seen that the evaluation of a decision cell is given by a number which is the *decision derivative* for that cell. Proceeding with the evaluation of the other decision cells, the decision derivatives for cells (1,3), (2,1), and (3,2), are found to be -1, $+1$, and $+5$, respectively.

For this state set, then, x_{13} is the only decision variable for which an increase will be advantageous. Increasing this variable decreases both x_{12} and x_{23}, and increases x_{22}; hence the largest allowable increase in x_{13} is 1, as this drives the state variable x_{23} to zero. Figure 5–24(c) shows the results of this change in the state set (which takes the place of the simplexing operations of linear programming); x_{23} is now a decision variable, and therefore cell (2,3) is left blank. The reader may verify that this is the optimal solution, since an increase in the value of any decision variable will increase the total cost y. Notice that in this optimal solution, no shipment is made from origin 2 to destination 1, even though zero cost would be incurred for such a shipment. In this simple problem, one can see that any shipments made through cell (2,1) will decrease the shipments through cells (1,1) and (2,2) while increasing the amount shipped through cell (1,2), causing a net increase in the total cost. In larger problems, the analysis is far more complex, and consequently less intuitive.

If an increase in the value of a decision variable drives more than one state variable to zero, it is important that only one of these variables be dropped from the state set, so that at all times we will retain a total of $M + N - 1$ state variables. We may choose arbitrarily which of the zero-valued variables to drop from the state set, keeping the others as part of a degenerate basic feasible solution. Thus, if in Fig. 5–24(b), both x_{12} and x_{23} had been equal to 2, the decision variable x_{13} would have been increased to 2, and we would have retained either x_{12} or x_{23} in the state set at a zero level, and made the other a decision variable (left its cell blank).

5-28 A Simplified Method for Evaluating
Decision Derivatives

The process just described for evaluating the decision cells can become tedious in even moderate-sized transportation problems. We now present a simplified method (Dantzig, 1951) for making these evaluations. By writing the Lagrangian function for the transportation problem, designating as u_m the Lagrange multiplier for the mth row constraint, and as v_n the Lagrange multiplier for the nth column constraint, and taking partial derivatives, we obtain as necessary conditions for an optimal solution:

$$x_{mn}(c_{mn} - u_m - v_n) = 0; \qquad m = 1, \ldots, M; \qquad n = 1, \ldots, N \quad (5\text{-}125)$$

$$c_{mn} - u_m - v_n \geq 0; \qquad m = 1, \ldots, M; \qquad n = 1, \ldots, N \quad (5\text{-}126)$$

Notice that the u_m and v_n are *not* required to be nonnegative, and that this relaxation of the nonnegativity restriction is due to the absence of slack variables in the constraints (5-119) and (5-120); all constraints in the transportation problem are equations rather than inequalities.

Equation (5-125) states that if any x_{pq} is positive, then $c_{pq} - u_p - v_q = 0$. Thus, for all state variables, a necessary condition for optimality is:

$$u_p + v_q = c_{pq}; \qquad \text{where } x_{pq} \text{ is a state variable} \quad (5\text{-}127)$$

From Eq. (5-124), the unit change in the objective function as a consequence of increasing a decision variable x_{mn} is given by

$$\frac{\delta y}{\delta x_{mn}} = c_{mn} - c_{ms} + c_{ps} - c_{pt} + \cdots + c_{wr} - c_{wn} \quad (5\text{-}128)$$

which, by Eq. (5-127), becomes

$$\frac{\delta y}{\delta x_{mn}} = c_{mn} - (u_m + v_s) + (u_p + v_s) - (u_p + v_t) + \cdots + (u_w + v_r) - (u_w + v_n)$$

$$= c_{mn} - u_m - v_n \quad (5\text{-}129)$$

since each of the "stepping stones" in the path is in a state cell. Comparison of Eqs. (5-128) and (5-129) with Eq. (5-15) shows that the number $c_{mn} - u_m - v_n$ is the *decision derivative* associated with cell (m, n). (Recall that all nonzero α_{mn} are ± 1 in the transportation problem.)

Equation (5-126) thus provides a simple means for checking the optimality of a solution; simply compute the sum $u_m + v_n$ for each decision cell, and if this sum exceeds the unit cost c_{mn} of that cell, then the total cost y can be decreased by increasing x_{mn}. Therefore, at each iteration, we need find only the closed loop path for the one decision variable which is to be increased. The numbers u_m and v_n, of course, are found from Eq. (5-127). Since there will be a total of $M + N$ such numbers, and each basic solution will contain exactly $M + N - 1$ state variables, Eqs. (5-127) will always consist of $M + N - 1$ equations in $M + N$ unknowns. Hence, these equations have one degree of freedom, and any one of the u_p or v_q may be chosen arbitrarily.

For example, in the problem of Fig. 5-24(b), we might choose $u_1 = 0$; because cells (1,1) and (1,2) are state cells, v_1 and v_2 must then be 1 and 4, respectively. Cell (2,2) is also a state cell, and since $v_2 = 4$, we must set $u_2 = -2$; this in turn forces $v_3 = 7$, as (1,3) is a state cell, and finally, $u_3 = -2$, so that $u_3 + v_3 = c_{33} \equiv 5$. The results of these calculations are shown in Fig. 5-25(a).

Using these numbers, we may now evaluate each decision cell without needing to trace out the entire closed loop path for the cell. For example, the decision derivative for cell (3,1) is $c_{31} - (u_3 + v_1) = 2 - (-2 + 1)$

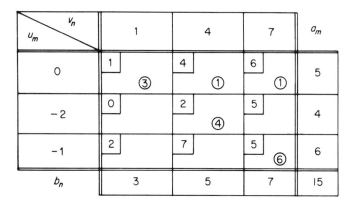

(a) First feasible solution as given by northwest corner rule

(b) Optimal solution

Figure 5-25. Evaluation of independent cells using u_m and v_n numbers.

= 3, and the decision derivative for cell (1,3) is $6 - (0 + 7) = -1$. Since among all the blank cells, only (1,3) has a negative decision derivative, x_{13} is the only decision variable which can be increased to improve the solution. The procedure for bringing this variable into the state set is exactly the same as that described previously, and it produces the tableau of Fig. 5–25(b). With this change in the state set, we must recalculate at least some of the u_m and v_n numbers; here it was necessary to change only u_3 and v_3. From Fig. 5–25(b), we see that all decision derivatives are positive, indicating that the optimal solution has been reached.

The decision derivatives in a transportation problem may, of course, be used to perform sensitivity analyses just as in the more general linear programming problem. For example, the reader may easily verify that the solution given in Fig. 5–24(c) will remain optimal so long as c_{32} is no less than 3, or c_{13} is any nonnegative number, etc. Again, if some unit cost is changed by an amount large enough to render the solution nonoptimal, then the new optimal solution can be obtained from the final tableau without re-solving the problem. As an illustration, suppose that c_{23} were changed from 5 to 3 in this problem, causing the decision derivative for cell (2,3) to become negative. Beginning with the tableau of Fig. 5–24(c), this cell is brought into the state set, and a new optimal solution obtained: $x_{11}^* = 3$, $x_{12}^* = 2$, $x_{22}^* = 3$, $x_{23}^* = 1$, $x_{33}^* = 6$, and $y^* = 50$.

5-29 Vogel's Method

We now describe what would seem to be a more effective method for obtaining a first feasible solution than is the northwest corner rule, since it takes the unit cell costs into consideration. We shall refer to this method as *Vogel's method* (Reinfeld and Vogel). In practice, the method has often been more successful in determining an initial solution that requires fewer iterations to reach the optimum than do other methods. It is not possible, however, to prove any general theorem to this effect as problems can be devised (by placing the smallest c_{mn} numbers along the main diagonal of the transportation tableau) for which the northwest corner rule yields the best beginning solution.

We shall use the problem described by the tableau of Fig. 5–26(a) to illustrate Vogel's method as well as some computational simplifications which can result from making scale changes in the problem parameters. For example, if in Eq. (5–118) we replace each c_{mn} with $c'_{mn} \equiv kc_{mn} + K$, there results the modified objective function:

$$y' = \sum_{m=1}^{M} \sum_{n=1}^{N} (kc_{mn} + K)x_{mn} = ky + KT \qquad (5\text{-}130)$$

where y is the original objective function, k and K are arbitrary constants, and T is the sum of the x_{mn} as defined by Eq. (5–115). Clearly, minimizing y' is equivalent to minimizing y so long as k is a positive number (K may be any real number). In addition, both sides of the constraint equations (5–119) and (5–120) may be multiplied by the same positive constant $\Re$ with the only effect being that of multiplying the optimal solution $\{x_{mn}^*\}$ by $\Re$. Hence, we may make use of these scale effects to simplify the calculations required to solve transportation problems by hand. For this illustrative problem, let us choose $k = 10$, $K = -5$, and $\Re = \frac{1}{6}$, to produce the modified problem shown in Fig. 5–26(b).

To obtain a first feasible solution by Vogel's method, we proceed as follows: For each row, compute the absolute value of the difference between the lowest unit cell cost and the next lowest unit cell cost in the row, and write this number to the left of the row. For example, in Fig. 5–26(b), this difference

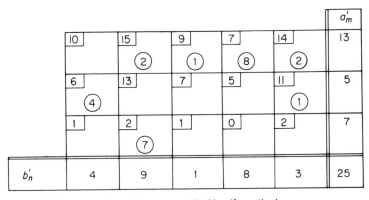

	a_m
	78
	30
	48
b_n	150

Values in row 1: 1.5, 2.0, 1.4, 1.2, 1.9 — a_m = 78
Row 2: 1.1, 1.8, 1.2, 1.0, 1.6 — a_m = 30
Row 3: 0.6, 0.7, 0.6, 0.5, 0.7 — a_m = 48
b_n: 24, 54, 6, 48, 18 — 150

(a) Original transportation tableau

Modified problem (b):
Column Vogel numbers: 5, 11, 6, 5, 9
Row Vogel numbers: 2, 1, 1

10	15	9	7	14	13
6	13	7	5	11	5
1	2	1	0	2	7
b'_n 4	9	1	8	3	25

a'_m: 13, 5, 7 — 25

(b) Modified problem including first Vogel numbers

First feasible solution (c):
a'_m = 13, 5, 7; total 25

Row 1: 10, 15 (2), 9 (1), 7 (8), 14 (2) — 13
Row 2: 6 (4), 13, 7, 5, 11 (1) — 5
Row 3: 1, 2 (7), 1, 0, 2 — 7
b'_n: 4, 9, 1, 8, 3 — 25

(c) First feasible solution as given by Vogel's method

Figure 5-26. Scale effects and Vogel's method.

for the first row is $9 - 7 = 2$. Repeat this procedure for the columns, writing the differences just above the corresponding columns, thus obtaining a total of $M + N$ nonnegative Vogel numbers for all the rows and columns, as shown in Fig. 5–26(b).

Put as much allocation as possible through the cell having the *smallest* unit cost in the row or column which has the *largest* Vogel number. This allocation will then satisfy either a row or a column constraint (not necessarily the row or column corresponding to the largest Vogel number). In the present problem, this process selects column *two*, and we would allocate 7 units to cell (3,2), since it has the lowest c_{mn} cost in that column, and min $(a_3, b_2) = 7$. None of the remaining cells in row three can be included in this first feasible solution, so these cells should be marked in some way as to exclude them from further consideration in carrying out the remaining steps in the method. This means that at each step, either a row or a column is eliminated from the computational procedure, and new Vogel numbers are computed. The process is repeated until all constraints are satisfied. The Vogel numbers may be looked upon as penalty costs which would be incurred if an allocation were not made to the cell having the lowest unit cost in a particular row or column. By analogy with the argument advanced for the northwest corner rule, this process of adding state cells one at a time will produce (in the absence of degeneracy) a total of exactly $M + N - 1$ such cells. As stated earlier, degeneracy occurs only if the addition of a state cell satisfies simultaneously both a row and a column constraint. Under such circumstances, one again perturbs the row constraint, a_m, by an amount ϵ, and continues with Vogel's method. At the conclusion of this procedure, setting the ϵ's to zero will always yield an initial feasible solution containing exactly $M + N - 1$ cells (Eisemann).

Continuing with Vogel's method on the foregoing problem, we obtain the initial solution shown in Fig. 5–26(c), which also happens to be the optimal solution, as the reader may verify by computing the u_m, v_n, numbers. (It is important not to confuse these evaluation numbers with the Vogel numbers used to obtain a feasible solution.) The resulting total minimum cost for this derived problem is readily found to be $y' = 172$. Since the original objective function y is related to this modified function through the expression $y' = \Re(ky + KT)$, and the optimal solution $\{x_{mn}^*\}$ to the original problem is given in terms of the derived optimum by $\{x_{mn}^*\} \equiv \Re\{x_{mn}'^*\}$, we have at once

$$y^* = \frac{1}{10}\left[\frac{172}{1/6} - (-5)(150)\right] = 178.2; \qquad x_{12}^* = 12 \ \ x_{13}^* = 6, \ \ x_{14}^* = 48,$$

$$x_{15}^* = 12, \ \ x_{21}^* = 24, \ \ x_{25}^* = 6,$$
$$\text{and} \quad x_{32}^* = 42$$

In some transportation or distribution problems, it is desired to *maximize* the objective function (5–118) rather than to minimize it (that is, the c_{mn} then represent unit *profits*). For such problems, one may replace each c_{mn} with $c_{mn}' \equiv c_{rs} - c_{mn}$ where c_{rs} is the largest of the c_{mn}, and then employ the foregoing solution algorithm to minimize $\sum_{m=1}^{M} \sum_{n=1}^{N} c_{mn}' x_{mn}$. Alternatively, one may work with the original c_{mn} and merely reverse the direction of the inequality signs in Eq. (5–126) which prescribes the conditions for optimality. In this case, the Vogel numbers would be computed as the absolute value of the difference between the *largest* and the *next largest* c_{mn} in each row and column. Vogel's method would then consist of allocating as much as possible to the cell having the largest unit profit in the row or column with the largest Vogel number. This latter procedure is better for hand computation; the former may be simpler when a computer program for minimizing the objective function is available.

5-30 Inequality Constraints

The description of the transportation problem constraints as given by Eq. (5-119) and Eq. (5-120) may appear somewhat artificial in that the total shipping requirements are always exactly equal to the total amount available for shipment, as shown in Eq. (5-115). This is not generally the case in practical problems, as when, for example, more units are available at the origins than are required at the destinations. In such a case, Eq. (5-120) remains unchanged, but Eq. (5-119) becomes:

$$\sum_{n=1}^{N} x_{mn} \leq a_m; \qquad m = 1, \ldots, M \qquad (5\text{-}131)$$

In order to obtain equality constraints, and thus satisfy the requirements of the solution algorithm, one merely adds slack variables, $x_{m,\,N+1}$ to Eq. (5-131), much as in the simplex method. Equation (5-115) then becomes

$$\sum_{m=1}^{M} \sum_{n=1}^{N+1} x_{mn} = \sum_{m=1}^{M} a_m = \sum_{n=1}^{N+1} b_n = T \qquad (5\text{-}132)$$

from which follows the expected result

$$\sum_{m=1}^{M} x_{m,\,N+1} = \sum_{m=1}^{M} a_m - \sum_{n=1}^{N} b_n = b_{N+1} \qquad (5\text{-}133)$$

where b_{N+1} is the total of the slack variables (that is, the total available quantity that is *not* shipped). By adding an $N+1$st column to the M by N transportation tableau, the $a_1, \ldots, a_M, b_1, \ldots, b_{N+1}$ are once again the row and column totals required for the new tableau, and the standard solution algorithm may be used on this modified problem. The following numerical example will clarify these concepts.

Orders for 15, 20, and 10 automobile engines have come in from three assembly plants, A, B, and C, respectively. These orders are to be met from three factories, 1, 2, and 3, which have respective availabilities of 35, 30, and 10 engines. The shipping distances in miles from the various factories to each assembly plant are shown in Fig. 5-27(a). The cost for shipping each engine is 10 cents per mile, and it is desired to find which factories should supply which plants so as to minimize the total cost of shipping the 45 engines on order.

In this problem, 30 more engines are available than are required to be shipped, so a column must be added to the transportation tableau to represent a dummy destination to which no engines will be sent. Since no cost is associated with such fictitious shipments, the c_{mn} in the dummy column will all be zero, as shown in Fig. 5-27(b). Application of Vogel's method and the

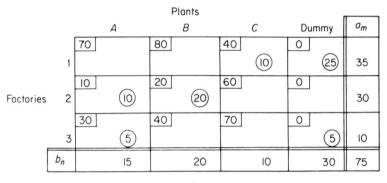

(a) Shipping distances from factories to assembly plants

(b) Optimal solution; $y^* = \$1,050$

Figure 5-27. Transportation problem illustrating inequality constraints.

stepping-stone algorithm to this modified tableau produces the optimal solution given by the circled numbers in Fig. 5–27(b), which shows that 25 of the 35 engines available at factory 1, and 5 of the 10 engines available at factory 3, will not be shipped.

An interesting situation has arisen in this problem; the decision derivative for cell (3,2) is *zero*. The reader will recall that this indicates the existence of an *alternate optimum*, for it means that the value of y^* would not change if the decision variable x_{32} were brought into the state set. Indeed, one can easily see that all optimal solutions to this problem may be written as $x_{21}^* = 10 + Z$, $x_{22}^* = 20 - Z$, $x_{31}^* = 5 - Z$, $x_{32}^* = Z$, $x_{13}^* = 10$, $x_{14}^* = 25$, and $x_{34}^* = 5$, where $Z = 0, 1, \ldots, 5$. As we stated earlier in this chapter, alternate optima are especially common in practical problems of high dimensionality.

Other inequalities in the constraints of a transportation problem are handled in an analogous manner. For example, if more units are demanded at the destinations than are available at the origins, a dummy *row* is added (to take care of shipments from a nonexistent source) which converts the constraints to equalities, as required by the solution algorithm. For a further discussion of inequalities in transportation problems, as well as a generalized version of this type of problem, see the thorough treatment by Hadley.

5-31 Dual Linear Problems

Duality relations arise in many mathematical systems, and these relations are subject to various interpretations, depending upon the particular context represented by the mathematical model. Here we are concerned with duality only as it relates to linear programming problems, although dual problems have also been devised for nonlinear programming problems (Wolfe, 1961; Dorn). Indeed, the fundamental ideas can be obtained directly from Legendre's dual transformation (Lanczos). Dennis presents an interesting discussion of duality in electrical networks; Sinden has described the relationship between duality in convex programming problems and geometric point-hyperplane duality.

We consider two linear programming problems:

(I) maximize
$$p = \sum_{n=1}^{N} c_n x_n \tag{5-134}$$

subject to

$$\sum_{n=1}^{N} a_{mn} x_n \leq b_m; \qquad m = 1, \ldots, M \tag{5-135}$$

$$x_n \geq 0; \qquad n = 1, \ldots, N \tag{5-136}$$

(II) minimize
$$y = \sum_{m=1}^{M} b_m z_m \tag{5-137}$$

subject to

$$\sum_{m=1}^{M} a_{mn} z_m \geq c_n; \qquad n = 1, \ldots, N \tag{5-138}$$

$$z_m \geq 0; \qquad m = 1, \ldots, M \tag{5-139}$$

where the c_n, b_m, and a_{mn} are given constants. Problems I and II are said to be *dual* linear programming problems; each is the dual of the other.

The nature of this duality may be derived by writing out the Lagrangian functions for problem I and II and computing the appropriate partial derivatives. Designating the Lagrange multipliers for Problem I as λ_m, we find the conditions for optimality in that problem to be

$$x_n \left(c_n - \sum_{m=1}^{M} \lambda_m a_{mn} \right) = 0; \qquad n = 1, \ldots, N \tag{5-140}$$

$$c_n - \sum_{m=1}^{M} \lambda_m a_{mn} \leq 0; \qquad n = 1, \ldots, N \tag{5-141}$$

$$f_m \lambda_m = 0; \qquad m = 1, \ldots, M \tag{5-142}$$

$$\lambda_m \geq 0; \qquad m = 1, \ldots, M \tag{5-143}$$

where the f_m are the slack variables for Eqs. (5–135). It can now be seen that Eqs. (5–141) and (5–143) are the constraint Eqs. (5–138) and (5–139) of *dual* Problem II, and that the Lagrange multipliers λ_m are the decision variables, z_m, of that problem. Equations (5-140) and (5-142) are complementary slackness conditions, and the former of these suggests that the decision variables x_n of *primal* Problem I are the Lagrange multipliers for the constraints of Problem II. It is left as an exercise to show that this is indeed the case, and that Eqs. (5-135) and (5-136) are optimality conditions for Problem II. This leads to the important result that the conditions for *feasibility* of the dual solution are also the conditions for *optimality* of the primal solution, and vice versa. Thus, for any linear programming problem, the (absolute) values of the dual variables are given by the *sensitivity coefficients* corresponding to the slack variables of the primal. (These values may be *opposite in sign*, depending upon the direction of the constraint inequalities and whether the objective function is to be minimized or maximized.)

Introducing the slack variables f_m and w_n into constraint Eqs. (5-135) and (5-138) respectively, and then multiplying the former through by z_m, and the latter through by x_n we may sum the resulting equations over m and n respectively, to obtain

$$\sum_{m=1}^{M} \sum_{n=1}^{N} a_{mn} x_n z_m + \sum_{m=1}^{M} f_m z_m = \sum_{m=1}^{M} b_m z_m \tag{5-144}$$

$$\sum_{n=1}^{N} \sum_{m=1}^{M} a_{mn} z_m x_n - \sum_{n=1}^{N} w_n x_n = \sum_{n=1}^{N} c_n x_n \tag{5-145}$$

If the double summation terms in these equations are equated, there results

$$\sum_{m=1}^{M} b_m z_m - \sum_{m=1}^{M} f_m z_m = \sum_{n=1}^{N} c_n x_n + \sum_{n=1}^{N} w_n x_n \tag{5-146}$$

We now observe that since $z_m \equiv -\delta p/\delta f_m$, the product $f_m z_m$, for $m = 1, \ldots, M$, must at all times be zero. To see this, note that if f_m is nonzero, it must necessarily be a state variable, and its sensitivity coefficient z_m will be zero, whereas, if z_m is nonzero, then f_m must be a decision variable, and hence have a value of zero. An analogous argument shows that the products $w_n x_n$ must likewise be zero, since $x_n \equiv \delta y/\delta w_n$. Accordingly, we have shown that at all times

$$\sum_{n=1}^{N} c_n x_n = \sum_{m=1}^{M} b_m z_m \tag{5-147}$$

Corresponding to an optimal-feasible solution to either Problem I or II, all the x_n and z_m in Eq. (5-147) will be nonnegative. A solution which is feasible but not optimal for Problem I will have dual variables z_m which provide an optimal but not feasible (since some of them will be negative) solution to Problem II, and vice versa. When a linear programming problem is solved using the simplex method, the final tableau contains the optimal (and feasible) solutions to both the primal and the dual problem.

The following statements (Hadley, pp. 221–66) concerning dual linear problems are of particular importance.

1. The primal problem has a finite optimal-feasible solution if and only

if the dual has a finite optimal-feasible solution, and in such a case, the optimal values are equal.

2. When one problem has no feasible solution, then the other either has no feasible solution, or has an unbounded optimal-feasible solution.

3. If one problem has an unbounded optimal-feasible solution, then the other has no feasible solution.

As an illustration of dual linear problems, consider the following:

maximize $p = 35x_1 + 60x_2 + 30x_3$

subject to

$$3x_1 + 5x_2 + 2x_3 \leq 50$$

$$2x_1 + 6x_2 + 3x_3 \leq 40$$

$$x_1, x_2, x_3 \geq 0$$

The dual to the preceding problem is then:

minimize $y = 50z_1 + 40z_2$

subject to

$$3z_1 + 2z_2 \geq 35$$

$$5z_1 + 6z_2 \geq 60$$

$$2z_1 + 3z_2 \geq 30$$

$$z_1, z_2 \geq 0$$

The optimal simplex tableaux for these problems are given in Fig. 5-28, and one can see that the complete solution to both problems can be obtained from either tableau.

x_1	x_2	x_3	f_1	f_2	
1	3/5	0	3/5	-2/5	14
0	8/5	1	-2/5	3/5	4
0	9	0	9	4	610

(a) Primal problem

z_1	z_2	w_1	w_2	w_3	
1	0	-3/5	0	2/5	9
0	1	2/5	0	-3/5	4
0	0	-3/5	1	-8/5	9
0	0	-14	0	-4	610

(b) Dual problem

Figure 5-28. Optimal tableaux for illustrative dual problems.

The reader may be interested in solving this two-dimensional dual problem graphically to see that the second constraint is dominated by the other two, and thus to infer that x_2, the dual variable for this constraint, must be zero.

5-32 Integer Programming

Some linear programming problems require that the decision variables take on only *integral* values, and this additional restriction actually makes the programming problem nonlinear. In spite of this nonlinearity, the name *linear* is still attached to such problems, since both the objective function (5-1) and the constraints (5-2) are linear; the only change in the mathematical description of the problem is that the nonnegativity conditions are replaced by the requirements

$$x_n = 0, 1, 2, \ldots; \qquad n = 1, \ldots, N \tag{5-148}$$

Integer programming problems in which the objective function or the constraints may be quadratic have also been studied (Witzgall). The integrality requirements usually result from combinatorial considerations, such as those found in replacement and inventory problems, which will be discussed in Chapter 8, using a dynamic programming formulation. Many other practical problems require integer solutions; for example, scheduling and sequencing problems involve ordering restrictions which are often formulated by the introduction of a variable (Kronecker delta) that may take on only the values 0 or 1. Although the dynamic programming solution algorithm works quite efficiently for problems of this type, it is computationally infeasible if more than three state variables are present. Since each constraint Eq. (5-2: i) corresponds to one state variable, only a limited (but important) class of integer programming problems can be solved with this algorithm.

A systematic method for solving the general integer linear programming problem has been given by Gomory. In this method, the simplex algorithm is used to obtain the solution which is optimal when the integrality requirements (5-148) are ignored, and then a new constraint is added to Eqs. (5-2) which eliminates a portion of the feasible region near this solution point. The result of this procedure is to render this optimal point nonfeasible, and the dual-simplex method of Lemke is then employed to move from this point to an extreme point of the modified feasible set. If this is a lattice point, the process terminates; if not, another constraint ("cut") is added, and the foregoing procedure is repeated. Gomory has shown that this method will converge to the optimal integer solution in a finite number of steps, although in practice the number of iterations is usually large. Also, this method enlarges the size of the original simplex tableau considerably, because of the number of additional constraints required. As a consequence, the solution of even moderate-sized integer problems in not practical unless they contain few enough constraints to be handled by dynamic programming.

Another approach to this type of problem is simply to round off each nonintegral value in the optimal solution obtained by the simplex method. Care must be taken to round off to integral values that will satisfy the constraints, of course, and if the noninteger values are large, the resulting solution may not be far from the true integer optimum. This method cannot, however, be used in the important class of combinatorial problems that require some of the variables to be restricted only to the values 0 and 1. Furthermore, rounding to the nearest integer can be misleading, especially in higher dimensions. Consider the difficulties encountered in the following *two*-dimensional problem:

$$\text{maximize } p = -7x_1 + 106x_2$$

subject to
$$-x_1 + 15x_2 \leq 90$$
$$x_1 + 2x_2 \leq 35$$
$$-3x_1 + 4x_2 \leq 12$$

x_1, x_2, to be nonnegative integers

Using the simplex method, three iterations are required to reach the nonintegral optimal solution, $x_1 = \frac{345}{17}$, $x_2 = \frac{125}{17}$. If these values are now rounded to the nearest feasible lattice point, one finds $\hat{x}_1 = 20$, $\hat{x}_2 = 7$, giving the objective function a value of $\hat{p} = 602$. By drawing a graph of this problem, the reader will be interested to see that the optimal integer solution is actually $x_1^* = 15$, $x_2^* = 7$, for a value of $p^* = 637$.

5-33 Concluding Summary

This chapter, the last of three on inequality constraints, outlined the many special consequences of linearity. The differential algorithm becomes very effective when linearity allows accurate extrapolation of local information. Known as the *simplex method*, the linear algorithm was demonstrated as part of the sensitivity analysis of a hypothetical petroleum refinery. The example shows quantitatively how scarcity enhances the value of a critical commodity, and how small changes in cost can lead to violent upsets in the optimal production schedule. Often the most valuable result of a linear programming analysis is not the optimal plan, but rather the insight gained through intelligent sensitivity analysis.

Linearity also facilitates breaking a large system down into subsystems for decentralized optimization. The decomposition principle helps local managers plan their operations to harmonize with larger considerations concerning the entire system, about which detailed knowledge is not available at the local level. The procedure distills information on how the subsystems interact into a set of quantitative penalties assessed against the use of critical materials locally. These penalties guide local management toward production schedules making best use of resources and markets shared with other plants. An example showed how farsighted planning prevented the shutdown of a superficially obsolete plant. Restraint on the newer facility brought the older into production, with a company-wide profit improvement of over 60 per cent.

Transportation and allocation problems are not only linear, but also have unit coefficients that lead to algorithms even simpler than the simplex method. Linearity also makes duality relations elegant and clear.

In treating the linear case as a special part of the general nonlinear situation, we have run opposite to the historical development of the subject. Terminology suitable for any nonlinear problem has been applied even to the simpler linear case, which can be handled very well by the techniques of linear algebra. We justify this different approach on the grounds that, although less clear for the easy linear problems, it provides a better foundation for solving the difficult nonlinear ones.

BIBLIOGRAPHY

Beightler, C. S., and D. J. Wilde, "Sensitivity analysis gives better insight into linear programming," *Hydrocarbon Proc. Petrol. Ref.*, **44** (February, 1965), 111–26.

Boot, J. C. G., "On sensitivity analysis in convex quadratic programming problems," *Opns. Res.*, **11** (September, 1963), 771–86.

Charnes, A., "Optimality and degeneracy in linear programming," *Econometrica*, **20** (1952), 160–70.

——, and W. W. Cooper, *Management Models and Industrial Applications of Linear Programming*, Vol. 2 (Wiley, New York, 1961).

——, and ——, "The stepping stone method of explaining linear programming calculations in transportation problems," *Man. Sci.*, **1** (January, 1954), 49–69.

Dantzig, G. B., *Linear Programming and Extensions* (Princeton Univ. Press, Princeton, N. J., 1963).

——, "Maximization of a linear function of variables subject to linear inequalities," in *Activity Analysis of Production and Allocation*, ed. T. C. Koopmans (Wiley, New York, 1951), pp. 339–47.

——, and P. Wolfe, "Decomposition principle for linear programming," *Opns. Res.*, **8** (January, 1960), 101–111.

Dennis, J. B., *Mathematical Programming and Electrical Networks* (Wiley [Technology Press], New York, 1959).

Dorn, W. S., "Duality in quadratic programming," *Q. Appl. Math.*, **18**, 2 (July, 1960), 155–62.

Eisemann, K., "Simplified treatment of degeneracy in transportation problems," *Quart. App. Math.*, **14**, 4 (1957).

Gass, S. I., and T. L. Saaty, "The computational algorithm for the parametric objective function," *Naval Res. Logistics Quart.*, **2** (June, 1955), 39–45.

Goldman, A. J., and D. Kleinman, "Examples relating to the simplex method," *Opns. Res.*, **12** (January, 1964), 159–61.

Gomory, R. E., "An algorithm for integer solutions to linear programs," *Princeton—IBM Mathematics Research Project*, Technical Report No. 1, Nov. 1958.

Hadley, G. H., *Linear Programming* (Addison-Wesley, Reading, Mass., 1962).

Hoffman, A. J., "Cycling in the simplex algorithm," *Nat. Bur. Standards Report No. 2974* (December, 1953).

Lanczos, C., *The Variational Principles of Mechanics*, 2nd ed. (Toronto, 1962), pp. 161–65.

Lemke, C. E., "The dual method of solving the linear programming problem," *Naval Res. Logistics Quart.*, **1** (March, 1954), 48–54.

Quandt, R. E., and H. W. Kuhn, "On upper bounds for the number of iterations in solving linear programs," *Opns. Res.*, **12** (January, 1964), 161–65.

Reinfeld, N. V., and W. R. Vogel, *Mathematical Programming* (Prentice-Hall, Inc., Englewood Cliffs, N.J., 1958).

Saaty, T. L., "The number of vertices of a polyhedron," *Amer. Math. Monthly*, **62** (May, 1955), 326–31.

Sinden, F. W., "Duality in convex programming and in projective space," *J. Soc. Ind. Appl. Math.*, **11** (1963), 535–52.

Symonds, G. H., *Linear Programming: The Solution of Refinery Problems* (Esso, New York, 1955).

Wehl, H., "Elementare Theorie der konvexen Polyeder," *Comm. Math. Helv.*, **7** (1934), 290–306.

Wilde, D. J., "Production planning of large systems," *Chem. Engng. Prog.*, **59**, 1 (January, 1963), 46–51.

Witzgall, C., "An all-integer programming algorithm with parabolic constraints," *J. Soc. Indust. Appl. Math.*, **11** (1963), 855–71.

Wolfe, P., "A duality theorem for non-linear programming," *Quart. Appl. Math.*, **19** (1961), 239–44.

EXERCISES

5-1. (a) Solve the following problem, using the simplex method:

$$\text{maximize } p = 2x_1 + x_2$$

subject to the constraints:

$$x_1 + x_2 \leq 14$$

$$x_1 - 2x_2 \leq 4$$

$$x_1, x_2 \geq 0$$

(b) Re-solve the problem when the first constraint is changed to:

$$x_1 + x_2 \leq 15$$

What is the change in the optimal value of the objective function p? Compare this change with the value of the sensitivity coefficient for the slack variable in the first constraint, as found in the optimal tableau in part (a).

5-2. The Relthgieb Company produces four products, I through IV. The raw material requirements, space needed for storage, production rates, and profits are given in the accompanying table. The total amount of raw material available per day for all four products is 360 lb, the total storage space for all products is 475 sq ft, and a maximum of 7 hr per day can be used for production. Assume that all products manufactured each day are shipped out of the storage area at the end of the day. Thus, the four products must share the total available storage space, production time, and raw material.

	Product			
	I	II	III	IV
Raw material (pounds per piece)	4	4	3	5
Storage space (square feet per piece)	4	5	4	3
Production rate (pieces per hour)	30	60	20	30
Profit (dollars per piece)	10	13	10	11

(a) Find the number of pieces of each of the products which the company should produce per day in order to maximize the total profit.
(b) What hourly rate could the company afford to pay for more production time?
(c) How much should the company be willing to pay for additional storage space?
(d) What premium could the company pay for more raw material?

5-3. (a) Solve the following linear programming problem, using the simplex method.
Find nonnegative numbers x_1, x_2, and x_3 which *maximize* the function

$$p = 2x_1 + x_2 + x_3$$

and which satisfy the constraints:

$$x_1 + x_2 + x_3 \leq 10$$

$$x_1 + 5x_2 + x_3 \geq 20$$

(b) Find the optimal solution to part (a) if the first constraint is changed to: $x_1 + x_2 + x_3 \leq 5$, without re-solving the entire problem. (Assume that the second constraint is left unchanged.)

(c) What would be the effect on the optimal solution to part (a) of a change Δc_1 in the coefficient of x_1 ($c_1 = 2$) in the objective function?

5-4. A company has five warehouses, numbered $1, \ldots, 5$, containing 40, 50, 90, 30, and 60 units of its product, respectively. In the next month 20, 30, 40, 80, 60, 25, and 15 units respectively must be shipped to seven retail outlets numbered $1, \ldots, 7$.

The unit cost of shipment from any warehouse to any retail outlet is contained in the following matrix:

Outlet

		1	2	3	4	5	6	7
	1	8	6	10	12	9	11	5
	2	3	7	6	9	8	7	8
Warehouse	3	5	4	2	6	3	9	3
	4	17	12	11	13	9	10	12
	5	7	11	4	5	6	5	7

Find the minimum-cost shipping schedule. What is the minimum cost?

5-5. The Bergwerk Corporation operates three coal mines, A, B, and C, which provide 400, 500, and 700 tons, respectively, per week. Orders for 500, 400, 300, 300, and 600 tons per week have been received from customers I through V, respectively. A schedule of transportation costs in dollars per ton from each mine to each customer is given in the following table:

Customer

		I	II	III	IV	V
	A	4	16	1	16	14
Mine	B	18	10	8	12	12
	C	6	1	4	13	2

The company will ship all available tonnage each week, but will obviously not be able to satisfy the demands of all five customers, resulting in a loss of future business which is estimated to cost one dollar for each ton demanded but not supplied.

Find the weekly shipping schedule which minimizes the total cost.

5-6. A machine-tool manufacturer has received orders for 190, 110, 150, 50, and 70 lathes of types I-V, respectively. These orders must be filled by the end of the month, and the manufacturer has four production lines, A, B, C, and D, each of which is capable of producing all five different types of lathe.

The monthly production capacities of these lines are 110, 150, 230, and 190 lathes, respectively, regardless of the type(s) made. The dollar profit resulting from the manufacture of a given type of lathe on a given production line is shown in the following table:

| | | Lathe type | | | | |
		I	II	III	IV	V
	A	340	410	260	590	470
	B	375	445	300	600	450
Production line	C	345	400	270	545	500
	D	330	420	250	570	445

Find how many lathes of each type each production line should produce so as to maximize the total profit.

5-7. Write out and solve the dual of the following linear programming problem:
minimize $y = 20z_1 + 3z_2 + 21z_3 + 6z_4$
subject to the constraints:

$$5z_1 + z_2 + 2z_3 - 4z_4 \geq 3$$
$$2z_1 - z_2 + 7z_3 + 3z_4 \geq 4$$
$$z_1 \geq 0$$
$$z_2 \geq 0$$
$$z_3 \geq 0$$
$$z_4 \geq 0$$

5-8. Show that the dual of the linear programming problem described by Eqs. (5-137)-(5-139) is the problem given by Eqs. (5-134)-(5-136). (Rewrite the former problem as a maximization problem by multiplying both the objective function and the constraints through by -1.)

5-9. Write out the dual of the refinery problem described in Fig. 5-6, and give an economic interpretation of this dual problem.

5-10. Show that the dual variable associated with a primal *equality* constraint is unrestricted in sign (a "free" variable). Do this by writing the constraint as two equivalent *inequality* constraints, and thus explain the absence of nonnegativity requirements on the dual variables u_m, v_n of the transportation problem.

5-11. Show that the following problem is the dual of the transportation problem described by Eqs. (5-118)-(5-121):
Find the values of u_m and v_n which maximize

$$p = \sum_{m=1}^{M} a_m u_m + \sum_{n=1}^{N} b_n v_n$$

and which satisfy the constraints:

$$u_m + v_n \leq c_{mn}; \quad m = 1, \ldots, M; \quad n = 1, \ldots, N$$

5-12. (a) Attempt to solve the following problem using the simplex method. Then, make a change of variable to show why the solution is unbounded.
Maximize $p = 4x_1 + 3x_2 + 2x_3 - 2x_4$ subject to:

$$-7x_1 + 2x_2 + 5x_3 + 4x_4 \leq 7$$
$$-9x_1 - x_2 + 4x_3 + 7x_4 \leq 4$$
$$x_1 + 3x_2 + 2x_3 - x_4 \leq 8$$
$$x_1, x_2, x_3, x_4 \geq 0$$

(b) Show that the constraints of the problem which is dual to the one in part (a) have no solution.

5-13. (a) Solve the following problem by starting at the origin ($z_1 = 0$, $z_2 = 0$), and using the *dual-simplex* method.
Minimize $y = 3z_1 + 2z_2$ subject to the constraints:

$$2z_1 + z_2 \geq 6$$
$$z_1 + z_2 \geq 4$$
$$z_1 + 2z_2 \geq 6$$
$$z_1, z_2 \geq 0$$

(b) Write out the *dual* to the linear programming problem in part (a). Solve this dual problem using the simplex method.
Compare each iteration tableau in part (a) with the corresponding tableau in part (b).

5-14. Solve the following problem:

maximize $p = 3x_1 + 6x_2 + 2x_3$

subject to

$$3x_1 + 4x_2 + x_3 \leq b_1$$
$$x_1 + 3x_2 + 2x_3 \leq b_2$$

for $b_1 = 2$ and $b_2 = 1$.
(a) For what simultaneous changes Δb_1, Δb_2, in the values of b_1 and b_2, respectively, will the final state set be optimal? Draw a graph of this region in b_1, b_2 space. How will the optimal value of p change within this region?
(b) If only b_1 is changed, show the optimal simplex tableaux for all values of b_1 and plot the optimal values of x_1, x_2, x_3, and p as functions of b_1.
(c) Write out the dual of the given problem, keeping b_1 as a parameter (with $b_2 = 1$). Solve this dual both graphically and by the simplex method. Compare the results with those obtained in part (b).

5-15. (a) Solve the following linear programming problem, choosing x_2 as the first variable to enter the state set (to simplify the calculations).

Maximize $p = 12x_1 + 9x_2 + 7x_3$

subject to the constraints:

$$3x_1 + 2x_2 + x_3 \leq 20 \; (= b_1)$$
$$x_1 + x_2 + x_3 \leq 11 \; (= b_2)$$
$$12x_1 + 4x_2 + x_3 \leq 48 \; (= b_3)$$
$$x_j \geq 0, \qquad j = 1, 2, 3$$

(b) Assume that the optimal state set found in part (a) cannot be changed, but that *any two* of b_1, b_2, b_3 may be changed by any amounts so long as none of the x_j are driven out of the state set. For what values of Δb_1, Δb_2, Δb_3 (not all nonzero) will p be maximized?

(c) Re-solve the problem given in (a) when the following constraints are added to the original three:

$$2x_1 + x_2 + x_3 \leq 12 \quad \text{and} \quad 4x_1 + 3x_2 + 2x_3 \leq 33$$

Do this by starting with the final optimal tableau from part (a).

(d) Suppose that c_1 and c_2 (the coefficients of x_1 and x_2 in p) are subject to market fluctuations. What must be the relation between their values if the original optimal solution in (a) is to remain optimal?
In this range of fluctuation of c_1 and c_2, by how much does p vary?

(e) Starting with the optimal tableau from (a), write the equation for p as a function of Δb_1 and Δc_1 and draw the line for $p = 97$.

(f) In solving the problem given in (a), we ignored the variable x_4, where $c_4 = 10$, $a_{14} = 2$, $a_{24} = 1$, and $a_{34} = 5$. Re-solve the problem, taking into account this new variable, by starting with the optimal tableau from (a).

5-16. The Hindernis company employs three classes of workers, A, B, and C. Work is divided into two major types, I and II. Type I work may be performed by class A workers acting alone, or by teams consisting of one class A worker and two class B workers. (Class C workers are not permitted to do this type of work.) Type II work may be performed by either class A or class B men working alone, or by teams consisting of one class B man and three class C men. The hourly pay rates are $10, $5, and $2 for classes A, B, and C, respectively. All men work 40 hours per week, but the A, B, and C workers actually turn out the weekly equivalent of 40, 30, and 20 production hours, respectively.

Each week, the company needs a total of 1000 productive hours on type I work, and 2000 productive hours on type II work, in order to meet its production quotas. Because of labor shortages, no more than 30 class A and 40 class B men can be hired. How many workers of each class should be employed in order to minimize the total cost?

Set up the mathematical statement of the foregoing problem. (Note that this is an *integer* programming problem.)

Direct Elimination 6

The superior man, when he sees what is good, moves toward it; and when he sees his errors, he turns from them.

THE BOOK OF CHANGES, APPENDIX II, HEXAGRAM 42 (CHINA, *c*. 1200 B.C., J. LEGGE, TRANS.)

Past chapters have shown how to take maximum advantage of knowledge about the objective function and the domain of feasibility. Such prior knowledge, usually in the form of analytic functions and inequalities, enabled us to replace the original optimization problem by others easier to solve. Without advance information, indirect methods of this sort cannot be used, and the next two chapters survey what to do when such knowledge is unavailable. The strategies developed tend to follow the three-thousand-year-old advice from the *I Ching* quoted at the beginning of this chapter. As information is accumulated, one moves into regions where the optimum may lie and eliminates areas where it cannot be.

Imagine then an optimization problem where an analytic expression for the objective function is either unavailable or too complicated to manipulate by indirect methods. Assume, however, that given a specific set of values of the independent variables, one can compute the corresponding value of the objective function. The computation device may be a table of numbers, a set of graphs in a handbook, a complicated computer program, a manufacturing process, or the estimating department of an engineering design firm. In such circumstances there are two approaches to optimization. One may evaluate the objective at many points in order to approximate it by an expres-

215

sion amenable to indirect methods. Or, one may eschew such attempts at complete description and drive directly toward the peak, using incomplete information generated along the way. Methods based on the former approach will be called *approximation techniques;* those embodying the latter viewpoint, *direct methods.*

Since approximation techniques are founded on curve-fitting procedures well known to engineers and numerical analysts (see the books of Lapidus and of Southworth and Deleeuw), little space is given to them here. Most of the next two chapters concern direct methods, which fall into two major categories: (1) the *elimination* techniques, which by bold moves continually strive to shrink the region in which the peak must lie; (2) the *climbing* procedures which cautiously move in directions where, based on local measurements, the objective appears to be improving. This chapter deals with the elimination techniques; the next, with climbing. Since elimination methods are extremely effective when there is but one independent variable, this chapter is principally, although not exclusively, concerned with this one-dimensional case. Although few practical optimization problems involve only one decision variable, many multidimensional climbing procedures involve one-dimensional optimizations as subroutines. Hence, study of the present chapter is essential for understanding the next. But aside from their usefulness, unidimensional elimination methods are of great interest because their effectiveness as optimization procedures can itself be optimized. It is therefore possible to develop *optimum* elimination techniques, which can rarely be done for hill-climbing methods.

Interest in elimination procedures began with Kiefer's 1953 publication of an optimal scheme based on the Fibonacci numbers, dating back to thirteenth-century Pisa. Many early developments are summarized at an elementary level in Wilde's *Optimum Seeking Methods* (1964, chap. 2) from which come many of the figures, problems, and ideas of this chapter. They are organized, however, according to Avriel's more general results, which include the simpler situations as special cases. Recent results also show how to handle rounding errors in the objective function, rather than in the decision variable alone as in the past. This leads to a procedure which is optimum in an economic sense (Wilde, 1966). Special situations involving semi-infinite intervals, convexity, optimum use of poorly placed measurements, and simple multidimensional schemes have also been added to the previous material. In contrast to *Optimum Seeking Methods*, this chapter gives optimality proofs for the procedures described.

6-01 Explicit and Implicit Objectives

When the objective function $y\langle x \rangle$ can be computed directly from the N independent variables, it is said to depend on them *explicitly*. Most of the elimination methods described here will be appropriate for explicit objective functions, which occur often in practice. There are two major ways to calculate the gradient ∇y at a point $\mathbf{x}$. One can differentiate the objective directly and substitute the components of $\mathbf{x}$ into the resulting equations. Alternatively, one can perturb each coordinate x_i a small amount, say, ϵ_i, and estimate the partial derivatives as difference quotients. Let $\boldsymbol{\epsilon}_i$ represent an N vector having its ith component equal to ϵ_i, the others being zero. Then the quotient approximating the partial derivative $\partial y / \partial x_i$, evaluated at $\mathbf{x}$, is

$$\frac{(y\langle \mathbf{x} + \boldsymbol{\epsilon}_i \rangle - y\langle \mathbf{x} \rangle)}{\epsilon_i} \approx \left. \frac{\partial y}{\partial x_i} \right|_{\mathbf{x}} \qquad (6\text{-}1)$$

By either method, N additional computations are needed to find the N components of the gradient, which is needed whenever a climbing technique is employed. Most elimination techniques do not bother with the gradient, preferring to invest the computations saved in evaluating the objective at more points, spread widely over the feasible region.

Horn has pointed out that a different situation arises when the objective function is implicit rather than explicit. This means that the objective appears together with the independent variables in a function which cannot be solved directly for y, as in the equations following:

$$f\langle y, \mathbf{x} \rangle = 0 \qquad (6\text{-}2)$$

To find the value of y at a given point $\mathbf{x}$, one must substitute the numerical value of $\mathbf{x}$ into the expression and determine the value of y making $f\langle y, \mathbf{x}\rangle$ zero. This problem in solving a nonlinear equation numerically is handled most conveniently by the Newton-Raphson method described in Section 2–06. As a by-product of the Newton-Raphson procedure one obtains the derivative $\partial f/\partial y$. If the derivatives $\partial f/\partial x_i$ are easy to compute, one can therefore calculate $\partial y/\partial x_i$ from the relation

$$\frac{\partial y}{\partial x_i} = -\frac{\partial f/\partial x_i}{\partial f/\partial y} \qquad (6\text{-}3)$$

since the numerical value of $\partial f/\partial y$ is known. It is therefore easier to compute the gradient at a point where y has been evaluated than to try to find y at a new point, which would involve the relatively long numerical solution of Eq. (6–2) again. Hence, elimination methods using gradients are attractive whenever the objective function is implicit. In each circumstance for which an explicit technique is indicated in this chapter, there is often a modified version appropriate for implicit objectives. Any such implicit methods will be described along with the corresponding explicit procedure.

6-02 Polynomial Approximation

Before developing the elimination techniques, let us describe the sort of approximation methods which would occur naturally to most people faced with an optimization problem and disciplined in mathematics. By *polynomial approximation* is meant fitting a polynomial of degree K to the objective function, for simplicity considered here a function of a single variable x. The polynomial is

$$p\langle x\rangle \equiv \alpha_0 + \alpha_1 x + \alpha_2 x^2 + \cdots + \alpha_K x^K$$

$$= \sum_{k=0}^{K} \alpha_k x^k \qquad (6\text{-}4)$$

To determine it, one must measure $y\langle x\rangle$ at $K+1$ points, say $x_0, x_1, \ldots, x_K$, and solve the following $K + 1$ equations linear in the $K + 1$ coefficients α_k.

$$\sum_{k=0}^{K} \alpha_k x_j^k = y\langle x_j\rangle; \qquad j = 0, 1, \ldots, K \qquad (6\text{-}5)$$

Where to place the measurements, a subject covered in most books on numerical analysis (see Lapidus), need not concern us here, except to point out that the computations are simplified by spacing them equally. Suffice it to say that once the approximating polynomial $p\langle x\rangle$ has been determined, one can apply the appropriate indirect method, such as setting its first derivative to zero. Since high-degree polynomials require many measurements, most of which will be far from the desired optimum, and since finding the roots of the $K - 1$ degree polynomial for the first derivative is a tedious task, approximations usually stick to low-degree polynomials. If for example four points are taken, $p\langle x\rangle$ is cubic.

$$p\langle x\rangle = \alpha_0 + \alpha_1 x + \alpha_2 x^2 + \alpha_3 x^3 \qquad (6\text{-}6)$$

Since its first derivative is quadratic,

$$\frac{\partial p}{\partial x} = \alpha_1 + 2\alpha_2 x + 3\alpha_3 x^2 \qquad (6\text{-}7)$$

the predicted optimum $\hat{x}$ is one of the roots given in closed form by

$$\hat{x} = \frac{-\alpha_2 \pm \sqrt{\alpha_2^2 - 3\alpha_1\alpha_3}}{3\alpha_3} \qquad (6\text{-}8)$$

One could take a new measurement at $\hat{x}$, throwing away the point farthest from this prediction in order to keep the approximating polynomial cubic. The new values of α_1, α_2, and α_3 can then be substituted into Eq. (6–8) for an adjusted prediction.

When the objective is implicit, one need take measurements at only two points to find all four coefficients of a cubic approximation, because each point furnishes not only y, but $\partial y/\partial x$ as well—two independent pieces of data. Hence Eqs. (6–6) and (6–7) give four equations in the four unknown coefficients. Equation (6–8) can be used as before for predicting the location of the optimum once α_1, α_2, and α_3 have been estimated.

Many such procedures can be imagined. They would work very well on smooth functions which are approximated well by low-degree polynomials, but they could behave badly on arbitrary objective functions. Brooks has shown how much in error such methods can be whenever the prediction falls outside the range of the measurements, since in this case extrapolation is called for. Another objection is that there is no good way to estimate how far the prediction is from the true optimum. Approximation methods must be viewed as quick paths to rough guesses in which luck plays a large part.

6-03 Interval Elimination

In this section, and throughout most of the chapter, our attention focuses on unimodal objective functions of a single variable defined in a closed interval. Suppose to be definite we seek the location x^* where $y\langle x\rangle$ achieves its maximum value y^* in the unit interval $0 \leq x \leq 1$. The unimodality of $y\langle x\rangle$ assures us that there is only one local maximum; in addition we assume, for the sake of the explicit elimination methods to be developed, that there are no intervals of finite length in which the slope of y is zero, that is, where y is horizontal. More precisely, $y\langle x\rangle$ is assumed to increase monotonically up to the maximum, after which it decreases monotonically. That is, if

$$x_1 < x_2 < x^* \tag{6-9a}$$

then

$$y_1 < y_2 < y^* \tag{6-9b}$$

whereas, if

$$x^* < x_1 < x_2 \tag{6-10a}$$

then

$$y^* > y_1 > y_2 \tag{6-10b}$$

Functions satisfying this definition, which is slightly more restrictive than the definition of unimodality employed so far in this book, will be called *strictly unimodal*. Notice that this definition does not require smoothness or even continuity; Fig. 6–1 shows three unimodal functions of varying character.

Strict unimodality makes it possible to say, after examining the results of any pair of evaluations of the objective function, that the maximum lies in some interval shorter than the original one. Consider two points $x_1 < x_2$. The three possible outcomes are shown in Fig. 6–2: $y_1 > y_2$, $y_1 < y_2$, or $y_1 = y_2$.

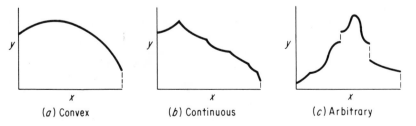

y		y		y	
x		x		x	
(a) Convex		(b) Continuous		(c) Arbitrary	

Figure 6-1. Unimodal functions.

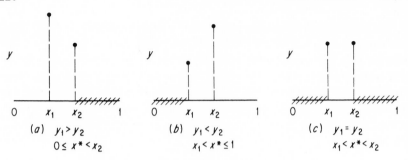

Figure 6-2. Possible outcomes of two experiments.

When $y_1 \geq y_2$, the maximum cannot lie to the right of y_2 without contradicting the definition of unimodality, and so we can conclude that $x^* < x_2$ in this case. Similarly, $y_1 \leq y_2$ implies that $x^* > x_1$. When the two outcomes are exactly equal ($y_1 = y_2$), the peak must lie between the points ($x_1 < x^* < x_2$).

To express these results in a form extendable to k function evaluations, let the left and right ends of the original interval be denoted by x_0 and x_{k+1} respectively. Let m_k be the location of the best point among them, and let l_k and r_k respectively be the points immediately to the left and right of m_k. Formally,

$$y\langle m_k \rangle = \max_{1 \leq j \leq k} (y\langle x_j \rangle) \tag{6-11}$$

$$l_k = \max_{x_j < m_k} (x_j) \tag{6-12}$$

$$r_k = \min_{x_j > m_k} (x_j) \tag{6-13}$$

Then if y is strictly unimodal, the true maximum must lie between l_k and r_k.

$$l_k < x^* < r_k \tag{6-14}$$

If $$y\langle m_k \rangle = y\langle r_k \rangle \tag{6-15}$$

then the interval is smaller:

$$m_k < x^* < r_k \tag{6-16}$$

Figure 6–3 shows all these relationships for $k = 7$.

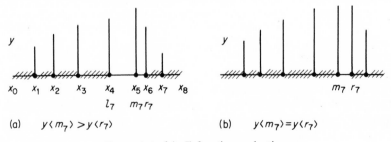

Figure 6-3. $k(=7)$ function evaluations.

The preceding development is relevant for explicit objectives; the implicit case requires only half as many function (and derivative) evaluations. Computation of y from an implicit function provides the derivative $y' (\equiv \partial y/\partial x)$ with relatively little additional effort. To take advantage of this, we must impose two additional restrictions on y; namely, that it be differentiable and that the derivative vanish only at the maximum. To emphasize this departure, let Eqs. (6–9) and (6–10) be replaced by the following definition of *differentiable unimodality*. If

$$x < x^* \tag{6-17a}$$

then $\qquad\qquad\qquad y'\langle x\rangle > 0 \tag{6-17b}$

and if $\qquad\qquad\qquad x > x^* \tag{6-18a}$

then $\qquad\qquad\qquad y'\langle x\rangle < 0 \tag{6-18b}$

From this it follows that $y'\langle x\rangle > 0$ implies $x^* > x$, that $y'\langle x\rangle < 0$ implies $x^* < x$, and $y'\langle x\rangle = 0$ implies $x^* = x$. When y and y' have been evaluated at k points, and with m_k, r_k, and l_k being defined as in Eqs. (6–11), (6–12), and (6–13), the true maximum x^* must lie in the interval immediately to the right or left of m_k according to whether $y'\langle m_k\rangle$ is positive or negative. That is, if

$$y'\langle m_k\rangle > 0 \tag{6-19a}$$

then $\qquad\qquad\qquad m_k < x^* < r_k \tag{6-19b}$

while if $\qquad\qquad\qquad y'\langle m_k\rangle < 0 \tag{6-20a}$

then $\qquad\qquad\qquad l_k < x^* < m_k \tag{6-20b}$

The range defined by Eq. (6–14) for explicit objectives and by Eqs. (6–19b) or (6–20b) for implicit objectives is called the *interval of uncertainty after k measurements* and denoted i_k. The ratio i_k/i_0 is a reasonable measure of the success of a particular deployment of k evaluations $x_1, \ldots, x_k$, which will be called a *k-measurement search plan*, abbreviated $\mathbf{x}_k$. With such a measure of effectiveness available, one can compare various schemes and look for a plan which is optimal in the sense of minimizing this ratio. Examination shows, however, that this ratio depends not only on the location of the measurements, but also upon the unknown location of the peak.

$$\frac{i_k}{i_0} = \frac{r_k - l_k}{x_{k+1} - x_0} \tag{6-21}$$

Specifically, the numerator $r_k - l_k$ is determined by where the sample maximum m_k happens to fall, which cannot be predicted in advance. In order to have a measure of *planning* effectiveness independent of such unknown factors, it is more reasonable to consider the worst (that is, longest) interval that might arise. This is given by

$$I_k\langle \mathbf{x}_k\rangle \equiv \max_{1 \le j \le k} (x_{j+1} - x_{j-1}) \tag{6-22}$$

called the *maximum interval of uncertainty after k measurements*. Since I_k depends only on the search plan $\mathbf{x}_k$, it is an a priori measure of any plan's effectiveness. Therefore any plan for which I_k attains its minimum I_k^* with respect to all other search schemes is in a sense optimal.

$$\frac{I_k^*}{I_0} \equiv \min_{\mathbf{x}_k} \frac{I_k\langle \mathbf{x}_k\rangle}{I_0} = \min_{\mathbf{x}_k}\left[\max_{1\leq j\leq k}\left(\frac{x_{j+1}-x_{j-1}}{x_{k+1}-x_0}\right)\right] \tag{6-23}$$

Because of the form of the right member of Eq. (6–23), a search plan giving such an interval is said to be *minimax*.

The minimax approach is completely conservative, chance determining only the *position* of the final interval, not its *length*. Despite this pessimistic point of view, the minimax concept leads to surprisingly effective search methods. Prudence of this sort is an ancient idea; in the *I Ching* (appendix III, sec. II, chap. V, hexagram 39) is written

> He who keeps danger in mind will rest safe in his seat;
> he who keeps ruin in mind will preserve his interests secure.

6-04 Simultaneous Elimination

Suppose that all k measurements are to be made at the same time—in a *single block*, in the terminology of the rest of the chapter. Since the optimal deployment depends on whether an odd or an even number of measurements is available, let p represent any natural number 1, 2, 3, . . . so that $k = 2p + 1$ is always odd and $k = 2p$ is always even. Thus p is the number of pairs contained in k objects. No generality is lost in assuming that the left end of the original interval of uncertainty is shifted so that

$$x_0 \equiv 0 \tag{6-24}$$

and in consequence

$$x_{k+1} = I_0 \tag{6-25}$$

Consider now the even-numbered evaluations $x_2, x_4, \ldots, x_{2p}$, which must be spaced no farther apart than I_k, the length of the final interval.

$$\begin{aligned} x_2 &\leq I_k \\ x_4 - x_2 &\leq I_k \\ \cdot \qquad \cdot \qquad \cdot \\ \cdot \qquad \cdot \qquad \cdot \\ \cdot \qquad \cdot \qquad \cdot \\ x_{2p} - x_{2p-2} &\leq I_k \end{aligned} \tag{6-26}$$

These p inequalities may be added to give

$$x_{2p} \leq pI_k \tag{6-27}$$

When k is odd, there is one more measurement $x_{2p+1}(\equiv x_k)$ to the right of x_{2p} so that

$$I_0 - x_{2p} \leq I_k \equiv I_{2p+1} \tag{6-28}$$

Hence addition of Eqs. (6–27) and (6–28) gives

$$I_0 \leq (p+1)I_{2p+1} \tag{6-29}$$

The final interval I_{2p+1} is minimized for any given initial interval I_0 by making Eq. (6–26) all strict equalities, for this forces equality in Eq. (6–29). Hence the minimax ratio is

$$\frac{I_0}{I_{2p+1}^*} = \frac{I_0^*}{I_{2p+1}} = p + 1 \tag{6-30}$$

and the optimal plan is to make

$$x_{2h} = hI_{2p+1}; \qquad h = 1, 2, \ldots, p \tag{6-31}$$

for the even measurements. The odd ones can be placed anywhere as long as they are no farther than I_{2p+1} from their adjacent odd-numbered neighbors.

$$(x_{2h+1} - x_{2h-1}) \leq I_{2p+1}; \qquad h = 1, 2, \ldots, p \tag{6-32}$$

Thus there is an infinity of minimax plans for an odd number of measurements. In particular they could be spaced equally in a *uniform search*.

$$x_j = \frac{jI_{2p+1}}{2} = \frac{jI_0}{2(p+1)}; \qquad j = 1, \ldots, 2p+1 \tag{6-33}$$

Examples of this and one other minimax simultaneous plan are given in Fig. 6–4 in which $I_0 = 1$.

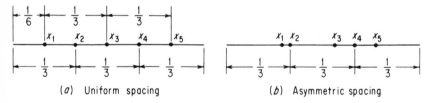

(a) Uniform spacing   (b) Asymmetric spacing

Figure 6-4. Minimax search plans for five simultaneous experiments.

When k is even $(= 2p)$, the minimax plan is unique and almost as effective as an odd plan having one more experiment. In this case Eq. (6–27) still holds, but Eq. (6–28) must be replaced by

$$I_0 - x_{2p-1} \leq I_k \equiv I_{2p} \tag{6-34}$$

Addition of Eqs. (6–27) and (6–34) gives

$$I_0 + x_{2p} - x_{2p-1} \leq (p+1)I_{2p} \tag{6-35}$$

To minimize I_{2p}/I_0, one must not only have equality in all Eqs. (6–26) and (6–34), but also place x_{2p-1} as close as possible to x_{2p} without having them coincide. Estimating this minimum distance is sometimes a difficult task (to be discussed in the next section), but for the time being, assume it is given as a known fraction ϵ of the initial interval.

Then
$$x_{2p} - x_{2p-1} \geq \epsilon I_0 \tag{6-36}$$

and
$$\frac{I_0}{I_{2p}^*} = \frac{p+1}{\epsilon+1} \tag{6-37}$$

Sometimes the minimum spacing is given as a fraction δ of the final interval instead, in which case Eq. (6–36) becomes

$$x_{2p} - x_{2p-1} \geq \delta I_{2p} \tag{6-38}$$

and
$$\frac{I_0^*}{I_{2p}} = p + 1 - \delta \tag{6-39}$$

Equation (6–37) is useful when the initial interval is known in advance, whereas Eq. (6–39) is more convenient when it is desired to find the largest initial interval that can be reduced to a known final interval. Comparison of Eqs. (6–30) and (6–39) shows that the advantage of $2p + 1$ rather than $2p$ experiments is very slight, the difference in initial interval that can be covered being only δI_{2p}, the minimum distance between two adjacent experiments. For this reason, odd numbers of experiments are rarely justified in practice for simultaneous search.

The reader can verify that the minimax plan calls for the even-numbered measurements to make strict equalities of Eqs. (6–26).

$$x_{2h} = h I_{2p} = \frac{h(\epsilon + 1) I_0}{p + 1}; \qquad h = 1, 2, \ldots, p \tag{6-40}$$

Each odd experiment is placed as close as possible to the even measurement on its right.

$$\begin{aligned} x_{2h-1} &= x_{2h} - \delta I_{2p} \\ &= (h - \delta) I_{2p} \tag{6-41} \\ &= x_{2h} - \epsilon I_0 \\ &= \frac{[h - (p + 1 - h)\epsilon] I_0}{p + 1}; \qquad h = 1, 2, \ldots, p \tag{6-42} \end{aligned}$$

This minimax *uniform pair* plan is illustrated in Fig. 6–5 for a unit starting interval and four or six measurements.

If derivatives are available, as when the objective function is implicit, each observation has the same power of elimination as two explicit measurements placed as close together as possible (a "uniform pair"). Hence implicit measurements should be equally spaced, and only half as many are needed as in the explicit case.

Here optimization theory, specifically the minimax approach, leads to a decision principle familiar to parents of small children—a cake is divided equally when the cutter gets the last piece. To paraphrase the *I Ching* again

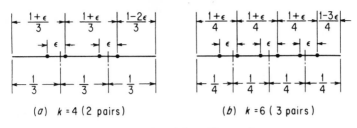

(a) $k = 4$ (2 pairs)   (b) $k = 6$ (3 pairs)

Figure 6-5. Search by uniform pairs.

(app. II, hexagram 15): "The superior man diminishes the excessive and increases the deficient, achieving balance in his actions."

6-05 Resolution and Distinguishability

In deriving the minimax simultaneous search plan we encountered a minimum separation $\delta I_k \ (= \epsilon I_0)$ to be maintained between adjacent measurements. This quantity, called the *resolution*, appears as a constraint on the search plan.

$$x_{j+1} - x_j \geq \delta I_k = \epsilon I_0; \qquad j = 1, \ldots, k - 1 \qquad (6\text{-}43)$$

If no good estimate of the resolution is available, the uniform search scheme involving an odd number of experiments can be employed. But when the resolution is known, and small, one can achieve a final interval almost as short with a search by uniform pairs, saving one measurement. On the other hand, if

$$\delta = \tfrac{1}{2} \qquad (6\text{-}44)$$

then the uniform pair scheme has all its evaluations equally spaced, and becomes a uniform search with an even number of measurements. This places an upper bound on δ which will be tacitly observed throughout the rest of the book.

$$\delta \leq \tfrac{1}{2} \qquad (6\text{-}45)$$

Let m be the maximum number of experiments which can be run without violating Eq. (6–45). A lower bound on this maximum is expressible in terms of ϵ by applying Eqs. (6–29) and (6–43) when m is odd ($m = 2p + 1$).

$$\frac{\delta}{\epsilon} = \frac{1}{2\epsilon} = \frac{I_0}{I_{2p+1}} \leq (p + 1) = \frac{m + 1}{2}$$

whence

$$m \geq \epsilon^{-1} - 1 \qquad (6\text{-}46)$$

The same lower bound is obtained when m is even (Exercise 6–1), and since m must be an integer, the upper bound cannot exceed the lower by more than unity. Hence the maximum number of measurements is the unique integer m lying in the interval

$$\epsilon^{-1} - 1 \leq m < \epsilon^{-1} \tag{6-47}$$

Suppose now $\delta < \frac{1}{2}$ so that there is some advantage in using a search by uniform pairs. The only time ϵ is directly predictable is when measurements can be taken at only a known, finite number of points, rather than anywhere in the initial interval. Since one cannot evaluate y anywhere between these points, it is convenient to respace them an equal unit distance apart in an interval of total length $P + 1$, where P is the number of possible points. In this case $I_0 = P + 1$ and $\epsilon I_0 = 1$, so that

$$\epsilon = (P + 1)^{-1} \tag{6-48}$$

The problem of matching the locations given by the uniform pair plan with the points where measurement is permitted is a little complicated, but these details, being of no present concern, can be delayed to the next section. For the moment it is enough to realize that these are the only circumstances in which ϵ is known with certainty in advance.

Even when y can be observed anywhere at all in the initial interval, one might be tempted to estimate ϵ in order to use the uniform pair scheme and save an experiment. Overestimation of ϵ will give a final interval slightly larger than necessary; whereas underestimation yields one greatly larger, since each pair of experiments too closely spaced behaves as if only one observation were present. Thus one should be sure to estimate ϵ large enough, not, however, exceeding $(k + 1)^{-1}$, which would make $\delta = \frac{1}{2}$ and force k to be the maximum number possible to run. For this value of ϵ, the uniform pair plan would reduce to a uniform scheme anyway.

One may, however, know the smallest detectable difference between values of the objective function, rather than the closest possible packing of measurements. This minimum difference in y will be called the *distinguishability* and denoted η. The distinguishability is such that for any pair of measurements x' and x'', one can say that

$$y\langle x' \rangle \neq y\langle x'' \rangle \tag{6-49a}$$

only if

$$|y\langle x' \rangle - y\langle x'' \rangle| \geq \eta \tag{6-49b}$$

When the difference is less than η, $y\langle x' \rangle$ and $y\langle x'' \rangle$ are said to be *indistinguishable*. If a simultaneous plan is to be used, the resolution (as either δ or ϵ) can be obtained from the distinguishability η by estimating the behavior of the function near the optimum, which can often be done even when the location of x^* is unknown. Specifically, ϵ is taken as the positive quantity satisfying the implicit relation

$$\min\{|y\langle x^* \rangle - y\langle x^* + \epsilon I_0 \rangle|, |y\langle x^* \rangle - y\langle x^* - \epsilon I_0 \rangle|\} = \eta \tag{6-50}$$

Figure 6–6 shows these quantities graphically.

The usual simultaneous procedures are usable with this choice of resolu-

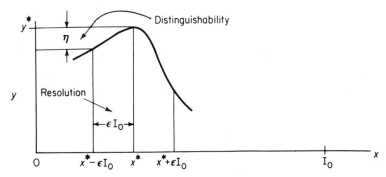

Figure 6-6. Resolution and distinguishability.

tion as long as the objective function does not flatten out too rapidly in the neighborhood of the optimum. To guarantee this, it is necessary to restrict $y\langle x\rangle$ somewhat. Therefore let a strictly unimodal function $y\langle x\rangle$ be called *regular* for k observations and resolution δ if

$$|y\langle x'\rangle - y\langle x''\rangle| \geq \eta \tag{6-51}$$

for all x' and x'' such that

$$(1) \quad \text{either } x^* \leq x' < x'' \quad \text{or} \quad x'' < x' \leq x^* \tag{6-52}$$

$$(2) \quad |x' - x^*| \leq (1 - \delta)I_k \tag{6-53}$$

$$(3) \quad |x'' - x'| \geq \delta I_k \tag{6-54}$$

One can readily show that convex functions satisfy these requirements (Exercise 6–2).

With this mild restriction, it is now possible to prove that if the best result m_k cannot be distinguished from the observation at $m_k + \delta I_k$ on its right, then the optimum x^* lies *between* m_k and $m_k + \delta I_k$. Formally, if

$$|y\langle m_k\rangle - y\langle m_k + \delta I_k\rangle| < \eta \tag{6-55a}$$

then $$m_k < x^* < m_k + \delta I_k \tag{6-55b}$$

This is proved by forcing a contradiction. Suppose that, contrary to Eq. (6–55b), either $x^* \leq m_k$ or $x^* \geq m_k + \delta I_k$. In the former case, Eqs. (6–52)–(6–54) hold with $x' \equiv m_k$ and $x'' \equiv m_k + \delta I_k$. This would imply Eq. (6–51), which contradicts the assumption that the two measurements are indistinguishable. A symmetric argument would also establish that x^* cannot be to the right of $m_k + \delta I_k$, which completes the proof of Eq. (6–55b). This, together with the fact that $\delta \leq \frac{1}{2}$ implies $(1 - \delta) \geq \delta$, guarantees that the observations at $m_k - (1 - \delta)I_k$ and $m_k + I_k$ will be distinguishable from that at m_k. Hence there is never any difficulty in identifying the best pair of measurements if y is regular.

When the maximum possible number of experiments is used, the sample maximum at m_m is indistinguishable from the true maximum at x^*, that is,

$$|y\langle x^*\rangle - y\langle m_m\rangle| < \eta \qquad (6\text{-}56)$$

as long as x^* is not at one end of the initial interval. Wilde (1966) gives a proof of this (see Exercise 6–3) which also uses the concept of indistinguishability to determine the optimal number of measurements. Suppose that both the resolution and distinguishability are perfect, so that the maximum number of experiments would be very large. In such cases one could use Eq. (6–56) to balance the cost c of each experiment against the loss of potential gain in the objective owing to an excessively large interval of uncertainty. Suppose it is possible to estimate a dummy resolution γ such that, by analogy with Eq. (6–50),

$$\min\{[y\langle x^*\rangle - y\langle x^* + \gamma\rangle], [y\langle x^*\rangle - y\langle x^* - \gamma\rangle]\} = c \qquad (6\text{-}57)$$

If the appropriate regularity condition can be assumed, the maximum number of experiments p for this dummy resolution γ will give a final interval such that

$$|y\langle x^*\rangle - y\langle m_p\rangle| \leq c \qquad (6\text{-}58)$$

with equality only if the true optimum is at one end of the initial interval. It would be economically pointless to make even a single additional measurement, for the outcome could never improve the sample maximum enough to justify the extra cost. Thus the search scheme proposed is optimal in the sense that it reaches the point of economically diminishing returns.

The concept of distinguishability also makes it possible to apply elimination methods when measurements of the objective are obscured by random experimental error. When the statistical distribution of this error can be predicted in advance, one can establish confidence limits about each estimate of y which correspond to the indistinguishability limits η. Doing this is a straightforward statistical task which will not be detailed here (see Mood or any other statistics text).

This long discussion of resolution and distinguishability is justified less because of the improvement it lends to simultaneous search than because of the improvement it gives to the sequential methods to follow. Simultaneous methods are so simple that they are good vehicles for developing the fundamentals of resolution and distinguishability for future reference. These ideas carry over easily to the more complicated procedures. Anyway, when it is absolutely impossible to guess ϵ or η, one can always go to a uniform plan with an odd number of measurements, at a cost of only one additional observation.

6-06 Scaling: Fictitious Points

The preceding two sections have shown both how to distribute a known number of observations for optimum effectiveness, and what the maximum number of measurements is for a given resolution or distinguishability. Before passing to more complicated schemes, let us examine the problem of placing observations to achieve a given ratio of initial to final interval I_0/I_k, where k is unknown. If the resolution ϵ is known, then one chooses the number $(p + 1)$ or $(p + 1)/(\epsilon + 1)$ which is the least upper bound on I_0/I_k for integral values of p. That is, p satisfies

either
$$\frac{p + 1}{\epsilon + 1} < \frac{I_0}{I_k} \leq (p + 1) \tag{6-59}$$

or
$$p < \frac{I_0}{I_k} \leq \frac{p + 1}{\epsilon + 1} \tag{6-60}$$

In the former case one uses a uniform search with an odd number of measurements $2p + 1$; the latter situation calls for a search with p uniform pairs ($2p$ observations). For example, if $I_0/I_k = 5.1$ and $\epsilon = 0.1$, then since

$$5 < 5.1 < \frac{6}{1.1}$$

one would use five uniform pairs ($k = 10$). But if $I_0/I_k = 4.9$, then nine uniformly spaced experiments would be in order because

$$\frac{5}{1.1} < 4.9 < 5$$

In neither case is the required reduction ratio attained exactly, but usually no one minds the slightly shorter final interval given by this procedure.

One time when one might wish a precise ratio I_0/I_k is when measurements can be taken only on a lattice of equally spaced points. Thus one might wish the final interval to contain exactly 3 points, starting with 57 original possibilities. Here it is convenient to scale the interval so that the points are one unit apart, in which case $I_0 = 58$, $I_k = 4$, and $\epsilon = \frac{1}{58}$. This gives $I_0/I_k = 14.5$, for which the procedure described in the last paragraph would require 14 uniform pairs (28 measurements), since

$$14 < 14.5 < \frac{15}{1 + (\frac{1}{58})}$$

Since such a scheme is actually designed to reduce 58, rather than 57 cases, to an interval containing 3 cases, at first glance it may not seem clear what to do. Experiments must be made at the integers, rather than at multiples of 57/58. The difficulty is overcome by adding a fictitious fifty-eighth case, artificially lengthening the initial interval to 59, the proper length for a 28-experiment search by uniform pairs. The observations are placed at 3, 4; 7, 8; 11, 12; ...; 51, 52; 55, 56 so that each final interval has exactly three points in it, as shown in Fig. 6–7. That the interval farthest to the right has one fictitious point (58) and only two real ones (56 and 57) need bother no one, for drawing this interval would merely be a stroke of good fortune, not a cause for alarm.

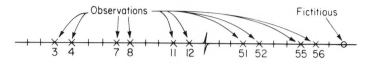

Figure 6-7. The method of fictitious points.

This idea of adding enough cases to bring the total up to the correct number for placement of the observations on the integers is called *the method of fictitious points*. It is not necessary to put the fictitious points at the end of the interval; they may be placed anywhere except where an experiment is to be made, including near any suspected location of the optimum. Hence the method of fictitious points generates a large number of search schemes, having equal effectiveness, that are approximately minimax. Anyone concerned about the word "approximately" may examine the minimax schemes in *Optimum Seeking Methods* (chap. 2). These procedures, however, involve the statistical technique of randomization which, although intellectually appealing, never saves as much as one experiment on the average. It is therefore of insufficient practical value to warrant discussion here.

6-07 Sequential Search: Bolzano's Method

Much more powerful search schemes are possible when observations can be made sequentially, that is, at different times rather than simultaneously. A *sequential* plan is one in which past results can be used to reduce the interval of uncertainty before new measurements are taken.

As an example of a sequential search situation, suppose the objective is implicit and differentiable so that each measurement yields both the value and first derivative of the objective function. Section 6–04 showed that simultaneous experiments should be equally spaced in the interval, and that reduction of the interval to 1 per cent of its original length would require 99 simultaneous observations. Suppose, however, that each measurement can be placed in an interval that has already been reduced by previous exploration. Then the first observation x^1, being a single simultaneous experiment search on the original interval I^0, should be made in the middle at $I^0/2$.

$$x^1 = \frac{I^0}{2} \tag{6-61}$$

The superscripts keep track of how many *sequential* observations have been made. The interval remaining runs either from 0 to x^1 or from x^1 to I^0, its length I^1 in either case being

$$I^1 = \frac{I^0}{2} \tag{6-62}$$

Let the origin of this new interval be shifted if necessary so that the ends are 0 and I^1. The second measurement x^2, being a single simultaneous observation in the new interval of length I^1, should be located in the center

$$x^2 = \frac{I^1}{2}$$

The interval remaining is of length

$$I^2 = \frac{I^1}{2} = \frac{I^0}{4} \tag{6-63}$$

The reader may prove by mathematical induction (Exercise 6–4) that after n implicit evaluations of this sort, the ratio of initial to final interval is

$$\frac{I^0}{I^n} = 2^n \tag{6-64}$$

Thus the number of observations needed to achieve a given reduction is

$$\begin{aligned}
n &= \frac{\log{(I^0/I^n)}}{\log 2} \\
&= 3.32 \log \frac{I^0}{I^n}
\end{aligned} \tag{6-65}$$

Since n must be an integer, it is more properly specified as the unique integer satisfying

$$3.32 \log \frac{I^0}{I^n} \le n < 1 + 3.32 \log \frac{I^0}{I^n} \tag{6-66}$$

Thus for a 100-to-1 reduction, only 7 implicit measurements are needed for sequential placement, certainly an improvement over the 99 required by a simultaneous plan to do the same job.

This scheme is called the *Bolzano search* plan because of its resemblance to the well-known Bolzano technique for finding the root of a monotonically decreasing function in a finite interval. Bolzano's root-finding method evaluates the function each time in the center of the remaining interval; eliminating the left (right) interval if the outcome is positive (negative). Since the peak of a differentiably unimodal function is at the root of the monotonically decreasing derivative curve, the optimum-seeking procedure described is a straightforward adaptation of Bolzano's method, hence the name.

It is not always possible to shorten the interval of uncertainty after each observation. Suppose, for instance, that each day the economic analysis department of a company has just enough time allocated on the available computer to evaluate the objective and its derivative at two points. Then the intelligent thing is to have the two results printed out for that day and use them to locate the reduced interval for the next day. This sort of scheme involving sequential blocks of simultaneous observations (two per block in the example) is called *block search* (Avriel and Wilde, 1966). Let superscripts denote the block number, and subscripts the number of experiments per block. Then, since each block of two implicit measurements (called a *diblock*) reduces the interval by a factor of 3, it follows that in the example

$$\frac{I_2^0}{I_2^n} = 3^n \tag{6-67}$$

For a reduction ratio of 100, only 5 diblocks are needed, since

$$3^4 = 81 < 100 < 3^5 = 243 \tag{6-68}$$

This is two fewer diblocks than for one experiment per block, but it requires in all 10 rather than 7 evaluations. Thus block search trades effort for time. In general, for n blocks of k measurements per block,

$$\frac{I_k^0}{I_k^n} = (k + 1)^n \tag{6-69}$$

and for given k,

$$\frac{\log (I_k^0/I_k^n)}{\log (k + 1)} \le n \le \frac{\log (I_k^0/I_k^n)}{\log (k + 1)} + 1 \tag{6-70}$$

If n is given, then the proper number of experiments per block is the integer k satisfying

$$\left(\frac{I_k^0}{I_k^n}\right)^{1/n} - 1 \le k < \left(\frac{I_k^0}{I_k^n}\right)^{1/n} \tag{6-71}$$

Thus if the hypothetical study must be completed in two days with 100-to-1 reduction, the computer must do nine evaluations per run—a total of eighteen in all. Such is the price of a crash program. The appropriate maxim is "Haste makes waste."

6-08 Even-Block Search

Bolzano's method and its extensions can be used only when each observation produces the derivative, as when the objective function is implicit. Explicit objectives require more observations since only values, not derivatives, of the objective are generated. When the blocks contain an even number of measurements ($k = 2p$; $p = 1, 2, \ldots$), the minimax sequential search procedure, called *even-block search* for short, resembles the Bolzano methods. The observations in each block are deployed in pairs, whose members are as close together as possible, placed in the vicinity of the Bolzano locations. Every pair approximates the sign of the derivative and gives the direction in which the optimum lies. Thus an even-block search requires twice as many observations to obtain roughly the same interval reduction as the implicit Bolzano method. Remember, however, an implicit function evaluation, being iterative, requires more than twice as much computation as an explicit one. Hence explicit objectives really take less total effort to eliminate than implicit ones.

Avriel's even-block procedure (Avriel and Wilde, 1966) gives a ratio of

$$\frac{I^0_{2p}}{I^n_{2p}} = (p+1)^n - \delta \tag{6-72}$$

bearing an obvious resemblance to Eq. (6–69) for implicit functions. Figure 6–8 shows how the method works in the specific case of two blocks of four experiments each. Placement of the first block (identified in Fig. 6–8 by circled 1's) differs slighly from that of the rest. It is, in fact, a search by uniform pairs. The even-numbered observations x^1_2, x^1_4, x^1_6, etc., are measured off from the left end at equal distances $(p+1)^{n-1} I^n_{2p}$.

$$x^1_{2h} = h(p+1)^{n-1} I^n_{2p}; \qquad h = 1, 2. \ldots, p \tag{6-73}$$

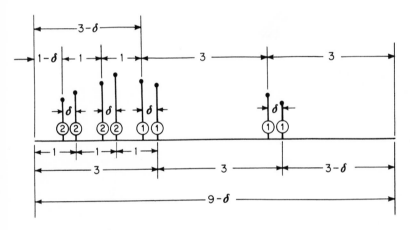

Figure 6-8. Two blocks of four measurements.

Each odd-numbered measurement is placed a distance δ to the left of those with an even number.

$$x^1_{2h-1} = x^1_{2h} - \delta \tag{6-74}$$

In the example in Fig. 6–8 the final interval I^2_4 has been taken as unity for simplicity, so the original interval is

$$I^0_4 = 9 - \delta$$

The even experiments in the first quadriblock are at

$$x^1_2 = 3; \qquad x^1_4 = 6$$

and the odd ones are at

$$x^1_1 = 3 - \delta; \qquad x^1_3 = 6 - \delta$$

As a result of this search by uniform pairs an interval of length $(p+1)^{n-1}$

(3 in the example) is obtained with a result located a distance δ from one end (the right end in the example).

The second and all subsequent blocks differ slightly from the first in that the search by uniform pairs is not performed on the full interval I_{2p}^2, but rather on the shorter interval $I_{2p}^2 - \delta$ bounded at one end by the best result from block one. Thus in Fig. 6–8 a search by uniform pairs is made on the interval of length $3 - \delta$ rather than on the full interval of uncertainty (3 units long). Half the experiments are equally spaced from the existing result, the modular distance being in general $(p+1)^{n-j}I_{2p}^n$ for quadriblock j (1 in the example). The other p observations are equally spaced in the same manner, starting from the end of the interval opposite to that where the existing measurement has been made. The circled 2's in Fig. 6–8 show the locations of the second (and last) quadriblock in the example:

$$x_1^2 = 1 - \delta, \quad x_2^2 = 1, \quad x_3^2 = 2 - \delta, \quad x_4^2 = 2$$

The result is an interval of length $(p+1)^{n-j}$ with a result only δ units from one end. Since this is the same configuration as before block j was performed, the procedure can be iterated until an interval of length $(p+1)^{n-n}I_0^n = I_0^n$ is obtained.

In case the resolution is given in terms of initial rather than final interval, Eq. (6–72) may be expressed as

$$\frac{I_{2p}^0}{I_{2p}^n} = \frac{(p+1)^n}{\epsilon + 1} \tag{6-75}$$

which may be rearranged to give

$$\frac{I_{2p}^n}{I_{2p}^0} = (p+1)^{-n}(\epsilon + 1) \tag{6-76}$$

The special case $p = 1$, in which each block consists of a single pair of measurements, was the only even-block procedure receiving any attention before Avriel's work. These *dichotomous procedures* (*OSM*, pp. 23–24) are not as efficient as Avriel's *diblock* method, the former technique giving $I_2^n/I_2^0 = 2^{-n} + (1 - 2^{-n})\epsilon$ rather than the improved $2^{-n}(1 + \epsilon)$ obtainable by Avriel. The even-block search technique is minimax; proof of that is omitted here because it resembles the proof for the odd-block case, given later in detail.

6-09 Population Explosion

There is an instructive analogy between rabbit breeding and not only the ratios I_k^0/I_k^n generated by the Bolzano type of methods in the two preceding sections, but also similar ratios associated with odd-block search. Suppose one has a pair of rabbits which produces k new pairs at the end of one month, making $k + 1$ couples in all. Imagine that at the end of the second month each pair alive at the end of the first month brings forth a litter of k new pairs, giving $k(k + 1)$ new couples in addition to the $k + 1$ old ones, making the total number of pairs

$$k(k + 1)^2 + (k + 1)^2 = (k + 1)^3$$

In general, assuming this process continues without change, there will be $(k + 1)^n$ rabbits on hand at the end of n months. By Eq. (6–69), this is the same as the ratio of initial to final interval after n blocks of k observations on an *implicit* objective function.

The implicit case was so easy to analyze that the rabbit analogy adds little to our understanding of the search procedure. If, however, the objective is *explicit*, then the derivatives are not obtained, and a different procedure must be used. Since individual measurements can no longer reduce the interval by themselves, but must instead be compared with existing results, reduction is slower than when derivatives are known. Correct procedures, derived in sections to follow, are based on sequences of numbers related to the sort of rabbit demography problem just studied. The slower reduction of an explicit objective corresponds, as we shall see, to the slower growth of population when the rabbits require time to mature before becoming fertile.

All this concern with animal husbandry has a sound basis in history, for it was as long ago as 1202 that Leonardo of Pisa solved such a problem. He assumed only one new couple per litter ($k = 1$), allowed a month for maturation, and computed the number of couples at the end of each month of the year. Table 6–1 gives the results. At time zero—midnight on New Year's Eve—there are no rabbits, but a newly born couple arrives on New Year's Day. It achieves maturity after one month, and at the beginning of March brings a new immature pair into the world—a total of 2 couples alive.

TABLE 6–1

FIBONACCI'S NUMBERS A_1^n

Months elapsed, n	0	1	2	3	4	5	6	7	8	9	10	11	12
Immature	0	1	0	1	1	2	③	5	8	13	21	34	55
Mature	0	0	1	1	2	③	5	8	13	21	34	55	89
Total, A_1^n	0	1	1	2	③	5	8	13	21	34	55	89	144

In April the original pair is blessed with another set of twins, as they will be during every month of the year; their first offspring reach adolescence and produce the first grandchildren in the fifth month. Hence each entry in the second row (the number of mature couples) appears again in the first row a month later as the young are born. Three couples alive in April mean 3 mature in May and 3 pairs of offspring in June.

Leonardo's nickname ("Fibonacci," or son of Bonacci) has been given to the sequence of numbers $A_1^n = 0, 1, 1, 2, 3, 5, 8, 13, \ldots$ in the third row, for they first appeared in his *Liber Abaci* (*Book of Numbers*), which helped introduce Arabic numerals into Europe. They are in general given by the recursion relation (Girard)

$$A_1^0 \equiv 0 \tag{6-77a}$$

$$A_1^1 \equiv 1 \tag{6-77b}$$

$$A_1^n = A_1^{n-1} + A_1^{n-2}; \quad n = 2, 3, \ldots \tag{6-77c}$$

That is, each is the sum of the two numbers preceding. Notice that if Fibonacci had not allowed a month for growing up, he would have computed $2^{12} = 4096$ instead of 144. On the other hand, if he had assumed that births occurred only in alternate months, doubling the population every two months would have given only $2^6 = 64$. It will be shown that the largest number (4096) is the sort associated with Bolzano's method, the smallest (64) with a diblock search, and the middle number (144) with a true sequential search having only one measurement per block.

6-10 Uniblock (Fibonacci) Search

The most effective allocation of search effort is to put each observation in its own block. A block containing but one measurement will be called a *uniblock*. For implicit objectives the Bolzano method is appropriate, and this section will show that the explicit case calls for a plan based on the Fibonacci numbers. The emphasis here is on plausibility rather than rigor, with formal proof postponed to Section 6–14 where the general odd-block case is developed. First we show how one might discover the minimax *uniblock* scheme. Then this optimal plan is described precisely for subsequent demonstration with an example in Section 6–11.

As in Section 6–08 on even-block search, let us, for simplicity, assume that the final interval is of unit length ($I_1^n = 1$). Once this situation has been analyzed, it is no trouble to rescale everything at the end. Johnson has suggested that the proper search plan is generated naturally by considering first two uniblocks, then three, etc, —an approach which is essentially the one called *dynamic programming* and studied in Chapter 8. His idea is coupled with one used by Leaton T. Oliver who, as an undergraduate chemical engineering student at the University of Texas, discovered the correct way to allow for the resolution δ. Oliver's insight was to consider a unimodal function with its maximum at the origin. Then, by proceeding backwards from the last observation, x_1^n, to the first, x_1^1, he was able to see the correct pattern for extension to general unimodal functions.

In this spirit let us seek the plan giving the largest starting interval I_1^0 reducible to a unit interval after n uniblocks. The case $n = 1$ is trivial, since at least two observations are needed for any reduction at all, and the case $n = 2$ has already been analyzed in section 6–04, for it is simply a search with one uniform pair ($p = 1$). Equations (6–72)—(6–74) show that an interval of length $2 - \delta$ can be reduced to a unit interval by measuring at $1 - \delta$ and at 1, locations marked with circled n and $n - 1$ in Fig. 6–9. The point $n - 2$ marks the right end of an interval reducible by two observations when the maximum is at the origin. Therefore

$$I_1^0 = I_1^1 = (2 - \delta)I_1^2$$

for $n = 2$. When there are more than two uniblocks, measurements x_1^n and x_1^{n-1} will be, respectively, the last and next to last to be performed, and the previous equation can be written more generally as

$$I_1^{n-1} = (2 - \delta)I_1^n \qquad (6\text{-}78)$$

Moreover there will be a measurement x_1^{n-2} at the right end of the next to last interval I_1^{n-1} when $n \geq 2$. Specifically, 3 uniblocks would call first for an observation at $x_1^{n-2} = x_1^1 = 2 - \delta$ and a second at $x_1^{n-1} = x_1^2 = 1$. They would be placed inside an initial interval longer than $2 - \delta$, whose maximum right end location can be determined by remembering that the experimenter does not know in advance which observation will give the best result. Since if, as in Fig. 6–9, $y\langle x_1^2 \rangle > y\langle x_1^1 \rangle$, the length remaining is $2 - \delta$, the distance from x_1^1 to the right end might as well be the same, since this is what would be left if $y\langle x_1^2 \rangle < y\langle x_1^1 \rangle$. That is,

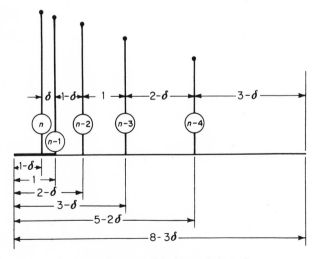

Figure 6-9. Uniblock search ($n \leq 5$).

$$I_1^1 - x_1^2 = x_1^1 = 2 - \delta$$

whence
$$I_1^1 = 2 - \delta + 1 = 3 - \delta$$

Therefore 3 uniblocks can reduce an interval of length $3 - \delta$, the first two experiments being made at $x_1^1 = 2 - \delta$ and $x_1^2 = 1$. With the maximum at the origin, this would give the interval $I_1^2 = 2 - \delta$, which in turn is cut down to unit length by an observation at $1 - \delta$. In general,

$$I_1^{n-2} = (3 - \delta)I_1^n$$

Repetition of this informal argument gives, for $n \geq 4$,

$$I_1^{n-3} = I_1^{n-2} + I_1^{n-1}$$
$$= (3 - \delta)I_1^n + (2 - \delta)I_1^n$$
$$= (5 - 2\delta)I_1^n$$

while, for $n \geq 5$,

$$I_1^{n-4} = I_1^{n-3} + I_1^{n-2}$$
$$= (8 - 3\delta)I_1^n$$

Thus an initial interval of $8 - 3\delta$ can be reduced to one of unit length after 5 uniblocks. The first two are placed at $x_1^1 = 5 - 2\delta$ and $x_1^2 = 3 - \delta$, and with the maximum at the left end, the others will be at $x_1^3 = 2 - \delta, x_1^4 = 1$, and $x_1^5 = 1 - \delta$, as shown in Fig. 6–9.

To generalize this, one must recognize that the key variable is not the number of measurements already taken, but instead the number yet to be made. Let j be the number remaining, so that $n - j$ is the number already used up. Then the succession of shrinking intervals is related by

$$I_1^{n-j} = I_1^{n-(j-1)} + I_1^{n-(j-2)} \tag{6-79}$$

That is, each interval is the sum of the next two following. Since Eq. (6–77) defining the Fibonacci numbers A_1^n has the same form, it is not surprising to find that

$$I_1^{n-j} = (A_1^{j+2} - A_1^j \delta)I_1^n; \qquad j = 0, 1, \ldots, n - 1 \tag{6-80}$$

In particular, the effectiveness of the reduction for all n uniblocks is obtained by setting $j = n - 1$.

$$\frac{I_1^0}{I_1^n} = \frac{I_1^1}{I_1^n} = A_1^{n+1} - A_1^{n-1} \delta \tag{6-81a}$$

$$= \frac{A_1^{n+1}}{A_1^{n-1} \epsilon + 1} \tag{6-81b}$$

Neglecting resolution, it would take at least 11 observations to reduce the interval to less than 1 per cent of its original length, compared to 7 Bolzano measurements or 14 of the diblock variety.

To achieve this performance, place the first experiment a distance I_1^2 from one end, say the left

$$x_1^1 = I_1^2 = (A_1^n - A_1^{n-2} \delta) I_1^n \qquad (6-82)$$

The second is located symmetrically with respect to the first, which, because of the nature of the Fibonacci sequence, happens to be exactly I_1^3 units from the left (see Exercise 6–6).

$$x_1^2 = I_1^3 = (A_1^{n-1} - A_1^{n-3} \delta) I_1^n \qquad (6-83)$$

After comparison of the two results, the interval remaining will be of length I_1^2 and will contain a measurement a distance I_1^3 from one end and I_1^4 from the other. Symmetric placement of the third measurement insures that the next interval will be I_1^4, etc. After $n - 1$ have been performed, the interval is

$$I_1^{n-1} = (A_1^3 - A_1^1 \delta) I_1^n = (2 - \delta) I_1^n$$

and the experiment within it is a distance I_1^n from one end. Placement of the other experiment guarantees attainment of a final interval of I_1^n, with the distance between x_1^n, the new measurement, and m_1^{n-1}, the old one, being exactly the resolution δI_1^n.

$$\begin{aligned} |x^n - m_1^{n-1}| &= I_1^n - (I_1^{n-1} - I_1^n) \\ &= 2I_1^n - I_1^{n-1} \\ &= [2 - (2 - \delta)] I_1^n = \delta I_1^n \end{aligned}$$

This scheme, called *Fibonacci search* for obvious reasons, was first devised and proved minimax for $\delta = 0$ by J. Kiefer. Oliver and Wilde showed informally how to include resolution, and the rigorous proof for this modification was given later by Avriel and Wilde, 1966. The formal proof is omitted here because it is a special case covered by the more general demonstration of Section 6–15. An example of Fibonacci search follows.

6-11 An Example of Fibonacci Search

Suppose one wishes to reduce an interval $5.11 \leq x \leq 23.64$ to one only 10 per cent as long, the resolution being 0.545 units. Then $I_1^0 = 18.53$, $I_1^n \leq 1.853$, and $\epsilon = (0.545)/(18.53) = 0.0294$. The number of observations n is the unique integer satisfying

$$A_1^n (A_1^{n-2} \epsilon + 1)^{-1} < \frac{I_1^0}{I_1^n} \leq A_1^{n+1} (A_1^{n-1} \epsilon + 1)^{-1} \qquad (6-84)$$

which gives $n = 6$, since (see Table 6–1)

$$8[3(0.0294) + 1]^{-1} = 7.35 < 10.00 < 13[5(0.0294) + 1]^{-1} = 11.33$$

The final interval can be shorter than 1.853, so rather than add fictitious points to the starting interval, we shall take the full reduction ratio of 11.33 and have a final interval of length $18.53(11.33)^{-1} = 1.636$. In terms of this final interval, the resolution is

$$\delta = \frac{\epsilon I_1^1}{I_1^6} = (0.0294)(11.33) = 0.334$$

Since $\delta < \frac{1}{2}$, there is no danger of having the last two observations too close together.

Fibonacci search places the first observation at

$$5.11 + x_1^1 = 5.11 + (A_1^6 - A_1^{6-2}\,\delta)I_1^6$$

$$= 5.11 + [8 - 3(0.334)](1.636)$$

$$= 5.11 + 11.45 = 16.56$$

The second is placed symmetrically at

$$23.64 - x_1^1 = 12.19$$

Suppose that $y\langle 16.56\rangle = 8.73$ and $y\langle 12.19\rangle = 9.07$. Then if we seek the maximum, there is no need to explore values greater than 16.56.

$$5.11 \le x^* < 16.56$$

The interval remaining resembles that in Fig. 6–9 with scale changed and origin shifted. The original length $13 - 5\delta$ has been reduced to $8 - 3\delta$, and there is an observation already at $5 - 2\delta$.

The third measurement is placed symmetrically with respect to the one still in the interval, namely at $16.56 - (12.19 - 5.11) = 9.48$, corresponding to the one at $3 - \delta$ in Fig. 6–9. Let the result be $y\langle 9.48\rangle = 7.89$. This eliminates the left portion and implies that

$$9.48 < x^* < 16.56$$

The best result is still at 12.19.

The fourth is located symmetrically at

$$9.48 + 16.56 - 12.19 = 13.85$$

If $y\langle 13.85\rangle = 9.32 > y\langle 12.19\rangle$, then

$$12.19 < x^* < 16.56$$

and the fifth observation is made at

$$12.19 + 16.56 - 13.85 = 14.90$$

If $y\langle 14.90\rangle = 9.27 < y\langle 13.85\rangle$, then

$$12.19 < x^* < 14.90$$

and the objective is measured finally at

$$12.19 + 14.90 - 13.85 = 13.24$$

Notice that this is 0.61 units from the nearest measurement at 13.85, a close approximation to the desired resolution 0.545. The discrepancy is owing to accumulated error caused by rounding off in the second decimal place.

Suppose the sixth result is $y\langle 13.24\rangle = 9.36 > y\langle 13.85\rangle$. Then the final interval is

$$12.19 < x^* < 13.85$$

Its length is 1.66, slightly above the predicted 1.64 because of rounding error, but still well below the 1.85 required.

6-12 Unknown Resolution

All the search schemes developed so far require prediction of the resolution δ or ϵ before beginning the search. When this information is unavailable, a slightly less efficient procedure due to Kiefer must be employed.

Since the length of the final interval cannot be predicted until, at the last observation, the resolution is known, the search plan must be scaled in terms of the original interval I_1^1. The first experiment is located at

$$x_1^1 = \frac{I_1^1 A_1^n}{A_1^{n+1}} \tag{6-85}$$

and the second symmetrically at

$$x_1^2 = I_1^1 - x_1^1 = \frac{I_1^1 A_1^{n-1}}{A_1^{n+1}} \tag{6-86}$$

and giving an interval after two uniblocks of

$$I_1^2 = \frac{I_1^1 A_1^n}{A_1^{n+1}}$$

This is repeated, giving in general after $n - 1$ uniblocks an interval of length

$$I_1^{n-1} = \frac{I_1^1 A_1^3}{A_1^{n+1}} = \frac{2 I_1^1}{A_1^{n+1}}$$

with an observation at

$$m^{n-1} = \frac{I_1^1 A_1^2}{A_1^{n+1}} = \frac{I_1^1}{A_1^{n+1}}$$

Since m^{n-1} is exactly in the middle of the interval, it would do no good to place the final observation x_1^n symmetrically because this would only duplicate effort without shortening the interval. Instead, one should put x_1^n as close as possible to m^{n-1}, either to the left or right. This involves estimating the resolution ϵI_1^1, presumably possible now after $n - 1$ measurements have given information about the objective and narrowed down the range containing the optimum.

$$x_1^n = m^{n-1} \pm \epsilon I_1^1$$

This will give two possible intervals—either $I_1^1[(A_1^{n+1})^{-1} + \epsilon]$ or $I_1^1[(A_1^{n+1})^{-1} - \epsilon]$. According to the cautious minimax approach, we must use the larger in measuring the effectiveness of the search plan, so

$$\frac{I_1^1}{I_1^n} = \frac{A_1^{n+1}}{1 + A_1^{n+1}\epsilon} \tag{6-87a}$$

$$= A_1^{n+1}(1 - \delta) \tag{6-87b}$$

Kiefer proved that this plan is minimax for any given $\epsilon > 0$. The slightly decreased effectiveness compared to Oliver's method (see Eq. 6–81) is the price of not knowing the resolution in advance.

If the resolution ϵ is estimated from the distinguishability η of the objective function as in Section 6–05, then the question of regularity must be reexamined. Equations (6–51)–(6–54) gave conditions unimodal functions had to meet if they were to be searched successfully with simultaneous observations, the resolution being estimated from the distinguishability. These regularity conditions excluded excessively flat unimodal functions which would give resolution problems during a search. When the sequential uniblock scheme is used, the regularity conditions of Section 6–05 are excessively restrictive. The greater reducing power of the sequential method permits it to tolerate more flatness at points far removed from the optimum than can a simultaneous plan, which must place a uniform lower bound on the slope throughout the original interval. The appropriate conditions for uniblock search involve the Fibonacci numbers.

A strictly unimodal function $y\langle x \rangle$ is said to be *regular* for an n uniblock search with resolution δ if

$$|y\langle x' \rangle - y\langle x'' \rangle| \geq \eta \tag{6-88}$$

for all x' and x'' such that

$$\text{(1)} \quad \text{either } x^* \leq x' < x'' \quad \text{or} \quad x'' < x' \leq x^* \tag{6-89}$$

$$\text{(2)} \quad |x' - x^*| \leq I_1^{n-j} = (A_1^{j+2} - A_1^j \delta)I_1^n \tag{6-90}$$

$$\text{(3)} \quad |x'' - x'| \geq I_1^{n-j-1} = (A_1^{j+3} - A_1^{j+1} \delta)I_1^n \tag{6-91}$$

for all $j = 2, 3, \ldots, n$. These milder conditions are satisfied by convex functions. As in Section 6–05, one can prove that if the best result m^j after j uniblocks cannot be distinguished from the observation on its right at $m^j + \delta I_1^n$, then the optimum x^* must lie between them. That is, if

$$|y\langle m^j \rangle - y\langle m^j + \delta I_1^n \rangle| < \eta \tag{6-92a}$$

then

$$m^j < x^* < m^j + \delta I_1^n \tag{6-92b}$$

(The proof is left as Exercise 6–8.)

6-13 The Golden Section

Often an experimenter begins searching for an optimum without knowing in advance exactly how many experiments to use. He simply keeps experimenting until the criterion of interest becomes good enough to satisfy him. But even when totally unconcerned about the interval of uncertainty itself, he would like to use a search plan that would rapidly close in on the optimum, since such a plan would reasonably give good values of the criterion as early as possible in the search.

Unfortunately, unless the number of experiments to be performed is known in advance, one cannot use the Fibonacci technique, because I_1^2, which must be known before the first experiment can be located, depends entirely on n, the number of trials [Eq. (6–82)]. One might be tempted to fall back on the dichotomous search method, which does not suffer from this defect. There is, however, another technique which, although nearly as effective as the Fibonacci method, is completely independent of the number of experiments available.

As before, let j represent the number of experiments already run. We may use the same reasoning as before to deduce that the experimental plan should place successive experiments such that [Eq. (6–79)]

$$I_1^{n-j} = I_1^{n-(j-1)} + I_1^{n-(j-2)}$$

just as for the Fibonacci technique. This time, however, we cannot invoke the final condition (Eq. 6–78) that

$$I_1^{n-1} = (2 - \delta)I_1^n$$

since we do not know what n is. Let us instead hold the ratio of successive lengths constant. Following Coxeter and calling this ratio τ (after τομη, the *section*), we have

$$\frac{I_1^{n-j}}{I_1^{n-(j-1)}} = \tau = \frac{I_1^{n-(j+1)}}{I_1^{n-j}} \tag{6-93}$$

By dividing Eq. (6–79) throughout by $I_1^{n-(j-2)}$ and noting that

$$\frac{I_1^{n-(j+1)}}{I_1^{n-(j-1)}} = \tau^2$$

we obtain $\tau^2 = \tau + 1$ as shown in Fig. 6-10. Only one root of this quadratic equation is positive, and so we see that

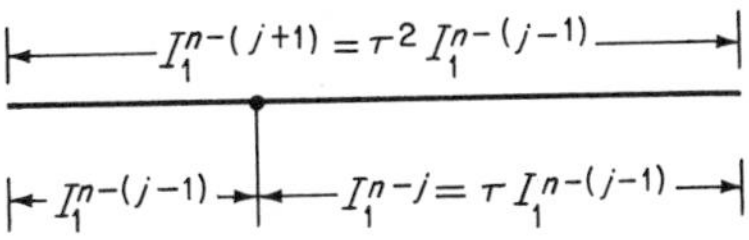

Figure 6-10. The Golden Section.

$$\tau = \frac{1 + \sqrt{5}}{2} = 1.618033989\ldots \tag{6-94}$$

Notice that the negative root is $-1/\tau$. The results of the two experiments will determine which segment is to be explored further. As usual, this remaining segment will contain one of the previous trials, and to continue the search one merely places the next experiments symmetrically in the interval. Once begun, this process may be continued as long as desired. After n experiments, the interval I_1^n remaining is given by

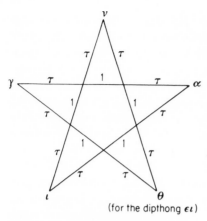

Figure 6-11. Badge of the Pythagoreans. Letters on the vertices spell ὑγίεια, meaning "health" (Ball).

(for the dipthong $\epsilon\iota$)

$$I_1^n = \frac{1}{\tau^{n-1}} \qquad (6\text{-}95)$$

This procedure is called *golden section search*.

Such a name demands justification. Although both Kiefer and Johnson have suggested this search technique in modern times, the ancient geometer Euclid knew how to divide a line segment in this way with only a ruler and compass. This ratio was in fact discovered two centuries before Euclid by the Pythagorean Brotherhood, whose star-shaped badge has all its lines divided in these proportions (Fig. 6-11). Coxeter describes how the many surprising properties of this construction gave it great mystical significance to ancient and medieval scholars, who accorded it the name "golden section." Architects have used it to design structures ranging from the Parthenon to the apartment houses of Le Corbusier. Thus, the venerable and respected "golden section" appears again in a modern application, and it is only right to combine old terms with new in the name "search by golden section."

In order to compare the performance of the search by golden section with the Fibonacci method, we make use of the following relation between the Fibonacci numbers and τ developed by Lucas:

$$A_1^n = \frac{\tau^n - (-\tau)^{-n}}{\sqrt{5}} \qquad (6\text{-}96)$$

When n is very large the second term becomes negligible, giving approximately

$$A_1^n \approx \frac{\tau^n}{\sqrt{5}} \qquad (6\text{-}97)$$

If G_1^n is the interval left after n trials in a search by golden section, and if I_1^n is that remaining after n Fibonacci experiments, then, for large n,

$$\frac{G_1^n}{I_1^n} = \frac{\tau^n}{\sqrt{5}\,\tau^{n-2}} = \frac{\tau^2}{\sqrt{5}} = 1.1708$$

Thus a search by golden section will give a final interval only about 17 per cent longer than that obtainable by Fibonacci search.

Lucas' formula also tells us that when n is large,

$$\frac{A_1^{n-1}}{A_1^n} \approx \frac{1}{\tau} \qquad (6\text{-}98)$$

Combining Eqs. (6–85) and (6–98) we have that for large n, $I_1^2 \approx 1/\tau$. But by Eq. (6–95) $I_1^2 = 1/\tau$ for a search by golden section; thus when n is large both the Fibonacci technique and the search by golden section start practically at the same point. By examining Table 6–1 we see that the ratio of successive Fibonacci numbers approaches 0.618 very soon; even for $n = 5$ the ratio is already 0.600—only 3 per cent low. We may therefore start a search using the golden section technique, switching to the Fibonacci method when we are sufficiently close to the optimum to fix the remaining number of experiments.

For example, we could begin with an indefinite number of experiments, placing early trials according to the golden section. At some point in the search we might be able to predict that four more experiments should be sufficient. We then would place the next trials according to the Fibonacci plan for five experiments (counting the one already in the interval). In this way we would recover most of the efficiency of the Fibonacci technique, even though we had started out with absolutely no idea how many experiments would be needed.

This section has shown how to seek an optimum without knowing in advance how many measurements are needed. Although the golden section scheme is less efficient than those presented earlier, it also requires the least prior information. Greater efficiency is obtainable by Kiefer's method when the number of experiments is predictable. When the resolution can also be estimated in advance, Oliver's plan gives the greatest reduction of all.

6-14 Infinite Starting Interval—Fibonacci Reversed

The methods described so far require knowledge of the length I_1^1 of the starting interval, but this information is not always available. In this case any rational guide to locating the observations can be based upon only two things: the length I_1^n of the final interval desired and the maximum number n of experiments to be expended. The *reverse Fibonacci* scheme to be described tries to establish a finite interval with the first three experiments and then reduce it to length I_1^n with the remaining $n - 3$.

Let the first measurement be made at the predicted location of the optimum, or, if no such estimate can be made, at random. The second should be placed a distance $(A_1^{n-2} - A_1^{n-4}\delta)I_1^n$ from the first, either to the right or left. Then if the two outcomes are distinguishable, the interval becomes bounded at the poorer measurement. No generality is lost in shifting the origin and, if necessary, changing the sign of x to place the optimum on the positive half line

$$0 < x^* < \infty \tag{6-99}$$

with the better result at

$$m_1^2 = (A_1^{n-2} - A_1^{n-4}\,\delta)I_1^n \tag{6-100}$$

Of course, if the first two results are indistinguishable, then the optimum must lie between the two experiments, and a Fibonacci search will finish the reduction with only $n - 3$ more measurements, making $n - 1$ in all. Suppose, however, that this does not happen.

The third measurement is taken at

$$x_1^3 = (A_1^{n-1} - A_1^{n-3} \delta) I_1^n \qquad (6\text{-}101)$$

If the original predictions are correct, then this result is no better than the one already at m_1^2, bracketing the optimum in a finite range.

$$0 < x^* < x_1^3$$

By Eqs. (6–80) and (6–81a), this can be reduced to I_1^n in $n - 3$ more experiments, not counting m_1^2, already in the proper position for Fibonacci search. Thus the final interval desired would be attained in n measurements as hoped.

On the other hand, if the third result is an improvement over the others then the interval is still semi-infinite

$$x_1^2 < x^* < \infty$$

and the next observation should be made at

$$x_1^4 = (A_1^n - A_1^{n-2} \delta) I_1^n + x_1^2 \qquad (6\text{-}102)$$

If it is no better than the others, the interval becomes finite; but the Fibonacci search would require $n - 2$ more observations to reduce the interval to the length desired. In all, this would be a total of $n + 2$ measurements. If only n are available, one must be satisfied with an interval of length $(3 - \delta) I_1^n$.

When the third result is still better, a fifth observation is placed at

$$x_1^5 = (A_1^{n+1} - A_1^{n-1} \delta) I_1^n + x_1^3 \qquad (6\text{-}103)$$

In general, as long as each new observation is better than the rest, the hth measurement is at

$$x_1^h = (A_1^{n+h-4} - A_1^{n+h-6} \delta) I_1^n + x_1^{h-2} \qquad (6\text{-}104)$$

If g is the index of the experiment at which the optimum is finally bracketed,

$$x_1^{q-2} < x^* < x_1^q \qquad (6\text{-}105)$$

Then it takes

$$n + 2(g - n) = 2g - n \qquad (6\text{-}106)$$

observations to achieve a final interval of the desired length I_1^n. If only n experiments are expended, the true final interval is longer than that desired by a factor of $(A_1^{2q+1} - A_1^{2q-1} \delta)$.

Since underestimation of the reduction ratio needed costs twice as many extra measurements as overestimation by the same amount, one should space the first two experiments generously. This requires courage, for one is deliberately forcing the second and third observations to be inferior to the first. Here is one case where boldness carries rewards.

Since the number of experiments is not really known with certainty in advance, one might be tempted to space the observations according to a reverse golden section scheme. This would be slightly wasteful, however, for as soon as the optimum is bracketed, the exact number of experiments needed to finish the job is known. A golden section modification would be in order only when no desired final interval is given. Lack of knowledge of the resolution could be handled by a reverse Kiefer search.

6-15 Odd-Block Search

Avriel has devised a minimax scheme using an odd number of measurements per block—1, 3, 5, 7, etc. It includes Fibonacci search as the special case when $b = 1$. The odd-block schemes are based on Avriel's generalization of Fibonacci's numbers. Let p be any positive integer, and let

$$A_p^0 \equiv 0 \qquad (6\text{-}107)$$

$$A_p^1 \equiv 1 \qquad (6\text{-}108)$$

$$A_p^n = p(A_p^{n-1} + A_p^{n-2}); \qquad n = 2, 3, \dots \qquad (6\text{-}109)$$

The integer p represents the number of pairs contained in a block, so b, the total number of experiments per block, is given by

$$b = 2p - 1 \qquad (6\text{-}110)$$

Clearly the A_1^n are the Fibonacci numbers. Table 6–2 gives values of Avriel's numbers up to 1000 for 1–9 measurements per block.

It will be proved that the following reduction ratio can be obtained with n blocks of b measurements:

$$\frac{I_b^0}{I_b^n} = A_p^{n+1} - p\,\delta A_p^{n-1} \qquad (6\text{-}111)$$

Thus Table 6–2 gives a rough estimate (with δ neglected) of the reduction ratio of 10^{-3}, which takes 16 uniblocks but requires only 8 triblocks, 6 pentablocks, 5 septablocks, or 4 nonablocks. Although increasing the observations per block speeds up the total elapsed time, the efficiency per measurement decreases. For instance, the 1000 to 1 reduction which requires 16 Fibonacci (uniblock) observations would need $3 \times 8 = 24$ observations in blocks of three, 30 in blocks of five, 35 in blocks of seven, and 36 in blocks of nine.

The Avriel numbers can be visualized in terms of rabbit populations by considering the effects of multiple births and birth control. Assume a pair of rabbits newly born on New Year's Eve can bring forth a litter of p pairs of offspring in only one month. After two litters have been born, the original couple is separated so that no more births occur to them after the first two months. This same procedure is followed for all succeeding rabbit generations

TABLE 6–2

AVRIEL'S NUMBERS A_p^n

Blocks required, $n-1$	n	Measurements per block, b	1	3	5	7	9
		Pairs, p	1	2	3	4	5
	0		0	0	0	0	0
0	1		1	1	1	1	1
1	2		1	2	3	4	5
2	3		2	6	12	20	30
3	4		3	16	45	96	185
4	5		5	44	171	464	1075
5	6		8	120	648	2240	
6	7		13	328	2457		
7	8		21	896			
8	9		34	2448			
9	10		55				
10	11		89				
11	12		144				
12	13		233				
13	14		377				
14	15		610				
15	16		987				
16	17		1597				

—they are permitted to give birth to only two litters before the sexes are segregated. The Avriel number A_{2p-1}^n therefore represents the total number of pairs born in each month, assuming p pairs for each couple of parents. Although this is not Fibonacci's model, it could be used to generate the Fibonacci numbers by setting $p = 1$. The principle to be drawn from this analogy between odd-block search and rabbit breeding is that the reduction power of block search, like the reproduction power of the rabbits, depends on the number of pairs in each block. Notice also that the effectiveness grows rapidly because it accumulates for two blocks (or generations) back in time.

Since odd-block search is hard to visualize abstractly, a concrete example (Avriel and Wilde) will be developed at the same time as the general description. Consider the minimax placement of 3 blocks each with 5 experiments per block ($n = 3$, $b = 5$, $p = 3$). For simplicity assume the final interval required to be of unit length

$$I_5^3 = 1 \qquad \qquad (6\text{-}112)$$

and let the resolution be

$$\delta = 0.2 \qquad \qquad (6\text{-}113)$$

Then Eq. (6-111) gives the initial interval as

$$I_5^0 = A_3^4 - 3\,\delta A_3^2$$
$$= 45 - 3(0.2)(3) = 43.2$$

The first measurement in the first block is placed at

$$x_1^1 = (A_p^n - p\,\delta A_p^{n-2})I_{2p-1}^n \qquad \qquad (6\text{-}114)$$

which in the example gives

$$x_1^1 = A_3^3 - 3\,\delta A_3^1$$
$$= 12 - 3(0.2)(1) = 11.4 \qquad \qquad (6\text{-}115)$$

The second measurement in the first block is located at

$$x_2^1 = (p^{-1}A_p^{n+1} - \delta A_p^{n-1})I_{2p-1}^n \qquad \qquad (6\text{-}116)$$

which in the example is

$$x_2^1 = 3^{-1}A_3^4 - \delta A_3^2$$
$$= (3^{-1})(45) - 0.2(3) = 14.4 \qquad \qquad (6\text{-}117)$$

The remaining experiments are performed in positions generated by these first two.

$$x_3^1 = x_1^1 + x_2^1 (= 25.8) \qquad \qquad (6\text{-}118)$$
$$x_4^1 = x_2^1 + x_2^1 (= 28.8) \qquad \qquad (6\text{-}119)$$
$$x_5^1 = x_3^1 + x_2^1 (= 40.2) \qquad \qquad (6\text{-}120)$$

or in general,

$$x_{h+2}^1 = x_h^1 + x_2^1; \qquad h = 1, \ldots, b - 2 \qquad \qquad (6\text{-}121)$$

The first block gives an interval whose length equals x_2^1.

$$I_{2p-1}^1 = x_2^1 = (p^{-1}A_p^{n+1} - \delta A_p^{n-1})I_{2p-1}^n \qquad \qquad (6\text{-}122)$$

It contains an observation a distance x_1^1 from one end which is a bench-mark for locating those of the second block. Figure 6-12 shows the location of the first of three pentablocks in the example.

As for Fibonacci search, which is after all a special case of odd-block search, deployment of the second block is different because of the observation already in the interval. The strategy for the second block is, however, typical of that for all those following the first. The first experiment is placed symmetrically with respect to m^{j-1}, the one already in the interval

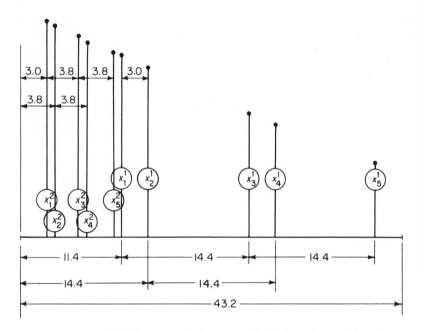

Figure 6-12. The first two of three pentablocks ($p = 3$) $\delta = 0.2$, unit final interval.

$$x_1^j = l^j + r^j - m^{j-1} \tag{6-123}$$

To simplify the discussion, assume that x_1^j is nearer the left end than the right so that in general

$$x_1^j = l^j + (A_p^{n-j+1} - p\,\delta A_p^{n-j-1})I_{2p-1}^n \tag{6-124}$$

In the example $m^1 = x_1^1 = 11.4$, $l^1 = 0$, and $r^1 = x_2^1 = 14.4$, so that

$$x_1^2 = 0 + 14.4 - 11.4 = 3.0$$

Next one computes the length of the interval to remain after the block has been evaluated. For the jth block ($j > 1$), this is given by the following generalization of Eq. (6–122):

$$I_{2p-1}^j = (p^{-1}A_p^{n-j+2} - \delta A_p^{n-j})I_{2p-1}^n \qquad (j > 1) \tag{6-125}$$

In the example this is

$$\begin{aligned}
I_5^2 &= 3^{-1}A_3^3 - \delta A_3^1 \\
&= (3^{-1})(12) - (0.2)(1) = 3.8
\end{aligned} \tag{6-126}$$

The second experiment is placed this distance from the end of the interval nearest x_1^j.

$$x_2^j = l^j + I_{2p-1}^j \tag{6-127}$$

The remaining $b - 2$ observations are spaced from the first two in multiples of the distance I_{2p-1}^j.

$$x_h^j = x_{h-2}^j + x_2^j$$
$$= x_{h-2}^j + I_{2p-1}^j; \qquad h = 3,\ldots,b \qquad (6\text{-}128)$$

Thus in the example $x_1^2 = 3.0$, $x_2^2 = 3.8$, $x_3^2 = 6.8$, $x_4^2 = 7.6$, and $x_5^2 = 10.6$. The measurement remaining from the first block is at 11.4. Evaluation of this block gives an interval of length 3.8, for illustrative purposes placed at the left to simplify Fig. 6–12.

The rules for the third (and subsequent) blocks are just like those for the second. At the last block $j = n$, and Eq. (6–125) reduces to

$$I_{2p-1}^n = (p^{-1}A_p^2 - \delta A_p^0)I_{2p-1}^n = I_{2p-1}^n$$

as required. The reader can verify that the third and final pentablock in the example should have its measurements at $x_1^3 = 0.8$, $x_2^3 = 1.0$, $x_3^3 = 1.8$, $x_4^3 = 2.0$, and $x_5^3 = 2.8$ ($m^2 = 3.0$), giving a unit final interval as required. Notice that the last block is always a search with p uniform pairs.

6-16 Minimax Proof

The preceding section described Avriel's odd-block search method and showed that it can achieve the reduction ratio given in Eq. (6–111). It remains to establish that the procedure is minimax among all procedures having a constant number of observations per block. Before doing this let us emphasize that, except for uniblock search, there are other procedures which can achieve the same, although not better, reduction ratio, but they are more difficult to describe mathematically. There are even plans by which one, if lucky, can achieve the same reduction ratio with fewer measurements in some blocks. Such schemes are excluded here because their advantages, depending on unpredictable good fortune, are not detected by the cautious minimax measure of effectiveness. (Exercise 6–9 describes a situation in which it may be possible to save an experiment in the second of two triblocks.)

The demonstration here closely follows Avriel's. No generality is lost in assuming the final interval is of unit length.

$$I_{2p-1}^n = 1 \qquad (6\text{-}129)$$

To avoid resolution difficulties, assume also that

$$\delta \leq \frac{1}{2} \qquad (6\text{-}130)$$

Let an overbar represent the observations and intervals for any n-block search plan with $2p - 1$ measurements per block which differs from Avriel's in the placement of at least one experiment and which is sure to give a unit final interval. That is, the search plan has locations $\bar{x}_1^1, \bar{x}_2^1, \ldots, \bar{x}_{2p-1}^1$; $\bar{x}_1^2, \ldots, \bar{x}_{2p-1}^n$ and yields intervals $\bar{I}_{2p-1}^0, \bar{I}_{2p-1}^1, \ldots, \bar{I}_{2p-1}^n \, (= 1)$. We must prove that

$$I_{2p-1}^0 \geq \bar{I}_{2p-1}^0 \tag{6-131}$$

for all possible search procedures. This means that Avriel's odd-block method gives the largest possible reduction ratio.

Since the first block is different from the others because it has one less measurement, the proof is slightly different from the usual inductive demonstration. Ordinary backward induction on j, the number of blocks performed, is used to establish that

$$I_{2p-1}^j \geq \bar{I}_{2p-1}^j \qquad \text{for } j = n - 1, \ldots, 1 \tag{6-132}$$

Then the result for $j = 1$ is used to generate the optimality proof of Eq. (6-131).

The induction starts by considering $j = n - 1$, since Eq. (6-132) is trivial for $j = n$. According to Eq. (6-125),

$$\begin{aligned}
I_{2p-1}^{n-1} &= p^{-1}A_p^3 - \delta A_p^1 \\
&= p^{-1}(p)(A_p^2 + A_p^1) - \delta A_p^1 \\
&= p + 1 - \delta
\end{aligned}$$

There is only one block, the last, to be placed, and there are $2p$ measurements to be taken, one of them the best of the first $n - 1$ blocks. In Section 6–06, Eq. (6–59), it was proved that the interval given above is the longest reducible to one of unit length with a single simultaneous block of p uniform pairs. As noted in Section 6–15, Avriel's method arranges the last block as a search by uniform pairs, so no other scheme can reduce a larger interval to unit length. Thus Eq. (6–132) is true for $j = n - 1$, which is the first phase of the induction.

To make the backward induction step, assume that Eq. (6–132) is true for $j = h$, with $1 < h \leq n - 1$. It will be shown that this implies the truth of Eq. (6–132) for $j = h - 1$. By Eq. (6–125),

$$I_{2p-1}^h = p^{-1}A_p^{n-h+2} - \delta A_p^{n-h} \tag{6-133}$$

No generality is lost in assuming that m^{h-1}, the point already measured in the hth interval, is nearer the right end than the left so that its location is given by Eqs. (6–123) and (6–124) as

$$\begin{aligned}
m^{h-1} &= r^h - (x_1^h - l^h) \\
&= I_{2p-1}^h + l^h - (A_p^{n-h+1} - p\,\delta A_p^{n-h-1}) \\
&= l^h + A_p^{n-h} - p\,\delta A_p^{n-h-2}
\end{aligned} \tag{6-134}$$

By the induction hypothesis, any competing search strategy must have placed the hth block so that no interval longer than I_{2p-1}^h could have occurred, which implies that

$$\bar{x}_2^h - \bar{l}^h \leq p^{-1}A_p^{n-h+2} - \delta A_p^{n-h} \tag{6-135}$$

$$\bar{x}_{g+2}^h - \bar{x}_g^h \leq p^{-1}A_p^{n-h+2} - \delta A_p^{n-h}; \qquad g = 1, 2, \ldots, 2p - 3 \tag{6-136}$$

$$\bar{m}^h - \bar{x}_{2p-2}^h \leq p^{-1}A_p^{n-h+2} - \delta A_p^{n-h} \tag{6-137}$$

$$\bar{r}^h - \bar{m}^h \leq A_p^{n-h+1} - p\,\delta A_p^{n-h-1} \tag{6-138}$$

To obtain the longest interval which can be covered by this competing plan add Eqs. (6-135), (6-137), and (6-138) to Eqs. (6-136) for even g.

$$\bar{r}^h - \bar{l}^h = \bar{I}_{2p-1}^{h-1} \leq p(p^{-1})A_p^{n-h+2} + A_p^{n-h+1} - p\delta(A_p^{n-h} + A_p^{n-h-1})$$
$$= p^{-1}A_p^{n-h+3} - \delta A_p^{n-h+1}$$

Hence $\qquad\qquad\qquad\qquad \bar{I}_{2p-1}^{h-1} \leq I_{2p-1}^{h-1}$

for $1 < h < n - 1$. This means that no competing scheme can start with an interval longer than Avriel's block method and still achieve a unit final interval. It completes the inductive proof of Eq. (6-132), in particular establishing that

$$\bar{I}_{2p-1}^1 \leq I_{2p-1}^1 \tag{6-139}$$

It remains to show that a similar relation holds for starting intervals, that is, that

$$\bar{I}_{2p-1}^0 \leq I_{2p-1}^0 \tag{6-140}$$

To prove this, observe that the $2p - 1$ experiments of the first block must be placed so as to give an interval $\bar{I}_{2p-1}^1$ no longer than that for Avriel's method I_{2p-1}^1. Otherwise Eq. (6-139) would be violated. Thus

$$\bar{x}_2^1 \leq I_{2p-1}^1 \tag{6-141}$$

$$\bar{x}_{g+2}^1 - \bar{x}_g^1 \leq I_{2p-1}^1; \qquad g = 1, \ldots, 2p - 3 \tag{6-142}$$

$$\bar{I}_{2p-1}^0 - \bar{x}_{2p-2}^1 \leq I_{2p-1}^1 \tag{6-143}$$

Addition of Eqs. (6-141), (6-142) for even g, and (6-143) gives

$$\bar{I}_{2p-1}^0 \leq pI_{2p-1}^1 = p[p^{-1}A_p^{n+1} - \delta A^{n-1}]$$
$$= A_p^{n+1} - p\,\delta A_p^{n-1}$$

But by Eq. (6-111) the right member of this inequality is I_{2p-1}^0, the initial interval for Avriel's procedure. Therefore $\bar{I}_{2p-1}^0 \leq I_{2p-1}^0$, as asserted in Eq. (6-131). Hence no procedure can reduce an initial interval larger than Avriel's to unit length in n blocks of $2p - 1$ measurements.

6-17 Gilding the Blocks

The block search methods described so far require prior knowledge of the number of blocks and the resolution. The modification needed when the resolution cannot be predicted is a straightforward extension of Kiefer's Fibonacci search. One simply ignores the terms involving δ until the last block is placed, obtaining a slightly larger final interval than would be possible if δ had been known in advance. When the number of blocks is not specified, a generalized version of the golden section procedure, named by Avriel the *golden block* search procedure, is appropriate.

To derive it let us begin by finding a simple equation for calculating large Avriel numbers directly, bypassing the tedious business of computing the entire sequence of smaller numbers. Consider the following function of a parameter z:

$$A_p^0 + A_p^1 z^{-1} + A_p^2 z^{-2} + \cdots = \sum_{n=0}^{\infty} A_p^n z^{-n} \equiv A_p^n \langle z \rangle \qquad (6\text{-}144)$$

This function is an infinite series in negative integer powers of the parameter z whose coefficients are the Avriel numbers A_p^n. Control engineers would recognize it as the "z transform" of the sequence of A_p^n; mathematicians would perhaps notice its resemblance to the "generating functions" of difference equation theory. The z transform of the sequence A_p^{n+1} can be written in terms of that for A_p^n as follows:

$$\begin{aligned} A_p^{n+1} \langle z \rangle \equiv \sum_{n=0}^{\infty} A_p^{n+1} z^{-n} &= z \sum_{n=0}^{\infty} A_p^n z^{-n} - zA_p^0 \\ &= zA_p^n \langle z \rangle \end{aligned} \qquad (6\text{-}145)$$

The last term vanishes because $A_p^0 = 0$ by definition. By similar reasoning the z transform of the sequence of A_p^{n+2} can be written (Exercise 6–10).

$$\begin{aligned} A_p^{n+2} \langle z \rangle &= z^2 A_p^n \langle z \rangle - zA_p^1 \\ &= z^2 A_p^n \langle z \rangle - z \end{aligned} \qquad (6\text{-}146)$$

The recursion relation generating the Avriel numbers is, Eq. (6–109)

$$A_p^{n+2} = p(A_p^{n+1} + A_p^n); \qquad n = 0, 1, 2, \ldots \qquad (6\text{-}147)$$

Taking the z transform of each term of Eq. (6–147) and then applying Eqs. (6–145) and (6–146) gives

$$z^2 A_p^n \langle z \rangle - z = p[zA_p^n \langle z \rangle + A_p^n \langle z \rangle]$$

which can be solved for $A_p^n \langle z \rangle$ as an algebraic function of z.

$$A_p^n \langle z \rangle = \frac{z}{z^2 - p(z + 1)} \qquad (6\text{-}148)$$

If the numerator were divided by the denominator, an infinite series in negative powers of z would result whose coefficients would be the Avriel numbers. It remains to find a simple formula for each coefficient.

Let τ_p be the positive root of the denominator of Eq. (6–148). That is, τ_p (> 0) satisfies

$$\tau_p^2 - p\tau_p - p = 0 \qquad (6\text{-}149)$$

Completion of the square gives

$$\tau_p = \tfrac{1}{2}[p + \sqrt{p^2 + 4p}] \tag{6-150}$$

There is also a negative root τ_p^- given by

$$\tau_p^- = \tfrac{1}{2}[p - \sqrt{p^2 + 4p}] \tag{6-151}$$

which is related in a simple way to the positive root. Multiply Eq. (6–151) by

$$(p + \sqrt{p^2 + 4p})(2\tau_p)^{-1} = 1$$

to obtain

$$\tau_p^- = [p^2 - (p^2 + 4p)](4\tau_p)^{-1} = -p\tau_p^{-1} \tag{6-152}$$

Hence the denominator of Eq. (6–148) can be written

$$z^2 - p(z + 1) = (z - \tau_p)(z + p\tau_p^{-1}) \tag{6-153}$$

which permits a partial fraction expansion of the z transform.

$$A_p^n\langle z \rangle = \frac{1}{\sqrt{p^2 + 4p}}\left[\frac{\tau_p}{z - \tau_p} + \frac{p}{\tau_p(z + p\tau_p^{-1})}\right] \tag{6-154}$$

Each term can be expanded as a geometric series in z:

$$\frac{\tau_p}{z - \tau_p} = \frac{\tau_p z^{-1}}{1 - \tau_p z^{-1}} = \tau_p z^{-1} + \tau_p^2 z^{-2} + \tau_p^3 z^{-3} + \cdots \tag{6-155}$$

$$\frac{p\tau_p^{-1}}{z + p\tau_p^{-1}} = p\tau_p^{-1}z^{-1} - p^2\tau_p^{-2}z^{-2} + p^3\tau_p^{-3}z^{-3} - \cdots \tag{6-156}$$

When Eqs. (6–155) and (6–156) are substituted into (6–154), the coefficients are the Avriel numbers.

$$A_p^n = \frac{\tau_p^n - (-p)^n\tau_p^{-n}}{\sqrt{p^2 + 4p}} \tag{6-157}$$

Values of τ_p for $1 \le p \le 10$ are given in Table 6–3.

TABLE 6-3

VALUES OF τ_p

p	1	2	3	4	5	6	7	8	9	10
τ_p	1.6180	2.73205	3.79129	4.82842	5.85410	6.87298	7.88745	8.89898	9.9084	10.9161

Since $\tau_p > p$ and $p/\tau_p < 1$, the second term of Eq. (6–157) becomes negligible with respect to the first even for small n, especially as p increases. Thus the ratios of successive Avriel numbers are approximately constant.

$$\frac{A_p^{n+1}}{A_p^n} \approx \tau_p \tag{6-158}$$

If the second term of Eq. (6–125), the resolution allowance in the formula for the interval remaining after j blocks $(j > 1)$, is neglected, then ratios of successive intervals after the first also are constant.

$$\frac{I_{2p-1}^{j+1}}{I_{2p-1}^{j}} \approx \frac{A_p^{n-j+1}}{A_p^{n-j+2}} \approx \tau_p^{-1} \tag{6-159}$$

This suggests the following generalization of the golden section method to blocks containing more than one experiment: Let the first measurement in the first block be taken at

$$x_1^1 = \tau_p^{-1} I_{2p-1}^0 \tag{6-160}$$

The second at

$$x_2^1 = p^{-1} I_{2p-1}^0 \tag{6-161}$$

and the rest according to

$$x_{h+2}^1 = x_h^1 + p^{-1} I_{2p-1}^0; \qquad h = 1, \ldots, 2p-3 \tag{6-162}$$

This gives a rightmost interval of length

$$I_{2p-1}^0 - x_{2p-2}^1 = I_{2p-1}^0 - p^{-1}(p-1)I_{2p-1}^0$$
$$= p^{-1} I_{2p-1}^0$$

which is also the length of every interval left after the first block.

Thus
$$I_{2p-1}^1 = p^{-1} I_{2p-1}^0 \tag{6-163}$$

and this interval will have in it a measurement a distance $\tau_p^{-1} I_{2p-1}^0$ from one end. For simplicity assume that it is nearer the right end so that

$$m^1 = l' + \tau_p^{-1} I_{2p-1}^0 \tag{6-164}$$

The first measurement in the second block is placed symmetrically with respect to m^1.

$$x_1^2 = l^1 + r^1 - (l^1 + \tau_p^{-1} I_{2p-1}^0)$$
$$= l^1 + (r^1 - l^1) - \tau_p^{-1} I_{2p-1}^0$$
$$= l^1 + (p^{-1} - \tau_p^{-1}) I_{2p-1}^0 \tag{6-165}$$
$$= l^1 + (1 - p\tau_p^{-1}) I_{2p-1}^1 \tag{6-166}$$

The second observation is made a distance from the left end equal to the interval to remain after the second block.

$$x_2^2 = l^1 + I_{2p-1}^2 = l^1 + p^{-1}\tau_p^{-1} I_{2p-1}^0$$
$$= l^1 + \tau_p^{-1} I_{2p-1}^1 \tag{6-167}$$

The rest are placed according to

$$x_{h+2}^2 = x_h^2 + p^{-1}\tau_p^{-1} I_{2p-1}^0$$
$$= x_h^2 + \tau_p^{-1} I_{2p-1}^1; \qquad h = 1, \ldots, 2p-3 \tag{6-168}$$

This gives a rightmost interval of

$$r^1 - x_{2p-1}^2 = \{1 - [(1 - p\tau_p^{-1}) + (p-1)\tau_p^{-1}]\} I_{2p-1}^1$$
$$= \tau_p^{-1} I_{2p-1}^1 = p^{-1}\tau_p^{-1} I_{2p-1}^0 \tag{6-169}$$

This is in fact the length of every interval possible, confirming Eq. (6–167). This time the interval has been reduced by a factor of τ_p^{-1} (the factor was p^{-1} the first time). The interval has in it a measurement placed a distance

$$(1 - p\tau_p^{-1})I^1_{2p-1} = p\tau_p^{-2}I^1_{2p-1} \tag{6-170}$$

from one end. For simplicity make it nearer the right end, so that

$$\begin{aligned}
m^2 &= l^2 + p\tau_p^{-2}I^1_{2p-1} \\
&= l^2 + p\tau_p^{-1}I^2_{2p-1} = l^2 + \tau_p^{-2}I^0_{2p-1}
\end{aligned} \tag{6-171}$$

In general, after the jth block ($j > 1$) the interval's length is

$$I^j_{2p-1} = p^{-1}\tau_p^{1-j}I^0_{2p-1} = \tau_p^{-1}I^{j-1}_{2p-1} \tag{6-172}$$

and there is an observation already in it either at

$$m^j = l^j + \tau_p^{-j}I^0_{2p-1} = l^j + p\tau_p^{-1}I^j_{2p-1} \tag{6-173}$$

or at

$$m^j = r^j - \tau_p^{-j}I^0_{2p-1} = r^j - p\tau_p^{-1}I^j_{2p-1} \tag{6-174}$$

In the former case (the latter is handled symmetrically), one places the experiments according to

$$x^{j+1}_1 = l^j + (1 - p\tau_p^{-1})I^j_{2p-1} \tag{6-175}$$

$$x^{j+1}_2 = l^j + \tau_p^{-1}I^j_{2p-1} \tag{6-176}$$

$$x^{j+1}_{h+2} = x^{j+1}_h + \tau_p^{-1}I^j_{2p-1}; \qquad h = 1,\ldots,2p - 3 \tag{6-177}$$

This gives an interval of length

$$I^{j+1}_{2p-1} = \tau_p^{-1}I^j_{2p-1} \tag{6-178}$$

consistent with Eq. (6–172). (See Exercise 6–11.) This golden block procedure gives a reduction ratio of

$$\frac{I^0_{2p-1}}{I^n_{2p-1}} = p\tau_p^{n-1} \tag{6-179}$$

For large n the Avriel numbers are approximated by [see Eq. (6–157)]

$$A^n_p \approx \tau_p^n(p^2 + 4p)^{-1/2} \tag{6-180}$$

so that according to Eq. (6–111) the ratio

$$\frac{\tau_p^{n+1}(p^2 + 4p)^{-1/2}}{p\tau_p^{n-1}} = p^{-1}\tau_p^{-2}(p^2 + 4p)^{-1/2} \tag{6-181}$$

measures the ratio of the final interval obtained by golden block to that given by the optimal block search procedure. The values of these quantities,

TABLE 6–4
RELATIVE EFFECTIVENESS OF GOLDEN BLOCK SEARCH

p	1	2	3	4	5	10
$p^{-1}\tau_p^{-2}(p^2 + 4p)^{-\frac{1}{2}}$	1.17	1.077	1.044	1.032	1.021	1.009

given in Table 6–4, show that the effectiveness of golden block search approaches that of optimal block search as p increases.

6-18 Multivariable Elimination

After seeing how effectively the elimination techniques cut down an interval of uncertainty when there is a single independent variable, one might ask how they behave in multivariable situations. The answer is disappointing, and scant space will be devoted to them. The principal difficulty is that it is much harder to eliminate portions of a square, cube, or multidimensional generalization than it is to cut away parts of a line. In the multivariable case, the class of functions on which elimination techniques can be used is more restricted than when there is but one variable. Moreover, the region of uncertainty remaining after several eliminations may be awkward to describe mathematically. In practice, multivariable problems are more usually attacked by the "hill-climbing" methods of Chapter 7 than by elimination techniques. Since, however, the data gathered to implement a hill-climbing procedure can often be used to eliminate part of the region, elimination techniques are discussed briefly here.

At present there are two principal multivariable elimination methods. The first, called the *contour tangents* procedure, closes in more rapidly on the optimum but produces irregularly shaped regions of uncertainty hard to visualize in multidimensional space. The second, called the *multivariable dichotomous* procedure, gives regions of uncertainty which are hypercubes (the multidimensional generalization of the square) of predictable size so that it is almost the only multivariable technique with measurable effectiveness. But this efficiency, although measurable, is not very high.

The descriptions to follow are shortened by treating only cases where the objective is differentiable and the first partial derivatives can be computed directly and accurately. In circumstances where such derivatives are not available, one can adapt these methods in ways described at the beginning of the next chapter.

6-19 Contour Tangents

Both multivariable elimination schemes are based on properties associated with a first-order approximation of the objective function in the neighborhood of a point $\mathbf{x}^0$, which is a vector of feasible values of the independent variables. Let the first partial derivatives $\partial y/\partial x_i$ be evaluated and assembled into a *gradient vector* ∇y.

$$\nabla y \equiv \left(\frac{\partial y}{\partial x_1}, \ldots, \frac{\partial y}{\partial x_N} \right) \qquad (6\text{-}182)$$

Let Δx be a vector of perturbations about x^0.

$$\Delta x \equiv (\Delta x_1, \ldots, \Delta x_N) \equiv (x_1 - x_1^0, \ldots, x_N - x_N^0) \qquad (6\text{-}183)$$

Then a first-order approximation of the change Δy in the objective resulting from this perturbation is

$$\Delta y = \nabla y \, \Delta x' = \sum_{n=1}^{N} \frac{\partial y}{\partial x_n} \Delta x_n \qquad (6\text{-}184)$$

Suppose y is to be maximized; then in the neighborhood of x^0, perturbations which improve the objective satisfy the inequality

$$\Delta y = \nabla y \, \Delta x' > 0$$

Whereas undesirable perturbations are those satisfying

$$\Delta y = \nabla y \, \Delta x' < 0$$

The boundary between these two groups of perturbations is the set of Δx satisfying

$$\Delta y = \nabla y \, \Delta x' = 0 \qquad (6\text{-}185)$$

Since at x^0 the components of ∇y are known constants, this equation is linear and describes a hyperplane of $N - 1$ dimensions passing through x^0. This hyperplane is called the *contour tangent* because it is tangent to the contour—the curved set of points x^0 satisfying

$$y\langle x \rangle = y\langle x^0 \rangle$$

that is, having the same value of y as at x^0. Figures 6–13 through 6–16 show contours and contour tangents for cases with two independent variables.

Suppose the objective function is known to be differentiably unimodal on the straight line passing through the point x^0 and the peak at x^*. Since all points on this line are given by $\lambda(x^* - x^0)$, where λ is a parameter taking on any real values (positive, negative, or zero), the assumption is that the function $y\langle \lambda(x^* - x^0) \rangle$ is strictly unimodal in the single variable λ. This means that $y\langle \lambda(x^* - x^0) \rangle$ strictly increases with increasing λ, and in particular that the slope at x^0 is positive.

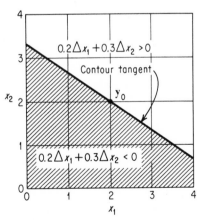

Figure 6-13. Projection of contour tangent.

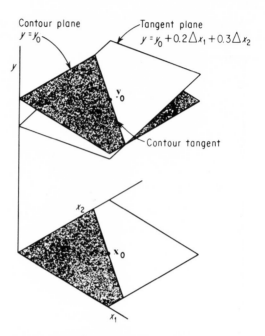

Figure 6-14. Contour tangent in space.

$$\frac{\partial y\langle \lambda(\mathbf{x}^* - \mathbf{x}^0)\rangle}{\partial \lambda} > 0 \tag{6-186}$$

But since along this path

$$\Delta \mathbf{x} = \lambda(\mathbf{x}^* - \mathbf{x}^0) \tag{6-187}$$

differentiation of Eq. (6–184) with respect to λ gives, after substitution of Eq. (6–187),

$$\frac{\partial y\langle \lambda(\mathbf{x}^* - \mathbf{x}^0)\rangle}{\partial \lambda} = \nabla y(\mathbf{x}^* - \mathbf{x}^0)' \tag{6-188}$$

Thus Eqs. (6–186) and (6–188) together establish that

$$\nabla y(\mathbf{x}^* - \mathbf{x}^0)' > 0 \tag{6-189}$$

This means that the maximum must be above the contour tangent, and Eq. (6–189) can be added to the original set of constraints defining the feasible region $\mathscr{F}$. Doing this eliminates all points below the contour tangent because they violate Eq. (6–189). Figure 6–15 illustrates this situation.

This elimination of a large fraction of the original feasible region is prudent only if one can be sure that the objective is differentiably unimodal on the straight line from $\mathbf{x}^0$ to $\mathbf{x}^*$. Fortunately many objective functions have this property at every point, in which case they are said to be *strongly unimodal*. Such functions (Figs. 6–15, 6–16, and 6–17) lend themselves to an iteration

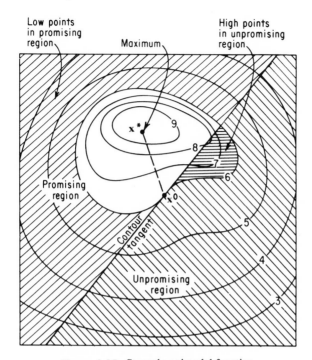

Figure 6-15. Strongly unimodal function.

of the elimination procedure which is called the method of *contour tangents* (Wilde, 1963; OSM, chap. 4). One determines the contour tangent at a point **x** in the interior of the feasible region, as at point 1 in Fig. 6–17, and cuts down the region of uncertainty. Then another contour tangent is measured at a point inside the remaining region (point 2 in Fig. 6–17). Repetition of this procedure gives successively smaller regions irregular in shape. Five applications of the method are illustrated in Fig. 6–17.

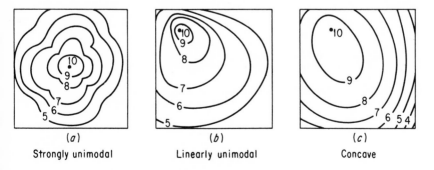

Figure 6-16. Strongly unimodal functions.

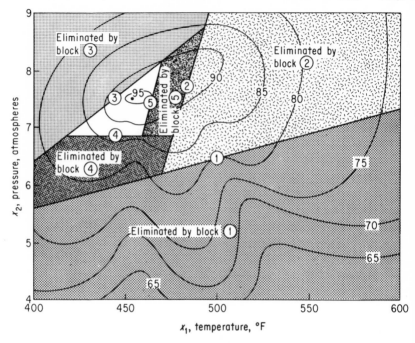

Figure 6-17. Contour tangent elimination.

The new point inside a cut-down region might be chosen in several ways (four are given in OSM), but discussion of such details is not warranted here because the method has not really been developed to the point of usefulness. Although the contour tangents procedure should reduce the region rapidly, it gives regions of such irregular shape that the area remaining cannot be predicted in advance. Thus there is no way to specify the "optimal" location of a new point.

The only quantitative result to date concerning the method of contour tangents is that of Newman, who locates each new point at the centroid of the region remaining. He requires the objective function to be strictly unimodal on every straight line, not just on those rays passing through the maximum. Such functions are called *quasi-concave* because each contour encloses a convex set of points (Arrow and Enthoven). Newman also considered the variant of the problem in which the function can be evaluated only on a finite set of points on a square lattice with k points in each dimension. He showed that, in the two-dimensional case, application of the contour tangents method using centroids will take less than

$$10 \ln (k + 1) + 6 \qquad (6\text{-}190)$$

evaluations of the function, where measurement of the function y and its gradient ∇y is counted as 3 evaluations in all. For 99 grid points in each direction (9801 points in all) the method could find the best after fewer than 29 observations (see Exercise 6–12). No results are yet available for contour tangents in cases with three or more independent variables. Newman has indicated, however, that upper bounds on the number of experiments grow as the logarithm of the number of lattice points k in each dimension. This is comforting because the total number of points is k^N.

6-20 Multivariable Dichotomous Elimination

By sacrificing efficiency for predictable preformance, one can modify the contour tangents method to give regions which are hypercubes of foreseeable size. Suppose the objective function to be differentiably unimodal on every straight line parallel to one of the coordinate axes. This property (to be described formally in the next paragraph), called *rectangular unimodality*, although not as restrictive as quasi-concavity, is more so than strong unimodality. Now consider the highest point u^{n-1} on any $(n-1)$-dimensional hyperplane perpendicular (orthogonal) to one of the coordinate axes. For simplicity, assume the feasible region is a unit hypercube in two dimensions, a square as in Fig. 6–18. A one-dimensional hyperplane is in this example simply a straight line; to be definite, assume its equation is $x_2 = \frac{1}{2}$ so that it is parallel to the x_1 axis as shown. The high point u^1 is, let us say, at $(\frac{2}{3}, \frac{1}{2})$. At u^1 the line is tangent to the contour there, for if it were not, it could not be the high point on the line (see Exercise 6–13). Hence the $(n-1)$-dimensional

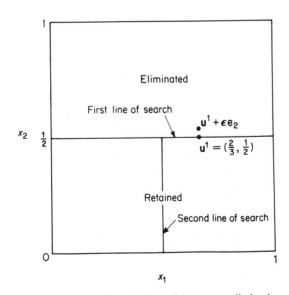

Figure 6-18. Two-variable dichotomous elimination.

hyperplane is the contour tangent passing through the point $\mathbf{u}^{n-1}$. In the method of contour tangents, one chooses a point and then determines the contour tangent passing through it. The procedure to be described chooses a hyperplane and then determines the point where it is tangent to a contour. Finding such a point is itself a maximization problem of one less dimension than the original one. This subproblem can be broken down into problems of lower dimension until ultimately unidimensional searches are employable.

Since the orientation and location of contour tangents can now be chosen, they are selected to give hypercubic regions. When the point of tangency $\mathbf{u}^{n-1}$ has been determined, a single additional measurement in the neighborhood, but not on, the hyperplane, is taken. If the new result is better, then the region on the other side of the hyperplane is eliminated; if worse, then the region on the same side is discarded. Iteration of the procedure gives ultimately a rectangular region as small as resolution will allow. It will be shown that successive hyperplanes should bisect each region remaining, so the procedure has the name *multivariable dichotomous elimination* (Wilde, January, 1965).

Formally, let $\mathscr{F}$ be an n-dimensional convex domain of points $\mathbf{x}$, and let $\mathbf{v}^h$ be a vector in $\mathscr{F}$ having its first h components variable but the last $n - h$ components fixed.

$$v_i^h = \begin{cases} x_i \text{ (variable)}; & i = 1, \ldots, h \\ c_i \text{ (constant)}; & i = h + 1, \ldots, n \end{cases} \tag{6-191}$$

The set of $\mathbf{v}^h$ form an h-dimensional hyperplane orthogonal to the x_{h+1}, $\ldots, x_n$ axes. Let $\mathbf{u}^h$ be the point where $y\langle\mathbf{v}^h\rangle$ is maximum in this hyperplane.

$$y\langle\mathbf{u}^h\rangle = \max_{\mathbf{v}^h} y\langle\mathbf{v}^h\rangle \tag{6-192}$$

Then $y\langle\mathbf{x}\rangle$ is said to be *rectangularly unimodal* if, for every set of $n - h$ constants c_i, for every ordering of the indices i, and for all $0 \leq \lambda \leq 1$,

$$y\langle\lambda\mathbf{u}^{h+1} + (1 - \lambda)\mathbf{u}^h\rangle \geq y\langle\mathbf{u}^h\rangle; \qquad h = 0, \ldots, n - 1 \tag{6-193}$$

with equality only when $\lambda = 0$. When $h = 0$, the minimax Bolzano procedure may be used to find $\mathbf{u}^1$, since Eq. (6–193) guarantees that $y\langle\mathbf{v}^1\rangle$ is unimodal on the straight line formed by the $\mathbf{v}^1$. If derivatives are not readily available, Fibonacci search can be used when $h = 0$. Differentiation of $y\langle\mathbf{x}\rangle$ with respect to λ and evaluation of $\partial y/\partial\lambda$ at $\mathbf{u}^h$ (where $\lambda = 0$) gives

$$\nabla y(\mathbf{u}^{h+1} - \mathbf{u}^h)' > 0 \tag{6-194}$$

where ∇y is evaluated at $\mathbf{v}^h = \mathbf{u}^h$. By Eqs. (6–191) and (6–192), the last $n - h - 1$ components of both $\mathbf{u}^h$ and $\mathbf{u}^{h+1}$ are identical, so that

$$u_i^{h+1} - u_i^h = 0; \qquad i = h + 2, \ldots, n \tag{6-195}$$

Moreover,

$$\frac{\partial y}{\partial x_i} = 0; \qquad i = 1, \ldots, h \tag{6-196}$$

because $y\langle \mathbf{v}^h \rangle$ is maximum at $\mathbf{u}^h$. Eqs. (6-194)–(6-196) together give

$$\frac{\partial y}{\partial x_{h+1}} (u_{h+1}^{h+1} - c_{h+1}) > 0; \qquad h = 1, \ldots, n \tag{6-197}$$

This suggests how to use knowledge of the location of $\mathbf{u}^h$, the maximum in an h-dimensional hyperplane, to narrow down the region known to contain $\mathbf{u}^{h+1}$, the maximum in the hyperplane of one higher dimension.

Let $\mathbf{e}_{h+1}$ be the $(h + 1)$th unit vector, having its $(h + 1)$th component unity and the rest zero. The differentiability of $y\langle \mathbf{x} \rangle$ guarantees that for a sufficiently small positive number ϵ,

$$\sigma\left\langle \frac{\partial y}{\partial x_{h+1}} \right\rangle = \sigma\langle y\langle \mathbf{u}^h + \epsilon \mathbf{e}_{h+1} \rangle - y\langle \mathbf{u}^h \rangle\rangle \tag{6-198}$$

where the *signum function* $\sigma\langle z \rangle$, encountered in Chapter 4, is defined in this context as

$$\sigma\langle z \rangle \equiv \frac{z}{|z|} \qquad (z \neq 0) \tag{6-199}$$

Equations (6-197) and (6-198) imply that

$$u_{h+1}^{h+1} > c_{h+1} \tag{6-200}$$

if and only if

$$y\langle \mathbf{u}^h + \epsilon \mathbf{e}_{h+1} \rangle > y\langle \mathbf{u}^h \rangle \tag{6-201}$$

Thus only one more measurement after finding $\mathbf{u}^h$ permits elimination of the entire $(h + 1)$-dimensional region not satisfying Eqs. (6-200) and (6-201). Since one does not know in advance which side of the dividing tangent hyperplane will be eliminated, it is best from the minimax point of view to center it.

That is, if $\mathcal{F}$ is the unit hypercube $0 \leq x_i \leq 1$ $(i = 1, \ldots, n)$, then half of the hypervolume can be eliminated by finding, in the $n - 1$-dimensional hyperplane $x_n = \frac{1}{2}$, the high point $\mathbf{u}^{n-1}$ and then evaluating $y\langle \mathbf{u}^{n-1} + \epsilon \mathbf{e}_n \rangle$. Figure 6–18 shows this for $n = 2$ and $\epsilon = 1/32$. Either all $0 \leq x_n \leq 1/2$ or $1/2 \leq x_n \leq 1$ will be eliminated, as shown in Fig. 6–18, in which the latter case obtains. The procedure is repeated in the region remaining, the lower rectangle in Fig. 6–18. This means finding the high point on the line segment $x_1 = 1/2$, $0 \leq x_2 \leq 1/2$.

In general one begins by finding the best point on the line $x_2 = x_3 = \ldots = x_n = 1/2$ by either Bolzano or Fibonacci search, depending on whether derivatives are available cheaply. Let x_1^* be the first coordinate at this high point $(x_1^* = 2/3$ in Fig. 6–18). Then comparison of $y\langle \mathbf{u}^1 \rangle \equiv y\langle x_1^*, 1/2, \ldots, 1/2 \rangle$ with $y\langle x_1^*, 1/2 + \epsilon, 1/2, \ldots, 1/2 \rangle$ will eliminate the points in the plane $(x_1, x_2, 1/2, \ldots, 1/2)$ where either $0 \leq x_2 \leq 1/2$ or $1/2 \leq x_2 \leq 1$. A new unidimensional search on the line bisecting the planar region remaining reduces the region containing $\mathbf{u}^2$ further. This is continued until $\mathbf{u}^2$ is located in the plane. Then a three-dimensional maximum is found by examining a sequence of planes parallel to the first, each two-dimensional maximum being found by a sequence of unidimensional Bolzano or Fibonacci searches. This is continued until the desired maximum $\mathbf{u}^n = \mathbf{x}^*$ is bracketed within a suitably small region.

The article cited gives the number of measurements $N\langle\epsilon\rangle$ needed to reduce a unit hypercube to one measuring ϵ on each side as

$$N\langle\epsilon\rangle = \frac{(\log 1.62\epsilon^{-1})(\log \epsilon^{-1})^{n-1}}{(\log 1.62)(\log 2)^{n-1}} + \sum_{h=1}^{n-1} \frac{(\log \epsilon^{-1})^h}{(\log 2)^h} \tag{6-202}$$

This assumes that golden section search is used for the unidimensional optimizations. If derivatives are available, Bolzano search can be used, and the number reduces to

$$N\langle\epsilon\rangle = \left(\frac{\log \epsilon^{-1}}{\log 2}\right)^n + \sum_{h=1}^{n-1} \frac{(\log \epsilon^{-1})^h}{(\log 2)^h} \tag{6-203}$$

A convenient upper bound is obtained by noting that the summation is always less than $(n-1)(\log \epsilon^{-1})^{n-1}/(\log 2)^{n-1}$ so that for golden section

$$N\langle\epsilon\rangle < \left(n - 1 + \frac{\log 1.62\epsilon^{-1}}{\log 1.62}\right)\left(\frac{\log \epsilon^{-1}}{\log 2}\right)^{n-1}$$

$$= \left(\frac{\log (1.62^n\epsilon^{-1})}{\log 1.62}\right)\left(\frac{\log \epsilon^{-1}}{\log 2}\right)^{n-1} \tag{6-204}$$

In the Bolzano case the appropriate upper bound is

$$N\langle\epsilon\rangle < \left(n - 1 + \frac{\log \epsilon^{-1}}{\log 2}\right)\left(\frac{\log \epsilon^{-1}}{\log 2}\right)^{n-1}$$

$$= \frac{[\log (2^{n-1}\epsilon^{-1})][\log \epsilon^{-1}]^{n-1}}{(\log 2)^n} \tag{6-205}$$

For golden section search, these bounds are

$$N\langle\epsilon\rangle < \begin{cases} (n + 9.5)(6.65)^{n-1} & \text{when } \epsilon = 10^{-2} \\ (n + 14.3)(9.97)^{n-1} & \text{when } \epsilon = 10^{-3} \\ (n + 19.5)(13.3)^{n-1} & \text{when } \epsilon = 10^{-4} \end{cases} \tag{6-206}$$

For Bolzano search, the bounds are

$$N\langle\epsilon\rangle < \begin{cases} (n + 5.65)(6.65)^{n-1} & \text{when } \epsilon = 10^{-2} \\ (n + 8.98)(9.97)^{n-1} & \text{when } \epsilon = 10^{-3} \\ (n + 12.30)(13.3)^{n-1} & \text{when } \epsilon = 10^{-4} \end{cases} \tag{6-207}$$

A rough comparison can be made between the dichotomous method and contour tangents when there are only two independent variables. For 99 grid points in a unit square, and $\epsilon = 10^{-2}$, Eqs. (6–206) and (6–207) predict upper bounds of 76 and 51 measurements respectively for golden section and

Bolzano search dichotomous procedures. For contour tangents the upper bound, computed in the preceding section, is 29. One would guess that this relative advantage of contour tangents would tend to increase with the number of independent variables, but there is as yet no proof that this is so.

6-21 Summary

This chapter has dealt with direct optimization methods which narrow down the region containing the optimum until it is acceptably small. Although the theory is almost complete for unimodal functions of a single variable, it is still primitive in the multivariable case. As far as economy of experimental effort is concerned, sequential search plans demonstrate great superiority over simultaneous ones, but an investigator in a hurry can buy time by making more than one observation in each time period. Oliver's method and its "block search" extension by Avriel give minimax reduction ratios when both the number of blocks and the resolution can be predicted in advance. Lacking prior knowledge of the resolution, one can do almost as well using Kiefer's Fibonacci scheme, historically the first of all plans to be developed. The golden section method and its golden block extension can be used when the number of blocks is not specified in advance.

Indistinguishability and its effect on resolution problems was discussed. This led to development of a quantitative definition of the economically optimum number of measurements. Mathematical proofs were given for Avriel's block search procedures, of which the Fibonacci methods form a special subclass.

Multidimensional elimination schemes depend on the properties of contour tangents when special forms of unimodality can be assumed. The contour tangent method chooses a point and finds the orientation of the contour tangent through it; the dichotomous method chooses a convenient hyperplane and finds where it is tangent to a contour. The former method is more efficient, but less well developed than the latter. Elimination methods can often be used in conjunction with the direct climbing techniques described in Chapter 7.

BIBLIOGRAPHY

Arrow, K. J., and A. C. Enthoven, "Quasi-concave programming," *Econometrica*, **29**, 4 (October, 1961) 779–800.

Avriel, M., and D. J. Wilde, "Optimal search for a maximum with sequences of simultaneous function evaluations," *Man. Sci.*, **12**, 9 (May, 1966), 722–31.

———, "Optimality proof for the symmetric Fibonacci search technique," *Fibonacci Q. Journ.* **4**, 3 (October, 1966), 265–69.

————, "Golden block optimization of unimodal functions, using an unknown number of blocks," *Chem. Engng. Dept. Rep.*, Stanford Univ., 1966.

Beightler, C. S., L. G. Mitten, and G. L. Nemhauser, "A short table of *z*-transforms and generating functions," *Opns. Res.*, **9**, 4 (August, 1961), 574–78.

Bell, E. T., *The Development of Mathematics* (McGraw-Hill, New York, 1940).

Bellman, R., *Dynamic Programming* (Princeton Univ., Princeton, N.J., 1957), p. 34.

Berge, Claude, *Topological Spaces*, E. M. Patterson, trans. (Oliver and Boyd, Edinburgh and London, 1963; French ed., 1959), pp. 199–200.

Brooks, S. H., "A comparison of maximum-seeking methods," *Opns. Res.*, **7**, 4 (July, 1959), 430–57.

Coxeter, H. S. M., "The Golden section, phyllotaxis, and Wythoff's game," *Scripta Mathematica* (1954), 135–43.

Euclid (365–275 B.C., Greek).

Fibonacci, Leonardo, *Algebra et almuchabala* (*liber abbaci*) (1202), cited in Bell, p. 160.

Girard, A., *L'arithmetique de Simon Stevin de Bruges* (Leiden, Holland, 1634), p. 667, cited by Coxeter, p. 139.

Horn, Friedrich (private communication, 1965).

Johnson, S. M., *Optimal search for a maximum is Fibonaccian*, RAND Corporation Report P-856 (1956); see also Bellman.

Kiefer, J., "Sequential minimax search for a maximum," *Proc. Am. Math. Soc.*, **4** (1953), 502–506.

Lapidus, L., *Digital Computation for Chemical Engineers* (McGraw-Hill, New York, 1962).

Legge, J., *The Chinese Classics*, Vol. 1 (Trübner and Co., London, 1861).

Lucas, E., "Note sur l'application des séries récurrents à la recherche de la loi de distribution des nombres prèmiers," *Compt. rend. Acad. Sci. Paris*, **82** (1876), 165–67, cited by Coxeter.

Mood, A. M., *Introduction to the Theory of Statistics* (McGraw-Hill, New York, 1950).

Newman, D. J., "Location of the maximum on unimodal surfaces," *J. Assn. Comp. Mach.*, **12**, 3 (July, 1965), 395–98.

Oliver, L. T., and D. J. Wilde, "Symmetric sequential minimax search for a maximum," *Fibonacci Quart.*, **2**, 3 (October, 1964), 169–75.

Pisano, Leonardo (Fibonacci), *Scritti*, Vol. 1 (1857), pp. 283–84, cited by Coxeter.

Pythagoras, cited by Turnbull.

Southworth, R., and S. Deleeuw, *Digital Computation and Numerical Methods* (McGraw-Hill, New York, 1965).

Turnbull, H. W., *The Great Mathematicians* (New York Univ., New York, 1961), pp. 8–15. (Thanks to M. Manoff for this reference.)

Wilde, D. J., "Optimization by the method of contour tangents," *Amer. Inst. Chem. Engrs. J.*, **9**, 2 (March, 1963), 186–90.

———, *Optimum Seeking Methods* (Prentice-Hall, Inc., Englewood Cliffs, N.J., 1964).

———, "A multivariable dichotomous optimum seeking method," *Inst. Electrical Electronic Engrs. G-AC Trans. AC-10*, 1 (January, 1965), 85–87.

———, "Objective function indistinguishability in unimodal optimization," in Recent Advances in Optimization Techniques, *Proc. IEEE—OSA Conf. Optimization*, A. Lavi, T. P. Vogl, eds. (Wiley, New York, 1966), pp. 341–50.

EXERCISES

6–1. Derive Eq. (6–46) when m is even.

6–2. Show that convex functions satisfy Eqs. (6–51)–(6–54).

6–3. Prove Eq. (6–56).

6–4. Prove Eq. (6–64).

6–5. Prove that the even-block search technique of Section 6–08 is minimax.

6–6. Prove that, in a Fibonacci search, $x_1^1 = I_1^2$ implies that $x_1^2 = I_1^3$.

6–7. Prove Eq. (6–87).

6–8. Prove Eq. (6–92). (Proof given in Wilde, 1966.)

6–9. Devise a search scheme with two triblocks in which it is not always necessary to perform all three experiments in the final block. The reduction ratio must be no worse than for Avriel's triblock procedure.

6–10. Derive Eq. (6–146).

6–11. Prove Eq. (6–178) from Eqs. (6–172)–(6–177).

6–12. Verify Newman's upper bound for $k = 99$, setting up the lattice in the first quadrant. (For definiteness, assume the contours are circles centered on the origin.) Suggest a smaller bound.

6–13. Prove that the line $x_2 = \frac{1}{2}$ is tangent to a contour only at $\mathbf{u}^1$, the high point, in Fig. 6–18.

6–14. Prove that all convex functions are unimodal.

6–15. Find a cubic function of x which is unimodal but not convex for $0 \le x \le 1$.

6–16. Search for the maximum of the function $y = 3 + 6x - 4x^2$ in the interval $0 \le x \le 1$ with four sequential experiments. Space all experiments at least 0.05 unit apart. What is the length of the final interval? What is the highest value of y attained?

6–17. Conduct the same search as in Exercise 6–16 with four lattice experiments. What is the highest value of y attained?

6–18. Could the preceding search have been conducted efficiently with five experiments? Why?

6–19. A medical research team is seeking the American with the highest concentration of exogen in the blood stream. Exogen concentration is known to be a unimodal function depending only on the date of birth of the individual, which is known to the team through U.S. Census Bureau records. What would be the least number of Americans that the team could examine and still find the one with the highest exogen content? Compare this figure to the number required if a dichotomous search were used.

Direct Climbing 7

*"How shall I reach the top?" No time for
thus reflecting! Start to climb!*

FRIEDRICH NIETZSCHE, "EXCELSIOR," 1882

Direct elimination procedures having been developed in Chapter 6, it is now time to follow Nietzsche's advice and "start to climb." Any direct optimization scheme using past information to generate better points is called a *climbing* procedure. From another point of view, the problem is to reach a specified minimum acceptable level of performance in as few trials as possible. Geometrically speaking, we would like to climb as quickly as possible, even though the only information we have about the mountain comes from the past experiments we have run.

Each climbing experiment has two purposes: (1) to attain an improved value of the objective; (2) to give information useful for locating future experiments where desirable values are likely to be found. Throughout the search we must continually be deciding whether to climb or to explore. If we expend all our experiments on exploration, we may guess where the peak is but have no measurements near it. On the other hand it would seem shortsighted to try to reach the top without exploring at all, for we might well end far from the peak through ignorance of the behavior of the function. We need a master search plan, or strategy, that properly combines achievement with exploration.

The character of the strategies considered here will change as the search progresses. At the beginning when nothing at all is known about the function, we must explore in some small region, chosen at random, so that we may place our next experiments where the objective is higher. In the middle of a

271

search, after having left the very low regions behind, we try to climb as fast as possible, exploring only when strictly necessary to guide our successive jumps. Toward the end of the search, when we are finally near the top, extensive exploration may be needed to attain any increase in elevation, the slope of the response surface often being slight near the maximum. Another reason for surveying rather closely the region near a supposed maximum is to check whether it really is a maximum or not.

Thus, multidimensional search strategy, like chess strategy, seems to have three phases: opening game, middle game, and end game. The opening moves set the stage; the middle ones push for advantages; the final ones strive to reach the goal. We shall see that the various search schemes differ from each other only in the middle phase, for each strategy always begins and ends with an exploration. This strategic approach, in which the experimenter changes tactics as the search moves on, seems to work well in practice, according to some empirical studies of Flood and Leon, and of Lapidus, *et al.*

Since climbing methods are designed to cope with problems involving many independent variables, a thorough understanding of multivariable functions is in order. There are two principal ways of studying such functions. The more general method involves expressing the dependent variable in terms of the independent variables, using algebraic equations. According to this approach, all analysis of the function is carried out by studying the equations. A second technique is to represent the function graphically, using cartesian coordinates. This latter method often gives deep insight into the nature of the function because it brings to bear the geometric intuition and visual experience more or less well developed in all of us. Unfortunately, graphical techniques are not practical when there are more than two independent variables. Thus we face the unhappy choice between geometric methods which are intuitively appealing but powerless to handle large numbers of variables, and algebraic methods which are generally applicable but difficult to visualize.

A compromise is definitely in order. We shall develop an algebraic apparatus of general applicability, each algebraic concept being illustrated geometrically for the special case in which there are exactly two independent variables. In this three-dimensional context, such geometric ideas as tangent, contour, gradient, curvature, and perpendicularity are easier to visualize than their algebraic counterparts. Once the algebra for two independent variables is understood, it can be extended quite simply to the general case, using the geometric concepts as a guide. Or, from another point of view, the geometric relations holding in three dimensions can be generalized readily in terms of their algebraic analogs.

After the algebra and geometry of multidimensional spaces have been developed, the chapter turns to describing and analyzing specific climbing procedures. *The gradient* method, going back to Cauchy, is treated first because most of the other techniques build upon it. The undesirable tendency of gradient techniques to oscillate can be overcome by *acceleration* procedures (Forsythe and Motzkin), which themselves have developed into the *ridge-following* methods of Hooke and Jeeves, Rosenbrock, Gelfand and Tsetlin, Humphrey, and Baer.

Two important techniques, the *parallel tangents* method of Shah, Buehler, and Kempthorne and the *deflected gradient* procedure of Fletcher and Powell, not only are good at following ridges, but also have ideal behavior on quadratic objectives, a property known as *quadratic convergence*. All the methods described in this chapter involve breaking a multidimensional search problem down into sequences of unidimensional optimizations solvable by the powerful elimination techniques of the preceding chapter.

An optimization problem arising often in empirical and numerical work is the *least-squares* problem, in which one wishes to minimize a sum of the squares of a set of functions. Gauss devised a highly effective *quadratic approximation* scheme for such problems which has been crossed with the gradient method by Levenberg to give the rapidly converging *damped ascent* procedure.

The "end game" of all climbing strategies involves checking the character of any stationary point found. This involves fitting a quadratic equation to the function and applying the tests developed in Chapters 2 and 3. This chapter gives an example showing the pitfalls of inadequate analysis of stationary points. Considerations of the second-order behavior of the objective in the neighborhood of maxima led Box to propose a method for continually monitoring an optimum in large systems plagued by measurement errors. This *evolutionary operations* idea led Spendley, Hext, and Himsworth to develop the *simplicial* procedure for finding and following an optimum which shifts as time passes.

Several procedures for adapting climbing procedures of the pattern search variety to constrained optimization problems have been developed by Wood, by Glass and Cooper, and by Klingman and Himmelblau. The Jacobian approach of Chapters 2 and 3 should also prove useful when there are constraints, for once the constrained gradient has been estimated, any of the unconstrained methods can be used to select new, improved points.

7-01 Multivariable Algebra and Geometry

Knowledge of the behavior of functions of many variables is useful, not only for visualizing direct experimental optimization methods, but for understanding many other topics in applied science as well. Indeed, one would be hard put to find in the complicated modern world a problem of any importance involving a function of a single variable. Most of the simple problems solvable by the graphical techniques so characteristic of basic engineering and economic analysis have already been solved. We therefore need to know something about the behavior of systems of many variables, especially since high-speed computers are now available to handle the calculations. Since multidimensional geometry is rarely discussed in college analytic geometry and calculus courses, at least in the United States, we must devote some time here to this elementary but exceedingly practical topic. Fortunately the few simple concepts needed can be developed quickly and without much effort.

It is difficult, using only line drawings on the flat pages of a book, to describe solid objects, but this is exactly what we must do before we can discuss the geometry of curves and surfaces in space. The isometric projection technique, with which most engineers are already familiar, is employed because of its simplicity and pictorial qualities. *Isometric projection* consists of representing three axes, mutually perpendicular in space, by a vertical line and two slanted lines as shown in Fig. 7–1. The slanted lines stand for the axes which are horizontal in space; the vertical line corresponds to the axis vertical in space. The independent variables, denoted x_1 and x_2, are plotted parallel to these horizontal axes, and values of the dependent variable y (the objective function) are measured vertically above the x_1-x_2 plane.

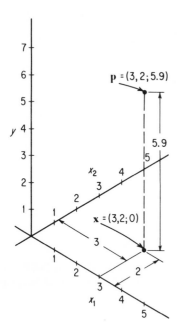

Figure 7-1. Isometric representation of a point in space.

In Fig. 7–1, the point **p** (notice the use of **boldface** type to denote points or vectors) has the coordinates $x_1 = 3$, $x_2 = 2$, and $y = 5.9$. Thus any ordered triplet of values $(x_1, x_2; y)$ can be represented graphically by a point in an isometric projection. The set of points corresponding to all possible ordered triplets forms a space of three dimensions. There are exactly *three* dimensions because at least three independent measurements, one for each coordinate, must be known to fix the location of a point.

Suppose y is a function of two independent variables x_1 and x_2.

$$y = y\langle x_1, x_2 \rangle$$

In this case not all of the points in the three-dimensional space satisfy the relation. Those that do will lie on a surface floating in the space as in Fig. 7–2, where the particular function depicted is

$$y = 5 - 0.2(x_1 - 3)^2 + 0.1(x_2 + 1)^2 \qquad (7-1)$$

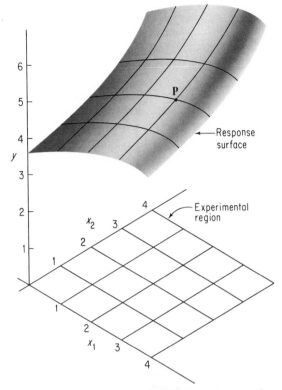

Figure 7-2. Isometric representation of a response surface.

The lines $x_1 = 0, 1, 2, 3, 4$ and $x_2 = 0, 1, 2, 3, 4$ have been drawn in the x_1-x_2 plane ($y = 0$) and projected onto the surface to make it easier to visualize. Notice that the point $\mathbf{p}$, already shown in Fig. 7-1, satisfies Eq. (7-1) and therefore lies on the surface. It is marked with a heavy dot at the intersection of $x_1 = 3$ with $x_2 = 2$ on the surface.

Biologists and statisticians, for whom y is often the response of a living organism to environmental factors x_1 and x_2, have come to call surfaces of this sort *response surfaces*, a name which found its way into engineering terminology because of the industrial applications of the work of G. E. P. Box (1954). The response surface of Fig. 7-2 is a two-dimensional object, because only two coordinates are needed to specify a point on it. For example, we may locate point $\mathbf{p}$ simply by stating that it lies on the response surface and then giving the two coordinates $x_1 = 3$ and $x_2 = 2$. This corresponds to the algebraic operation of finding y at the point $\mathbf{p}$ by substituting the values of x_1 and x_2 into Eq. (7-1).

In algebraic terminology the difference between the number of variables and the number of independent equations relating them is called the *number of degrees of freedom.* For the response surface there are three variables (x_1, x_2, and y) linked by Eq. (7–1), leaving two degrees of freedom. Since the number of degrees of freedom equals the number of coordinates which must be fixed to determine a point, it is the same as the number of dimensions. Therefore the space of all possible points (x_1, x_2; y) not necessarily satisfying Eq. (7–1) has three degrees of freedom, or dimensions, whereas the response surface has only two. Geometrically speaking, a surface is a two-dimensional object embedded in a three-dimensional space. For that matter, so is the x_1-x_2 plane on which $y = 0$, and the vertical plane on which $x_1 = 0$.

The intersection of two surfaces is a curve, which is one-dimensional because each surface is the representation of one equation relating the three variables. Points on the intersection belong to both surfaces and therefore must satisfy both equations, leaving only one degree of freedom. The space curves of Fig. 7–2 are at the intersections of the response surface with the equally spaced vertical planes $x_1 = 0, 1, 2, 3, 4$, and $x_2 = 0, 1, 2, 3, 4$.

By similar reasoning we can conclude that a point which is at the simultaneous intersection of three surfaces must be considered a zero-dimensional object, for it can have no degrees of freedom. The point **p** in Fig. 7–2 is at the intersection of the response surface with the two planar surfaces $x_1 = 3$, and $x_2 = 2$.

Figure 7–3 shows another way of depicting a response surface graphically. A front view of the surface as seen from the negative side of the x_2 axis is given in Fig. 7–3(a). It shows the five space curves on the surface for $x_2 = 0, 1, 2, 3$, and 4. Similarly the right side view in Fig. 7–3(b) consists of the projections of the space curves for $x_1 = 0, 1, 2, 3$, and 4 onto the y-x_2 plane, as they appear from the positive side of the x_1 axis. The curves shown in these views are the same as the ones in Fig. 7–2.

The curves in the top view, Fig. 7–3(c), are the projections onto the x_1-x_2 plane of intersections of the response surface with the horizontal planes on which $y = 4, 5, 6$, and 7. These curves, known as *contours*, are also shown in the isometric projection of Fig. 7–4. In Fig. 7–3(c) these contours are all viewed from above. Readers who have studied mechanical drawing will recognize this technique of describing a solid object by three mutually perpendicular views as the method of *orthogonal projection*.

Let us now generalize some of these geometric notions to situations where there are more than two independent variables. Suppose the objective y is a function of N variables $x_1, x_2, \ldots, x_N$.

$$y = y\langle x_1, \ldots, x_N \rangle \tag{7-2}$$

To represent this relation graphically one would need $N + 1$ axes all mutually perpendicular, which is physically impossible in our three-dimensional world. But even though we cannot construct such a coordinate system physically, we can certainly imagine a space of more than three dimensions if we are willing

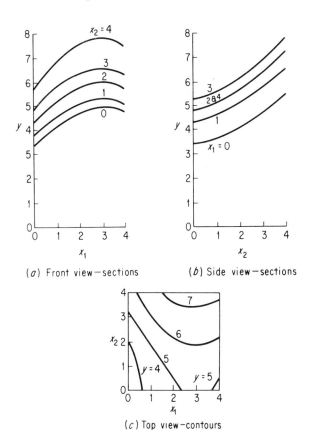

(a) Front view—sections (b) Side view—sections

(c) Top view—contours

Figure 7-3. Orthogonal projection (sections) of response surface.

to extend the geometric concept of dimensionality by using the algebraic idea of degrees of freedom. It is customary to use the prefix *hyper-* to indicate any extension of ordinary solid geometry to spaces with more than three dimensions. Thus the term $N + 1$-*dimensional hyperspace* refers to the set of all possible points $(x_1, \ldots, x_N; y)$. In this terminology the set of points satisfying the single Eq. (7–2) would be an N-dimensional *hypersurface* imbedded in an $N + 1$-dimensional hyperspace. Similarly we may conceive of the intersection of the response hypersurface with any hyperplane on which y is constant as a *hypercontour*, an object of $N - 1$ dimensions.

The multivariable search problem can now be stated in geometric terms. It is desired to find the optimum (to be specific, say the maximum) value of some objective y which depends on N independent variables $x_1, x_2, \ldots, x_N$. This function is unknown to us, but the value of y for any particular set of values of the $x_1, \ldots, x_N$ can be determined by an experiment, as in Fig. 7–1,

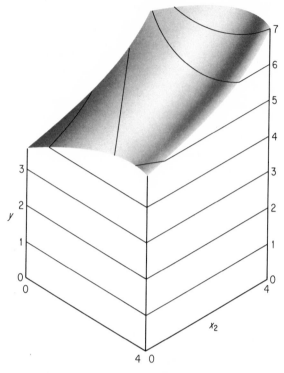

Figure 7-4. Contours in isometric representation.

where the experiment conducted for $x_1 = 3$ and $x_2 = 2$ gives 5.9 for the value of y. Thus each point in the $x_1, x_2, \ldots, x_N$ hyperplane (where $y = 0$) corresponds to a possible experiment, the point above it on the response hypersurface representing the experimental outcome. Commonly the possible experimental points are confined to a bounded portion of the $x_1, \ldots, x_N$ hyperplane which will be called the *experimental region*. Each experiment gives the elevation of the response surface above a new point in the experimental region. We wish to climb as high as possible on the response surface, using past information to guide the search for the summit.

7-02 Difficulties in Multivariable Optimization

At first glance one might think that the difference between multivariable search problems and the single-variable ones already analyzed is only one of degree, that with a little extra calculation one could extend single-variable methods to multivariable problems. Unfortunately this is not true, multivariable problems having a structure entirely different from that of a single-variable one. Bellman refers to the difficulties engendered by these differences as "the curse of dimensionality." This "curse" takes two forms in the problems of interest here.

One deleterious effect of multidimensionality is that we shall be unable to find a measure of search effectiveness that does not depend on the experimenter's luck in some way. Recall that the minimax methods developed for unimodal functions of a single variable gave the same length of final interval of uncertainty no matter where the peak happened to be. To see why the measures of effectiveness used previously are not valid in multidimensional problems, consider the two experiments $\mathbf{a} = (3, 2)$ and $\mathbf{b} = (1, 1)$ used to find, in the experimental region $0 \le x_1 \le 4$, $0 \le x_2 \le 4$, the maximum of the function given in Eq. (7–1). The values of y, respectively 5.9 and 4.6, are shown in Fig. 7–5. The function is unimodal above the straight line passing through $\mathbf{a}$ and $\mathbf{b}$, as is verified in Fig. 7–6, which shows the curve at the intersection of the response surface with the vertical plane passing through $\mathbf{a}$ and $\mathbf{b}$. Therefore we can conclude that the maximum sought cannot be above the line segment between $\mathbf{b}$ and $\mathbf{c}$, the latter point being where the line intersects the boundary of the experimental region. Unfortunately, the line segment

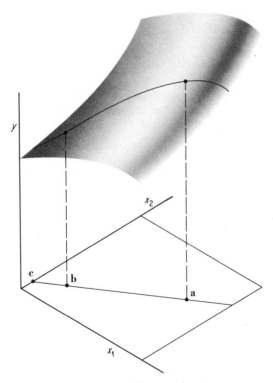

Figure 7-5. Two experiments.

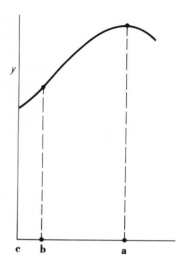

Figure 7-6. Vertical section along line through **a** and **b**.

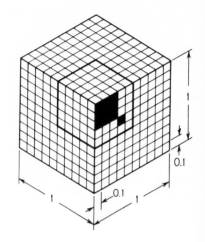

Figure 7-7. The second curse of dimensionality.

eliminated is negligible compared to the two-dimensional experimental region remaining. Thus multidimensionality overpowers the search techniques that were so effective when we had only lines to deal with.

The other difficulty is the very vastness of multidimensional spaces. This is a subtle point, difficult to visualize. To overcome our lack of multidimensional experience, let us attempt to imagine what happens as we pass from a one-dimensional line to a two-dimensional square and then to a three-dimensional cube.

Consider a line of unit length, the top edge of the cube in Fig. 7–7. Suppose we had a search method which would leave us with a final interval of uncertainty of 0.1, only one-tenth of the initial length. Such a technique would in effect select, from among 10 equally sized segments of the line, the interval containing the optimum, and this interval looks relatively small compared to the original one of unit length.

Next imagine a unit square divided into squares, each measuring 0.10 units on the side, as on one of the faces of the cube of Fig. 7–7. The darkened region shown comprises ten of these 100 squares—again, one-tenth of the original region. Somehow, this tenth of a square looks larger than the tenth of the line.

This effect is more marked in the unit cube of Fig. 7–7, which has been divided into 1000 cubes each measuring 0.10 unit on a side. To encompass 10 per cent of this region we must take 100 cubes, in Fig. 7–7 a volume measuring $0.4 \times 0.5 \times 0.5$. We see that a 10 per cent interval of uncertainty, which looked small enough on a line, appears rather large on a cube. If we were dealing with a function of 50 variables the hypercube containing only 10 per cent of the volume would measure $(0.1)^{1/50} = 0.91$ units on a side!

This phenomenon, which may appear paradoxical at first, arises from our application of a first-degree measure, namely, percentage, to a high-degree quantity, namely, volume, and its multidimensional generalization. Thus even if we had a search method guaranteed to cut down the multidimensional volume of uncertainty to a fixed fraction, this percentage would have to be extremely small before the ranges of the individual independent variables would be significantly reduced. This difficulty, which might be called the *vastness* of hyperspace, has been pointed out by Hooke and Jeeves (1958). Thus multidimensionality hurts us in two ways: it takes away the a priori measure of effectiveness which led to the powerful unidimensional minimax techniques, and it forces us to seek regions of uncertainty which are but tiny fractions of the original experimental region.

7-03 Opening Gambit : Estimating First Derivatives

Let us begin the discussion of search strategy by studying the problem of locating the first few experiments. Since we have no advance information about the objective function, the opening trials must be purely exploratory. We shall see that all they tell us is our elevation on the response surface and the way we need to move in order to go up from our initial group of experiments.

To avoid being too abstract at the very beginning, consider the particular problem of finding the maximum, in the square experimental region $0 \leq x_1 \leq 4$, $0 \leq x_2 \leq 4$, of an unknown function $y\langle x_1, x_2 \rangle$ of two independent variables x_1 and x_2. Since nothing is known about the function, one point in the experimental region is as good a place to begin as any other, but to be specific, let us start at the exact center, that is, at $(2.0, 2.0) \equiv \mathbf{x}_0$. Its first coordinate will be written x_{01}; its second, x_{02}.

$$\mathbf{x}_0 = (x_{01}, x_{02})$$

The outcome of the experiment $\mathbf{x}_0$ will be denoted by y_0. Suppose this result happens to be 5.70. The point $(x_{01}, x_{02}; y_0)$, which will be abbreviated $\mathbf{y}_0$, will be on the response surface directly above $\mathbf{x}_0$, as shown in Fig. 7–8.

Not much has been gained by this initial trial, for we still have no idea where to put the next experiment. Suppose, however, that we knew the general slope of the response surface in the neighborhood of the point $\mathbf{y}_0$. Then we would have at least a rough notion of which combination of changes in x_1 and x_2 might bring an increase in y. To find the slope in the direction parallel to the x_1 axis we need only run an experiment $\mathbf{x}_1 = (x_{11}, x_{12})$ whose second

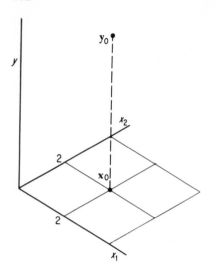

Figure 7-8. Result of first experiment.

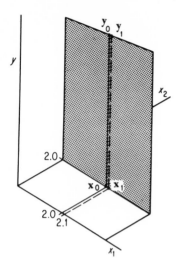

Figure 7-9. Approximate tangent to response surface at y_0 in plane $x_2 = 2.0$.

coordinate x_{12} is the same as for the initial trial. That is, we set $x_{12} = x_{02}$. The first coordinate x_{11} should, however, be slightly different from x_{01}. In order to get an accurate estimate of the slope we must place x_1 as close as possible to x_0, allowing just enough distance between them to make the outcome y_1 distinguishable from y_0. Let us take, in this example,

$$\mathbf{x}_1 = (2.1, 2.0)$$

and suppose that the result is

$$y_1 = 5.72$$

Then the situation after the first two experiments is that shown in Fig. 7–9. The straight line through the points $\mathbf{y}_0$ and $\mathbf{y}_1$ lies entirely in the vertical plane $x_2 = 2.0$ and is approximately tangent to the response surface at $\mathbf{y}_0$. Its slope is given by

$$\left(\frac{\partial y}{\partial x_1}\right)_0 \approx \frac{y_1 - y_0}{x_{11} - x_{01}} = \frac{5.72 - 5.70}{2.1 - 2.0} = 0.2,$$

where the subscript 0 indicates that the partial derivative is approximated at the point $\mathbf{y}_0$.

It would seem reasonable to locate the next experiment where x_1 is larger than at $\mathbf{x}_0$ and $\mathbf{x}_1$, since the objective y seems to be increasing in this direction. One could indeed conduct a one-dimensional search to find the high point of the response surface in the plane $x_2 = 2$. From this high point we could then carry out another one-dimensional search in the x_2 direction, holding the

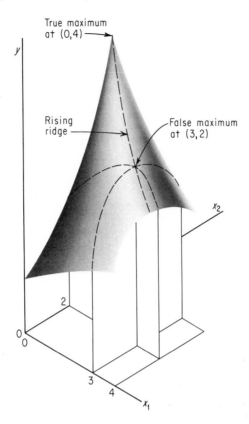

Figure 7-10. Response surface with rising ridge—isometric view.

coordinate x_1 at the value obtained on the previous search. This procedure could be continued, holding one variable constant and adjusting the other until the maximum is found. Unfortunately, as Box and Wilson have pointed out, this method, described more fully in Section 7-05, will fail to find the maximum of a function shaped like the rising ridge of Fig. 7-10. The initial search along the line $x_2 = 2$ will find a summit at the point $(3, 2)$ where the line crosses the ridge. Attempts to search for a higher point along the line $x_1 = 3$ would be doomed to failure, since $(3, 2)$ itself is higher than any other point on that line. Therefore the search would terminate at $(3, 2)$, far from the true maximum at $(0, 4)$. The contours of this ridge are shown in Fig. 7-11.

It seems then that we should alter the x_2 coordinate at the same time as we change the coordinate for x_1. To decide whether x_2 should be increased or decreased, we must perform another exploratory experiment very close to $\mathbf{x}_0$, this time varying the x_2 coordinate while holding the x_1 coordinate constant

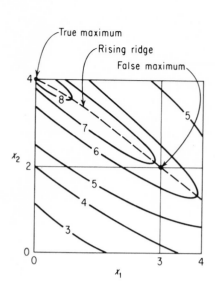

Figure 7-11. Contours for surface in Fig. 7-10.

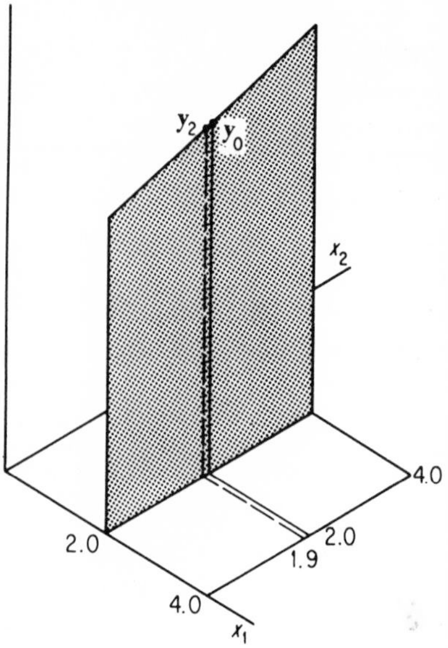

Figure 7-12. Approximate tangent to response surface at y_0 in plane $x_1 = 2.0$.

at x_{01}. Let us place an experiment at (2.0, 1.9), to be designated $\mathbf{x}_2$. The decision to decrease the x_2 coordinate rather than to increase it for this exploratory run was, of course, completely arbitrary. If we suppose the outcome to be 5.67, then the situation after this third exploratory experiment will be as shown in Fig. 7–12. The straight line passing through points $\mathbf{y}_0$ and $\mathbf{y}_2$, approximately tangent to the response surface at $\mathbf{y}_0$, has a slope given by

$$\left(\frac{\partial y}{\partial x_2}\right)_0 \approx \frac{y_2 - y_0}{x_{22} - x_{02}} = \frac{5.67 - 5.70}{1.9 - 2.0} = 0.3$$

This tangent lies in the vertical plane $x_1 = 2.0$.

We now know the slope of the response surface in two particular directions—parallel to the x_1 axis and parallel to the x_2 axis. What can we infer about the slope in other directions? The three points $\mathbf{y}_0$, $\mathbf{y}_1$, and $\mathbf{y}_2$ on the response surface are enough to determine the plane approximately tangent to the surface at $\mathbf{y}_0$. Let us find the equation of this tangent plane.

A plane in this three-dimensional space will satisfy an equation of the form

$$y\langle x_1, x_2 \rangle = m_0 + m_1 x_1 + m_2 x_2 \tag{7-3}$$

where m_0, m_1, and m_2 are constants. Notice that since a plane has two degrees of freedom, it is a special kind of surface, as our geometric experience readily verifies. The particular character of a plane follows from the special form of Eq. (7-3), which expresses y as a *linear* function of the independent variables x_1 and x_2. The word "linear" comes from the geometric fact that the intersection of two planes is a straight line. If any of the terms in Eq. (7–3) involved powers of x_1 and x_2 not equal to unity, or product of x_1 with x_2, then the equation would be *nonlinear* and the surface *curved*.

Knowing that the equation of the tangent plane must take the form of Eq. (7–3), we need evaluate only the three constants m_0, m_1, and m_2. One way to do this is to substitute into Eq. (7–3) the values of x_1, x_2, and y for the three exploratory experiments performed. This would give the following three independent equations in the three unknown coefficients m_0, m_1, and m_2:

$$y_0 = m_0 + m_1 x_{01} + m_2 x_{02} \tag{7-4a}$$

$$y_1 = m_0 + m_1 x_{11} + m_2 x_{12} \tag{7-4b}$$

$$y_2 = m_0 + m_1 x_{21} + m_2 x_{22} \tag{7-4c}$$

In the specific case under consideration, these equations would be

$$5.70 = m_0 + 2.0 m_1 + 2.0 m_2 \tag{7-5a}$$

$$5.72 = m_0 + 2.1 m_1 + 2.0 m_2 \tag{7-5b}$$

$$5.67 = m_0 + 2.0 m_1 + 1.9 m_2 \tag{7-5c}$$

It remains only to solve these equations simultaneously for m_0, m_1, and m_2.

In determining the equation of the tangent plane, it is convenient to deal only with the deviations of x_1, x_2, and y from the original point $\mathbf{y}_0$. For the experiment $\mathbf{x}_i = (x_{i1}, x_{i2})$ let us define the deviations

$$\Delta x_{i1} = x_{i1} - x_{01} \tag{7-6a}$$

$$\Delta x_{i2} = x_{i2} - x_{02} \tag{7-6b}$$

$$\Delta y_i = y_i - y_0 \tag{7-6c}$$

In our example, $\Delta x_{i1} = x_{i1} - 2.0$, $\Delta x_{i2} = x_{i2} - 2.0$, and $\Delta y_i = y_i - 5.70$. This translation of coordinates eliminates the need to determine the intercept constant m_0, for by subtracting Eq. (7–4a) successively from Eq. (7–4b) and (7–4c) and applying the Eqs. (7–6) we obtain

$$\Delta y_i = m_1 \Delta x_{i1} + m_2 \Delta x_{i2} \qquad \text{for } i = 1, 2 \tag{7-7}$$

A further simplification results because $\mathbf{x}_1$ was chosen to make $\Delta x_{12} = 0$ and $\mathbf{x}_2$ was chosen to make $\Delta x_{21} = 0$. For these special choices it is clear that

$$m_1 = \frac{\Delta y_1}{\Delta x_{11}} = 0.2 \approx \left(\frac{\partial y}{\partial x_1}\right)_0$$

$$m_2 = \frac{\Delta y_2}{\Delta x_{22}} = 0.3 \approx \left(\frac{\partial y}{\partial x_2}\right)_0$$

and therefore that the equation of the plane tangent to the response surface at $\mathbf{y}_0$ is

$$\Delta y = 0.2 \Delta x_1 + 0.3 \Delta x_2 \tag{7-8}$$

This tangent plane is shown in Fig. 7–13. The general equation of the tangent plane, obtained by combining Eqs. (7–3) and (7–6), is

$$\Delta y = m_1 \Delta x_1 + m_2 \Delta x_2 = \nabla y \, \Delta \mathbf{x}' \tag{7-9}$$

where $\nabla y \equiv (\partial y/\partial x_1, \, \partial y/\partial x_2)$ is the *gradient* of y.

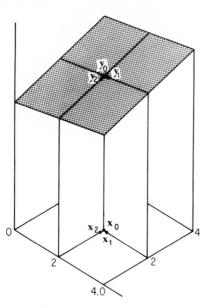

Figure 7-13. Tangent plane at $\mathbf{y}_0$.

Given Eq. (7–8) describing the tangent plane at $\mathbf{y}_0$, we could, if we wished, estimate changes in y for any combination of small deviations in x_1 and x_2. For example, we would expect the value of y at (2.1, 2.1) to be about $5.70 + 0.2(0.1) + 0.3(0.1) = 5.75$. There is no reason then to make any further slope measurements, since no additional information would be gained. Hence, in accordance with our geometric intuition, only three experiments are needed to determine the tangent plane at $\mathbf{y}_0$. Any three, not just the particular ones we chose, would have been acceptable as long as they did not all lie on the same straight line in the x_1-x_2 plane. The geometric reason for this restriction is that to determine a plane through a point one must have at least two different lines through the point. From an algebraic standpoint, three points on the same line would lead to Eqs. (7–7) that would not be linearly independent and which therefore could not give a unique solution for m_1 and m_2.

In order to guide our location of future experiments we shall use the tangent plane as an approximate representation of the response surface in the neighborhood of $\mathbf{y}_0$. It would be well at this point to examine the limitations on this approximation. Let us assume that the objective function y is a continuous function of x_1 and x_2 with continuous first partial derivatives everywhere in the experimental region. (This hypothesis will be weakened later on.) Then we may expand y in a Taylor's series about the point $\mathbf{y}_0$ as follows:

$$\Delta y = \left(\frac{\partial y}{\partial x_1}\right)_0 \Delta x_1 + \left(\frac{\partial y}{\partial x_2}\right)_0 \Delta x_2 + 0(\Delta x)^2 \tag{7-10}$$

where $(\partial y/\partial x_i)_0$ is the partial derivative of y with respect to x_i, evaluated at the point $\mathbf{y}_0$, and $0(\Delta x)^2$ represents terms of second order and higher. For sufficiently small deviations, these terms of higher order are negligible compared to the first-order, or linear terms, which have precisely the same form as the tangent plane Eq. (7–9). Hence the coefficients m_1 and m_2 can be interpreted as approximations to the first derivatives $(\partial y/\partial x_1)_0$ and $(\partial y/\partial x_2)_0$, or conversely, the linear terms of Taylor's expansion can be considered to be the equation of the tangent plane at $\mathbf{y}_0$. It follows that in the immediate vicinity of $\mathbf{y}_0$ the tangent plane approximates very closely the behavior of the objective y.

Generalization of the results of this section to functions of many independent variables is easy using the algebraic concepts already developed. Let $y\langle x_1, x_2, \ldots, x_N\rangle$ be a function of N independent variables, let $\mathbf{x}_0 = (x_{01}, x_{02}, \ldots, x_{0N})$ be the original experiment, and let y_0 be its outcome. Define the deviations

$$\Delta x_j = x_j - x_{0j} \quad \text{for } j = 1, 2, \ldots, N$$
$$\Delta y = y - y_0 \tag{7-11}$$

and let m_j be the derivative $(\partial y/\partial x_j)$ evaluated at $\mathbf{y}_0$. The linear approximation for y at $\mathbf{y}_0$ is

$$\Delta y = \sum_{j=1}^{N} m_j \, \Delta x_j = \nabla y \Delta \mathbf{x}' \tag{7-12}$$

To evaluate the coefficients m_j one must perform N experiments (not including $\mathbf{x}_0$) and solve the N simultaneous equations

$$\Delta y_i = \sum_{j=1}^{N} \Delta x_{ij} m_j \quad \text{for } i = 1, 2, \ldots, N \tag{7-13}$$

for the constants m_j, since the Δx_{ij} and Δy_i are given for each experiment. These computations can be simplified by choosing $\Delta x_{ij} = 0$ for all $i \neq j$, in which case Eq. (7–13) gives simply

$$m_i = \frac{\Delta y_i}{\Delta x_{ii}} \quad \text{for } i = 1, 2, \ldots, N \tag{7-14}$$

Once the m_j are known, one can state that the combinations of Δx_j giving increased y near $\mathbf{y}_0$ must satisfy the inequality

$$\nabla y \Delta \mathbf{x}' = \sum_{j=1}^{N} m_j \, \Delta x_j > 0 \tag{7-15}$$

Geometrically speaking, if one considers the $N + 1$-dimensional space of y and the x_j, Eq. (7–12) describes the N-dimensional hyperplane tangent to the response surface at $\mathbf{y}_0$. In terms of the experimental region, which is part of a space of N dimensions, the boundary between the upward region (that is, of increasing y) and the downward region is the $N - 1$-dimensional hyperplane satisfying the equation

$$\nabla y \Delta \mathbf{x}' = \sum_{j=1}^{N} m_j \, \Delta x_j = 0 \tag{7-16}$$

7-04 Gradient Method

In the preceding section, as well as throughout the early chapters, the vector of first partial derivatives $(\partial y/\partial x_1, \ldots, \partial y/\partial x_N) \equiv \nabla y$ has been given the name *gradient*. This vector gets its name because it points in the direction in which the response surface has the steepest slope. To see why this is so, consider the N-dimensional hypersphere of radius r, centered about the point $\mathbf{x}$. Points $\mathbf{x} + \partial \mathbf{x}$ on this sphere satisfy

$$\sum_{j=1}^{N} (\partial x_j)^2 = |\partial \mathbf{x}|^2 = r^2 \tag{7-17}$$

The first-order approximation of the objective function in the neighborhood of $\mathbf{x}$ gives the value of the objective function at various points on the sphere as

$$\Delta y = \nabla y \, \partial \mathbf{x}' \tag{7-18}$$

Let us seek the point on the hypersphere where Δy is maximum. At this point the following Lagrangian must be stationary.

$$L = \nabla y \partial \mathbf{x}' - \lambda[|\partial \mathbf{x}|^2 - r^2] \tag{7-19}$$

Hence the maximizing perturbation $\partial \mathbf{x}^*$ satisfies

$$\nabla L = \nabla y - 2\lambda \, \partial \mathbf{x}^* = 0$$

whence $$\partial \mathbf{x}^* = (2\lambda)^{-1} \nabla y \tag{7-20}$$

Since λ, the Lagrange multiplier, is a constant, the geometric interpretation of Eq. (7–20) is that the optimal perturbation vector $\partial \mathbf{x}^*$ points in the same direction as the gradient vector. The constraint Eq. (7–17) gives λ:

$$|\partial \mathbf{x}^*|^2 = (2\lambda)^{-2} |\nabla y|^2 = r^2$$

whence $$\lambda = \frac{|\nabla y|}{2r} \tag{7-21}$$

$$\partial \mathbf{x}^* = \frac{r \nabla y}{|\nabla y|} \tag{7-22}$$

and $$\Delta y^* = r|\nabla y| \tag{7-23}$$

The vector $\nabla y/|\nabla y|$ is called the *normalized gradient*. All these quantities are shown graphically in Fig. 7–14 for $\nabla y = (0.2, 0.3)$, the two-dimensional example of Section 7–03.

The *gradient method* for seeking a maximum is to determine the gradient at a point $\mathbf{x}_0$. The set of points in the gradient direction is given by

$$\Delta \mathbf{x}_0 = \rho \nabla y \langle \mathbf{x}_0 \rangle \equiv \rho \nabla y_0 \tag{7-24}$$

where ρ is a normalized hypersphere radius given by

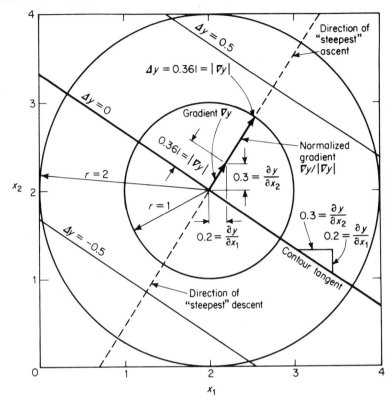

Figure 7-14. The gradient for $\Delta y = 0.2\Delta x_1 + 0.3\Delta x_2$.

$$\rho \equiv \frac{r}{|\nabla y|} \tag{7-25}$$

Positive values of the normalized radius ρ give locally increasing values of y, so the value of ρ maximizing Δy is found either by a one-dimensional (Fibonacci) search or, when possible, by direct differentiation. The latter alternative involves substituting Eq. (7–24) into the objective function, differentiating with respect to ρ, setting the derivative to zero, and solving for the minimizing value ρ^*. Thus one finds ρ^* satisfying

$$\frac{\partial y\langle \mathbf{x} + \rho\nabla y\rangle}{\partial \rho}\bigg|_{\rho=\rho^*} = 0 \tag{7-26}$$

At the new point $\mathbf{x}_1$ one evaluates a new gradient and iterates the gradient climbing procedure. That is,

$$\mathbf{x}_1 = \mathbf{x}_0 + \rho_0^* \nabla y_0 \tag{7-27}$$

$$\Delta \mathbf{x}_1 = \rho_1^* \nabla y_1 \tag{7-28}$$

etc. Figure 7–15 shows the progress of this method toward the minimum in the chemical plant design problem of Chapter 2. The technique, first proposed

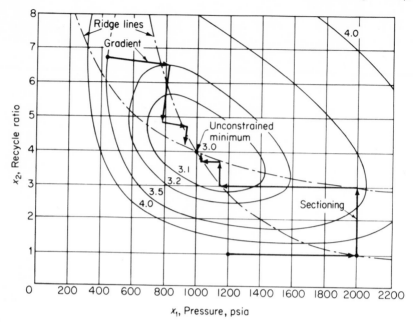

Figure 7-15. Sectioning and gradient methods.

by Cauchy in connection with solving simultaneous linear equations, was exhumed a century later by Courant for application to problems in mathematical physics. Its application to problems in industrial statistics has been due largely to the efforts of G. E. P. Box and K. B. Wilson.

7-05 Scale and Representation

It is instructive to study effects of linear transformations of the independent variables, that is, changes of scale and rotation of coordinates, on the behavior of the gradient method. The effect is so marked that often a preliminary transformation of the original problem is justified by the improvement in performance it brings. Investigation of this phenomenon in the case of objectives with ellipsoidal contours suggests ways of speeding up convergence simply by thoughtful choice of the functional representative of the objective. Briefly stated, in terms as yet ill-defined, the principles for preliminary preparation of a problem are three: remove interactions between independent variables, make the contours as spherical as possible by symmetric choice of scales of measurement, and represent the objective by a function well approximated by a low-order Taylor expansion in the neighborhood of the optimum. These suggestions were first made by Buehler, Shah, and Kempthorne in 1961.

First consider the consequences of a nonsingular linear transformation of the independent variables $\mathbf{x}$. Let $\mathbf{z}$ be the N-component column vector obtained by transforming the N-component column vector $\mathbf{x}$, using the transformation whose matrix is the N by N nonsingular matrix $\mathbf{L}$. Then,

$$\mathbf{z} = \mathbf{L}\mathbf{x} \tag{7-29}$$

Since the transformation is nonsingular, each vector $\mathbf{z}$ is the image of a unique $\mathbf{x}$ which can be found by using the inverse matrix $\mathbf{L}^{-1}$.

$$\mathbf{x} = \mathbf{L}^{-1}\mathbf{z} \tag{7-30}$$

Let the gradient method be applied in the image space of the $\mathbf{z}$. The points in the gradient direction are given by the chain rule as

$$\Delta\mathbf{z} = \rho_z \, \nabla y \langle \mathbf{z} \rangle$$

$$= \rho_z \frac{\partial \mathbf{x}}{\partial \mathbf{z}} \frac{\partial \mathbf{y}}{\partial \mathbf{x}} = \rho_z \mathbf{L}^{-1} \, \nabla y \langle \mathbf{x} \rangle \tag{7-31}$$

where ρ_z is the appropriate parameter in $\mathbf{z}$ space. This path may be transformed back into the $\mathbf{x}$ space to see how its points compare with those along the gradient there.

$$\Delta\mathbf{x} = \mathbf{L}^{-1} \, \Delta\mathbf{z} = \rho_z \mathbf{L}^{-2} \nabla y \langle \mathbf{x} \rangle \tag{7-32}$$

Since the gradient path in the $\mathbf{x}$ space is

$$\Delta\mathbf{x} = \rho_x \nabla y \langle \mathbf{x} \rangle \tag{7-33}$$

the two paths are the same if and only if

$$\mathbf{L}^2 = (\rho_z \rho_x^{-1})\mathbf{I} \tag{7-34}$$

where $\mathbf{I}$ is the N by N unit matrix. The only matrix having this property is a multiple of the unit matrix, so

$$\mathbf{L} = (\rho_z \rho_x^{-1})^{1/2}\mathbf{I} \tag{7-35}$$

In geometric terms this means that unless the linear transformation is merely a multiplication of all independent variables by the same constant, the two directions of "steepest" ascent will be different. Rotations of axes and unequal changes of scale are forbidden. The effect of compressing the x_2 axis by a factor of two in the example illustrated in Fig. 7–14 is shown in Fig. 7–16. Here

$$\mathbf{L} = \begin{pmatrix} 1 & 0 \\ 0 & \frac{1}{2} \end{pmatrix}$$

and the inverse is

$$\mathbf{L}^{-1} = \begin{pmatrix} 1 & 0 \\ 0 & 2 \end{pmatrix}$$

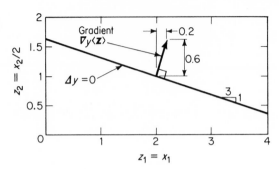

Figure 7-16a. The gradient for $z_1 = x_1$; $z_2 = x_2/2$; $\Delta y = 0.2\Delta z_1 + 0.6\Delta z_2$.

In the image space,

$$\Delta y = 0.2\,\Delta x_1 + 0.3\,\Delta x_2$$
$$= 0.2\,\Delta z_1 + 0.3(2\,\Delta z_2)$$
$$= 0.2\,\Delta z_1 + 0.6\,\Delta z_2$$

whence $\qquad \nabla y\langle \mathbf{z}\rangle = (0.2, 0.6)'$

as predicted by Eq. (7–31). Transformation of the path

$$\Delta \mathbf{z} = \rho_z(0.2, 0.6)'$$

back into the $\mathbf{x}$ space gives

$$\Delta x_1 = \Delta z_1 = 0.2\rho_z$$
$$\Delta x_2 = 2\,\Delta z_2 = 1.2\rho_z$$

which is clearly not the gradient direction, as shown in Fig. 7–16. (A fuller discussion of this phenomenon is given in *OSM*.) The important thing to realize at the moment is that *any* direction on the high side of the contour tangent can be made into a "gradient" direction by a linear transformation of the independent variables.

To discover what a reasonable transformation might be, consider next the relation of the gradient to an optimum of a quadratic objective function. Suppose

$$y = y_0 + \mathbf{c}'\mathbf{x} + \tfrac{1}{2}\mathbf{x}'\mathbf{Q}\mathbf{x} \qquad (7\text{-}36)$$

where $\mathbf{c}$ is an N vector and $\mathbf{Q}$ a positive definite N by N nonsingular symmetric matrix. Then y has a unique local minimum which is also the global minimum. At any point $\mathbf{x}$, the gradient is

$$\nabla y = \mathbf{c} + \mathbf{Q}\mathbf{x} \qquad (7\text{-}37)$$

Suppose one knows $\mathbf{Q}$ but not $\mathbf{c}$, and that the gradient $\nabla y\langle\mathbf{x}\rangle$ has been measured directly at some arbitrarily chosen point $\mathbf{x}$. Solution of Eq. (7–37) gives

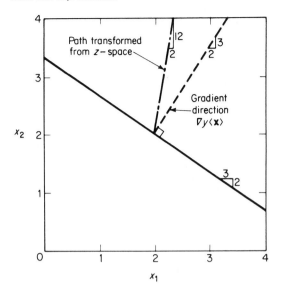

Figure 7-16b. Inverse transformation.

$$\mathbf{x} = \mathbf{Q}^{-1}(\nabla y - \mathbf{c}) \tag{7-38}$$

Since the gradient vanishes at the minimum $\mathbf{x}^*$, one can write

$$\mathbf{x}^* = -\mathbf{Q}^{-1}\mathbf{c} \tag{7-39}$$

Subtraction of Eq. (7-38) from (7-39) gives

$$\mathbf{x}^* - \mathbf{x} = \Delta\mathbf{x}^* = -\mathbf{Q}^{-1}\nabla y \tag{7-40}$$

Thus the minimum could in principle be achieved in one step in the direction indicated by Eq. (7-40). Notice that this would *not* be in the gradient direction ∇y unless $\mathbf{Q}$ happened to be a multiple of the unit matrix $\mathbf{I}$, in which case the contours would be concentric circles. Let us seek a linear transformation such that the gradient in the image space will point to the minimum.

Matrix theory (see Birkhoff and MacLane or Frazer, Duncan, and Collar) proves that for any symmetric matrix, such as $\mathbf{Q}$, there exists an N by N nonsingular matrix $\mathbf{T}$ such that

$$\mathbf{Q} = \mathbf{T}'\mathbf{T} \tag{7-41}$$

Finding $\mathbf{T}$ is not a simple task, requiring much more effort than computing the inverse $\mathbf{Q}^{-1}$, but suppose for the sake of argument that $\mathbf{T}$ is known. Then Eq. (7-36) can be written

$$y = y_0 + \mathbf{c}'\mathbf{x} + \tfrac{1}{2}\mathbf{x}'\mathbf{T}'\mathbf{T}\mathbf{x} \tag{7-42}$$

which suggests the transformation

$$\mathbf{z} = \mathbf{T}\mathbf{x} \tag{7-43}$$

whose inverse

$$\mathbf{x} = \mathbf{T}^{-1}\mathbf{z} \qquad (7\text{-}44)$$

may be substituted into Eq. (7–42) to give

$$y = y_0 + \mathbf{c}'\mathbf{T}^{-1}\mathbf{z} + \tfrac{1}{2}\mathbf{z}'\mathbf{z} \qquad (7\text{-}45)$$

Then $\nabla y\langle\mathbf{z}\rangle = (\mathbf{T}')^{-1}\mathbf{c} + \mathbf{z}$

whence $\mathbf{z} = \nabla y\langle\mathbf{z}\rangle - (\mathbf{T}')^{-1}\mathbf{c} \qquad (7\text{-}46)$

and $\mathbf{z}^* = -(\mathbf{T}')^{-1}\mathbf{c} \qquad (7\text{-}47)$

This gives

$$\mathbf{z}^* - \mathbf{z} = -\nabla y\langle\mathbf{z}\rangle \qquad (7\text{-}48)$$

so that the step to the minimum is the gradient vector itself.

The unique matrix $\mathbf{T}$ is found from quantities known as *eigenvalues* and *eigenvectors* of $\mathbf{Q}$. Let $\mu_1, \ldots, \mu_N$ be the N scalar eigenvalues of $\mathbf{Q}$, and let $\mathbf{P}$ be the N by N matrix of the corresponding eigenvectors. Form the diagonal matrix $\mathbf{D}$ whose nonzero elements are $\mu_1^{1/2}, \ldots, \mu_N^{1/2}$. The eigenvalues and eigenvectors are related to $\mathbf{Q}$ by

$$\mathbf{PQP}' = \mathbf{D}^2 \qquad (7\text{-}49)$$

Since $\mathbf{P}$ happens to be orthogonal,

$$\mathbf{P}'\mathbf{P} = \mathbf{PP}' = \mathbf{I} \qquad (7\text{-}50)$$

and Eqs. (7–49) and (7–50) may be combined to give

$$\mathbf{Q} = \mathbf{P}'\mathbf{D}^2\mathbf{P} \qquad (7\text{-}51)$$

Comparison of Eqs. (7–41) and (7–51) shows that

$$\mathbf{T} = \mathbf{DP} \qquad (7\text{-}52)$$

Methods for finding $\mathbf{D}$ and $\mathbf{P}$, and therefore $\mathbf{T}$, are well known but laborious. The point here is not that one should compute eigenvalues before beginning a search, but rather that ideal behavior of the gradient method is possible.

The quadratic term

$$\mathbf{z}'\mathbf{z} = \sum_{i=1}^{N} z_i^2 \qquad (7\text{-}53)$$

exposes the algebraic character of the ideal function. There are no cross-product terms $z_1 z_2$, etc., which means that the change in y resulting from adjusting a given variable z_i does not depend on what values the other variables z_j $(j \neq i)$ happen to have. When this happens, the variables are said to be *noninteracting*. Moreover, the equality of all coefficients of the quadratic terms implies that the contours are spherical, that is, completely symmetrical. At the optimum, a unit change in one variable produces the same effect on the objective as the same change in any other variable. Although in practice one rarely has an objective which is precisely quadratic, experience and preliminary study often suggest ways to reduce interaction between variables and to achieve approximate symmetry in the neighborhood of the optimum. Such preparation of the problem is, in view of the potentially increased convergence rate, often well worth the effort.

As an illustration consider the function

$$y = -2x_1^2 - x_2^2 - 3x_3^2 - 2x_4^2 \qquad (7\text{-}54)$$

Suppose we wish to search along the line of steepest ascent from the point $x_0 = (-1, 0, 3, -2)$. The linear approximation to y at this point is obtained by direct differentiation in this artificial example, since the function y has been given in advance. This approximation, which corresponds to Eq. (7–18), is

$$\Delta y = 4\,\Delta x_1 + 0\,\Delta x_2 - 18\,\Delta x_3 + 8\,\Delta x_4$$

with $\Delta x_1 \equiv x_1 + 1$, $\Delta x_2 \equiv x_2$, $\Delta x_3 \equiv x_3 - 3$, and $\Delta x_4 \equiv x_4 + 2$ in the usual manner. Equation (7–24) gives the parametric equations of the line of steepest ascent as

$$\Delta x_1 = 4\rho\,; \qquad \Delta x_2 = 0\,; \qquad \Delta x_3 = -18\rho\,; \qquad \Delta x_4 = 8\rho$$

or $\quad x_1 = -1 + 4\rho\,; \qquad x_2 = 0\,; \qquad x_3 = 3 - 18\rho\,; \qquad x_4 = -2 + 8\rho$

$$(7\text{-}55)$$

The four equations in the five variables have one degree of freedom, as we would expect for a line. A typical point on the line of steepest ascent is specified by selecting any positive ρ, say, $\rho = 2$. The corresponding point is $(7, 0, -33, 14)$. The reader may verify that the point $(-5, 0, 21, -10)$ is on the line of steepest *descent*. (What would be the corresponding ρ?)

Since all the points on the line have been expressed in terms of a single parameter, the values that the function y takes along the line can also be made a function of ρ alone. Equations (7–54) and (7–55) together give

$$y = -2(-1 + 4\rho)^2 - 3(3 - 18\rho)^2 - 2(-2 + 8\rho)^2$$

The value of ρ giving maximum y on the line can now be obtained by differentiating the preceding equation with respect to ρ:

$$\frac{dy}{d\rho} = 404 - 2264\rho = 0$$

whence $\rho = 0.179$ gives the highest value of y on the line of steepest ascent. The corresponding point is $(-0.28, 0, -0.22, -0.57)$.

The line of steepest ascent will always be characterized parametrically by one equation for each of the N coordinates. There being $N + 1$ variables in all (counting ρ), the set of points represented always has one degree of freedom. Since the equations are linear, the points must lie on a straight line in space. Parameterization enables us to work with one dimension instead of N coordinates, simplifying things both algebraically and conceptually. In practice, when the function is not known in advance, the high point on a gradient line can be found by the powerful unidimensional techniques developed in Chapter 6. Thus ρ may be used as the independent variable for a Fibonacci search. Most of the multivariable search methods we shall study will involve similarly breaking the problem down into a sequence of unidimensional searches.

A great advantage of gradient methods, and one not widely recognized, is that they will inherently stay away from saddlepoints. Zellnick, Sondak, and Davis found that their gradient search computer program avoids saddles so dependably that the only way they could test their subroutine for exploring the neighborhood of a pass was to start the search there.

Figure 7–17, in which gradient lines (dashed) are superimposed on the contours of a bimodal response surface, suggests why. Only one gradient line out of the infinite number possible actually passes through the saddle. The other lines all lead directly to one peak or the other. Hence the possibility of a gradient method's stumbling upon a saddle is remote, although the prudent experimenter should still check at the end of a search to see whether he has, by chance, found a saddle instead of a peak.

The simpler but related "sectioning" method, described by Friedman and Savage, involves altering only one variable at a time, holding all the others constant. One searches for the high point on the straight line described by $\Delta x_i = 0$ for all $i \neq j$, where j is the identifying index of the variable adjusted. Once this high point is found, x_j is fixed and some other variable altered. This procedure is continued until no further improvement is possible. Since each leg of the search will be parallel to one of the coordinate axes, for two independent variables the sectioning search path will resemble the staircase

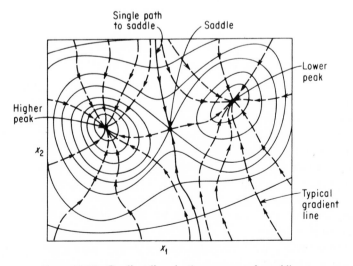

Figure 7-17. Gradient lines in the presence of a saddle.

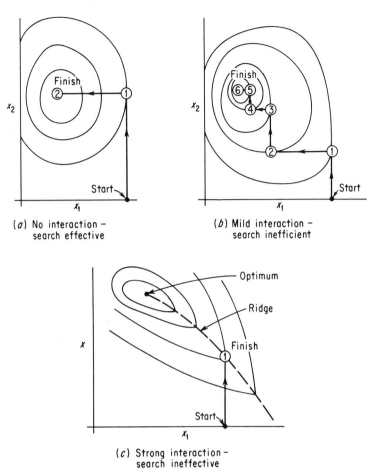

(a) No interaction –
search effective

(b) Mild interaction –
search inefficient

(c) Strong interaction –
search ineffective

Figure 7-18. Sectional search.

shown in Fig. 7–15. Figure 7–18 demonstrates how dependent the performance of the one-at-a-time method is on the shapes of the contours. It is highly effective for circles or ellipses having their major and minor axes parallel to the coordinate axes. This would mean that the independent variables are noninteracting. But when the major and minor axes are tilted, as in Fig. 7–18(b), the method is forced to change direction many times before reaching the optimum. The method fails completely when the response surface has a sharp ridge as in Fig. 7–18(c), for, being unable to move diagonally, it cannot find any higher places once it reaches the ridge where the contours come to a point. Buehler, Shah, and Kempthorne (1961) concluded that the method, uncombined with other techniques, is not suitable unless the experimenter knows in advance that such ridges are absent.

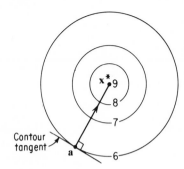

Figure 7-19. Circular contours.

To understand the third consideration in setting up a direct optimization problem, one must distinguish a *relationship* between variables from the various mathematical *representations* of that relationship. For example, if we are investigating the dependence of chemical process yield on the adjustable operating variables—pressure and temperature—then if y is yield in grams, p is pressure in atmospheres, π is the natural logarithm of p, and t is absolute temperature in degrees Kelvin, the following expressions are two different *representations of* the same *relationship:*

$$y = \varphi\langle p, t \rangle = y_0[1 - a(p - p_0)^2 - b(t - t_0)^2]$$

$$y = \psi\langle \pi, t \rangle = y_0[1 - a(e^\pi - p_0)^2 - b(t - t_0)^2]$$

It is wise to choose a representation that can be approximated readily, at least in the neighborhood of the optimum, by a fairly low-degree Taylor expansion, because most climbing techniques, like the gradient method, involve constructing approximations from measured estimates of first and second derivatives. By this rule, the quadratic representation is preferable to the other one involving the transcendental e^π term.

The three rules—noninteraction, symmetry, and low-order approximation—together tend to make the contours of the objective function spherical so that the gradient method will come close to the optimum in one step. Although it is rarely true that enough information is available beforehand to permit close application of these rules, they can guide educated guesses that will tend, if accurate, to speed up any climbing procedure. Figure 7–19 shows what would happen if the contours were spherical.

7-06 Least Squares

Before studying climbing methods for general unimodal functions, let us examine the important special case where the objective function is the sum of the squares of a set of functions. That is, there are M nonlinear functions $\phi_m\langle x \rangle$ $(m = 1, \ldots, M)$ of the N independent variables $\mathbf{x}$ such that

$$y\langle \mathbf{x} \rangle = \sum_{m=1}^{M} \phi_m^2 \tag{7-56}$$

Such objective functions arise often in practice because of the *least squares* curve-fitting method of Gauss and Legendre (see Davies). In this procedure each $\phi_m\langle x \rangle$ represents the difference between a prediction based on the adjustable parameters **x** and an actual experimental result. When there are as many measurements as adjustable parameters $(M = N)$, it is possible to drive each function to zero, and $y^* = 0$ since $\phi_m^2 \geq 0$ for all **x**. This fact is the basis of Booth's method for solving nonlinear equations by a gradient method. When $M > N$, which is usually the case in experimental work, one wants the **x** minimizing the sum of squared errors y.

Let $\boldsymbol{\phi}$ be the column vector of M functions $\phi_m\langle \mathbf{x} \rangle$ so that Eq. (7–56) becomes

$$y = \boldsymbol{\phi}'\boldsymbol{\phi} \tag{7-57}$$

Differentiation with respect to the **x** gives the N element gradient vector

$$\nabla y = \left(\frac{\partial y}{\partial \mathbf{x}} \right)$$
$$= 2\mathbf{J}\boldsymbol{\phi} \tag{7-58}$$

where $\mathbf{J}'$ is the M by N Jacobian matrix defined by Eq. (2–81). In the present context $\mathbf{J}$, having more columns than rows, is singular, and its various representations follow:

$$\mathbf{J} \equiv \left(\frac{\partial(\phi_1, \ldots, \phi_M)}{\partial(x_1, \ldots, x_N)} \right)'$$
$$= (\nabla\phi_1, \ldots, \nabla\phi_M) \tag{7-59}$$

Assume that the N rows are linearly independent so that the rank of $\mathbf{J}$ equals N. Gauss noticed that if the $\phi_m\langle \mathbf{x} \rangle$ are all linear functions of the **x**, so that $y\langle \mathbf{x} \rangle$ is quadratic, then the Jacobian matrix does not change from one point to another. Thus he suggested approximating the gradient at a point $\mathbf{x} + \Delta\mathbf{x}$ as follows [compare this with Eq. (7–58)]:

$$\nabla y \langle \mathbf{x} + \Delta\mathbf{x} \rangle \approx 2\mathbf{J}\langle \mathbf{x} \rangle \boldsymbol{\phi}\langle \mathbf{x} + \Delta\mathbf{x} \rangle \tag{7-60}$$

An approximation for $\boldsymbol{\phi}\langle \mathbf{x} + \Delta\mathbf{x} \rangle$ is obtained from the linear terms of the Taylor expansion about **x**.

$$\boldsymbol{\phi}\langle \mathbf{x} + \Delta\mathbf{x} \rangle \approx \boldsymbol{\phi}\langle \mathbf{x} \rangle + \frac{\partial \boldsymbol{\phi}'}{\partial \mathbf{x}} \Delta\mathbf{x}$$
$$\approx \boldsymbol{\phi} + \mathbf{J}'\Delta\mathbf{x} \tag{7-61}$$

Combination of Eqs. (7–60) and (7–61) gives an estimate of the gradient at $\mathbf{x} + \Delta\mathbf{x}$.

$$\nabla y \langle \mathbf{x} + \Delta\mathbf{x} \rangle \approx 2\mathbf{J}(\boldsymbol{\phi} + \mathbf{J}'\Delta\mathbf{x}) = 2(\mathbf{J}\boldsymbol{\phi} + \mathbf{J}\mathbf{J}'\Delta\mathbf{x}) \tag{7-62}$$

Since the N rows of $\mathbf{J}$ have been assumed linearly independent, the N by N matrix $\mathbf{J}\mathbf{J}'$ is nonsingular and has an inverse $(\mathbf{J}\mathbf{J}')^{-1}$. Therefore one can solve Eq. (7–62) for the correction $\Delta\mathbf{x}$ which drives all components of the gradient to zero and obtain

$$\Delta\mathbf{x} = -(\mathbf{J}\mathbf{J}')^{-1}\mathbf{J}\boldsymbol{\phi} \tag{7-63}$$

The point $\mathbf{x} + \Delta\mathbf{x}$ is where Gauss' approximation predicts the minimum to be, since the gradient ∇y would vanish there. Gauss' procedure is to measure the true values of $\boldsymbol{\phi}\langle\mathbf{x} + \Delta\mathbf{x}\rangle$ and $\mathbf{J}\langle\mathbf{x} + \Delta\mathbf{x}\rangle$ to see whether the gradient $2\mathbf{J}\boldsymbol{\phi}$ really vanishes. If it does, a stationary point has been found; if not, the information is used to generate a new approximation and further correction. If the functions of $\boldsymbol{\phi}$ are linear in $\mathbf{x}$, so that y is quadratic in $\mathbf{x}$—which is the case in the "linear regression" problem of statistics (Davies)—then Gauss' method finds the minimum in one move.

Harkins studied the behavior of Gauss' method on the following test function devised by Rosenbrock:

$$y = 100(x_2 - x_1^2)^2 + (1 - x_1)^2 \tag{7-64}$$

Figure 7–20 shows the response surface to have a shallow curved valley. Starting at the point $(-1.2, 1)$, Gauss' method found the minimum at $(1, 1)$ after 38 function evaluations. Since other methods to be described in this chapter required from two to ten times as much effort, Gauss' procedure seems to be about the best available for least-squares problems. It is also interesting that both the gradient and the sectioning methods stopped far short of finding the minimum, as shown in Fig. 7–20.

Powell (1965) has devised a variation of Gauss' method which does not require knowledge of the derivatives, equivalent information being generated during unidimensional searches. Powell's method required 70 function evaluations to minimize Rosenbrock's function.

To illustrate Gauss' method numerically, the computations needed to make the first step from the starting point $(-1.2, 1)$ are given. Here $\phi_1 = 10(x_2 - x_1^2) = -4.4$; $\phi_2 = 1 - x_1 = 2.2$

and $$\mathbf{J} = \begin{pmatrix} -20x_1 & -1 \\ 10 & 0 \end{pmatrix} = \begin{pmatrix} 24 & -1 \\ 10 & 0 \end{pmatrix}$$

Therefore $$\mathbf{JJ'} = \begin{pmatrix} 577 & 240 \\ 240 & 100 \end{pmatrix}$$

and $$(\mathbf{JJ'})^{-1} = \begin{pmatrix} 1 & -2.4 \\ -2.4 & 5.77 \end{pmatrix}$$

The step is given by

$$\Delta\mathbf{x} = -(\mathbf{JJ'})^{-1}\mathbf{J}\boldsymbol{\phi} = (2.2, -4.84)'$$

The new point is therefore

$$\mathbf{x} + \Delta\mathbf{x} = (1.0, -3.84)'$$

as shown in Fig. 7–20. Gauss' method has found the correct value of x_1, but because of the high-order behavior of the objective, it has overshot badly on x_2. The dashed contour, that for the straight ridged quadratic approximation, shows that it is the curvature of the ridge that causes the trouble. In

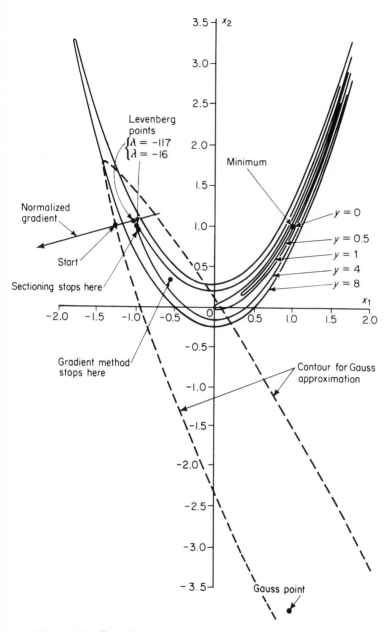

Figure 7-20. Rosenbrock's curved valley $y = 100\,(x_2 - x_1^2)^2 + (1 - x_1)^2$.

fact, the objective function actually *increases* from the point $(-1.2, 1)$ to the point $(1, -3.84)$. Still the method recovers rapidly and converges faster than any of the others tried. Incidentally, the nonlinear transformation $z_1 = x_2 - x_1^2$;

$z_2 = 1 - x_1$ would have straightened out the ridge so that either Gauss' method, or even the gradient method, would have found the minimum after one step.

If Gauss' quadratic approximation is poor, the procedure will behave erratically because of the unwarranted extrapolation. Levenberg proposed a modification which prevents steps far out of the region where the Gauss approximation is still reasonable. His strategem is to find where Gauss' approximation would predict a minimum on a hypersphere of radius r, chosen small enough to prevent leaving the range of validity of the quadratic approximation. Thus one tries to minimize y subject to the constraint

$$|\Delta \mathbf{x}|^2 = r^2 \tag{7-65}$$

The Lagrangian for this problem is

$$L = y - \lambda[|\Delta \mathbf{x}|^2 - r^2] \tag{7-66}$$

and its stationary point is achieved where [see Eq. (7-62)]

$$\nabla L = \mathbf{0}' = 2(\mathbf{J}\phi + \mathbf{JJ}'\Delta \mathbf{x} - \lambda \Delta \mathbf{x})$$

The step $\Delta \mathbf{x}$ is obtained as a function of λ by solving these linear equations. In matrix form,

$$\Delta \mathbf{x} = -(\mathbf{JJ}' - \lambda \mathbf{I})^{-1}\mathbf{J}\phi \tag{7-67}$$

Another equation involving the Lagrange multiplier λ is obtained by substituting Eq. (7-67) into Eq. (7-65).

$$r^2 = |\Delta \mathbf{x}|^2 = \phi'\mathbf{J}'(\mathbf{JJ}' - \lambda \mathbf{I})^{-2}\mathbf{J}\phi \tag{7-68}$$

In principle one would have to solve Eq. (7-68) for λ before being able to find the step from Eq. (7-67). But r, the radius of validity of the approximation, is only an estimate anyway, so such detailed computations are hardly justified. Instead Levenberg suggests ignoring Eq. (7-68) and simply choosing a value of the Lagrange multiplier λ, which is known in this context as the *Levenberg parameter*.

To guide the intelligent choice of λ, let us consider the values of the radii r corresponding to very small and to very large values of λ. When $\lambda = 0$, the Lagrangian of Eq. (7-66) becomes simply the unconstrained objective function. Hence the step would take us exactly to the point given by Gauss' method, in which case Eq. (7-63) gives

$$|\Delta \mathbf{x}| = r = |(\mathbf{JJ}')^{-1}\mathbf{J}\phi| \tag{7-69}$$

This is an upper bound on r, which, in the example, would be $|2.2, -4.84|$ $= 5.32$. At the other extreme, let λ become very large so that $(\mathbf{JJ}' - \lambda \mathbf{I})$ approaches the diagonal matrix $-\lambda \mathbf{I}$. Then λ^2 can be factored out of the right member of Eq. (7-68).

$$r^2 = \lambda^{-2}\phi'\mathbf{J}'\mathbf{J}\phi = \frac{\lambda^{-2}|\nabla y|^2}{4} \tag{7-70}$$

Hence the radius approaches zero for large values of λ. Moreover, Eq. (7–67) becomes

$$\Delta \mathbf{x} = \lambda^{-1} \mathbf{J} \boldsymbol{\phi} = \tfrac{1}{2} \lambda^{-1} \nabla y \qquad (7\text{-}71)$$

The positive (negative) value of λ is taken for maximization (minimization). In this case the step is in the gradient direction, and Eq. (7–71) closely resembles Eq. (7–20) giving the step for the gradient method. Thus, as the Levenberg parameter varies from zero to infinity, the step shifts continuously from the Gauss step to that for the gradient method as the step length shrinks to zero.

Most experimenters would rather guess r than λ, since the step length is easier to visualize and an upper bound on it is easily computed from Eq. (7–69). An estimate of λ for a given r can be obtained by solving Eq. (7–70).

$$\lambda = \pm \frac{|\mathbf{J}\boldsymbol{\phi}|}{r} = \pm \frac{|\nabla y|}{2r} \qquad (7\text{-}72)$$

In the example, a reasonable choice would be $r = 1$, in which case

$$\lambda = \frac{-|\nabla y|}{2} = - |-107.8, -44| = -117$$

Then
$$\mathbf{J}\mathbf{J}' - \lambda \mathbf{I} = \begin{pmatrix} 694 & 240 \\ 240 & 217 \end{pmatrix}$$

and
$$(\mathbf{J}\mathbf{J}' - \lambda \mathbf{I})^{-1} = \begin{pmatrix} 0.00233 & -0.00258 \\ -0.00258 & 0.00746 \end{pmatrix}$$

The step is therefore

$$\Delta \mathbf{x} = -10^{-3} \begin{pmatrix} 2.33 & -2.58 \\ -2.58 & 7.46 \end{pmatrix} \begin{pmatrix} -107.8 \\ -44 \end{pmatrix} = \begin{pmatrix} 0.138 \\ 0.050 \end{pmatrix}$$

Its length (0.147) is considerably less than the unit step expected due to the error in approximating λ by Eq. (7–72). The next point is at $(-1.062, 1.050)$, not very far off the gradient line, showing that λ is so large that the Gauss approximation is not really being used. Even so, considerable improvement in the objective function has been achieved by this first short step—a decrease from 24.2 down to 4.80. To take a longer step closer to the unit length desired, one could decrease λ to, say, $-117(0.14) = -16$ and recompute the step. The reader can verify (Exercise 7–10) that in this case the step would be

$$\Delta \mathbf{x} = - \begin{pmatrix} 0.01032 & -0.0213 \\ -0.0213 & 0.0527 \end{pmatrix} \begin{pmatrix} -107.8 \\ -44 \end{pmatrix} = \begin{pmatrix} 0.186 \\ 0.000 \end{pmatrix}$$

Although the step is not much longer than before, the direction has changed considerably; the new point is at $(-1.02, 1)$. The objective function has been decreased to 4.24, and as Fig. 7–20 shows, the point is now right on the floor of the valley.

Several improvements on this method can be visualized. One can continue to decrease λ until the specified radius is obtained. This in effect would be an iterative technique for solving Eq. (7–68) for the correct value of the Levenberg parameter. Levenberg also proposed finding the value of λ minimizing the true value of the objective function. Since only the single parameter λ is involved, Fibonacci search could be used, even though the line of search will not be straight. This scheme would not require an a priori guess of the proper radius, since the procedure would find the radius optimizing the objective function along the curved line of search generated by Levenberg's method. Rubin has applied this technique to highly nonlinear problems in chemical kinetics.

The Gauss and Levenberg methods are powerful but they are limited to least-squares problems. Subsequent sections will describe techniques available for more general objective functions.

7-07 Acceleration Along a Ridge

When the objective function is too general for least-squares representation, extensions of the gradient method can be used to search for the peak. The various methods have in common a propensity for finding a "ridge," to use geographic imagery, and following it upwards until it reaches the summit. This seems to be effective because the ridges of many objective functions encountered in practice tend to point toward the peak.

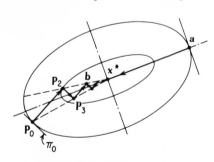

Figure 7-21. Elliptical contours.

Consider the objective function with concentric ellipsoidal contours shown in Fig. 7-21. If, as at point **a**, the first point for a gradient search happens to be precisely on one of the axes of the system of ellipses, the gradient line will pass right through the peak and the search will be over in one ascent. Otherwise the search will follow a zigzag course such as the one from $\mathbf{p}_0$ to $\mathbf{p}_2$ to $\mathbf{p}_3$ to **b**, etc. It is interesting to notice that, in principle, gradient search will not reach the peak in a finite number of steps because the steps shorten as the maximum is approached. The peak can, however, be approached as closely as desired, and if the starting point is not too near the major axis, the neighborhood of the peak is attained rapidly.

Notice that the crooked path is bounded by two straight lines which intersect at the peak. This suggests that the search from point $\mathbf{p}_3$ be conducted, not in the gradient direction toward **b**, but along the straight line from $\mathbf{p}_0$

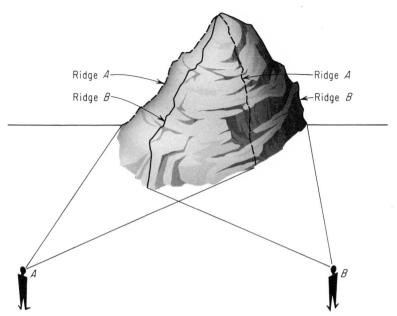

Figure 7-22. Geographic "ridges."

through $\mathbf{p}_3$. In this way, the peak would be located exactly after three uni-dimensional searches: first from $\mathbf{p}_0$ to $\mathbf{p}_2$ along the gradient at $\mathbf{p}_0$, then from $\mathbf{p}_2$ to $\mathbf{p}_3$ along the gradient at $\mathbf{p}_2$, and finally from $\mathbf{p}_3$ along the line through $\mathbf{p}_0$ and $\mathbf{p}_3$. This sort of acceleration of gradient search was first proposed by Forsythe and Motzkin. It is the two-dimensional version of what will later be called *gradient partan*. In this exposition we have identified the starting point as $\mathbf{p}_0$ rather than $\mathbf{p}_1$ for reasons that will become clear later when we generalize the technique to many dimensions.

In a manner of speaking, the acceleration path can be said to "follow a ridge." But the geographic concept of "ridge" is not sufficiently precise for our purposes, so we must define the special idea of a *resolution ridge* in order to discuss ridge-following methods unambiguously. Before introducing this new concept, let us see what is unsuitable about the geographic one.

Consider two men viewing a mountain from two different positions, as in Fig. 7-22. Mr. A would say that the points on curve A would be on the "ridge," since from where he stands these points form the profile of the mountain. On the other hand, Mr. B would see a different "ridge." In fact, any point on the mountain which can be seen at all will, from some viewpoint, be on a "ridge." If there are some points that appear to be a ridge when seen from many different angles, they will often be called the "crests of the ridge," and if the points are all about the same elevation the whole mountain may be called a *ridge*. Thus the geographic idea of "ridge," although helping us picture the formation or response surface with which we are dealing, is not precise enough to be useful in analyzing ridge-climbing techniques.

We prefer to define a *principal ridge* as the locus of points where the sectioning method will stop before reaching the optimum. Hence any point on a *principal ridge* will be the best attainable in any direction parallel to the coordinate (hence "principal") axes. Such a ridge is shown in Fig. 7–18(c); the other two response surfaces in Fig. 7–18 do not have principal ridges according to this definition.

A ridge of this sort can occur only where the contour lies entirely in one quadrant (for two variables; the multidimensional generalization of the quadrant is called an *orthant*). This can happen only if the contour comes to a sharp point, meaning that the first derivatives are discontinuous there. Since, practically speaking, observations must be a finite distance from each other to be distinguishable, this can cause sectioning to stick on the ridge even when the contours are smooth. Let $\epsilon_i(> 0)$ be the closest distance between two points on a line parallel to the x_i axis for which a difference between the results can be detected. That is, ϵ_i, the *resolution* in the x_i direction, is such that for all $x_1, \ldots, x_i, \ldots, x_N$ it can be asserted that

$$y\langle x_1, \ldots, x_i, \ldots, x_N \rangle \neq y\langle x_1, \ldots, x_i + \epsilon_i, \ldots, x_N \rangle$$

A point $(x_1, \ldots, x_i, \ldots, x_N)$ will be said to be on a *principal resolution ridge* if it is above all points $(x_1, \ldots, x_i + \epsilon_i, \ldots, x_N)$ and $(x_1, \ldots, x_i - \epsilon_i, \ldots, x_N)$. If a point is *below* all such neighboring points it will be said to be in a *principal resolution valley*. Principal resolution ridges are important in maximization problems, and they may be regions rather than lines. As shown in Fig. 7–23, a principal resolution ridge becomes narrower as the resolution is made finer. With sufficient resolution, a ridge may even vanish.

The sectioning method will not reach the peak if it runs into a principal resolution ridge. On the other hand, the contour tangent elimination method of Chapter 6 is not particularly confounded by a ridge; it will merely lead to a long narrow region of uncertainty. Gradient methods can safely navigate a ridge, but unless one fortunately steers right up the ridge there is likely to be much inefficient zigzagging, as shown in Fig. 7–21. The techniques about to be described will find the trend of a principal resolution ridge and move rapidly along it.

Suppose one conducts two sectioning searches, each starting from a different point, and suppose that each search encounters the principal resolution ridge at a different point. Consider the consequences of finding the best point on the line of search determined by the two points. If the resolution ridge is straight, then this acceleration step will find a point close to the true optimum. This is the basic idea behind the "principle of nonlocal search" of Gelfand and Tsetlin. They do not restrict themselves to sectioning searches, however, and in general, other procedures might be used to find the resolution ridge.

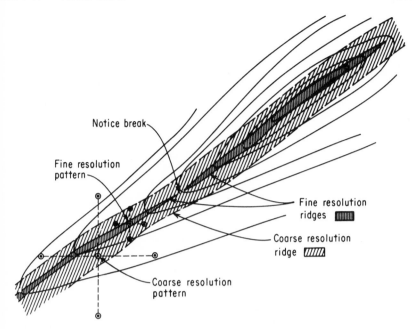

Figure 7-23. Coarse and fine resolution ridges.

7-08 Pattern Search

An easily programmed accelerated climbing technique with ridge-following properties is the *pattern search* method of Hooke and Jeeves (1961). Their technique is based on the hopeful conjecture that any set of moves, that is, adjustments of the independent variables, which have been successful during early experiments, will be worth trying again. This strategy is successful on straight ridges because an early pattern of moves can succeed only if it lies along the crest. Hence, further moves in the same direction will be worthwhile if the ridge is straight.

Although the method starts cautiously with short excursions from the starting point, the steps grow with repeated success. Subsequent failure indicates that shorter steps are in order, and if a change in direction is required, the technique will start over again with a new pattern. In the vicinity of the peak the steps become very small to avoid overlooking any promising direction.

In visualizing what is meant by a "pattern," it is helpful to think of an arrow, its base at one end and its head at the other. The search begins at a base point $\mathbf{b}_1$ which may be chosen arbitrarily; as yet the pattern has not been established. The experimenter chooses a step size δ_i for each independent variable $x_i (i = 1, 2, \ldots, N)$. Let $\boldsymbol{\delta}_i$ be the vector whose ith component is δ_i, all the rest being zero. After measuring the criterion at the initial base $\mathbf{b}_1$, one takes an observation at $\mathbf{b}_1 + \boldsymbol{\delta}_1$. If this new point is better than the base, we call $\mathbf{b}_1 + \boldsymbol{\delta}_1$ the *temporary* head $\mathbf{t}_{11}$, where the double subscript shows that we are developing the first pattern and that we have already perturbed the first variable x_1. Now $\mathbf{b}_1 + \boldsymbol{\delta}_1$ may not be as good as $\mathbf{b}_1$, in which case we forget $\mathbf{b}_1 + \boldsymbol{\delta}_1$ and try $\mathbf{b}_1 - \boldsymbol{\delta}_1$. If this new point is better than $\mathbf{b}_1$, we make it the temporary head; otherwise, $\mathbf{b}_1$ is designated temporary head. In summary, when we are maximizing,

$$\mathbf{t}_{11} = \begin{cases} \mathbf{b}_1 + \boldsymbol{\delta}_1 & \text{if } y\langle \mathbf{b}_1 + \boldsymbol{\delta}_1 \rangle > y\langle \mathbf{b}_1 \rangle & \text{(7-73a)} \\ \mathbf{b}_1 - \boldsymbol{\delta}_1 & \text{if } y\langle \mathbf{b}_1 - \boldsymbol{\delta}_1 \rangle > y\langle \mathbf{b}_1 \rangle > y\langle \mathbf{b}_1 + \boldsymbol{\delta}_1 \rangle & \text{(7-73b)} \\ \mathbf{b}_1 & \text{if } y\langle \mathbf{b}_1 \rangle > \max \left[y\langle \mathbf{b}_1 + \boldsymbol{\delta}_1 \rangle, \ y\langle \mathbf{b}_1 - \boldsymbol{\delta}_1 \rangle \right] & \text{(7-73c)} \end{cases}$$

In Fig. 7–24, Eq. (7–73b) governs.

Perturbation of x_2, the next independent variable, is now carried out in a similar manner, this time about the temporary head $\mathbf{t}_{11}$ instead of the original base $\mathbf{b}_1$. In general the jth temporary head $\mathbf{t}_{1j}$ is obtained from the preceding one $\mathbf{t}_{1,j-1}$ as follows:

$$\mathbf{t}_{1j} = \begin{cases} \mathbf{t}_{1,j-1} + \boldsymbol{\delta}_j & \text{if } y\langle \mathbf{t}_{1,j-1} + \boldsymbol{\delta}_j \rangle > y\langle \mathbf{t}_{1,j-1} \rangle & \text{(7-74a)} \\ \mathbf{t}_{1,j-1} - \boldsymbol{\delta}_j & \text{if } y\langle \mathbf{t}_{1,j-1} - \boldsymbol{\delta}_j \rangle > y\langle \mathbf{t}_{1,j-1} \rangle > y\langle \mathbf{t}_{1,j-1} + \boldsymbol{\delta}_j \rangle & \text{(7-74b)} \\ \mathbf{t}_{1,j-1} & \text{if } y\langle \mathbf{t}_{1,j-1} \rangle > \max \left[y\langle \mathbf{t}_{1,j-1} + \boldsymbol{\delta}_j \rangle, y\langle \mathbf{t}_{1,j-1} - \boldsymbol{\delta}_j \rangle \right] & \text{(7-74c)} \end{cases}$$

This expression covers all $1 \leq j \leq N$ if we adopt the convention that

$$\mathbf{t}_{10} \equiv \mathbf{b}_1$$

In Fig. 7–24, Eq. (7–74a) applies for $j = 2$. When all the variables have been perturbed, the last temporary head point $\mathbf{t}_{1N}$ is designated the *second base point* $\mathbf{b}_2$.

$$\mathbf{t}_{1N} \equiv \mathbf{b}_2$$

The original base point $\mathbf{b}_1$ and the newly determined base point $\mathbf{b}_2$ together establish the first pattern. Reasoning that if a similar exploration were conducted from $\mathbf{b}_2$ the results are likely to be the same, we skip the local excursions and extend the arrow from $\mathbf{b}_1$ to $\mathbf{b}_2$, immediately doubling its length. This establishes a new temporary head $\mathbf{t}_{20}$ for the second pattern based at $\mathbf{b}_2$. This initial temporary head is given by

$$\mathbf{t}_{20} \equiv \mathbf{b}_1 + 2(\mathbf{b}_2 - \mathbf{b}_1) = \mathbf{b}_2 + (\mathbf{b}_2 - \mathbf{b}_1) = 2\mathbf{b}_2 - \mathbf{b}_1$$

The double subscript 20 indicates that we are building a second pattern and that we have not yet begun to perturb the variables. A local exploration about $\mathbf{t}_{20}$ is now carried out to correct the tentative second pattern if necessary, as shown in Fig. 7–24. The logical equations governing establishment of the new temporary heads $\mathbf{t}_{21}$, $\mathbf{t}_{22}$, ..., $\mathbf{t}_{2N}$ will be similar to Eqs. (7–74), the only difference being that the first subscript will be 2 instead of 1. The recon-

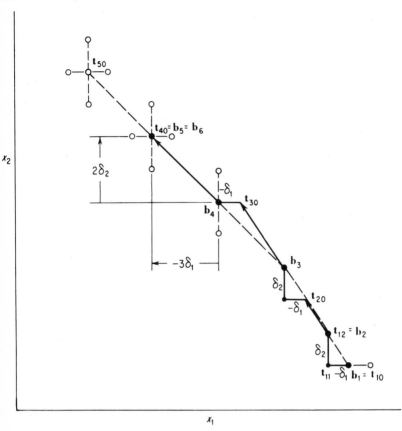

Figure 7-24. Finding a ridge.

naissance is completed when all the variables have been perturbed, and the last temporary head t_{2N} is designated the third base point b_3, if, as in Fig. 7-24, the outcome there is better than at b_2.

As before, a new temporary head t_{30} is established by extrapolating from b_2 through b_3.

$$t_{30} = 2b_3 - b_2$$

In Fig. 7-24 the new base b_3 is colinear with b_2 and b_1, indicating that the direction of the pattern is not to be changed. Notice that the repeated success in this direction causes the pattern to grow, because

$$b_3 - b_2 = 2(t_{20} - b_2) = 2(b_2 - b_1)$$

The procedure is iterated for the third pattern. Suppose that perturbation of x_2 fails to produce any improvement over temporary head t_{31}, as in Fig. 7-24, but that t_{31} is still a better point than b_3. Then,

$$\mathbf{b}_4 = \mathbf{t}_{32} = \mathbf{t}_{31}$$

and the pattern will veer to the left, still growing in length.

For the fourth pattern imagine that none of the perturbations about the initial temporary head $\mathbf{t}_{40}$ improve the outcome, but that $y\langle\mathbf{t}_{40}\rangle > y\langle\mathbf{b}_4\rangle$. Then,

$$\mathbf{b}_5 = \mathbf{t}_{42} = \mathbf{t}_{41} = \mathbf{t}_{40}$$

and the pattern will maintain its direction and length without any growth. The fourth pattern $\mathbf{b}_5 - \mathbf{b}_4$ has components $(-3\delta_1, 2\delta_2)$, representing the cumulative effect of three successful steps in the negative x_1 direction (that is, to the left) and two in the positive x_2 direction (that is, upward).

Suppose that none of the temporary heads, $\mathbf{t}_{50}$, $\mathbf{t}_{51}$, or $\mathbf{t}_{52}$, is any better than the fifth base $\mathbf{b}_5$, as in Fig. 7–24. Then $\mathbf{b}_6 = \mathbf{b}_5$ and the pattern is destroyed. Since this could mean we are either at the peak or crossing a resolution ridge, new maneuvers are in order.

Unable to continue the old pattern from $\mathbf{b}_5$ even by modifying it, we must abandon it entirely and try to build a new one using $\mathbf{b}_5$ as the base point, but designating it $\mathbf{b}_6$ since we now are working with the sixth pattern. We start all over again, making $\mathbf{b}_6$ the initial temporary head $\mathbf{t}_{60}$ for a local exploration. If this scouting expedition locates a better point, then we can begin a new pattern. But if, as in Fig. 7–25, no better point is found then the steps must be shortened in an attempt to break the resolution ridge, if there is one. In Fig. 7–25 we have cut the steps in half and are able to obtain improvement, which starts us off on a fresh, albeit tiny pattern.

After a few minor modifications of direction and rapid growth in size, the pattern coincides with the trend of the ridge from the ninth through eleventh pattern moves and hence holds its length constant. At $\mathbf{b}_{12}$ the ridge starts to curve, and the pattern swerves sharply to follow the crest, shortening up as necessary until $\mathbf{b}_{16}$, where the ridge straightens out again. The sixteenth pattern lengthens rapidly on the straight ridge, but the seventeenth pattern fails to find a better point. Again the pattern must be destroyed.

As before, we retreat to the last successful base point, in this case $\mathbf{b}_{17}$ (now designated $\mathbf{b}_{18}$) and try to establish a nineteenth pattern by shortening the exploratory steps. When this fails to resolve the ridge, we retrench further, again with no improvement. The search terminates when the step sizes fall below a preselected minimum, as after the second reduction in Fig. 7–25. In our case, $\mathbf{b}_{17}$ is actually at the maximum, at least as far as we can tell with the finest resolution available.

This example shows how smoothly pattern search finds the trend of a ridge and follows it to the top. Although performance of the method does not depend on the choice of scale, it certainly would be sensitive to the step size selected and the speed at which the grid is reduced to resolve a ridge. In the original form described here, pattern search occasionally has difficulty establishing a new pattern after arriving at the resolution ridge. To correct this

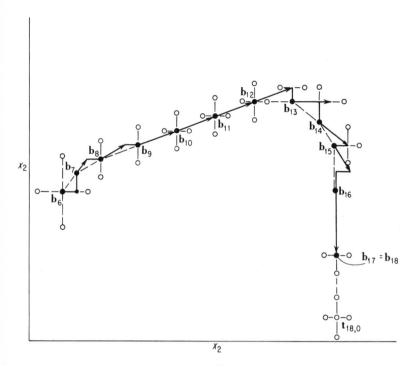

Figure 7-25. Following a ridge.

shortcoming, Wood has incorporated a quadratic strategy into the routine that uses second-order information to detect the trend of the resolution ridge and restart the pattern. These techniques are developed in Section 7-09.

Hooke and Jeeves found empirically, in a curve-fitting problem involving neutron flux in a nuclear reactor, that the computation time for pattern search increased only as the *first* power of the number of variables. This is striking because, with classical minimization techniques, the computations grow with the *cube* of the dimensionality. This phenomenon may be rationalized by observing that a ridge is really a one-dimensional object, since it may be characterized by a single parameter. Thus the empirically-observed efficiency of pattern search may be due precisely to its ability to follow a ridge and reduce the effective dimensionality of the problem.

This approach is mechanized in the "Opcon" device, developed by the Westinghouse Corporation, which has been applied to the automatic optimization of a Dow Chemical Co. pilot plant for making the chemical *styrene* by catalytic dehydrogenation of ethylbenzene (Hooke, 1959). Opcon could vary, within limits, any pair of the independent variables among heating rate (steam flow), reactor temperature, or ethylbenzene feed rate. The styrene production as measured by refractometers was to be maximized. The same machine has been used to optimize operation of a distillation column (Weiss, Archer, and Burt). Elliott Automation, Ltd. has developed a similar device called *Optimat* (cf. D. A. Bell).

Rosenbrock has devised a ridge-following procedure which has proved effective at finding the minimum of his test function

$$y = 100(x_2 - x_1^2)^2 + (1 - x_1)^2 \qquad (7\text{-}75)$$

having its low point at (1,1) in the shallow, curving valley shown in Fig. 7–20. His *method of rotating coordinates* differs from pattern search mainly in the way it carries out local explorations. Instead of perturbing each of the original variables independently as in pattern search, Rosenbrock rotates the coordinate system so that one axis points along the direction of the ridge as estimated by the previous trial. The other axes are arranged in directions normal to the first. Naturally, excursions in these normal directions are effective in correcting the estimate of the trend of the ridge, as indicated in Fig. 7–20.

Instead of taking a fixed step in each direction, Rosenbrock in effect tries to find the optimum point on each line. This procedure continuously adjusts what in pattern search would be the step size. The combined rotation of the ridge-tracking vector and scale adjustment proves extremely effective on the test function. Table 7–1 shows where several schemes, all started at the point $(-1.2, 1)$, ended after 200 moves. The pattern search trials were recorded by Wood in his 1962 report. Gauss' method, which happens to be applicable to Rosenbrock's function, gets as close to the minimum with only a tenth of the effort.

TABLE 7–1

PERFORMANCE OF VARIOUS SEARCH SCHEMES AFTER 200 TRIALS
ON $y = 100 \, (x_2 - x_1^2)^2 + (1 - x_1)^2$

Method	x_1	x_2	y
Sectioning	−0.970	0.945	3.882
Gradient	−0.605	0.371	2.578
Ordinary pattern	------	-----	0.803
Pattern with adjusted steps	-----	-----	0.0103
Rotating coordinates	0.995	0.991	0.000022
Optimum	1	1	0

The mathematical details of the method of rotating coordinates may be found in Rosenbrock's article and in OSM. O'Hagan has had considerable success with a simplified version called *spider*, developed together with C. Moler. The computer program has several precomputed exploration plans which call for perturbations in oblique directions rather than those parallel to the coordinate axes. At each exploration move, one of these plans is chosen at random, but the acceleration moves are made just as in pattern search. Introduction of this randomness apparently keeps the search from sticking on a resolution ridge while still preserving the ridge-following characteristics. The technique, which might be called *random pattern* search, has been applied successfully to the following problems at Texas Instruments:

1. Determining the equilibrium position of up to twenty particles constrained to lie on a sphere
2. Design of microwave matching networks
3. Design of a gallium-arsenic light source
4. Maximum likelihood estimation
5. Curve fitting of diode and transistor characteristics
6. Design of digital filters
7. Optimal parts replacement

This completes discussion of the "middle game" strategies for organizing first-order information into climbing procedures. By acceleration and by following ridges, they scale the response surface rapidly in steeply sloped regions and bring the investigator to the vicinity of a stationary point. There, where the tangent plane is almost horizontal and the first derivatives become small, a change in tactics is called for which is the topic of Section 7-09.

7-09 Exploration Near a Stationary Point

Both the beginning and the end of a climb involve local exploration, the former being a simple linear study near an arbitrary point; the latter, a nonlinear exploration of the vicinity of the optimum. Thus a fairly simple extension of the concepts already developed enables us to dispose of the end game tactics in this section. Moreover, some of the geometric and algebraic ideas connected with nonlinear exploration will be of value in Section 7-11 on quadratic convergence.

Box and Wilson have remarked that often an experimenter is not satisfied merely with locating the optimum; he needs also to know how the objective function behaves at points nearby. Since the tangent plane will be horizontal at a peak, curvature, asymmetry, and other nonlinear effects become important there, and the investigator is led to fit quadratic or higher-degree expressions to the unknown function. Even an investigator totally unconcerned about the objective's behavior near the summit would be reckless not to examine the supposed optimum closely, for there may actually be better points nearby. We shall study an example where the fitting of a quadratic expression signals the presence of higher ground which otherwise would have been overlooked.

First we measure the curvature by considering only the first- and second-degree terms of the Taylor expansion in the region of interest. If the function is asymmetric, cubic terms might be necessary, but we will find this out later when we check our quadratic predictions against actual observations. Box (1954) has discussed the dangers of trying to approximate a high-degree expression with a lower-degree polynomial. Since the work required to construct a nonlinear approximation grows rapidly with its degree, choice of a good algebraic representation for the function may well justify the initial research and reflection needed to obtain it, as pointed out in Section 7–01.

We shall develop the principles of nonlinear exploration by studying a specific example. An investigator wishes to find the combination of temperature and chemical reactor volume for which the maximum profit, considering value of product less operating and construction costs, is obtainable. He has constructed a complicated mathematical model relating profit (y, \$/day) to the *logarithm* of temperature in degrees centigrade (x_1, dimensionless) and the reactor volume (x_2, cubic feet). The logarithm was chosen because theoretical considerations, namely, the Arhennius relation of chemical kinetics (McCutcheon, Seltz, and Warner), indicate that reaction rate is an exponential function of temperature. Use of the logarithm is more likely to give a representation which can be fitted by a low-degree polynomial.

Suppose that, according to a pattern search, the optimum appears to be near the point (2.45, 8.5), where the profit is \$756/day, the highest measured. The daily profits at the four nearest points are as follows: $y\langle 2.49, 8.5\rangle = 574$; $y\langle 2.45, 8.9\rangle = 742$; $y\langle 2.41, 8.5\rangle = 646$; $y\langle 2.45, 8.1\rangle = 702$. In the experimental region obtained by plotting x_2 against x_1 the five points form a cross. As we saw in Section 7–08, many search strategies give this sort of pattern in the neighborhood of a candidate for the optimum.

Consider the Taylor series for a function of two variables with the terms of higher than second degree neglected.

$$\Delta y = m_1 \, \Delta x_1 + m_2 \, \Delta x_2 + \tfrac{1}{2}[m_{11}(\Delta x_1)^2 + 2m_{12}(\Delta x_1)(\Delta x_2) + m_{22}(\Delta x_2)^2]$$

$$(7\text{-}76)$$

This expression has five constants, but there are available only four points different from the base point, which we shall take to be (2.45, 8.5) in the center of the cross. We must either take another observation or throw out one term. As a first trial let us neglect the interaction term involving both Δx_1 and Δx_2. Thus we would have

$$\Delta y = m_1 \, \Delta x_1 + m_2 \, \Delta x_2 + \tfrac{1}{2}[m_{11}(\Delta x_1)^2 + m_{22}(\Delta x_2)^2] \qquad (7\text{-}77)$$

This approximation will be used to estimate the location of the true optimum. A check measurement there will tell us whether the approximation is good enough; if it isn't, we shall use the check point to evaluate the constants when the interaction term is included.

The crosslike arrangement permits great simplification in the computations. Consider first the constants m_1 and m_{11} associated with the variable x_1.

Let the base point (2.45, 8.5) be designated x_0; let the point (2.49, 8.5) to its right be x_{11}; and let (2.41, 8.5) on the left be x_{12}. With Δy_{ij} denoting $y\langle x_{ij}\rangle - y\langle x_0\rangle$ and Δx_{ij} being the distance from the base to the point x_{ij}, we may write Eq. (7–77) for x_{11} and x_{12} as follows

$$\Delta y_{11} = m_1 \Delta x_{11} + \tfrac{1}{2}m_{11}(\Delta x_{11})^2 \tag{7-78a}$$

$$\Delta y_{12} = m_1 \Delta x_{12} + \tfrac{1}{2}m_{11}(\Delta x_{12})^2 \tag{7-78b}$$

But $\Delta x_{12} = -\Delta x_{11}$; hence the latter equation becomes

$$\Delta y_{12} = -m_1 \Delta x_{11} + \tfrac{1}{2}m_{11}(\Delta x_{11})^2 \tag{7-78c}$$

Adding (7–78a) to (7–78c) gives

$$m_{11} = \frac{\Delta y_{11} + \Delta y_{12}}{(\Delta x_{11})^2} \tag{7-79a}$$

Subtracting (7–78c) from (7–78a) gives

$$m_1 = \frac{\Delta y_{11} - \Delta y_{12}}{2\,\Delta x_{11}} \tag{7-79b}$$

In general if there are N independent variables arranged so that there are points x_{i1} and x_{i2} such that

$$x_{i1} = x_0 + \Delta x_{i1}e_i \quad \text{and} \quad x_{i2} = x_0 - \Delta x_{i1}e_i$$

where e_i is the ith unit vector,

then
$$m_{ii} = \frac{\Delta y_{i1} + \Delta y_{i2}}{(\Delta x_{i1})^2} \tag{7-80a}$$

and
$$m_i = \frac{\Delta y_{i1} - \Delta y_{i2}}{2\Delta x_{i1}} \tag{7-80b}$$

In the example at hand, the approximation would be

$$\Delta y = -900\Delta x_1 + 50\Delta x_2 - 90{,}000(\Delta x_1)^2 - 200(\Delta x_2)^2 \tag{7-81}$$

This quadratic expression may be differentiated partially with respect to Δx_1 and Δx_2, the derivatives set equal to zero, and the two equations solved simultaneously to give the coordinate changes Δx_1^0 and Δx_2^0 to reach the apparent optimum. Thus,

$$\frac{\partial \Delta y}{\partial \Delta x_1} = -900 - 180{,}000\Delta x_1 = 0$$

whence
$$\Delta x_1^0 = -0.005$$

and similarly
$$\Delta x_2^0 = 0.125$$

In general, for this cruciform pattern,

$$\Delta x_i^0 = -\frac{m_i}{m_{ii}} = \frac{(\Delta y_{i2} - \Delta y_{i1})\,\Delta x_{i1}}{2(\Delta y_{i2} + \Delta y_{i1})} \tag{7-82}$$

Since the expression fit indicates that the optimum is indeed quite close to $\mathbf{x}_0$, we may be tempted to conclude that the optimum has been found. It is prudent, however, to test another point first. Although the predicted optimum may seem like a good place to test, it is so close to the point $\mathbf{x}_0$ that it would be of little value in subsequent surface fitting should the prediction be invalid. Thus we shall try the point (2.41, 8.9), obtained by *decreasing* x_1 an amount $\Delta \mathbf{x}_{11}$ and *increasing* x_2 by $\Delta \mathbf{x}_{21}$. This puts the new point not only in the same quadrant as the predicted optimum, but also where it will make future computations convenient. Equation (7-81) forecasts that at the new point the profit will be \$636/day —\$120 less than at the best point so far. Evaluation of this point shows the profit to be only \$492/day, indicating that the variables are interacting so strongly that the simple model should not be used.

Equation (7-77) having failed, we are forced to use Eq. (7-76) with its additional interaction term $m_{12}(\Delta x_1)(\Delta x_2)$. Fortunately the calculations are quite simple, for, since the interaction term will still be zero in equations such as (7-78), the expressions (7-80) for m_i and m_{ii} remain valid. In fact the numerical values of m_1, m_2, m_{11}, and m_{22} already computed will be unchanged in the new expression. To evaluate m_{12} we need merely write Eq. (7-76) for the new point $\mathbf{x}^{12}$, substituting the values of the known constants.

$$\Delta y^{12} = -264 = -900\,(-0.04) + 50(0.4)$$
$$- 90{,}000(0.04)^2 - 200(0.4)^2 + m_{12}(-0.04)(0.4)$$

whence $m_{12} = 9000$, clearly not negligible.

Before finding the optimum according to the new expression, let us indicate how to handle interaction when there are more than two independent variables. For N variables there will be $N(N-1)/2$ interaction terms each requiring a point. To evaluate the coefficient m_{ij}, place a new point at

$$\mathbf{x}_{ij} \equiv \mathbf{x}_0 \pm \Delta x_i \mathbf{e}_i \pm \Delta x_j \mathbf{e}_j$$

where the $\pm$ indicates that the sign is arbitrary. Equation (7-76), when written for this point, will have m_{ij} as its only unknown, since all the constants m_i and m_{ii} have already been determined.

Next we reestimate the location of the optimum by differentiating Eq. (7-76), which in this case is now

$$\Delta y = -900\,\Delta x_1 + 50\,\Delta x_2 - 90{,}000(\Delta x_1)^2 + 9000(\Delta x_1)(\Delta x_2)$$
$$- 200(\Delta x_2)^2 \tag{7-83}$$

Solution of the two simultaneous equations resulting gives

$$\Delta x_1^0 = -0.01 \quad \text{and} \quad \Delta x_2^0 = -0.10$$

A test at the corresponding point $\mathbf{x}^0 = (2.44, 8.4)$ verifies the slight profit improvement of \$2/day predicted by Eq. (7-83). Hence we shift our coordinate system to put $\mathbf{x}^0$ at the origin, defining

$$\Delta \bar{x}_1 \equiv x_1 - x_1^0 = \Delta x_1 + 0.01 \qquad (7\text{-}84a)$$

$$\Delta \bar{x}_2 \equiv x_2 - x_2^0 = \Delta x_2 + 0.10 \qquad (7\text{-}84b)$$

To obtain a quadratic expression valid in the vicinity of this apparent optimum we could invoke Taylor's theorem, using Eq. (7–83) to give us the first and second derivatives we need. But we know that at the optimum the first derivatives vanish, and the values of the second derivatives of a quadratic expression are necessarily the same no matter where they are evaluated. Therefore,

$$\Delta \bar{y} \equiv y - y^0 = y - 756 = -90{,}000(\Delta \bar{x}_1)^2 + 9000(\Delta \bar{x}_1)(\Delta \bar{x}_2)$$
$$- 200(\Delta \bar{x}_2)^2 \qquad (7\text{-}85)$$

The right member is a *homogeneous quadratic form* in two variables because each term is of second degree. In Section 3–16 it was shown how to identify the character of a stationary point by completing the square on the quadratic terms, which in this case gives

$$\Delta \bar{y} = -90{,}000(\Delta \bar{x}_1)^2 + 9000(\Delta \bar{x}_1)(\Delta \bar{x}_2) - 200(\Delta \bar{x}_2)^2$$
$$= -[90{,}000(\Delta \bar{x}_1)^2 - 9000(\Delta \bar{x}_1)(\Delta \bar{x}_2) + 225(\Delta \bar{x}_2)^2] + 25(\Delta \bar{x}_2)^2$$
$$= -(300\Delta \bar{x}_1 - 15\Delta \bar{x}_2)^2 + 25(\Delta \bar{x}_2)^2 \qquad (7\text{-}86)$$

This expression is indefinite because the two squared terms have different signs. Hence the point $\mathbf{x}^0$ is not a peak; it is a saddle. Notice that the expression would have been different if we had eliminated x_2 first. This does not matter because we are interested merely in the arrangement of signs, which is known as the *signature* of the function (Birkhoff and MacLane).

Since $\mathbf{x}^0$ is in reality a saddle, there is the possibility of further improvement of the profit. To do this we must choose a combination of $\Delta \bar{x}_1$ and $\Delta \bar{x}_2$ which will make Eq. (7–86) positive. Let us, for the sake of convenience, simply nullify the first term by taking

$$\Delta \bar{x}_2 = 20 \, \Delta \bar{x}_1 \qquad (7\text{-}87)$$

Since the second term must always be positive, any pair of values satisfying Eq. (7–87) will be satisfactory: we shall choose $\Delta \bar{x}_1 = 0.02$ and $\Delta \bar{x}_2 = 0.4$. Equation (7–86) predicts $\Delta \bar{y} = 4$ at this point; hence, if this value is verified, we should search in this direction. Notice that if opposite signs were chosen the improvement would be the same, which indicates that there are two possible peaks to be examined.

If the experiments do not confirm the predictions of the equation, then the observer is forced to consider fitting a cubic equation, but we shall not go into this matter here. It is important to notice that the direction of improvement was found from data which at first glance would suggest that no better profit was possible. Directions of improvement can be found only if the interaction term is taken into account; the simpler no-interaction

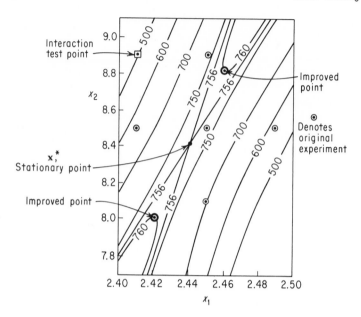

Figure 7-26. The objective function.

model is unsuitable because it involves only squared terms. Figure 7–26 shows the contours of the objective function.

7-10 Evolution and the Simplicial Method

In most large-scale industrial operations any observations are obscured by appreciable experimental error. One must make many repeated measurements to distinguish between true changes in optimum conditions and the spurious fluctuations caused by random noise. Since experimentation with a full-sized manufacturing plant is a costly business, monitoring a moving optimum would be out of the question but for the large amount of data available for small changes in the independent variables. Hence if the experimenter is patient and uses good statistical techniques in gathering and analyzing his information, he may be able to make the plant slowly follow shifts in optimum conditions.

This idea of letting a system adapt to changing conditions without unduly upsetting it dynamically or sacrificing profits is due to G. E. P. Box (1957), who named the procedure *evolutionary operations*, perhaps in the spirit of the Darwin Centennial being celebrated at that time. The bookkeeping details of evolutionary operations are not within the scope of this text, which assumes no statistical background on the part of the reader. The method deserves attention, however, for it has proved itself valuable in industrial optimization.

Its principles are very close to those we have described for fitting a nonlinear function to the response surface near the optimum.

The concept of evolutionary operations inspired Spendley, Hext, and Himsworth to devise a simple system for approaching a nearby optimum and following it if it drifts. Their scheme involves placing observations on the vertices of a *simplex*, which is the N-dimensional generalization of the equilateral triangle ($N = 2$) and the regular tetrahedron ($N = 3$). To describe algebraically where to put the measurements, define the quantities (Spendley, Hext, and Himsworth),

$$p_N \equiv \frac{\sqrt{N+1} - 1 + N}{N\sqrt{2}} \tag{7-88}$$

$$q_N \equiv \frac{\sqrt{N+1} - 1}{N\sqrt{2}} \tag{7-89}$$

Then the $N + 1$ vertices of a simplex with unit edge are specified by

$$x_0 = 0 \tag{7-90}$$

$$x_1 = (p_N, q_N, q_N, \ldots, q_N) \tag{7-91}$$

$$x_2 = (q_N, p_N, q_N, \ldots, q_N) \tag{7-92}$$

$$\cdot$$
$$\cdot$$
$$\cdot$$

$$x_N = (q_N, \ldots, q_N, p_N) \tag{7-93}$$

That is, the nth component of x_n is p_N, the others being q_N ($n \neq 0$). For $N = 2$, the three points are

$$x_0' = (0, 0)$$

$$x_1' = \frac{\sqrt{3} + 1, \sqrt{3} - 1}{2\sqrt{2}} = (0.965, \ 0.259)$$

$$x_2' = \frac{\sqrt{3} - 1, \sqrt{3} + 1}{2\sqrt{2}} = (0.259, \ 0.965)$$

They are shown graphically in Fig. 7–27. Notice that they are a unit distance apart (Exercise 7–12).

Next consider $N + 1$ *complementary points* $\hat{x}_n$ defined by

$$\hat{x}_n = \sum_{j=0}^{N} x_j - \left(\frac{N+2}{N}\right)x_n \tag{7-94}$$

For $N = 2$, the three complementary points are:

$$\hat{x}_0' = \sum_{j=0}^{2} x_j - 2(0, 0) = (1.224, \ 1.224)$$

$$\hat{x}_1' = (1.224, \ 1.224) - 2(0.965, \ 0.259)$$

$$= (-0.706, \ 0.706)$$

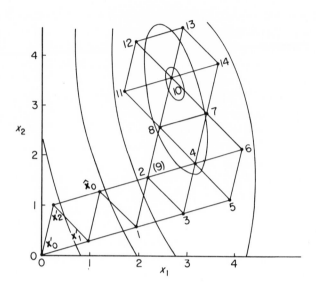

Figure 7-27. Simplicial search.

$$\hat{x}_2' = (1.224, 1.224) - 2(0.259, 0.965)$$
$$= (0.706, -0.706)$$

Let the typical point $\mathbf{x}_n$ be deleted from the original set. The remaining N points, together with the complementary point $\hat{\mathbf{x}}_n$, form a new regular unit simplex as in Fig. 7-27. Suppose the objective function is measured at each point $\mathbf{x}_n$ in the original simplex, and let the index of the worst value be w. That is, if y is to be maximized, then

$$y_w \equiv y\langle \mathbf{x}_w \rangle \equiv \min_{0 \leq n \leq N} y\langle \mathbf{x}_n \rangle \tag{7-95}$$

The strategy is to measure next at $\hat{\mathbf{x}}_w$, the point complementary to the worst one in the original set. Then one finds the worst point in the new set, measures at its complement, and continues. If started in a nonoptimal region, this procedure will migrate upward, as shown for points $\hat{\mathbf{x}}_0$, 1, 2, 3, 4, 5, and 6, until it crosses a ridge. There it changes direction so that for the first time the current simplex (points 4, 7, and 6) does not contain all of the most recently measured points. The next two simplices are (4, 8, 7) and (4, 8, 9), the point numbers being arranged in order of decreasing value. Notice that the procedure is beginning to circle around the aging point 4. The point 9 is in fact identical with the former point 2.

Here there is danger of oscillation, for the points 7 and 9 are mutually complementary in the simplices formed together with points 8 and 4. To prevent an endless exchange between simplices (4, 8, 9) and (4, 8, 7), a second rule is invoked. If the newest point in a simplex has the worst value, then proceed to the complement of the *second* worst point. This prevents return to the simplex immediately preceding and subsequent oscillation. In the example, the second worst point in (4, 8, 9) is 8, and so the new simplex is (4, 9, 10), where point 10 is identical with the older point 3.

Here again the anti-oscillation rule applies, and since the next simplex (4, 5, 10) would be identical with the older one (4, 5, 3), the procedure would circle the point 4 forever if something were not done. Spendley, Hext, and Himsworth give a stopping rule which terminates the search whenever a given point has remained in the number of successive simplices given by Table 7–2. These numbers seem low to us, for in Fig. 7–27 the rule would stop the search at the simplex (4, 6, 5) before it has had a chance to go up the ridge. They probably do not intend to stop the search and declare point 4 the optimum, which it certainly isn't, but rather to make a quadratic approximation to determine the character of the apparent stationary point. The end game procedure would in this case predict greener pastures in directions of increased x_2 which would justify points 7 and 8.

TABLE 7–2

STOPPING AGES FOR SIMPLICIAL METHOD

Number of independent variables	2	3	4	5	6	7	8	9	10	15	20	30
Maximum age	3	5	7	9	11	13	16	18	21	36	52	92

This time, when point 9 gives such poor results that the anti-oscillation rule would be called for, the quadratic prediction is used to suggest a new point instead. This directs the search to point 10, a radical move because the point 4, best until now, is left behind. In Fig. 7–27 this gamble pays off, since point 10 is really better than point 4 and the search can resume. Simplices (10, 8, 11), (10, 11, 12), and (10, 12, 13) follow from the usual logic. At this juncture, point 10 has aged sufficiently to justify another shift to end game strategy, which would indeed verify that (10, 12, 13) contains the optimum. Spendley, Hext, and Himsworth give several second-order experimental designs for the end game which build upon simplices.

This technique is called the *sequential simplex* method by its inventors. To avoid confusing it with Dantzig's simplex method for linear programming problems, we prefer to call it the *simplicial method*. Since it does not accelerate its steps, it is probably too slow for ordinary optimization problems free from experimental error. It does fit in well with Box's evolutionary operations philosophy when there is experimental error present. In this case the stopping rule is replaced by the dictum that any over-age point be rechecked, since it may be spuriously high owing to sampling error. In evolutionary operations there is no need for a stopping rule, since measurement continues forever. The simplicial method will circle around an optimum, gathering more information until a quadratic fit suggests trying a point off the beaten path. In Fig. 7–27, dropping the stopping rule would generate simplices (10, 13, 14), (10, 7, 14), and finally (10, 8, 7) again. Here the cycle would be completed, and the procedure would continue circling about point 10 until the optimum moved outside the hexagon of points 7, 8, 11, 12, 13, and 14.

7-11 Quadratic Convergence

A quadratic function $q\langle \mathbf{x} \rangle$ of N variables $\mathbf{x}$ has in it one constant term, N linear terms, and $N(N + 1)/2$ quadratic terms—$(N + 1)(N + 2)/2$ in all. If values of a quadratic objective function are known at $(N + 1)(N + 2)/2$ points, then the coefficients can be found by solving the resulting linear simultaneous equations, provided that the points have been located so as to make the equations linearly independent. This done, one could predict the precise location of the optimum by setting the first derivatives to zero.

Next consider an objective which is a monotonic function $m\langle q \rangle$ of a quadratic function $q\langle \mathbf{x} \rangle$ of N variables $\mathbf{x}$.

$$y\langle \mathbf{x} \rangle = m\langle q\langle \mathbf{x} \rangle \rangle \tag{7-96}$$

Such an objective is called *quasi-quadratic*, its contours being N-dimensional ellipsoids. If the form of the function $m\langle q \rangle$ is known, then it is in principle possible to invert it because of its monotonicity. Application of this inverse $m^{-1}\langle q \rangle$ gives

$$m^{-1}\langle y\langle \mathbf{x} \rangle \rangle = m^{-1}\langle m\langle q\langle \mathbf{x} \rangle \rangle \rangle \tag{7-97}$$
$$= q\langle \mathbf{x} \rangle$$

In this case one can determine the $(N + 1)(N + 2)/2$ coefficients of $q\langle \mathbf{x} \rangle$ by evaluating $y\langle \mathbf{x} \rangle$, and consequently $m^{-1}\langle y\langle \mathbf{x} \rangle \rangle$, at $(N + 1)(N + 2)/2$ points. Then one could optimize $q\langle \mathbf{x} \rangle$ directly, the monotonicity of $m\langle q \rangle$ insuring that the same point $\mathbf{x}^*$ would optimize $y\langle \mathbf{x} \rangle$.

In practice these ideal situations rarely arise. Usually $m\langle q \rangle$ either is not known in advance or is too complicated to be inverted. Yet quadratic or quasi-quadratic functions are useful as standards against which to compare the performances of competing climbing techniques. For example, Section 7–07 showed that on a quasi-quadratic function the gradient method may not achieve the optimum in a finite number of steps, whereas, for $N = 2$, the accelerated gradient technique will always reach the optimum after three straight-line unidimensional searches (see Fig. 7–21). Any climbing procedure capable of finding the optimum of a (quasi-) quadratic function after measuring N gradients is said to *converge* (*quasi-*) *quadratically* or to have (*quasi-*) *quadratic convergence.*

The next two sections describe two methods, one with quasi-quadratic, the other with quadratic convergence. The first procedure is the *method of parallel tangents* or *partan* of Shah, Buehler, and Kempthorne; the second, the *deflected gradient method* of Fletcher and Powell. Partan is appropriate when the objective function is explicit and gradients must be measured by perturbation; the deflected gradient approach is more effective when precise gradients can be obtained easily, as when the objective is implicit. Partan requires more measurements, involving N gradient searches and $N - 1$ acceleration steps. The accelerations are not needed by the deflected gradient method, which does, however, require certain straightforward matrix multiplications not needed by partan. Although the deflected gradient method involves measurement of N gradients, the N unidimensional optimizations are not in the gradient directions. Partan's convergence properties are stronger, being quasi-quadratic. Fletcher and Powell proved quadratic convergence for their procedure, but the question of its quasi-quadratic convergence has not yet been studied.

7-12 Parallel Tangents

The first technique to be described is the method of parallel tangents, which combines many desirable properties of the simpler methods already described. It climbs like the ascent methods. Its over-all performance on quasi-quadratic functions is invariant to changes in scales of measurement. Since the basic geometric properties measured are contour tangents, the technique can be used as an elimination technique. For quasi-quadratic functions, partan will find the optimum exactly after a fixed, small number of measurements. But even when the contours are not precisely elliptical, the technique has certain ridge-following properties which make it attractive. Consequently partan may be considered a master strategy integrating and guiding the opening, middle, and end game tactics already described. Although partan has many forms, the discussion will be confined here to a version called *gradient partan*, which amounts to a multidimensional extension of the accelerated gradient method of Section 7–07 and Fig. 7–21.

In three dimensions the partan strategy is first to locate a plane containing the center and then to apply plane partan to find the center exactly. The first four steps of three-dimensional partan are exactly like a plane search. The fifth step locates a plane containing the peak $\mathbf{x}^*$. The search is so conducted that when this plane is located there are already three points in it placed where they can be used for plane partan. Hence the center $\mathbf{x}^*$ is found at the sixth point, $\mathbf{p}_6$.

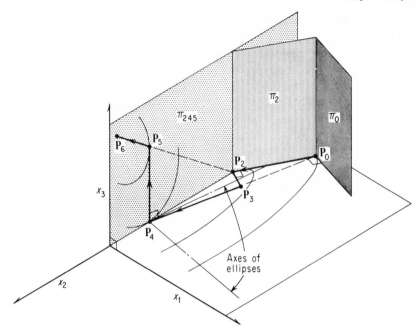

Figure 7-28. Gradient partan in space.

Figure 7–28 shows an example of gradient partan in three dimensions. The first four steps constitute a gradient partan search in a plane, which for pictorial convenience has been taken to be horizontal in the isometric representation. Since the traces of the ellipsoids on any intersecting plane must be ellipses, point $\mathbf{p}_4$ is where the objective is maximum in the horizontal plane. Intuition would suggest locating the next point $\mathbf{p}_5$ by another uni-dimensional search along the vertical gradient at $\mathbf{p}_4$. It is important to observe that this line is parallel to the intersection of the tangent planes π_0 and π_2.

Notice that the points $\mathbf{p}_2$, $\mathbf{p}_4$, and $\mathbf{p}_5$ are in position for an ordinary plane partan search in the plane π_{245} containing them. This is because the vertical plane π_2 tangent to $\mathbf{p}_2$ intersects π_{245} in a vertical line which is necessarily parallel to the vertical line $\mathbf{p}_5 - \mathbf{p}_4$. Hence by searching along the line $\mathbf{p}_5 - \mathbf{p}_2$ we can find the point $\mathbf{p}_6$ where the objective is maximum in π_{245}. If we can show that the peak $\mathbf{x}^*$ is in this plane π_{245}, then it will follow immediately that $\mathbf{p}_6$, the last point, is actually the peak. We shall do this by proving the four points $\mathbf{p}_2$, $\mathbf{p}_4$, $\mathbf{p}_5$ and $\mathbf{x}^*$ to be coplanar, using the geometric proof of Shah, Buehler, and Kempthorne in their 1961 report.

The coplanarity proof is accomplished by studying the behavior of general partan on spherical contours. Imagine that the original ellipsoidal contours are first rotated until their axes are parallel to those of the coordinate system. Then change the scales of the variables x_2 and x_3 until all three axes of the ellipsoids are equal. The contours will in this way be transformed into concentric spheres. Although the perpendicularity relations of gradient partan no longer hold, lines parallel before transformation are still parallel afterwards, and the colinearity and coplanarity of points is also preserved. Thus if $\mathbf{p}_2$, $\mathbf{p}_4$, $\mathbf{p}_5$, and $\mathbf{x}^*$ are coplanar after transformation, they must have been coplanar before. Moreover, general partan is applicable in the plane π_{0234} containing the first four points, as well as in the plane π_{2456} containing $\mathbf{p}_2$, $\mathbf{p}_4$, $\mathbf{p}_5$, and $\mathbf{p}_6$.

The instructions for three-dimensional general partan, illustrated in Fig. 7–29 are

1. Locate $\mathbf{p}_2$ at the high point on any line from the arbitrary starting point $\mathbf{p}_0$, making sure the line is not in the tangent plane π_0 at $\mathbf{p}_0$.
2. Place $\mathbf{p}_3$ at the high point on any line from $\mathbf{p}_2$ parallel to π_0 but not in the tangent plane π_2 at $\mathbf{p}_2$.
3. Put $\mathbf{p}_4$ at the summit along the line through $\mathbf{p}_0$.
4. Locate $\mathbf{p}_5$ at the high point on the *unique* line from $\mathbf{p}_4$ parallel to the intersection of π_0 and π_2.
5. Place $\mathbf{p}_6$ at the high point of the line from $\mathbf{p}_2$ through $\mathbf{p}_5$. This final point will be at the center $\mathbf{x}^*$ of the system of three-dimensional ellipsoids.

The advantage of using spherical contours for the sake of the proof is that

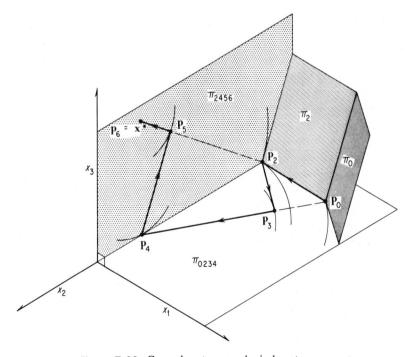

Figure 7-29. General partan on spherical contours.

the line from the center $\mathbf{x}^*$ to any tangent point $\mathbf{p}_i$ is perpendicular to the tangent plane π_i there. In particular, $\mathbf{p}_2 - \mathbf{x}^*$ is perpendicular to π_2, and $\mathbf{p}_4 - \mathbf{x}^*$ is normal to π_4. Since the line $\mathbf{p}_2 - \mathbf{p}_0$ is in both these planes, it must also be perpendicular to the plane $\pi_{24\mathbf{x}^*}$ containing the points $\mathbf{p}_2, \mathbf{p}_4$, and $\mathbf{x}^*$. Now the line $\mathbf{p}_5 - \mathbf{p}_4$ was constructed parallel to the intersection of the tangent planes π_0 and π_2. Since π_0 is perpendicular to $\mathbf{p}_0 - \mathbf{x}^*$, and π_2 is normal to $\mathbf{p}_2 - \mathbf{x}^*$, this intersection will be perpendicular to the plane $\pi_{02\mathbf{x}^*}$, which contains the line $\mathbf{p}_2 - \mathbf{p}_0$. Hence $\mathbf{p}_5 - \mathbf{p}_4$ must be perpendicular to $\mathbf{p}_2 - \mathbf{p}_0$, which in turn implies that $\mathbf{p}_5 - \mathbf{p}_4$ must be in $\pi_{24\mathbf{x}^*}$, also perpendicular to $\mathbf{p}_2 - \mathbf{p}_0$. It follows that $\mathbf{p}_5$ is in $\pi_{24\mathbf{x}^*}$, or equivalently, that $\mathbf{x}^*$ is in the plane π_{245} containing $\mathbf{p}_2, \mathbf{p}_4$, and $\mathbf{p}_5$. Since $\mathbf{p}_6$ is the highest point in π_{245}, the peak $\mathbf{x}^*$ must be at $\mathbf{p}_6$, which establishes the validity of both general and gradient partan.

The gradient option has an advantage over any other version of partan. If any of the axes of the ellipsoid system are equal, gradient partan will reach the center sooner. This is clearly true when all the axes are equal, for in this case, the contours are spherical and the first gradient line from $\mathbf{p}_0$ passes right through $\mathbf{x}^*$, that is, $\mathbf{p}_2 = \mathbf{x}^*$.

Consider the situation when only two of the axes are equal, and the contours are ellipsoids of revolution. The first four points of a gradient partan search determine a plane, and the traces of the ellipsoidal contours on this plane will be ellipses centered at $\mathbf{p}_4$. Figure 7-30, in which such a plane has, for pictorial convenience, been taken to be horizontal, shows that the tangent planes at $\mathbf{p}_0$ and $\mathbf{p}_2$ will be perpendicular to π_{024} when gradient partan is used. Any set of ellipsoids of revolution must have their contours through $\mathbf{p}_0$ and $\mathbf{p}_2$ tangent to the respective tangent planes. We can construct such a contour system by rotating the plane ellipses about the line passing through $\mathbf{p}_4$ and bisecting the angle $\mathbf{p}_0\mathbf{p}_4\mathbf{p}_2$. This line is, of course, one of the axes of the system of ellipses. Alternatively, an acceptable set of contours could be obtained by rotating the ellipses about their other axis, which is the line in π_{024} at right angles to the first axis, as shown in Fig. 7-30.

An ellipsoid of revolution is by definition generated by rotating an ellipse about one of its axes. No other line will do. Hence we have exhausted the number of ways that ellipsoids of revolution can be formed from the ellipses in π_{024}. It follows that $\mathbf{p}_4$ is the only point which can be the center of the contour system. Therefore $\mathbf{p}_4 = \mathbf{x}^*$ when the ellipsoidal contours have only two axes equal.

This result can be extended to functions of any number of variables. That is, when only two axes are unequal, gradient partan will locate the peak after only a planar search, because the plane of the search will necessarily pass through $\mathbf{x}^*$. General partan does not have this property because the tangent planes π_0 and π_2 will not be perpendicular to π_{024} unless gradients are used to determine search directions.

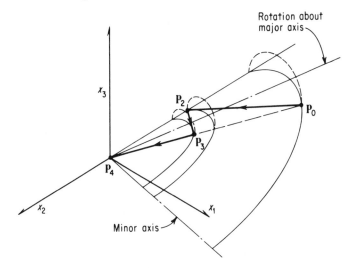

Figure 7-30. Gradient partan on ellipsoids of revolution.

Until now our arguments have been entirely geometric, and since it may not yet be clear how to carry out the corresponding algebra, we shall study two numerical examples of gradient partan. The first involves maximizing $y = -2x_1^2 - x_2^2 - x_3^2$, which requires only a planar search because two of the axes are equal. The second needs a three-dimensional search because it concerns maximizing $y = -2x_1^2 - x_2^2 - 3x_3^2$, whose contours have three different axes. The functions are clearly negative-definite, and both their peaks are at the origin $(0, 0, 0)$.

For simplicity, and to focus attention on the search method itself, the problems chosen are somewhat artificial. Generally we do not know what the function is; if we did, as in these examples, we could find the center immediately by setting the three partial derivatives of y equal to zero. Working with a known function saves us from having to measure the slopes m_1, m_2, and m_3 of the tangent plane at a point, for in our artificial example we can obtain them simply by evaluating the partial derivatives $\partial y/\partial x_i$ $(i = 1, 2, 3)$ at the point. Thus if the coordinates of a point a are (a_1, a_2, a_3), the slopes for the function $-2x_1^2 - x_2^2 - x_3^2$ are $m_1 = -4a_1$, $m_2 = -2a_2$, and $m_3 = -2a_3$. The equation of the tangent plane at a is therefore

$$-4a_1(x_1 - a_1) - 2a_2(x_2 - a_2) - 2a_3(x_3 - a_3) = 0 \qquad (7\text{-}98)$$

where $\mathbf{x} \equiv (x_1, x_2, x_3)$ is any point in the tangent plane. In a real problem these slopes would be determined experimentally by the methods of Section 7–03.

Another convenience arising from the artificiality of the problems is that the high point on a line of search can be found by expressing the points on the line as functions of a single parameter ρ (as in Section 7–04), writing the objective function $y\langle x_1, x_2, x_3\rangle$ in terms of this parameter as $y\langle\rho\rangle = y\langle x_1\langle\rho\rangle, x_2\langle\rho\rangle, x_3\langle\rho\rangle\rangle$, and then finding the value of ρ for which $dy\langle\rho\rangle/d\rho = 0$. This technique will be illustrated in the problems. Keep in mind, however, that in an actual problem the high point would be found, not by differentiation, but by one of the unidimensional search methods of Chapter 6.

Let us begin the search for the maximum of $y = -2x_1^2 - x_2^2 - x_3^2$ arbitrarily at the point $\mathbf{p}_0 = (-1, 1, -1)$. From Eq. (7–98) the equation of the tangent plane at $\mathbf{p}_0$ is

$$4(x_1 + 1) - 2(x_2 - 1) + 2(x_3 + 1) = 0$$

By Eq. (7–24) the parametric equations of the gradient line at $\mathbf{p}_0$ are

$$x_1 = -1 + 4\rho, \quad x_2 = 1 - 2\rho, \quad x_3 = -1 + 2\rho$$

where ρ is the parameter of the line. In terms of ρ the objective function y may be written

$$y = -2(-1 + 4\rho)^2 - (1 - 2\rho)^2 - (-1 + 2\rho)^2$$

whence the high point can be found (artificially) by solving

$$\frac{dy}{d\rho} = -8[2(4\rho - 1) + (2\rho - 1)] = 0$$

The solution is $\rho^* = 0.3$, and

$$\mathbf{p}_2 = (-1 + 4(0.3), 1 - 2(0.3), -1 + 2(0.3)) = (0.2, 0.4, -0.4).$$

From $\mathbf{p}_2$ we again climb along the gradient, whose parametric equations are now

$$x_1 = 0.2 - 0.8\rho, \, x_2 = 0.4 - 0.8\rho, \, x_3 = -0.4 + 0.8\rho$$

Along this line, $y\langle\rho\rangle$ is maximum when $\rho^* = 0.375$, as the reader can verify. Hence,

$$\mathbf{p}_3 = (-0.1, 0.1, -0.1)$$

Next comes the first acceleration step in which we search along the line from $\mathbf{p}_0$ through $\mathbf{p}_3$. The vector equation of this line is

$$\mathbf{x} - \mathbf{p}_0 = \rho(\mathbf{p}_3 - \mathbf{p}_0)$$

whence $\qquad\qquad \mathbf{x} = (-1 + 0.9\rho, 1 - 0.9\rho, -1 + 0.9\rho)$

The objective function on this line reduces to

$$y = -4(1 - 0.9\rho)^2$$

which is clearly maximum when $\rho^* = 10/9$.

Hence $\qquad\qquad\qquad \mathbf{p}_4 = (0, 0, 0)$

In determining the tangent equation at $\mathbf{p}_4$ we find that all the first derivatives vanish, and we are already at the peak, that is, $\mathbf{x}^* = \mathbf{p}_4$, even though a three-dimensional search ordinarily would need two more steps. This is no coincidence. The equality of two of the contour axes has made it possible to save steps by gradient partan.

For the second function, $y = -2x_1^2 - x_2^2 - 3x_3^2$, the peak is not found until $\mathbf{p}_6$. The gradient line at a point $\mathbf{a}$ will have the vector equation

$$\mathbf{x} = \mathbf{a} + \rho(-4a_1, -2a_2, -6a_3)$$

Thus if we start again at $\mathbf{p}_0 = (-1, 1, -1)$, the gradient line will be described by

$$\mathbf{x} = (-1 + 4\rho, 1 - 2\rho, -1 + 6\rho)$$

The maximum on this line occurs when $\rho^* = 0.1944$,

whence $\mathbf{p}_2 = (-0.22222, 0.61111, 0.16666)$

The next point $\mathbf{p}_3$ is located at the summit of the gradient line from $\mathbf{p}_2$. We find that

$$\mathbf{p}_3 = (0.01807, 0.28071, -0.10366)$$

The first acceleration step locates

$$\mathbf{p}_4 = (0.1084, 0.2169, -0.0241)$$

which, as the reader can confirm, is colinear with $\mathbf{p}_0$ and $\mathbf{p}_3$. Since the derivatives at $\mathbf{p}_4$ do not vanish, $\mathbf{p}_4$ is clearly not at the peak; hence another gradient search must be conducted along the line

$$\mathbf{x} = (0.1084 - 0.4337\rho, 0.2169 - 0.4337\rho, -0.0241 + 0.1446\rho)$$

The summit is attained when $\rho^* = 0.3167$, and

$$\mathbf{p}_5 = (-0.0289, 0.0795, 0.0217)$$

The second, and in this three-dimensional case the final, acceleration step is along the line from $\mathbf{p}_2$ through $\mathbf{p}_5$. Since we know, in this artificial example, that $\mathbf{x}^* = (0, 0, 0)$, let us simply verify that $\mathbf{p}_2$ and $\mathbf{p}_5$ are colinear with the origin, for if they are, then $\mathbf{p}_6$ will be placed at $\mathbf{x}^*$. By direct calculation, we find that

$$\mathbf{p}_5 = 0.130\mathbf{p}_2,$$

which confirms that $\mathbf{p}_2$ and $\mathbf{p}_5$ are on the same ray from the origin. Hence

$$\mathbf{p}_6 = \mathbf{x}^* = (0, 0, 0)$$

Shah, Buehler, and Kempthorne have shown how to extend the method of parallel tangents to ellipsoidal functions of any number of independent variables. The strategy of gradient partan is to follow each climb from a tangent plane with an acceleration step along the gradient. The points have been numbered such that the odd-numbered ones $\mathbf{p}_3$, $\mathbf{p}_5$, $\mathbf{p}_7$, etc. are the result of a climb, whereas the even-numbered ones following $\mathbf{p}_2$ (that is, $\mathbf{p}_4$, $\mathbf{p}_6$, $\mathbf{p}_8$, etc.) are obtained by acceleration. Thus in finding the maximum of a function of four variables the searcher would locate point $\mathbf{p}_6$ exactly as in a three-dimensional search. Since $\mathbf{p}_6$ would, however, not be at the peak when there are four dimensions, a point $\mathbf{p}_7$ would be located at the summit of the line from $\mathbf{p}_6$ parallel to the intersection of tangent planes π_0, π_2, and π_4. The final point $\mathbf{p}_8$, at the peak of the acceleration line from $\mathbf{p}_4$ through $\mathbf{p}_7$, would fall at the optimum $\mathbf{x}^*$.

Figure 7–31, a schematic diagram due to the inventors of partan, may help the reader picture the sequence of unidimensional searches. Contour tangent planes π_{2k} are measured at all the even-numbered points $\mathbf{p}_{2k}$ ($k = 0$, $1, \ldots, N - 1$, where N is the number of independent variables). The gradient ascents from even-numbered points p_{2k} are on lines parallel to the tangents $\pi_0, \pi_2, \ldots, \pi_{2k-2}$ ($k = 1, 2, \ldots, N - 1$), which explains the name "parallel tangents."

The even points $\mathbf{p}_{2k}$ are determined by acceleration from $\mathbf{p}_{2k-4}$ through $\mathbf{p}_{2k-1}$ ($k = 2, 3, \ldots, N$). To start the process, $\mathbf{p}_2$ is placed at the summit of any line from the starting point $\mathbf{p}_0$. For quasi-quadratic objectives, the process terminates at the point $\mathbf{p}_{2N}$ after $2N - 1$ unidimensional searches and measurement of N contour tangents, counting the last one at $\mathbf{p}_{2N}$.

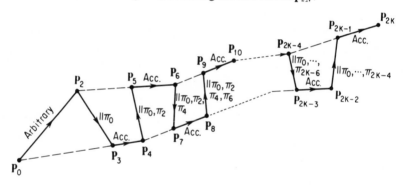

Figure 7-31. Schematic diagram of general partan.

On unimodal functions which do not happen to be quasi-quadratic, partan will not necessarily reach the optimum in $2N - 1$ steps. In this case one can either start over again or continue the cycle of gradient search and acceleration. The former procedure is called *iterated partan;* the latter, *continued partan.* The instructions for continued partan are simpler because they do not depend on the number N of independent variables. Harkins tested continued partan on Rosenbrock's curved valley function, Eq. (7–75), Fig. 7–20, and found the performance comparable with that of pattern search and the method of rotating coordinates. Naturally partan was no match for Gauss' method, which is especially efficient on a least-squares function like Rosenbrock's. Harkins also observed that it is best *not* to determine the high point on a line too precisely.

The inaccuracy seems to introduce a bit of randomness into the problem which prevents sticking on a resolution ridge. He recommends expending no more than five Fibonacci experiments on any line of search. Finally Harkins remarked that he found continued partan easier to program than the method of rotating coordinates.

7-13 Deflected Gradients

Partan is appropriate when gradients must be estimated by perturbation methods, but the *deflected gradient* method of Fletcher and Powell appears more efficient when accurate gradients are relatively easy to obtain. The latter situation arises when the objective is implicit, making function evaluations so costly that the extra effort needed to find the gradient is relatively small. The deflected gradient method requires N gradient measurements and subsequent unidimensional searches, but unlike partan, no acceleration steps are needed. The searches, although in directions of locally improving values of the objective, are rarely exactly along the gradient—hence the name "deflected" gradient. Fletcher and Powell developed the procedure from some earlier ideas of Davidon and gave proofs of its quadratic convergence. It required only 18 iterations (gradient measurements) to find the optimum for Rosenbrock's function. To compare this with other procedures one should multiply this number by three, the number of function evaluations needed to measure a gradient by perturbation in two dimensions. The 54 or so equivalent evaluations are almost as low as the 38 needed by Gauss' method, and certainly better than the 200 needed by partan and the simple ridge-following techniques.

To understand the strategy involved, consider the quadratic objective

$$y = y_0 + \mathbf{c}'\mathbf{x} + \tfrac{1}{2}\mathbf{x}'\mathbf{Q}\mathbf{x}$$

In Section 7-05 it was shown [Eq. (7-40)] that the step $\Delta\mathbf{x}^*$ needed to go to the optimum $\mathbf{x}^*$ from a point $\mathbf{x}_0$ where the gradient $\nabla y\langle\mathbf{x}_0\rangle(\equiv\nabla y_0)$ is known is

$$\Delta\mathbf{x}^* \equiv (\mathbf{x}^* - \mathbf{x}_0) = -\mathbf{Q}^{-1}\nabla y_0 \qquad (7\text{-}99)$$

In practice, however, $\mathbf{Q}$ is not known in advance, which makes the foregoing relation unusable. This analysis does suggest, however, that one proceed in a direction which is not along the gradient. Fletcher and Powell suggest using an N by N matrix $\mathbf{H}_0$ such that

$$\mathbf{x}_1 - \mathbf{x}_0 \equiv \Delta\mathbf{x}_1 = -\mu_1\mathbf{H}_0\nabla y_0 \qquad (7\text{-}100)$$

The matrix $\mathbf{H}_0$ is chosen to be positive-definite so that the new direction will give local improvement of y, whereas μ_1 is the search parameter chosen to optimize $y\langle\Delta\mathbf{x}_1\rangle$ along the line of search defined by Eq. (7-100). If the investigator has some idea in which direction the optimum might be, he should select H_0 accordingly. In the absence of such information he might as well choose the N by N unit matrix I, it being the simplest to deal with. This means that the first step is an ordinary gradient optimization after all.

The deflected gradient method generates a sequence of points $x_1, \ldots, x_n$ such that the gradient ∇y_n at each point x_n is orthogonal (perpendicular) to all preceding steps $\Delta x_1, \ldots, \Delta x_n$.

$$(\nabla y_n)' \Delta x_i = 0; i = 1, \ldots, n; n = 1, \ldots, N \tag{7-101}$$

The Nth gradient ∇y_N must therefore be orthogonal to N vectors Δx, which are constructed to be linearly independent. Hence ∇y_N must vanish, indicating that x_N is the minimum sought in this ideal quadratic case. Moreover, a sequence of N by N positive definite matrices $H_1, \ldots, H_N$ is generated such that the last one is precisely the inverse of the originally unknown Hessian matrix Q.

$$H_N = Q^{-1} \tag{7-102}$$

In ideal circumstances one need not compute this matrix, but in practice ∇y_N may not vanish, say because of accumulated round-off errors, and an $(N+1)$th step using H_N would be justified. In this case,

$$\Delta x_{N+1} \equiv x_{N+1} - x_N \equiv -\mu_{N+1} H_N \nabla y_N$$
$$= -\mu_{N+1} Q^{-1} \nabla y_N$$
$$= \mu_{N+1}(x^* - x_N)$$

Thus if $\mu_{N+1} = 1$,

$$x_{N+1} = x^* \tag{7-103}$$

and the search terminates after $N + 1$ steps. Further correction for rounding errors can be made by minimizing with respect to μ_{N+1}, which in practice may differ from unity.

When y is not quadratic, the procedure will not end so soon, but after N steps the deflection matrices H usually become increasingly better estimates of the curvature at the minimum, as measured by the inverse of the Hessian matrix of second derivatives there. Thus the method converges rapidly as soon as it gets close enough to make a quadratic approximation valid. Following is a detailed description of the method and its behavior in ideal quadratic circumstances.

After the nth step has been taken ($n = 1, \ldots, N$) the location of the nth point x_n is known. The gradient ∇y_n is determined there, as are two new N by N matrices A_n and B_n used to form the new deflection matrix H_n from the preceding one H_{n-1}.

$$H_n = H_{n-1} + A_n + B_n \tag{7-104}$$

The role of the A_n is to generate the inverse Q^{-1} in N steps. In fact, the A_n will be chosen so that their sum will be Q^{-1}.

$$\sum_{n=1}^{N} \mathbf{A}_n = \mathbf{Q}^{-1} \tag{7-105}$$

The sequence of matrices $\mathbf{B}_n$ is intended to cancel out the initial assumption for $\mathbf{H}_0$. Their sum is therefore the negative of $\mathbf{H}_0$.

$$\sum_{n=1}^{N} \mathbf{B}_n = -\mathbf{H}_0 \tag{7-106}$$

To see that Eqs. (7–105) and (7–106) do give a sequence converging to $\mathbf{Q}^{-1}$, write

$$\begin{aligned}
\mathbf{H}_N &= \mathbf{H}_{N-1} + \mathbf{A}_N + \mathbf{B}_N \\
&= \mathbf{H}_{N-2} + (\mathbf{A}_N + \mathbf{A}_{N-1}) + (\mathbf{B}_N + \mathbf{B}_{N-1}) \\
&\quad\cdot \\
&\quad\cdot \\
&\quad\cdot \\
&= \mathbf{H}_0 + \sum_{n=1}^{N} \mathbf{A}_n + \sum_{n=1}^{N} \mathbf{B}_n = \mathbf{Q}^{-1}
\end{aligned} \tag{7-107}$$

It remains to find how to compute the $\mathbf{A}_n$ and $\mathbf{B}_n$ from information generated along the way. The principal agent for this is the *gradient difference* vector $\mathbf{g}_n$, defined as the difference between the gradients at the beginning and at the end of the nth step.

$$\mathbf{g}_n \equiv \nabla y_n - \nabla y_{n-1} \tag{7-108}$$

The gradient difference can be related to the unknown matrix $\mathbf{Q}$ by differentiating the objective function to obtain the gradients.

$$\begin{aligned}
\mathbf{g}_n &= (\mathbf{c} + \mathbf{Q}\mathbf{x}_n) - (\mathbf{c} + \mathbf{Q}\mathbf{x}_{n-1}) \tag{7-109} \\
&= \mathbf{Q}\Delta\mathbf{x}_n
\end{aligned}$$

This furnishes N linear equations, not enough to determine all the N^2 elements of $\mathbf{Q}$. One can see that N such gradient differences would be needed, and any of the previous methods would yield an estimate of $\mathbf{Q}$ after N steps if gradient differences were tabulated and the resulting N^2 equations were solved. The advantage of the deflected gradient method is that, in effect, it solves these equations in a stepwise fashion that does not require storage of data from all previous steps. Updating the matrices $\mathbf{A}_n$ and $\mathbf{B}_n$ is all that is needed.

To find $\mathbf{A}_n$, write, using Eqs. (7–105) and (7–109),

$$\begin{aligned}
\Delta\mathbf{x}_n = \mathbf{I}\Delta\mathbf{x}_n &= \mathbf{Q}^{-1}\mathbf{Q}\Delta\mathbf{x}_n \\
&= \sum_{i=1}^{N} \mathbf{A}_i \mathbf{Q}\,\Delta\mathbf{x}_n \tag{7-110} \\
&= \sum_{i=1}^{N} \mathbf{A}_i \mathbf{g}_n
\end{aligned}$$

But if $\mathbf{A}_n$ is to depend only upon information generated at the nth step, then only the nth term of the sum should be nonzero. That is,

$$\Delta \mathbf{x}_n = \mathbf{A}_n \mathbf{g}_n \tag{7-111}$$

and
$$\mathbf{A}_i \mathbf{g}_n = 0 \quad \text{for } i \neq n \tag{7-112}$$

Multiplication of $\Delta \mathbf{x}_n$ by unity (written in a complicated way) gives

$$\Delta \mathbf{x}_n = \Delta \mathbf{x}_n \left[\frac{\Delta \mathbf{x}_n' \mathbf{g}_n}{\Delta \mathbf{x}_n' \mathbf{g}_n} \right] = \left[\frac{\Delta \mathbf{x}_n \Delta \mathbf{x}_n'}{\Delta \mathbf{x}_n' \mathbf{g}_n} \right] \mathbf{g}_n$$

which by comparison with Eq. (7–111) gives

$$\mathbf{A}_n = \frac{\Delta \mathbf{x}_n \Delta \mathbf{x}_n'}{\Delta \mathbf{x}_n' \mathbf{g}_n} \tag{7-113}$$

The inductive proof of orthogonality Eq. (7–112), given by Fletcher and Powell, will not be detailed here. It depends on the fact that the gradient at $\mathbf{x}_n$ must be orthogonal to the preceding step $\Delta \mathbf{x}_n$ because y is optimized along the line of search. That is,

$$(\nabla y_n)' \Delta \mathbf{x}_n = 0 \tag{7-114}$$

Success of the deflected gradient method depends on the fact that the steps $\Delta \mathbf{x}_1, \Delta \mathbf{x}_2, \ldots, \Delta \mathbf{x}_n$ are related to $\mathbf{H}_n$ by

$$\mathbf{H}_n \mathbf{Q} \Delta \mathbf{x}_i = \Delta \mathbf{x}_i ; \quad i = 1, 2, \ldots, n \tag{7-115}$$

In particular, at the last step $(n = N)$

$$\mathbf{H}_N \mathbf{Q} \Delta \mathbf{x}_i = \Delta \mathbf{x}_i \tag{7-116}$$

which can be true for N linearly independent steps $\Delta \mathbf{x}_i$ only if $\mathbf{H}_N \mathbf{Q}$ is the unit matrix. This proves that

$$\mathbf{H}_N = \mathbf{Q}^{-1} \tag{7-117}$$

In matrix jargon, the steps $\Delta \mathbf{x}_i$ are called *eigenvectors* of $\mathbf{H}_n \mathbf{Q}$, each with unit eigenvalue. Arranging things so that Eq. (7–115) holds gives a way to compute the sequence of $\mathbf{B}_n$. Equation (7–104), (7–109), and (7–111) give

$$\mathbf{H}_n \mathbf{Q} \, \Delta \mathbf{x}_n = \mathbf{H}_n \mathbf{g}_n$$
$$= \mathbf{H}_{n-1} \mathbf{g}_n + \mathbf{A}_n \mathbf{g}_n + \mathbf{B}_n \mathbf{g}_n \tag{7-118}$$
$$= \mathbf{H}_{n-1} \mathbf{g}_n + \Delta \mathbf{x}_n + \mathbf{B}_n \mathbf{g}_n$$

Equations (7–115) and (7–118) imply that

$$\mathbf{B}_n \mathbf{g}_n = - \mathbf{H}_{n-1} \mathbf{g}_n \tag{7-119}$$

The obvious solution $(\mathbf{B}_n = -\mathbf{H}_{n-1})$ must be ruled out because of its uninteresting consequences, but there is a nontrivial possibility obtained by multiplying the right member of Eq. (7–119) by unity, written in a way even more complicated then before. Observe that for any N vector $\mathbf{z}$ it is true that

$$1 = \frac{\mathbf{z}' \mathbf{g}_n}{\mathbf{g}_n' \mathbf{z}} \quad (\mathbf{g}_n' \mathbf{z} \neq 0) \tag{7-120}$$

Equations (7–119) and (7–120) together give

TABLE 7–3

DEFLECTED GRADIENT METHOD EXAMPLE

$\mathbf{x}_0 = (-1, 1, -1)$ $y\langle \mathbf{x}_0 \rangle = 6.0000$ $\nabla y_0 = (-4, 2, -6)$ $\mathbf{H}_0 = \begin{pmatrix} 1 \\ 0 & 1 \\ 0 & 0 & 1 \end{pmatrix}$

	$n=1$	$n=2$	$n=3$
$\mathbf{H}_n \nabla y_{n-1}$	-4.0000 2.0000 -6.0000	-1.0612 1.2653 0.6122	0.2641 0.5281 -0.0587
μ_n	0.1944	0.3116	0.4106
$\mathbf{x}_n$	-0.2222 0.6111 0.1667	0.1084 0.2169 -0.0241	0.0000 0.0000 0.0000
$y\langle \mathbf{x}_n \rangle$	0.5556	0.0723	0.0000
∇y_n	-0.8889 1.2222 1.0000	0.4337 0.4337 -0.1446	0.0000 0.0000 0.0000
$\mathbf{g}_n$	0.3111 -0.7778 7.0000	1.3226 -0.7885 -1.1446	-0.4337 -0.4337 0.1446
$\mathbf{A}_n$	0.0556 -0.0278 0.0139 0.0833 -0.0417 0.1250	0.1131 -0.1349 0.1608 -0.0652 0.0778 0.0377	0.0813 0.1627 0.3253 -0.0181 -0.0361 0.0040
$\mathbf{B}_n$	-0.1633 0.0408 -0.0102 -0.3673 0.0918 -0.8265	0.6387 0.3553 -0.1976 0.3233 -0.1798 -0.1637	-0.1980 -0.3961 -0.7922 0.0440 0.0880 -0.0098
$\mathbf{H}_n$	0.8923 0.0130 1.0037 -0.2840 0.0502 0.2985	0.3667 0.2334 0.9669 -0.0259 -0.0519 0.1724	0.2500 0.0000 0.5000 0.0000 0.0000 0.1667

$$\mathbf{B}_n \mathbf{g}_n = -\frac{\mathbf{H}_{n-1}\mathbf{g}_n \mathbf{z}' \mathbf{g}_n}{\mathbf{g}_n' \mathbf{z}}$$

whence, by comparing matrices,

$$\mathbf{B}_n = -\frac{\mathbf{H}_{n-1}\mathbf{g}_n \mathbf{z}'}{\mathbf{g}_n' \mathbf{z}} \qquad (7\text{-}121)$$

Notice that the numerator is a (singular) N by N matrix, whereas the denominator is a scalar. Since $\mathbf{H}_n$, $\mathbf{H}_{n-1}$, and $\mathbf{A}_n$ are all required to be symmetric, the vector $\mathbf{z}$ must be selected to make $\mathbf{B}_n$ symmetric. The correct choice is

$$\mathbf{z} = \mathbf{H}_{n-1}\mathbf{g}_n \qquad (7\text{-}122)$$

which gives

$$\mathbf{B}_n = -\frac{\mathbf{H}_{n-1}\mathbf{g}_n \mathbf{g}_n' \mathbf{H}_{n-1}'}{\mathbf{g}_n' \mathbf{H}_{n-1}\mathbf{g}_n} \qquad (7\text{-}123)\dot{}$$

The reader may wish to test his understanding of the deflected gradient method by applying it to the same problem solved earlier by partan; namely, to minimize

$$y = 2x_1^2 + x_2^2 + 3x_3^2$$

starting at the point $(-1, 1, -1)$ where $\nabla y_0 = (-4, 2, -6)$. Table 7–3, prepared by B. A. Williams while a graduate student at Stanford, shows the computations involved.

On nonquadratic functions convergence cannot be guaranteed any more than it can for any other climbing methods. Yet Fletcher and Powell have had success with it even on helical ridges and with functions of up to 50 variables. In all cases the number of steps increased only linearly with the number of variables. Progress toward the optimum, although slow during early iterations when data are being gathered for estimates of $\mathbf{Q}^{-1}$, often speeds up remarkably as the quadratic approximation gets better. It appears to be the best method available when accurate gradients are relatively easy to obtain. Powell(1964) has devised a variation not requiring explicit evaluation of the gradients, equivalent information being generated during the unidimensional searches. This modification required 140 function evaluations to minimize Rosenbrock's function, a performance comparable to that of partan.

This completes the description of climbing techniques for finding interior optima. Section 7–14 discusses the handling of inequality constraints.

7-14 Inequality Constraints

The procedures described earlier in the chapter, which were developed for finding interior optima, can be extended to handle optimization problems with inequality constraints. One merely works with the constrained derivatives developed in Sections 2–10, 2–11, 2–12, and 3–01, using the Kuhn-Tucker necessary conditions of Section 3–02 and the sufficiency conditions of Sections 3–03 and 3–04 to choose feasible directions of improvement. Existing nonlinear programming routines could be used to guide the search, the required constrained derivatives being obtained by perturbation or direct measurement. As a matter of fact, many nonlinear programming procedures now being used could be improved by incorporating some of the climbing tactics developed for unconstrained functions. For example, Sections 3–13 and 3–14, which deal with curing oscillation in a differential algorithm for quadratic programming, introduce an acceleration technique. E. M. L. Beale reports that Gauss-Levenberg subroutines have improved the effectiveness of nonlinear programming algorithms.

In this section our concern is with climbing rather than nonlinear programming. The Jacobian approach to constrained direct methods has been suggested by Wilde (September, 1965) and by King. Wood has modified pattern search to handle constraints simply by treating infeasible points as failures, even though the value of the objective may be better there. Mugele's PROBE method is somewhat similar, although he gives special rules governing particular situations that might arise. The same artifice can be used to adapt the simplicial method of Spendley, Hext, and Himsworth so that it will handle constraints. The trouble with this simple idea is that one can be very easily stopped before reaching even a local optimum, as illustrated in Fig. 7–32. Even for the linear objective function and linear constraint shown, the pattern stops as soon as it hits the constraint, since all its exploratory moves fail to find a feasible point where the objective function is improved. The crosses indicate infeasible trials; the circles, economically unsuccessful ones.

When this happens, Glass and Cooper use the perturbations to estimate the gradients ∇y of the objective and ∇f_m of the constraint functions from which the Jacobian matrix $\mathbf{J}$ can be computed. Using the last successful point as the origin of new changes $\Delta \mathbf{x}$, they solve the following linear programming problem:

$$\max_{\Delta \mathbf{x}} \nabla y \, \Delta \mathbf{x}$$

subject to $\mathbf{x} \geq 0$ and $\mathbf{J} \, \Delta \mathbf{x} \geq \mathbf{f}$

Here $\nabla y \, \Delta \mathbf{x}$ is the linear approximation of the objective function, whereas $\mathbf{J} \, \Delta \mathbf{x}$ is the linear approximation of the vector of constraint functions $\mathbf{f}\langle \mathbf{x} \rangle$. The local value $\mathbf{f}$ of the constraint functions is known at $\mathbf{x}$. This procedure may be considered an end game tactic for testing a proposed optimum and finding new, improved, feasible moves if any are possible. In solving the linear programming problem, the constrained derivatives will be developed, so an alternative approach is to choose state and decision variables and use con-

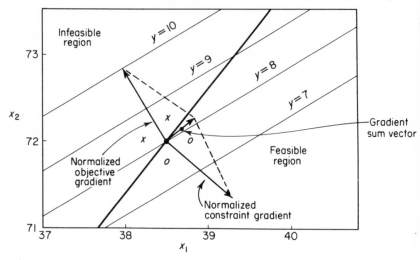

Figure 7-32. Gradient sum method.

strained derivatives computed from the Jacobian formulas to guide feasible moves in directions of improvement. If the steps generated by the Glass-Cooper method move immediately into the infeasible region because of curvature of the constraints, a positive constant vector should be added to **f**, the right member of the constraint equation. This will keep moves away from the boundaries and permit larger feasible steps.

The *multiple-gradient summation* technique of Klingman and Himmelblau is also intended to handle this problem. It moves in the direction which is the vector sum of the normalized gradients of all the functions, objective and constraint. The direction is

$$\Delta \mathbf{x} = \frac{\nabla y}{|\nabla y|} + \sum_{m=1}^{M} \frac{\nabla f_m}{|\nabla f_m|}$$

As shown in Fig. 7-32, this tends to generate feasible moves in the right direction. On several problems tested by Klingman and Himmelblau, the procedure converged rapidly, although not always to the optimum. Difficulties were experienced when the objective function contours were nearly parallel to the constraints, making the region of feasible improvement too small to find. This situation would be hard to deal with no matter what procedure were used because the Jacobian matrix would be approaching singularity. The rapid convergence probably results from the simplicity of the computations. The gradient sum technique effectively causes the constraints to repel any close approach which might lead to infeasibility. In this regard it resembles C. W. Carroll's created response surface method of Chapter 3, which accomplished the same thing using nonlinear penalty functions. In the same vein, the SUMT method of Fiacco and McCormick could be adapted to constrained direct optimization problems.

7-15 Concluding Summary

The climbing methods begin by measuring a gradient and end with estimating curvature by second-order approximations. The most effective techniques have ridge-following properties, and one of them, gradient partan, also has quasi-quadratic convergence. When gradients are relatively easy to measure, or when the objective function is particularly difficult to measure, the deflected gradient procedure with its quadratic convergence seems best. For least-squares problems, Levenberg's method is highly effective. In the presence of experimental error, and for continual monitoring of a shifting optimum, the simplicial method is suitably cautious and easy to implement. Constraints can be handled by straightforward adaptations of the Jacobian procedures of nonlinear programming, by local linearization, or by methods which repel the search path away from the constraints. Many climbing methods could be combined with elimination techniques if one wanted to know the region of uncertainty. The climbing procedures, originally developed for unconstrained objectives, may also be useful in nonlinear programming computer codes because of their ability to adjust several variables at once.

No matter how sophisticated the climbing procedure used, one should always be careful in setting up the problem. By removing interaction, by scaling variables to make contours approximately circular, and by choosing representations easy to approximate quadratically, one can cut down the searching effort significantly. There is no need to make the problem difficult unnecessarily.

With absolutely perfect preparation of the problem, the number of function evaluations needed is proportional to N, the number of independent variables. Imperfect scaling drives the number up to N^2, even for quasi-quadratic functions, which is about as good as one could hope for. Linear programming computations increase as N^3, so all of the procedures described so far must be confined to problems with a number of independent variables much smaller than those encountered in most practical problems. The next two chapters show how to break very large optimization problems down into pieces of a size solvable by the methods developed so far. When this is done, the computation effort grows only linearly, not quadratically or cubically, with the number of pieces.

BIBLIOGRAPHY

Baer, R. M., "Note on an extremum locating algorithm," *Comp. J.*, **5**, 3 (1962), cited by Flood and Leon.

Ball, Walter W. Rouse, *A Short Account of the History of Mathematics* (Macmillan, London, 1888).

Bell, D. A., *Intelligent Machines* (Blaisdell Publishing Company, New York, 1962), pp. 62–63.

Bellman, Richard, *Dynamic Programming* (Princeton, N.J., Princeton Univ., 1957).

Booth, A. D., "An application of the method of steepest descents to the solutions of systems of nonlinear simultaneous equations," *Quart. J. Mech. Appl. Math.*, **2**, 4 (1949), 460.

Booth, A. W., and T. I. Peterson, "Nonlinear estimation," IBM 704 program WL NLI (1960), cited by Harkins.

Box, G. E. P., "The exploration and exploitation of response surfaces," *Biometrics*, **10** (1954), 16.

———, "Evolutionary operation: a method for increasing industrial productivity," *Appl. Statist.*, **6**, (1957), 81–101.

———, and K. B. Wilson, "On the experimental attainment of optimum conditions," *J. Roy. Stat. Soc.*, **B13** (1951), 1.

Buehler, R. J., B. N. Shah, and O. Kempthorne, "Some properties of steepest ascent and related procedures for finding optimum conditions," Iowa State University Statistical Lab., Ames, Iowa (April, 1961).

Cauchy, A., "Méthode générale pour la résolution des systèmes d'équations simultanées," *Compt. rend. Acad. Sci. Paris*, **25** (1847), 536–38. Also in *Oeuvres completes d'Augustin Cauchy*, **10** (Gauthier-Villars, Paris, 1901), 399–406.

Davidon, W. C., "Variable metric method for minimization," AEC Res. and Dev. Report Anl-5990 (December, 1959). Cited by Fletcher and Powell.

Davies, Owen L., *The Design and Analysis of Industrial Experiments* (Oliver and Boyd, London, 1956).

Fletcher, R., and M. J. D. Powell, "A rapidly convergent descent method for minimization," *Comp. J.*, **6**, 2 (1963), 163–68.

Flood, M. M., and A. Leon, "A universal adaptive code for optimization (GROPE)," Lavi and Vogl, pp. 101–30.

Friedman, M., and L. S. Savage, "Planning experiments seeking maxima," in *Selected Techniques of Statistical Analysis*, C. Wisenhart, M. W. Hastay, and W. A. Wallis, eds. (McGraw-Hill, New York, 1947), cited by Shah, Buehler, and Kempthorne.

Forsythe, G. E., and T. S. Motzkin, "Acceleration of the optimum gradient method," preliminary report (abstract) *Bull. Amer. Math. Soc.*, **57** (1951), 304–305, cited by Shah, Buehler, and Kempthorne.

Gauss, C. F., *Werke*, Vol. 4 (Göttingen, 1821), cited in Davies, p. 578.

Gelfand, I. M., and M. L. Tsetlin, "The principle of nonlocal search in automatic optimization systems," *Doklady Akad. Nauk, SSSR*, **137**, 2 (March, 1961), 295–98.

Genocchi, Angelo, and G. Peano, *Calcolo Differenziale e principii di Calcolo Integrale* (1884), app., prob. 133–6; cited by Hancock, pp. 33 *et seq.*

Glass, H., and L. Cooper, "Sequential search: a method for solving constrained optimization problems," *J. Assoc. Comp. Mach,.* **12** (1965), 71.

Harkins, A., "The use of parallel tangents in optimization," *Optimization Techniques* (see Blakemore and Davis) (1964), pp. 35–40.

Himsworth, F. R., "Empirical methods of optimization," *Trans. Inst. Chem. Engrs.,* **40** (1962), 345–49.

Hestenes, M. R., and E. Stiefel, "Method of conjugate gradients for solving linear systems," *J. Res. Natl. Bur. Standards,* **49** (1952), 409–36.

Hooke, R., and T.A. Jeeves, "Comments on Brooks' discussion of random methods," *Opns. Res.,* **6**, 6 (November, 1958), 881–82.

———, "Progress report on Opcon," *Control Engng.,* **6** (November, 1959), 124.

———, and T. A. Jeeves, " 'Direct search' solution of numerical and statistical problems," *J. Assn. Comp. Mach.,* **8**, 2 (April, 1961), 212–29.

Humphrey, W. E., "A general minimizing routine-Minfun," University of California, Lawrence Radiation Laboratory, Berkeley; internal memorandum (September, 1962), 9 pp. Cited by Flood and Leon.

Kelley, H. J., "Method of gradients," in Leitman, G., ed., *Optimization Techniques with Applications to Aerospace Systems* (New York, Academic Press, 1962), pp. 205–254.

King, R. P., "Necessary and sufficient conditions for inequality constrained extreme values," *Ind. Engng. Chem. Fund. Q.*

Klingman, W. R., and D. N. Himmelblau, "Nonlinear programming with the aid of a multiple-gradient summation technique," *J. Assn. Comp. Mach.,* **11**, 4 (October, 1964), 400–15.

Lapidus, L., E. Shapiro, S. Shapiro, and R. E. Stillman, "Optimization of process performance," *A.I. Ch. E. J.,* **7**, 2 (June, 1961), 288–94.

Lavi, A., and T. P. Vogl, eds., *Recent Advances in Optimization Techniques* (Wiley, New York, 1966).

Leitman, G., ed., *Optimization Techniques with Applications to Aerospace Systems* (New York, Academic Press, 1962).

Leon, A., "A classified bibliography on optimization," Lavi and Vogl, pp. 599–649. Univ. of California (Berkeley), Space Sciences Laboratory, Working Paper No. 11 (April, 1964).

Levenberg, K., "A method for the solution of certain nonlinear problems in least squares," *Quart. Appl. Math.,* **2** (1944), 164–68.

McCutcheon, T. P., H. Seltz, and J. C. Warner, *General Chemistry* (Van Nostrand, Princeton, N.J., 1939), p. 236.

Nietzsche, Friedrich, "Excelsior" (1882), from *Joyful Wisdom*, Thomas Commons, trans. Poetry versions by Paul V. Cohn and Maude D. Petrie (New York, F. Ungar, 1964).

Phillips, H. B., *Vector Analysis* (Wiley, New York, 1933), pp. 35 *et seq.*

Powell, M. J. D., "An efficient method for finding the minimum of a function of several variables without calculating derivatives," *Comp. J.*, **7** (1964), 155–62.

————, "A method for minimizing a sum of squares of nonlinear functions without calculating derivatives," *Comp. J.*, **7** (1965), 303–7.

Raphson, Joseph, *Analysis aequationem universalis*, cited in Cajori, p. 203.

Rosenbrock, H. H., "An automatic method for finding the greatest or least value of a function," *Comp. J.*, **3**, 3 (October, 1960), 175–84.

Rubin, D. I., "Nonlinear least squares parameter estimation and its application to chemical kinetics," *Chem. Eng. Prog. Symp. Ser. No.* 42, **59** (1963), 90–94. (Thanks to G. Blau.)

Scheefer, Ludwig, "Über die Bedeutung der Begriffe Maximum and Minimum in der Variationsrechnung," *Math. Ann.*, **26** (1886), 197–208, cited in Hancock, chap. 4.

Shah, B. V., R. J. Buehler, and O. Kempthorne, "Some algorithms for minimizing a function of several variables," *J. Soc. Ind. Appl. Math.*, **12**, 1 (March, 1964), 74–92.

Spendley, N., G. R. Hext, and F. R. Himsworth, "Sequential application of simplex design in optimization and evolutionary operations," *Technometrics*, **4**, 4 (November, 1962), 441–59.

Weiss, E. A., D. H. Archer, and D. A. Burt, *Petr. Ref.*, **40**, 10 (October, 1961).

Wilde, D. J., *Optimum Seeking Methods* (Prentice-Hall, Inc., Englewood Cliffs, N.J., 1964).

————, "Jacobians in constrained nonlinear optimization," *Opns. Res.*, **13**, 5 (September, 1965), 848–56.

Wood, E. F., "Application of direct search to the solution of engineering problems," Westinghouse Scientific Paper 64–1210–1–P (1960).

————, "Recent developments in direct search techniques," Westinghouse Res. Rep. 62–159–522–R1 (1962).

EXERCISES

7-1. Draw an isometric projection and the three orthogonal views for the following functions in the region $-2 \leq x_1 \leq 2$, $-2 \leq x_2 \leq 2$. Indicate all the maxima, minima, and saddles in the region.

(a) $y = x_1 x_2$
(b) $y = x_1^2 + x_2^2$
(c) $y = \exp(-x_1^2 + x_2^2)$
(d) $y = \ln(x_1^2 + x_1 x_2 - 2x_2^2)$
(e) $y = x_1^3 + x_2^3$
(f) $y = x_1^2 x_2^2$

7-2. Find the equation of the contour tangent through the point $(1, -2, 3)$ for the functions
(a) $y = x_1^2 + x_2^2 + x_3^2$
(b) $y = \exp[x_1^2 + x_3^2 - x_1 + 3x_2 + 2]$
(c) $y = \ln(x_1^2 + x_1 x_2 + x_2^2)$
(d) $y = x_1^3 + x_2^3$

7-3. Find the equation of the contour tangent through the point $(-2, 1, -1, 4)$, using the following data:

x_1	x_2	x_3	x_4	y
-2	1	-1	4	10.0
-1.9	1	-1	4	10.3
-2	1.1	-1	4	9.8
-2	1	-0.9	4	9.7
-2	1	-1	4.1	10.4

7-4. Estimate the value of y in the previous problem at the point
$$(-1.5, 0.5, -0.5, 4.5)$$

7-5. Construct a quadratic approximation to the function $y = \exp[2x_1^2 + 2x_2^2 + x_1 - 5x_2 + 10]$ in the vicinity of $(0, 1)$. Where does the approximation predict the minimum to be? Compare the predicted value at this point with the actual value.

7-6. From the accompanying data, construct both a noninteracting and an interacting quadratic approximation. Compare the stationary points predicted by these approximations. Is the stationary point a maximum, minimum, or saddle?

x_1	x_2	y
1.0	4.0	5.85
1.0	3.0	5.85
1.0	2.0	6.00
2.0	4.0	6.10
2.0	3.0	6.10
2.0	2.0	6.10
3.0	4.0	5.85
3.0	3.0	6.05

7-7. A function y depends on four independent variables x_1, x_2, x_3, and x_4, and the following table gives the measured value of y at eight different points.
(a) Give the coordinates of any point on the line of steepest ascent passing through $(0, 1, -1, 3)$. [Do not give $(0, 1, -1, 3)$ as answer.]

(b) Give the coordinates of any point [except $(0, 1, -1, 3)$] in the contour tangent hyperplane passing through $(0, 1, -1, 3)$.

x_1	x_2	x_3	x_4	y
0	1	−1	3	5
1	1	−1	3	7
2	1	−1	3	9
−1	2	−1	3	2
0	−1	−1	3	7
0	1	1	3	7
0	1	−1	2	5
0	2	0	3	5

7-8. It is desired to find the point where an unknown function y is maximum on the line between the two points $(1, -1, 0, 2)$ and $(-5, -1, 3, 1)$.

(a) Assuming perfect resolution and unimodality of the function on the line, give the coordinates of the points where you would measure the function next, assuming you are going to conduct a total of five new experiments in sequence.

(b) What is the final interval of uncertainty of the coordinate x_1?

7-9. Use the sectioning method and the gradient method to find the minimum of the following functions, starting from the points given: (Make no more than four linear searches.)

(a) $y = x_1^2 + 3x_2^2 + 2x_3^2$; $(2, -2, 1)$
(b) $y = 2x_1^2 + 2x_1x_2 + 5x_2^2$; $(2, -2)$

7-10. Verify the step $\Delta\mathbf{x}' = (0.186, 0.000)$ given in Section 7-06.

7-11. Calculate the Levenberg step for the example in Section 7-06 for the following values of the Levenberg parameter λ:

(a) $\lambda = 1$
(b) $\lambda = 0.1$
(c) The value of λ minimizing y

7-12. Prove that the points given in Fig. 7-27 are a unit distance apart.

7-13. Using the results in Table 7-3 for the deflected gradient example, verify Eqs. (7-105), (7-106), (7-112), (7-116), and (7-117).

7-14. Use gradient partan to minimize the following functions, starting at the points given.

(a) $x_1^2 + x_2^2 + x_3^2 + x_4^2$; $(2, -2, 1, -1)$
(b) $x_1^2 + x_2^2 + x_3^2 + 2x_4^2$; $(2, -2, 1, -1)$
(c) $2x_1^2 + x_2^2 + 3x_3^2$; $(2, -2, 1)$
(d) $2x_1^4 + 2x_1^2x_2^2 + 5x_2^4$; $(2, -2)$

7-15. On the functions of Exercise 7-1 use the following procedures, making no more than 5 moves:

(a) Pattern search (set $\delta_1 = \delta_2 = 0.1$ and use second-order check at apparent optimum)
(b) The Gauss-Levenberg method
(c) Deflected gradients

Partial Optimization
of Multistage Systems

8

> *The toe bone's connected to the* foot *bone,*
> *The foot bone's connected to the* heel *bone,*
> *The back bone's connected to the* neck *bone,*
> *The neck bone's connected to the* head *bone,*
> *Now hear the word of the Lord!*

ANONYMOUS AMERICAN SPIRITUAL

Like the "dry bones" in the song, decisions are often connected to each other. What we decide tomorrow and in the future depends upon choices we make today, and vice versa. Any planning problem, be it corporate expansion program, manufacturing plant layout, or family vacation trip, involves many decisions, each affecting the other. In guiding their lives, people continually balance immediate pleasures against future advantages. This chapter and the next show how sequences of interacting decisions can be optimized when timing is important.

Problems of this nature can be attacked by methods developed in preceding chapters, as long as there are not too many decisions. But since the computing effort grows as the square, cube, or higher power of the number of variables, the procedures already described have ceilings on the size of problem they can solve. Large systems must be decomposed into components small enough for optimization by previous methods, taking proper account of how the different parts interact.

In planning problems, the components are arranged in series, each representing the same technological complex at a different point in time. This serial structure, in which decisions at any stage affect the condition of all later ones, occurs also in processes having manufacturing units in series. Serial systems lend themselves to decomposition by the partial optimization schemes of this chapter. The earliest and best-known example of the partial optimization approach to serial problems is Bellman's "dynamic programming," the first method to be described here. Once understood for serial systems, partial optimization can be extended to branching or even cyclic structures by the methods of Mitten, Nemhauser, Aris, Beightler, and Wilde. Such complex arrangements are often analyzed by cutting them into serial subsystems, although excessive interconnection may render decomposition impractical.

The distinction between state and decision variables, somewhat arbitrary in the methods described previously, is more clearly marked in partial optimization problems. A *state variable* is one which, being both an input to one component and an output from another, transmits information between stages. Only variables which can be manipulated directly qualify as decisions. Partial optimization of a stage involves finding the optimal values of its decisions for every possible value of its input state variables. Although decisions can be guided efficiently by any appropriate optimization method, state variables must be searched exhaustively to avoid overlooking an optimal possibility. Hence the distinction between states and decisions is very important in structured decision problems.

In this world of rapidly increasing complexity, it is hard to improve one thing without affecting others. The study of partial optimization gives insight into the wise selection of interacting alternatives for the good of the whole.

8-01 Serial Systems: The Initial Value Problem

A *serial multistage system* involves a series of decisions, each affecting the circumstances under which the next in the sequence must be made. In such problems, the output from one stage becomes the input to the next and thus affects all those following. This type of system and the technique for solving it are most clearly illustrated by the sort of network problem (Beckwith) shown in Fig. 8–1(a). The numbers on the links give the cost of shipping one unit of a given commodity between the indicated nodes (cities). For simplicity of discussion, the nodes have been divided horizontally by dashed lines into northern (N), central (C), and southern (S) cities, and vertically by dashed lines into five east-west zones, I through V; the boundaries of these zones represent the *stages* of this problem.

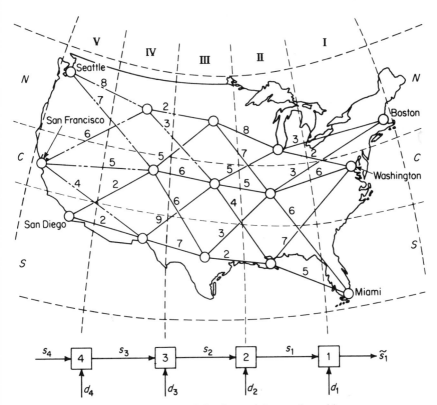

Figure 8-1(a). Network for first serial example problem.

An example of an *initial value serial optimization problem* is the following: starting in the southern city at stage 4 (San Diego), find the least-cost shipping path to any east coast (stage 1) city. Thus, a path would consist of five links, where motion is restricted to easterly (NE, E, or SE) directions. This is called *an initial-value problem* because the initial condition (San Diego) is fixed, but the final condition is not. We merely wish to ship to the east coast via the least expensive route, whether this minimum cost path terminates in Boston, Washington, or Miami. The restriction that the process must originate in San Diego effectively deletes some links from the system; these infeasible links are shown as double-dashed lines in Fig. 8–1(a).

In this problem there are just three possible inputs or outputs at each state, namely, north (N), central (C), or south (S). The problem is solved recursively beginning with the last stage (1), computing the optimal (minimum) cost for each possible entering condition, s_1. The decisions are concerned with selecting the appropriate link leading out of the stage. The decision variables can take on at most one of three discrete values, L(left), F(forward),

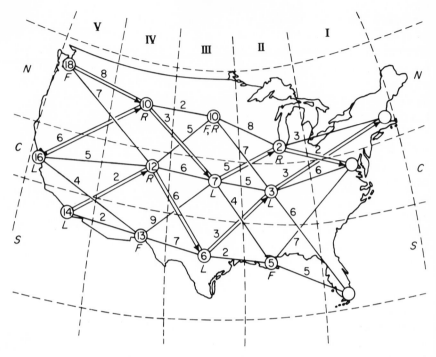

Figure 8-1(b). Solution to network problem of Fig. 8-1(a).

or R(right), depending upon whether the decision is to move northeasterly, easterly, or southeasterly, respectively. For example, if $s_1 = C$(central; that is, the shipment is in Cairo, Illinois), the decisions $d_1 = L$, F, and R would be associated with one-stage costs of 3, 6, and 6, respectively. Nodes representing northern and southern cities are restricted to only two possible decision choices; thus, for $s_1 = N$(Chicago), d_1 can take on only the values F and R. The solution procedure begins with the nodes in zone II, for each of which we find the least-cost path to an east coast node. Then, the problem is solved by moving iteratively stage by stage from the east coast to the west coast. Since at this point we do not know through which nodes the optimal path will pass, we must find the best decision to make at each one.

The optimal one-stage decisions are readily seen to be $d_1^*\langle N\rangle = R$, $d_1^*\langle C\rangle = L$, and $d_1^*\langle S\rangle = F$, producing the corresponding optimal returns (costs) of 2, 3, and 5. Next, we compute, for each node at stage 2 (zone III), the cost to a stage 1 node plus the minimum cost from that stage 1 node to the east coast. For example, if $s_2 = C$, the decision $d_2 = L$ sends the shipment to Chicago at a cost of 5 plus the 2 incurred in getting the shipment from Chicago to the east coast via the least-cost path. Thus, this decision results in a total cost of 7, whereas the decision $d_2 = C$ produces a total two-stage cost of $5 + 3 = 8$, and the decision $d_2 = S$ yields a cost of $4 + 5 = 9$. Hence, for $s_2 = C$, the optimal decision is $d_2 = L$. The same analysis is carried out at the remaining two stages (3 and 4). For each node at each stage we compute, for each possible decision, the sum of the link cost to the next adjoining stage plus the minimum total cost from that node to the east coast. The decision which produces the smallest such cost is then the optimal decision to make at that node, and it is recorded.

In working network problems, it is convenient to write the values of the optimal cumulative costs and decisions on the network nodes, as shown in Fig. 8–1(b). From this figure we see, for example, that the minimum shipment cost from Denver to the east coast is 12, and the optimal decision at that point is $d_3^* \langle C \rangle = R$. The figure also shows the optimal solution to the initial value problem $s_4 = S$: the least-cost shipping path from San Diego to the east coast has a total cost of 14, and the path may be traced out by following the optimal decision at each node. The optimal set of decisions is thus L, R, L, L, as shown by the arrows in Fig. 8–1(b). Also shown on this figure are the solutions to the other two initial value problems, $s_4 = C$ and $s_4 = N$, and their associated costs of 16 and 18, respectively.

The reader can verify how efficient and rapid is this computational procedure by solving the network problem given in Fig. 8–2 and checking the answers printed in the nodes. Further examples are provided in the exercises at the end of this chapter.

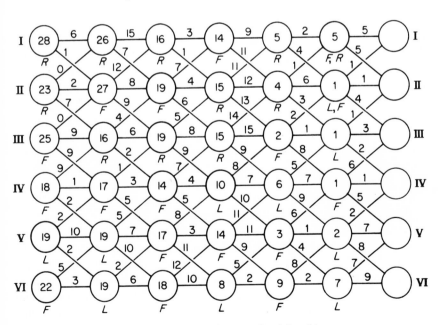

Figure 8-2. Network for second serial problem.

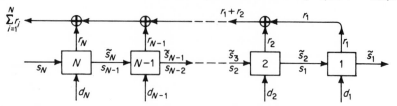

Figure 8-3. A serial system.

We may now generalize both the solution technique just employed and the type of problem for which it is applicable. The most general form of a serial multistage decision problem is shown in Fig. 8–3, in which the stages are represented schematically by appropriately numbered rectangles, with arrows used to indicate inputs and outputs to the various stages. Associated with the ith stage is an output r_i, called the *stage return*, which is a function of the inputs to the stage. All outputs which are not returns are called *state* variables, written $\tilde{s}_i$, where i is the index of the inputs generating the state, and the tilde ($\sim$) identifies this as an output. The transformation having the state $\tilde{s}_i$ as its output is given the name *transition* function and written T_i. Many states act also as inputs; a state serving as an input to stage i is written s_i. All inputs which are not states are called *decision* variables and written d_i, the index i identifying the return and transition having d_i as an input. Thus we may write

$$r_i = R_i \langle d_i, s_i \rangle \qquad (8\text{-}1\text{:}\,i)$$

$$\tilde{s}_i = T_i \langle d_i, s_i \rangle \qquad (8\text{-}2\text{:}\,i)$$

The set of all transformations carrying the same index i is called the ith *stage*, and the set of all stages is called the *system*.

Since a state variable is usually the output of some stage (say, i) and the input to at least one other (say, j), it can be represented by more than one symbol—either $\tilde{s}_i$ or s_j, for example. The identification of the several symbols with each other ($\tilde{s}_i \equiv s_j$) defines precisely how the stages i and j interact, and such a relation will be called an *incidence identity*. A system is specified completely by its stages and incidence identities. For the serial system of Fig. 8–3, the incidence identities are

$$\tilde{s}_{i+1} \equiv s_i; \qquad i = 1, 2, \ldots, N - 1 \qquad (8\text{-}3\text{:}\,i)$$

This means that the stages are numbered in the direction opposite to the flow of information shown by the arrows in Fig. 8–3. Although this backward numbering is confusing at first, it leads to simpler notation for the proofs. In Chapter 9 the more natural order is used.

In the *initial value* problem, the value of the initial state s_N, the total system input, is given, and the decision problem is to find the optimal sequence $d_1^* \langle s_N \rangle, \ldots, d_N^* \langle s_N \rangle$ maximizing the *total return* R, defined by

$$R = \sum_{i=1}^{N} R_i \langle d_i, s_i \rangle \qquad (8\text{-}4)$$

Eqs. (8–1) and (8–2) show that for a given input s_i, the value chosen for d_i determines not only the return r_i, but also the value of T_i which maps the input s_i onto the output $\bar{s}_i$. Thus, although a given decision d_i may maximize the return at that particular stage, it may also affect adversely the inputs to all subsequent stages, leading to a nonoptimal total return for the system. An optimal sequence, or *policy*, $\{d_i^*\langle s_N \rangle\}$ can be found only by taking into account the transitions coupling the stages together.

Eqs. (8–1)–(8–4) can be combined to express the total return as a function of the various inputs

$$R = \sum_{i=1}^{N} R_i \langle T_{i+1} \langle T_{i+2} \cdots \langle T_N \langle s_N, d_N \rangle, d_{N-1} \rangle \rangle, \cdots d_i \rangle \qquad (8\text{-}5)$$

so that for a given value of the initial state s_N, R is a function only of the decisions d_i

$$R \equiv R \langle d_i, s_N \rangle \qquad (8\text{-}6)$$

The *initial value maximum return function* is $R^* \langle s_N \rangle$, defined as the function which, for *all* values of $d_1, \ldots, d_N$ and for any *particular* value of s_N is such that

$$R^* \langle s_N \rangle = \max_{d_i} \{ R \langle d_i, s_N \rangle \} \qquad (8\text{-}7)$$

The functions $d_i^* \langle s_N \rangle$ form an *initial value optimal policy*, and since there are N functions of the single state variable s_N to be specified by the policy, the problem is said to be an *N-decision, one-state optimization problem*. The number of decisions plus the number of states equals the number of degrees of freedom.

Strictly speaking, s_N, not being the output of any stage, should be called a decision rather than a state. If one can choose freely among the many possible values of s_N, then s_N will be called a *choice* variable and written c_N instead of s_N. Although there is no difference between a choice variable and a decision variable so far as actual computations are concerned, the distinction in notation will be preserved for analytical reasons to be made apparent later.

Multiple decision or state variables may be distinguished from each other by adding a second subscript (d_{i1}, d_{i2}, etc.). A stage can have several transition functions (Beightler, Mitten), given double subscripts where necessary to avoid confusion. Each stage has only one return function, and the returns are always scalar. Every decision and state is, for simplicity, treated as a single variable here, although under circumstances discussed later the relations derived hold for vector variables as well.

8-02 Decomposition by Dynamic Programming

The sequential structure of a serial system can be exploited to transform the N-decision, one-state initial value optimization problem into a set of N

one-decision, one-state problems. This is accomplished by the procedure called *dynamic programming*, due to Richard Bellman.

Let S_n be the sum of the returns from stages 1 through n.

$$S_n \equiv \sum_{i=1}^{n} R_i\langle d_i, s_i\rangle; \qquad n = 1, \ldots, N \qquad (8\text{-}8\!:\!n)$$

$$S_n = S_n\langle d_1, \ldots, d_n, s_n\rangle; \qquad n = 1, \ldots, N \qquad (8\text{-}9\!:\!n)$$

Let state s_n be treated as a parameter, and let $f_n\langle s_n\rangle$ be such that

$$f_n\langle s_n\rangle \geq S_n\langle d_1, \ldots, d_n, s_n\rangle$$

for all $d_1, \ldots, d_n; \qquad n = 1, \ldots, N$ $(8\text{-}10\!:\!n)$

with equality achieved at each stage for at least one set of decisions. The function $f_n\langle s_n\rangle$, which is the *n-stage maximum return*, can be made to depend on the input and decision for the *previous* stage $n + 1$ by substitution of the transition function $(8\text{-}2\!:\!n + 1)$ for s_n:

$$f_n\langle s_n\rangle = f_n\langle T_{n+1}\langle d_{n+1}, s_{n+1}\rangle\rangle \equiv f_n\langle d_{n+1}, s_{n+1}\rangle; \qquad n = 1, \ldots, N-1 \qquad (8\text{-}11\!:\!n)$$

where state s_{n+1} is regarded as a parameter. Addition of the return r_{n+1} from stage $n + 1$ to both sides of inequality $(8\text{-}10\!:\!n)$ and subsequent application of definition $(8\text{-}8\!:\!n)$ and Eq. $(8\text{-}11\!:\!n)$ gives

$$R_{n+1}\langle d_{n+1}, s_{n+1}\rangle + f_n\langle d_{n+1}, s_{n+1}\rangle \geq S_{n+1}\langle d_1, \ldots, d_{n+1}, s_{n+1}\rangle$$

for all $d_1, \ldots, d_n; \qquad n = 1, \ldots, N-1$ $(8\text{-}12\!:\!n)$

Notice that this upper bound holds for the last n decisions, but not for d_{n+1}. Moreover, the upper bound depends only upon the independent decision variable d_{n+1} and the state parameter s_{n+1}. Thus it is only a one-decision, one-state optimization problem to find the function $U_{n+1}\langle s_{n+1}\rangle$, defined to be such that

$$U_{n+1}\langle s_{n+1}\rangle \geq R_{n+1}\langle d_{n+1}, s_{n+1}\rangle + f_n\langle d_{n+1}, s_{n+1}\rangle$$

for all $d_{n+1}; \qquad n = 1, \ldots, N-1$ $(8\text{-}13\!:\!n)$

with equality achieved at each stage for at least one set of decisions. Inequalities $(8\text{-}12\!:\!n)$ and $(8\text{-}13\!:\!n)$ together establish $U_{n+1}\langle s_{n+1}\rangle$ as a least upper bound on the $n + 1$ stage return S_{n+1} for all of the last $n + 1$ decisions, *including* d_{n+1}.

$$U_{n+1}\langle s_{n+1}\rangle \geq S_{n+1}\langle d_1, \ldots, d_{n+1}, s_{n+1}\rangle$$

for all $d_1, \ldots, d_{n+1}; \qquad n = 1, \ldots, N-1$ $(8\text{-}14\!:\!n)$

Hence by definition $(8\text{-}10\!:\!n)$, $U_{n+1}\langle s_{n+1}\rangle$ must be the $n + 1$ stage maximum return function $f_{n+1}\langle s_{n+1}\rangle$, providing it exists.

$$U_{n+1}\langle s_{n+1}\rangle \equiv f_{n+1}\langle s_{n+1}\rangle; \qquad n = 1, \ldots, N-1 \qquad (8\text{-}15\!:\!n)$$

Therefore one can find f_{n+1} from f_n by determining the one parameter decision function $d^*_{n+1}\langle s_{n+1}\rangle$ which is such that

$$f_{n+1}\langle s_{n+1}\rangle = R_{n+1}\langle d^*_{n+1}\langle s_{n+1}\rangle, s_{n+1}\rangle + f_n\langle d^*_{n+1}\langle s_{n+1}\rangle, s_{n+1}\rangle;$$

$$n = 1, \ldots, N - 1 \qquad (8\text{-}16\text{: } n)$$

for any value of s_{n+1}.

Equation (8–16:n) may also be written as

$$f_{n+1}\langle s_{n+1}\rangle = \max_{d_{n+1}} \{R_{n+1}\langle d_{n+1}, s_{n+1}\rangle + f_n\langle d_{n+1}, s_{n+1}\rangle\};$$

$$n = 1, \ldots, N - 1 \qquad (8\text{-}17\text{: } n)$$

Since the return $R_1\langle d_1, s_1\rangle$ depends only on one decision variable, determination of $f_1\langle s_1\rangle$ is a one-decision, one-state optimization problem. With $f_1\langle s_1\rangle$ known, one can find $f_2\langle s_2\rangle$ and $d^*_2\langle s_2\rangle$ by another one-decision, one-state optimization involving Eq. (8–16:1). After N such optimizations, one obtains the N decision functions $d^*_1\langle s_1\rangle, \ldots, d^*_N\langle s_N\rangle$ and the N stage maximum return $f_N\langle s_N\rangle$.

Equation (8–17) is a mathematical statement of Bellman's *Principle of Optimality* for serial multistage systems. This principle states that the optimal policy, $d^*_N\langle s_N\rangle, \ldots, d^*_1\langle s_1\rangle$, for an N-stage system must be such that the subset of decision functions $d^*_n\langle s_n\rangle, \ldots, d^*_1\langle s_1\rangle, (n = 1, \ldots, N)$ is optimal for the last n stages of the N-stage system, for *any* input s_n. Starting with $d^*_N\langle s_N\rangle$, the recursive substitution of $d^*_N\langle s_N\rangle$ into transition Eq. (8–2) to beget the optimal input function $s_{n-1}\langle s_n\rangle$, which is in turn put into $d^*_{n-1}\langle s_{n-1}\rangle$ to give $d^*_{n-1}\langle s_n\rangle$, eventually generates the entire initial value optimal policy.

In practice one rarely needs to know $R^*\langle s_N\rangle$ for every possible value of s_N. Usually either s_N is specified to be a particular constant value k_N or else it can be selected at will and is therefore really a choice variable c_N amenable to search techniques. In the former case one simply determines the constant $R^*\langle k_N\rangle$ and the corresponding optimal policy. The latter situation, formulated in the previous section, can be solved by dynamic programming with one modification. Since stage N has a choice c_N and a decision d_N as inputs, the optimum return R^* is the result of a two-decision, no-state optimization.

$$R^* = \max_{d_N, c_N}\{R_N\langle d_N, c_N\rangle + f_{N-1}\langle d_N, c_N\rangle\} \qquad (8\text{-}18)$$

8-03 Partial Optimization

Now define the *maximand*

$$M_n \equiv M_n\langle s_n, d_n\rangle \equiv R_n\langle s_n, d_n\rangle + f_{n-1}\langle T_n\langle s_n, d_n\rangle\rangle; \qquad n = 2, \ldots, N$$

$$(8\text{-}19\text{: } n)$$

The maximand can be regarded as an objective function in the two

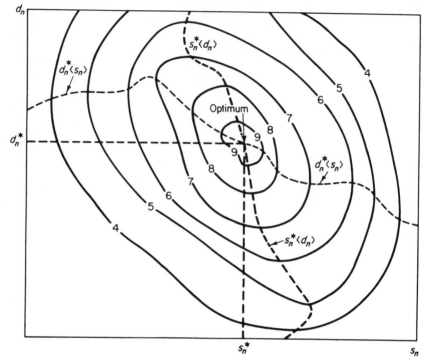

Figure 8-4. Graphic illustration of commutativity.

variables s_n and d_n. Contours of a typical maximand are shown in Fig. 8–4. Suppose that for each possible input state s_n the decision $d_n^*\langle s_n\rangle$ is found which maximizes (in general, *optimizes*) M_n. That is,

$$M_n\langle s_n, d_n^*\langle s_n\rangle\rangle \geq M_n\langle s_n, d_n\rangle \qquad (8\text{-}20\text{: } n)$$

for every s_n. The left member of Eq. (8–20) depends only upon the input state s_n, and we symbolize this by defining

$$M_n^*\langle s_n\rangle \equiv M_n\langle s_n, d_n^*\langle s_n\rangle\rangle \qquad (8\text{-}21\text{: } n)$$

We shall refer to the process of finding $d_n^*\langle s_n\rangle$ and $M_n^*\langle s_n\rangle$ as "partial optimization with respect to d_n." It corresponds graphically to determining the locus of points where the maximand contour tangents are parallel to the d_n axis in Fig. 8–4. Notice that this partial optimization produces a functional relationship, $d_n^*\langle s_n\rangle$, between d_n and s_n which removes one degree of freedom, so that specification of only *one* variable (the input state s_n) completely determines the value of M_n. By analogy with the phrase "integrated out" we can say that d_n has been "optimized out" of the return function. Optimization with respect to d_n may be considered an operator mapping M_n from the two-dimensional set of all possible d_n and s_n onto the one-dimensional set of the allowable s_n. We lose no generality in assuming that we are dealing with a *maximization* problem; then we may write

$$\max_{d_n} \{M_n\langle s_n, d_n\rangle\} \equiv M_n^*\langle s_n\rangle \qquad (8\text{-}22\text{: } n)$$

Maximization of $M_n^*\langle s_n \rangle$ with respect to the remaining variable s_n gives the optimum return, M_n^*, a constant for all s_n

$$\max_{s_n} \{M_n^*\langle s_n \rangle\} \equiv M_n^* \geq M_n^*\langle s_n \rangle \qquad (8\text{-}23\colon \text{n})$$

The optimal input state s_n^* is defined by

$$M_n^*\langle s_n^* \rangle \equiv M_n^* \qquad (8\text{-}24\colon \text{n})$$

The optimal decision d_n^* is obtained from substituting s_n^* into $d_n^*\langle s_n \rangle$.

$$d_n^* \equiv d_n^*\langle s_n^* \rangle$$

It is important to notice that the two optimization operations previously described are commutative; that is, the order in which the partial optimizations are carried out is immaterial. This may be stated formally as

$$\max_{d_n} \{\max_{s_n} [M_n\langle s_n, d_n \rangle]\} = \max_{s_n} \{\max_{d_n} [M_n\langle s_n, d_n \rangle]\} \qquad (8\text{-}25\colon \text{n})$$

To prove this, first define $s_n^*\langle d_n \rangle$ by a partial optimization with respect to s_n:

$$M_n\langle s_n^*\langle d_n \rangle, d_n \rangle \equiv M_n^*\langle d_n \rangle \geq M_n\langle s_n, d_n \rangle \qquad (8\text{-}26\colon \text{n})$$

for every allowable decision d_n. Optimization of $M_n^*\langle d_n \rangle$ with respect to d_n gives the optimal decision d_n^* such that

$$M_n^*\langle d_n^* \rangle \geq M_n^*\langle d_n \rangle \qquad (8\text{-}27\colon \text{n})$$

for all d_n.

Since by Eqs. (8–26) and (8–27),

$$M_n^*\langle d_n^* \rangle \geq M_n^*\langle d_n \rangle \geq M_n\langle s_n, d_n \rangle$$

and by definition of Eq. (8–23),

$$M_n^* \geq M_n\langle s_n, d_n^* \rangle$$

it follows that

$$M_n^*\langle d_n^* \rangle = M_n^* = M_n^*\langle s_n^* \rangle$$

which proves Eq. (8–25) and the commutativity property. This commutativity is demonstrated graphically in Fig. 8–4, which shows how both functions $s_n^*\langle d_n \rangle$ and $d_n^*\langle s_n \rangle$ intersect at the optimum value of the maximand.

In serial problems, one first optimizes stage 1 partially with respect to d_1, the maximand being the stage 1 return r_1. This gives $d_1^*\langle s_1 \rangle$ and $f_1\langle s_1 \rangle$, from which the maximand $M_2\langle s_2, d_2 \rangle$ can be constructed by adding the stage 2 return. A new partial optimization determines $d_2^*\langle s_2 \rangle$ and $f_2\langle s_2 \rangle$, and the procedure is iterated until stage N has been reached.

8-04 Serial Networks

In order to visualize clearly how much computational effort is saved by partial optimization, consider a network of 100 nodes, arranged in 10 columns, with 10 nodes per column. Further, let each node in every column be joined via a link to each node in the nearest adjacent columns, for a total of 900 links. For a given initial state s_9 there are then 10^9 total paths (here a path consists of 9 links) to the final column (stage), and to find the shortest path, all one billion must be examined if a complete enumeration method is used. Now consider the solution by dynamic programming. Beginning with the last stage, we must examine a total of 10 links for each of the 10 possible input states s_1, or 100 links to obtain $f_1\langle s_1\rangle$. For the two-stage returns, 100 values of $r_2\langle s_2, d_2\rangle + f_1\langle T_1\langle s_2, d_2\rangle\rangle$ must be calculated to find $f_2\langle s_2\rangle$, 100 values of $r_3 + f_2$ will be needed to find $f_3\langle s_3\rangle$, etc.

Thus, to find the length of the shortest path, $f_9\langle s_9\rangle$, only 900 partial paths need be evaluated, resulting in savings which, for hand computations, mark the difference between solving and not solving the problem. Numerous prob-

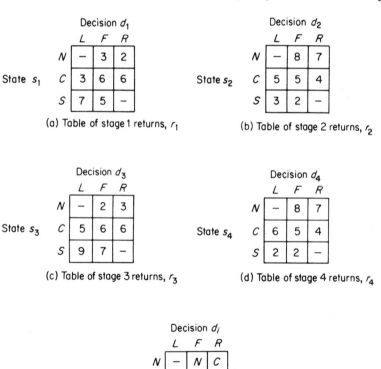

Decision d_1

State s_1	L	F	R
N	–	3	2
C	3	6	6
S	7	5	–

(a) Table of stage 1 returns, r_1

Decision d_2

State s_2	L	F	R
N	–	8	7
C	5	5	4
S	3	2	–

(b) Table of stage 2 returns, r_2

Decision d_3

State s_3	L	F	R
N	–	2	3
C	5	6	6
S	9	7	–

(c) Table of stage 3 returns, r_3

Decision d_4

State s_4	L	F	R
N	–	8	7
C	6	5	4
S	2	2	–

(d) Table of stage 4 returns, r_4

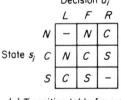

Decision d_i

State s_i	L	F	R
N	–	N	C
C	N	C	S
S	C	S	–

(e) Transition table for output
$\tilde{s}_i$ $(i = 1, ..., 4)$

Figure 8-5. Transition and stage return tables for network problem of Fig. 8-1(a).

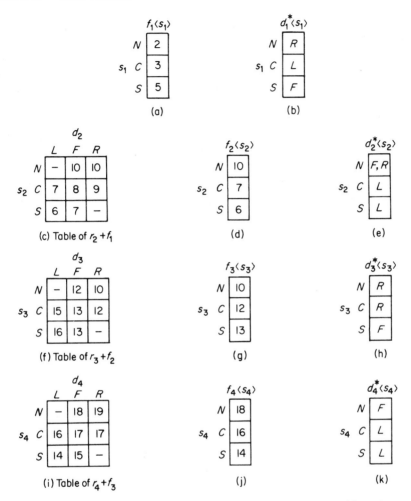

Figure 8-6. Optimal stage returns and decisions for network problem of Fig. 8-1(a).

lems have appeared in applications which would defy solution by the largest electronic computers, were they to be solved by total enumeration.

Network problems also provide an excellent transition to the more general serial optimization problem. The relation between the general initial value problem and the network problem is best illustrated by writing the $f_i\langle s_i\rangle$ and $d_i^*\langle s_i\rangle$ in tabular form. This is, in fact, the way a digital computer would be programmed to solve any discrete variable serial optimization problem. For example, consider the tabular solution of the network given in Fig. 8-1. The input data to the computer (whether electronic or human) are the tables of returns and transitions for each of the four stages shown in Fig. 8-5. In general, a different transition table would be required for each stage, but in this simple problem the transitions are identical at each stage.

The computer first determines, for each row (state) in the r_1 table, the minimum return, $f_1\langle s_1\rangle$, and the corresponding optimal decision, $d_1^*\langle s_1\rangle$ and enters them in a tabular array as shown in Fig. 8–6(a), (b). Next, a working table of the two-stage returns, $r_2\langle s_2, d_2\rangle + f_1\langle T_1\langle s_2, d_2\rangle\rangle$, (abbreviated as $r_2 + f_1$) is prepared as shown in Fig. 8–6(c). The entries in this table are obtained using Tables (b) and (e) of Fig. 8–5 and (a) of Fig. 8–6. For example, for $s_2 = C$, $d_2 = L$, we find the two-stage return to be the sum of 5 and 2, as obtained from the tables cited. The computer now finds $f_2\langle s_2\rangle$ by locating the minimum entry in each row and records it, along with the optimal decision, $d_2^*\langle s_2\rangle$ as shown in Fig. 8–6(d), (e). This process is now continued, producing the remaining tables of Fig. 8–6. Owing to its repetitive nature, this procedure is well adapted to computer work, and the working tables may be destroyed as soon as they have been used, since only the $f_i\langle s_i\rangle$ tables need be stored. (The $d_i^*\langle s_i\rangle$ tables may be printed out or stored on tape for later use in tracing out the optimal path.) The reader may verify that the values in Fig. 8–6 are the same as those shown on the network of Fig. 8–1.

8-05 Discrete Variable Problems

The analysis used in constructing the tables of Fig. 8–6 may now be employed to solve a more general class of problems. The analytic approach and computational procedure to be used on discrete variable problems are best illustrated by a few examples.

First consider a highly simplified example of the replacement type of problem (Bellman, 1955) that occurs in almost every industrial organization. A factory is interested in developing an optimal replacement policy for a certain type of equipment which costs 12 units when new, and which has a resale value of $4 - t$, for $0 \leq t \leq 4$ (no resale value after four years) when it is t years old. The net profit from one year of operation of a t-year-old piece of equipment has been found to be $16 - t^2 (0 \leq t \leq 4)$. Assuming that this type of equipment will be discontinued after 4 years, it is desired to find the optimal replacement policy to maximize the total net profit if the present equipment is two years old.

In this problem, the decision variable at each stage (year) can take on only one of two values, *Keep*(K) or *Replace*(R). If n is the number of years remaining before discontinuance of the equipment, define $f_n\langle t\rangle$ as the total net profit from n years of operation beginning with a t-year-old piece of equipment, when an optimal replacement policy is used. Assuming that the equipment will be sold at the end of the final year ($n = 0$), then for a one-stage process we have

$$f_1\langle t \rangle = \max \begin{cases} K: & 19 - t - t^2 \\ R: & 11 - t \end{cases}$$

The value associated with the decision to replace is the sum of the net profit from one year of operation with a new piece of equipment, 16, plus the resale value this year, $4 - t$, plus the resale value next year, 3, minus the cost of the new equipment, 12. By a similar analysis, we find:

$$f_n\langle t \rangle = \max \begin{cases} K: & 16 - t^2 + f_{n-1}\langle t + 1 \rangle \\ R: & 8 - t + f_{n-1}\langle 1 \rangle \end{cases} \quad n = 2, 3, 4$$

Since the decisions in this problem are all limited to just two possible values, all optimal returns and associated decisions can be conveniently placed in one table as shown in Fig. 8–7. The values in this table are computed by comparing the returns (profits) produced by the decisions K and R and retaining the larger. For example, $f_1\langle 2 \rangle$ is the maximum of the values $19 - 2 - 4$ and $11 - 2$, associated with the decisions K and R, respectively, and $f_4\langle 2 \rangle$ is the maximum of $16 - 4 + 33$ and $8 - 2$ + 38, produced by the respective

n \ t	1	2	3	4
1	17 ⓚ	13 ⓚ	8 R	7 R
2	28 ⓚ	23 R	22 R	21 R
3	38 ⓚ	34 ⓚ R	33 R	32 R
4	49 ⓚ	45 ⓚ	43 R	42 R

Figure 8-7. Optimal returns and decisions for the equipment replacement problem.

decisions, K and R. Beginning with a two-year-old piece of equipment, the optimal policy for four years of operation is shown by the arrows in Fig. 8–7 as $K R K K$, for a total net profit of 45. This value can be checked by computing the individual returns for each of the four years: 12, 5, 15, and 12, plus the resale value of the three-year-old piece of equipment at the end of the four years, 1, which sum to 45.

As a second example, consider the problem of loading a space capsule having a total capacity of W tons with scientific instruments in such a way as to maximize the total value of the payload. Note that this same type of problem occurs in numerous other contexts, such as the selection of items to go into survival kits, the selection of machinery types for factory departments, and, in general, the optimal choice of components under capacity (usually dollar) restrictions. For illustration we again select a much simplified example which, however, completely describes the computational procedure.

Four kinds of items are available for loading into the capsule, where the ith item has weight w_i (in tons, say) and value v_i, as shown in Fig. 8–8(a).

It is not so obvious what constitutes a stage in this problem, but this can be made clear by considering the solution procedure to be inductive as follows: having found the optimal cargo selection when considering only the

i	w_i	v_i
1	4	7
2	3	4
3	1	1
4	5	9

(a) Weights and values of the four components

n_1\\W_1	0	1	2	3	4	5	6	7	8	9	10	11	12	13	14	15	16	17	18	19	20
0	0	0	0	0	0																
1					7	7	7	7													
2									14	14	14	14	14	14	14	14	14	14	14	14	14

(b) Stage 1

n_2\\W_2	0	1	2	3	4	5	6	7	8	9	10	11	12	13	14	15	16	17	18	19	20
0	0	0	0	0	(7)	(7)	7	7	(14)	(14)	14	14	14	14	14	14	14	14	14	14	14
1				(4)	4	4	4	(11)	11	11	11	(18)	(18)	(18)	18	18	18	18	18	18	18
2							(8)	8	8	8	(15)	15	15	15	(22)	(22)	(22)	(22)	(22)	(22)	(22)

(c) Stage 2

n_3\\W_3	0	1	2	3	4	5	6	7	8	9	10	11	12	13	14	15	16	17	18	19	20
0	0	0	0	(4)	(7)	7	8	(11)	(14)	14	15	(18)	18	18	(22)	22	22	22	22	22	22
1		(1)	1	1	5	(8)	8	9	12	(15)	15	16	(19)	19	19	(23)	23	23	23	23	23
2			(2)	2	2	6	(9)	9	10	13	(16)	16	17	(20)	20	20	(24)	(24)	(24)	(24)	(24)

(d) Stage 3

n_4\\W_4	0	1	2	3	4	5	6	7	8	9	10	11	12	13	14	15	16	17	18	19	20
0	0	(1)	(2)	(4)	7	8	9	(11)	(14)	15	16	18	19	20	22	23	24	24	24	24	24
1						(9)	(10)	(11)	13	(16)	17	18	(20)	(23)	24	25	(27)	28	29	31	32
2											(18)	(19)	(20)	22	(25)	(26)	(27)	(29)	(32)	(33)	(34)

(e) Stage 4

Figure 8-8. Input data and stage returns for the space capsule problem.

first $i - 1$ items and a weight restriction W_{i-1}, we can now use partial optimization to find the optimal cargo for the first i items under the weight limitation W_i. Thus the stages are the individual items under consideration, whereas the states are the total remaining unused weight capacity.

Let $f_i\langle W_i \rangle$ be the maximum total cargo value obtainable from the first i items when the weight restriction is W_i, and let n_i be the number of type i

items selected. Then, if no more than one of each item is desired, or available, we have for $f_0 = 0$ and W_i a positive integer:

$$f_i\langle W_i\rangle = \max_{n_i=0,1} \{n_i v_i + f_{i-1}\langle W_i - n_i w_i\rangle\}; \qquad i = 1, 2, 3, 4$$

when $w_i \leq W_i$. (Clearly, for $w_i > W_i$, $f_i\langle W_i\rangle = f_{i-1}\langle W_i\rangle$.) If the n_i may be any nonnegative integer, the recurrence relation must be written as

$$f_i\langle W_i\rangle = \max_{n_i=0,1,\ldots} \{n_i v_i + f_{i-1}\langle W_i - n_i w_i\rangle\}$$

$$n_i \leq \left[\frac{W_i}{w_i}\right]$$

where the symbol $[x]$ indicates the greatest integer in x. For example, $[\frac{7}{3}] = 2$, $[\frac{1}{2}] = 0$, and $[4] = 4$. Assume that for the present problem, the decision variable n_i can take on only the values 0, 1, or 2, and consider the solution of the problem for values of the initial state, W, up to a maximum of 20.

Beginning with the last stage, that is, considering only item 1, if the remaining unused capacity after loading the other three item types is W_1, then

$$f_1\langle W_1\rangle = \max_{\substack{n_1=0,1,2 \\ n_1 \leq [W_1/4]}} \{7n_1\}$$

$$= \begin{cases} 7\left[\dfrac{W_1}{4}\right], & W_1 \leq 8 \\ 14, & W_1 > 8 \end{cases}$$

where the restriction $W_1 \leq 8$ is derived from $[W_1/4] \leq 2$. From this equation, values of $f_1\langle W_1\rangle$ can be computed as shown in Fig. 8–8(b). The optimal two-stage returns, involving items 1 and 2, are then found from the relation

$$f_2\langle W_2\rangle = \max_{n_2} \{4n_2 + f_1\langle W_2 - 3n_2\rangle\}$$

where $n_2 = 0, 1, \ldots, \min(2,[W_2/3])$ as shown by the *circled* values in Fig. 8–8(c) which contains all of the two-stage returns, $r_2\langle W_2, n_2\rangle + f_1\langle T_1\langle W_2, n_2\rangle\rangle$. As an example of the procedure, consider the calculations for the two-stage input, $W_2 = 7$. For $n_2 = 0$, we find $r_2 = 0$, and $f_1\langle 7\rangle = 7$ (from (a)); for $n_2 = 1$: $r_2 = 4$, $f_1\langle 4\rangle = 7$; for $n_2 = 2$: $r_2 = 8$, $f_1\langle 1\rangle = 0$. When $W_2 < 6$, the upper limit $[W_2/3] < 2$, and when $W_2 < 3$, this limit is zero, so that n_2 must be less than 2 when $W_2 < 6$, and must be zero when $W_2 < 3$, as common sense would dictate. Continuing in this manner, the optimal four-stage returns are found as shown by the circled values in Fig. 8–8(e) where, of course, $W_4 \equiv W$.

Thus, if the capsule has a weight capacity W of 13 tons, the optimal payload will have a total value of 23. From (e), we find $n_4^* = 1$, so that the state input to the remaining three stages is $W_3 = 8$, resulting in $n_3^* = 0$, which makes $W_2 = 8$, $n_2^* = 0$, and finally, $W_1 = 8$, $n_1^* = 2$. As a check, we compute $2 \cdot 7 + 0 \cdot 4 + 0 \cdot 1 + 1 \cdot 9 = 23$. If for some secondary consideration we should desire to have $n_4 = 2$, the total return will be 22, and by tracing through the remaining stages, we find that this is produced by the policy: $n_4 = 2$,

$n_3 = 0$, $n_2 = 1$, $n_1 = 0$. Note that if the weight limitation is 16 tons, there are two alternate optimal policies which will produce the maximum return of 27: $n_4 = 2$, $n_3 = 2$, $n_2 = 0$, $n_1 = 1$, and $n_4 = 1$, $n_3 = 0$, $n_2 = 1$, $n_2 = 2$. The reader should convince himself that the solution procedure used on this problem is independent of the ordering of the items by re-solving the problem after the items have been renumbered in some arbitrary way.

8-06 Problems in Continuous Variables

In many problems, the decision variables are not restricted to discrete values, but are continuous within various ranges. In this case, Eqs. (8-1) and (8-2) are given as algebraic functions, rather than in tabular form. For example, consider the problem (L.G. Mitten) of maximizing $\sum_{i=1}^{4} r_i$, where

$$r_i = 0.5s_i - 0.2d_i, \qquad i = 1, \ldots, 4$$

and $$\tilde{s}_i = 0.7s_i + 0.4d_i, \qquad i = 1, \ldots, 4$$

The initial value is given as $s_4 = 100$, and each decision may take on any value in the open interval $[0, s_i]$.

Then in this problem, Eq. (8–17) is simply

$$f_n\langle s_n \rangle = \max_{0 \le d_n \le s_n} \{0.5s_n - 0.2d_n + f_{n-1}\langle 0.7s_n + 0.4d_n \rangle\}$$

for $n = 2, 3, 4$

and $$f_1\langle s_1 \rangle = \max_{0 \le d_1 \le s_1} \{0.5s_1 - 0.2d_1\} = 0.5s_1; \qquad d_1^* = 0$$

since the coefficient of d_1 is negative. The two-stage return is $0.5s_2 - 0.2d_2 + 0.5(0.7s_2 + 0.4d_2) = 0.85s_2$, which is completely independent of d_2. Hence, *any* feasible decision at stage 2 is also an optimal decision. By a similar analysis, the three-stage return is $1.095s_3 + 0.14d_3$; to maximize this, d_3 is is chosen as large as possible: $d_3^* = s_3$, making $f_3\langle s_3 \rangle = 1.235s_3$. Continuing in this manner, we find $d_4^* = s_4$, which produces an optimal four-stage return of $f_4\langle s_4 \rangle = 1.6585s_4$.

Notice that we have solved a larger problem than that given in the problem definition, for we have the optimal solution for *any* initial input s_4; thus, the original problem has been imbedded in a much larger problem. By tracing through the system from left to right, one finds the optimal decisions to be $d_4^* = s_4$, $d_3^* = 1.1s_4$, $0 \le d_2^* \le 1.21s_4$, and $d_1^* = 0$. The optimal four-stage return of 165.85, corresponding to the given input, $s_4 = 100$, may be verified by adding the individual returns produced by this policy.

Problems involving decisions to be made at specified time intervals usually exhibit a serial structure and are therefore amenable to the type of analysis associated with dynamic programming. The following is an example of an *allocation* type of problem. The particular formulation of the example given here is due to L. G. Mitten. Multistage allocation problems were first formulated as dynamic programming problems by Bellman, 1954.

In a certain (highly simplified) economy, the following rules apply: commodity K can be produced by either or both of two industries, A and B. Each dollar of capital invested in Industry A at the beginning of the year yields, at the end of that year and each succeeding year, 2 tons of commodity K and $0.50 capital; each dollar of capital invested in Industry B at the beginning of a year yields, at the end of that year and each succeeding year, 1 ton of commodity K and $0.90 capital. Given an initial capital of $$s_5$, how should the available capital at the beginning of each year be allocated between the two industries so as to maximize the total amount of commodity K produced during the next five years?

For this program, let s_i be the amount of capital available at the beginning of the ith year, $\bar{s}_i$ the amount of capital available at the end of the ith year, r_i the tons of commodity K produced during year i, and $0 \leq d_i \leq s_i$ the capital invested in Industry A at the beginning of the ith year. Then a total of $s_i - d_i$ dollars will be invested in Industry B at the start of year i, since it will always pay to invest all available funds. This problem differs somewhat from those considered previously because of the production of the commodity in years subsequent to the initiating decision. The method of solution is unchanged, however, and the accumulation feature may be treated as follows;

$$r_i = \sum_{j=i}^{5} [2d_j + 1 \cdot (s_j - d_j)] = \sum_{j=i}^{5} (s_j + d_j)$$

and the transitions are defined by

$$\bar{s}_i = 0.5d_i + 0.9(s_i - d_i) + s_i = 1.9s_i - 0.4d_i, \qquad i \neq 5$$

since the total capital available at the end of the year is that available at the beginning of the year plus the amount of capital produced during the year. There is no accumulation of the initial capital available, however, so, for the first year,

$$\bar{s}_5 = 0.9s_5 - 0.4d_5$$

The recurrence relations for the problem are now

$$f_n\langle s_n \rangle = \max_{0 \leq d_n \leq s_n} \left\{ \sum_{i=n}^{5} (s_i + d_i) + f_{n-1}\langle \bar{s}_n \rangle \right\}$$

where, as always, $f_0 \equiv 0$.
Then, recursively, we find

$$f_1\langle s_1 \rangle = \max_{0 \leq d_1 \leq s_1} \left\{ s_1 + d_1 + \sum_{i=2}^{5} (s_i + d_i) \right\}$$

which has the value $2s_1 + \sum_{i=2}^{5} (s_i + d_i)$, for $d_1^* = s_1$, and

$$f_2\langle s_2 \rangle = \max_{0 \le d_2 \le s_2} \left\{ s_2 + d_2 + \sum_{i=3}^{5} (s_i + d_i) + 2(1.9s_2 - 0.4d_2) + \sum_{i=2}^{5} (s_i + d_i) \right\}$$

$$= \max_{0 \le d_2 \le s_2} \left\{ 5.8s_2 + 1.2d_2 + 2 \sum_{i=3}^{5} (s_i + d_i) \right\}$$

which has the value $7s_2 + 2 \sum_{i=3}^{5} (s_i + d_i)$ produced by the optimal decision $d_2^* = s_2$.

In this same manner we then find

$$f_3\langle s_3 \rangle = 16.5s_3 + 3 \sum_{i=4}^{5} (d_i + s_i); \qquad d_3^* = s_3$$

and
$$f_4\langle s_4 \rangle = 35.35s_4 + 4(s_5 + d_5); \qquad d_4^* = 0$$

Then, since

$$f_5\langle s_5 \rangle = \max_{0 \le d_5 \le s_5} \{ 5(s_5 + d_5) + 35.35(0.9s_5 - 0.4d_5) \}$$

the optimal first-year decision is $d_5^* = 0$ so that $f_5\langle s_5 \rangle = 36.815s_5$ tons, for any initial capital s_5.

This problem may be approached from another point of view by defining $\hat{r}_i$ as the total amount of commodity K produced *as a consequence* of the decision d_i (rather than the amount produced *during* year i). Then the recurrence relations become

$$f_n\langle s_n \rangle = \max_{0 \le d_n \le s_n} \{ n(s_n + d_n) + f_{n-1}\langle 1.9s_n - 0.4d_n \rangle \}, \quad n \ne 5$$

and
$$f_5\langle s_5 \rangle = \max_{0 \le d_5 \le s_5} \{ 5(s_5 + d_5) + f_4\langle 0.9s_5 - 0.4d_5 \rangle \}$$

As the reader can see, these relations require exactly the same computational work as those given before, the only difference being that the summation terms need not be carried along in the computations. Thus, with this approach we find $f_1\langle s_1 \rangle = 2s_1, f_2\langle s_2 \rangle = 7s_2, f_3\langle s_3 \rangle = 16.5s_3, f_4\langle s_4 \rangle = 35.35s_4$, and $f_5\langle s_5 \rangle = 36.815s_5$, with the same optimal decisions as before.

Finally, consider an initial-value problem for which the stage returns are nonlinear. (All discrete variable problems are naturally nonlinear, but the computational details require somewhat different handling in the case of continuous variables.) Specifically, we wish to maximize

$$p = \sum_{i=1}^{3} r_i$$

where $r_i = 5d_i - id_i^2$ and $\tilde{s}_i = s_i - 0.4d_i$

and where each decision variable is restricted to nonnegative values which cannot exceed the stage input: $0 \le d_i \le s_i$. This is the usual restriction found in allocation problems, since no more can be allocated than is available, and negative allocations have no meaning.

In this problem, unlike the linear problems previously considered, the optimal decision at a given stage is not the same function of the stage input for all inputs. Thus at the last stage, the optimal return must be written

$$f_1\langle s_1 \rangle = \begin{cases} 6.25 \quad ; & s_1 \geq 2.5 \quad (d_1^* = 2.5) \\ 5s_1 - s_1^2; & s_1 \leq 2.5 \quad (d_1^* = s_1) \end{cases}$$

Then the two-stage return with input s_2 is

$$M_2 = \begin{cases} 5d_2 - 2d_2^2 + 6.25; & s_2 - 0.4d_2 \geq 2.5 \\ 3d_2 - 2.16d_2^2 + 5s_2 - s_2^2 + 0.8s_2d_2; & s_2 - 0.4d_2 \leq 2.5 \end{cases}$$

For the *upper* branch, we find $f_2\langle s_2 \rangle = 9.375$ when $s_2 \geq 3$, with the corresponding $d_2^* = 1.25$; when $s_2 < 3$, the two-stage return will be maximized by keeping d_2 at the largest possible value (consistent with $s_1 = 2.5$), so that $d_2^* = 2.5s_2 - 6.25$, producing an optimal return of $f_2\langle s_2 \rangle = 75s_2 - 12.5s_2^2 - 103.125$. This latter value of d_2^* becomes negative when the input falls below 2.5, so that the total restriction is $2.5 \leq s_2 \leq 3$.

For the *lower* branch, the optimal stage 2 decision is found by differentiation to be $d_2^* = 0.185s_2 + 0.695$, producing the return $f_2\langle s_2 \rangle = 5.556s_2 - 0.926s_2^2 + 1.042$, which is valid in the range $0.853 \leq s_2 \leq 3$ (since for s_2 below 0.853, $d_2^* = 0.185s_2 + 0.695$ would be greater than s_2). When s_2 is below 0.853, the two-stage return is again maximized by keeping d_2 at the largest possible value: $d_2^* = s_2$, for an optimal return of $f_2\langle s_2 \rangle = 8s_2 - 2.36s_2^2$. We have now generated two different optimal returns $f_2\langle s_2 \rangle$ for the range $2.5 \leq s_2 \leq 3$; namely, $75s_2 - 12.5s_2^2 - 103.125$, and $5.556s_2 - 0.926s_2^2 + 1.042$, but since the former never exceeds the latter, it may be dropped as nonoptimal, so that in summary we have

$$f_2\langle s_2 \rangle = \begin{cases} 9.375; & 3 \leq s_2 \leq \infty \quad (d_2^* = 1.25) \\ 5.556s_2 - 0.926s_2^2 + 1.042; & 0.853 \leq s_2 \leq 3 \\ & (d_2^* = 0.185s_2 + 0.695) \\ 8s_2 - 2.36s_2^2; & 0 \leq s_2 \leq 0.853 \quad (d_2^* = s_2) \end{cases}$$

The foregoing analyses and results are shown graphically in Fig. 8–9; note that d_2^* is piecewise continuous and linear in s_2.

The three-stage returns must now be computed separately for the three different outputs $3 \leq s_3 - 0.4d_3 \leq \infty$, $0.853 \leq s_3 - 0.4d_3 \leq 3$, and $0 \leq s_3 - 0.4d_3 \leq 0.853$, which form the input to the last two stages. The procedure is exactly like that previously given for $f_2\langle s_2 \rangle$, and again, when different expressions are generated for $f_3\langle s_3 \rangle$ over the same range of s_3, they must be compared and only the one producing the larger value retained. For example, in the range $0.853 \leq s_3 \leq 1.082$, one finds $f_3\langle s_3 \rangle = 44.454s_3 - 18.75s_3^2 - 19.16$, and $f_3\langle s_3 \rangle = 8.503s_3 - 2.096s_3^2 + 0.241$, generated by the decisions $d_3^* = 2.5s_3 - 2.13$ and $d_3^* = 0.28s_3 + 0.267$, respectively, where the former will be found to be nonoptimal and is accordingly dropped from the solution.

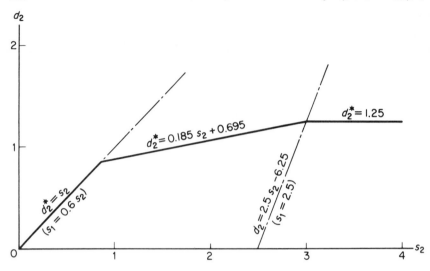

Figure 8-9. Optimal stage 2 decisions for nonlinear initial value problem.

The complete solution to this three-stage problem is given below, and in Fig. 8–10 the optimal decisions and stage restraints are shown graphically.

$$f_3\langle s_3\rangle = \begin{cases} 11.46; & 3.33 \le s_3 \le \infty \quad (d_3^* = 0.833) \\ 5.89s_3 - 0.883s_3^2 + 1.657; & 1.082 \le s_3 \le 3.33 \\ & (d_3^* = 0.118s_3 + 0.442) \\ 8.503s_3 - 2.096s_3^2 + 0.241; & 0.371 \le s_3 \le 1.082 \\ & (d_3^* = 0.28s_3 + 0.267) \\ 9.8s_3 - 3.849s_3^2; & 0 \le s_3 \le 0.371 \quad (d_3^* = s_3) \end{cases}$$

Notice that $f_3\langle s_3\rangle$ is sectionally continuous and that it increases monotonically with s_3. That $f_3\langle s_3\rangle$ is concave follows from the concavity of the transition functions and stage returns (Bellman, 1957).

The partial optimizations of dynamic programming emphasize how different is the role of a decision variable from that of a state variable when the computations are done numerically. For every possible value of an input state, s_i, for instance, one finds the value of the decision variable d_i maximizing the function $R_i\langle d_i, s_i\rangle + f_{i-1}\langle d_i, s_i\rangle$. Since d_i is a system input, unaffected by any stage outputs, none of its values are important except the optimal ones, which may be found efficiently by direct optimum-seeking methods. On the other hand, since s_i is an output from other parts of the system, one cannot know which of its values might be optimal until the entire problem has been solved. Hence an optimal decision $d_i^*\langle s_i\rangle$ must be found for every value of s_i, which rules out using direct search techniques on the state variable. Furthermore $d_i^*\langle s_i\rangle$ must be saved for all i and every value of s_i

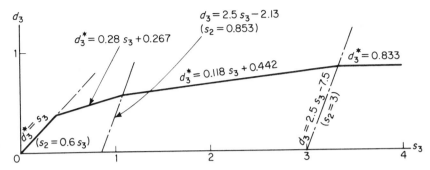

Figure 8-10. Optimal stage 3 decisions for nonlinear initial value problem.

in order to generate the optimal policy. This storage requirement can exceed the rapid access memory of large digital computers.

The states and decisions may in general be vectors (written in **boldface**) whose components are single variables. Except for obvious changes in notation the partial optimization procedure is no different than before, although the number of computations certainly increases. But state dimensionality is more of a computational and storage burden than decision dimensionality.

8-07 Final Value Problem: State Inversion

Consider the problem of obtaining the maximum return from a serial process as a function of $\bar{s}_1$, called the *final state* because it is the only state not a stage input. Suppose there exist N *inverse transition functions* $\tilde{T}_i\langle d_i, \bar{s}_i\rangle$ which express the input s_i as a function of the decision and output.

$$s_i = \tilde{T}_i\langle d_i, \bar{s}_i\rangle; \qquad i = 1, \ldots, N \qquad (8\text{-}28\!:\!i)$$

Finding such a function for a stage is called *state inversion* because the roles of the input and output states are interchanged. The inverse transitions can be used to express the stage returns in terms of decision and *output* state.

$$\tilde{R}_i\langle d_i, \bar{s}_i\rangle = R_i\langle d_i, \tilde{T}_i\langle d_i, \bar{s}_i\rangle\rangle; \qquad i = 1, \ldots, N \qquad (8\text{-}29\!:\!i)$$

A total return function $\tilde{R}\langle d_i, \bar{s}_1\rangle$ depending only on the decisions and the final state, $\bar{s}_1$, can be obtained by adding the inverted stage returns and using the inverse transitions and incidence identities to eliminate states s_1 through s_N. The corresponding *final value maximum return function*, given $\bar{s}_1$, is

$$\tilde{R}^*\langle \bar{s}_1\rangle = \max_{d_1, \ldots, d_N} \{\tilde{R}\langle d_i, \bar{s}_1\rangle\} \qquad (8\text{-}30)$$

The *final value optimization problem* is to find a set of functions $d_1^*\langle \bar{s}_1\rangle$, $\ldots$, $d_N^*\langle \bar{s}_1\rangle$ for which

$$\tilde{R}\langle d_i^*\langle \bar{s}_1\rangle, \bar{s}_1\rangle = \tilde{R}^*\langle \bar{s}_1\rangle \tag{8-31}$$

The N functions $d_i^*\langle \bar{s}_1\rangle$ form a *final-value optimal policy,* and like the initial value case, finding them is an N-decision, one-state problem. As before there are $N + 1$ degrees of freedom.

When every stage has been inverted, the final-value problem can be put into the same notational form as the initial-value problem by renumbering the stages in reverse. Then the final-value problem can be decomposed into N one-decision, one-state problems by partial optimization in the manner already described.

8-08 State Inversion: Network Routing Problems

Consider the network shipping problem of Fig. 8–11, which is identical to that discussed in connection with Fig. 8–1 except that now it is the *final* state which is fixed, and the *initial* state that is free. In this problem, the given final condition is $\bar{s}_1 \equiv C$; the shipment may originate in *any* west coast city, but it must terminate in Washington D.C. As before, the solution procedure begins

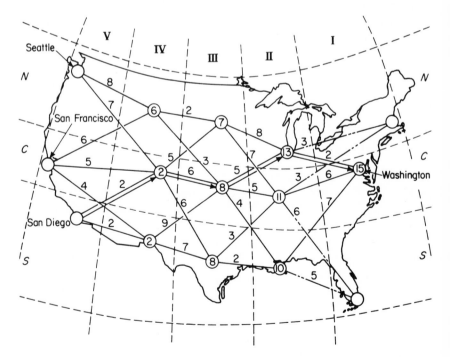

Figure 8-11. Solution of network routing problem by state inversion.

at the free end and proceeds recursively toward the fixed end, infeasible links being shown as double-dashed lines. Using state inversion, one begins at stage 4 and finds the optimal one-stage return (and optimal decision) for a given *output* $\bar{s}_4$. Thus, if $\bar{s}_4 = C$ (Denver), the optimal decision, d_4, is L (that is, *if* the shipment has arrived in Denver, we would prefer that it had been shipped *from* San Diego) and the associated return is 2. The problem is then solved just as were the initial-value problems, except that one now proceeds from left to right.

The optimal return (least cost) is 15, and by tracing back through the path shown by the arrows, one finds $s_4^* = S$; San Diego is the best city from which to start if Washington is to be the destination. Comparison of Figs. 8–1 and 8–11 illustrates the fundamental difference between initial- and final-value problems.

In an initial-value problem, the initial state s_N is fixed, and the final state is free to take on any value which the optimal stage decisions may produce as a consequence of optimizing the sum of the stage returns. For example, given the initial state $s_4 = C$ (San Francisco), Fig. 8–1 shows that the optimal return of 16 is achieved by selecting a path which terminates at $\bar{s}_1 = C$ (Washington). In a final-value problem, the final state $\bar{s}_1$ is fixed, and the initial state is free to take on whatever value results from making the optimal set of decisions. Here it is instructive to select as the final state the one which resulted when it was treated as a free end in the earlier initial-value problem: $\bar{s}_1 \equiv C$. From Fig. 8–11 we find an optimal return of 15 produced by a path that originates not at San Francisco but at San Diego. In other words, for a shipment which originates in San Francisco, the optimal route will terminate at Washington, whereas the optimal route which must terminate in Washington will originate in San Diego.

8-09 Initial-Value–Final-Value Theorem

This property may now be set down formally as follows: for an initial-value problem, let the initial state be $s_N \equiv k_N$. Then the set of optimal decisions for this problem generates a final state, $\bar{s}_1\langle k_N \rangle$, and an optimal return of $f_N\langle k_N, \bar{s}_1\langle k_N \rangle\rangle$. For the same problem worked as a final-value problem, fix the final state at $\bar{s}_1 \equiv \bar{s}_1\langle k_N \rangle$. Then the optimal solution to this problem will generate an initial state, $s_N\langle k_N \rangle$, and an optimal return, $f_N\langle s_N\langle k_N \rangle, \bar{s}_1\langle k_N \rangle\rangle$.

Then for maximization problems, we have the

THEOREM:

$$f_N\langle s_N\langle k_N \rangle, \bar{s}_1\langle k_N \rangle\rangle \geq f_N\langle k_N, \bar{s}_1\langle k_N \rangle\rangle$$

Proof: If the left member is less than the right member, then it cannot be an optimal policy for the final-value problem, since one could always select $s_N = k_N$ and obtain a larger return.

The converse is also true: if for a final-value problem $\tilde{s}_1 \equiv K$, and the optimal solution is $f_N \langle s_N \langle K \rangle, K \rangle$, where $s_N \langle K \rangle$ is the optimal initial state generated by the solution, then let the initial value problem for $s_N \equiv s_N \langle K \rangle$ generate $\tilde{s}_1 \langle K \rangle$ as the resulting final state, and $f_N \langle s_N \langle K \rangle, \tilde{s}_1 \langle K \rangle \rangle$ as the optimal return. Then, by the previous reasoning,

$$f_N \langle s_N \langle K \rangle, \tilde{s}_1 \langle K \rangle \rangle \geq f_N \langle s_N \langle K \rangle, K \rangle$$

8-10 State Inversion: Allocation Problems

As another example of a final-value problem solved by state inversion, let it be required to maximize the function $p = \sum\limits_{i=1}^{4} r_i$, where $r_i = 0.5s_i - 0.2d_i$, $\tilde{s}_i = 0.7s_i + 0.4d_i$, $\tilde{s}_1 \equiv c_1$, and $0 \leq d_i \leq s_i$, $i = 1, \ldots, 4$. Then Eqs. (8–28) and (8–29) are $s_i = 1.43\tilde{s}_i - 0.572d_i$, and $r_i = 0.715\tilde{s}_i - 0.486d_i$; the restriction $0 \leq d_i \leq s_i$ becomes $0 \leq d_i \leq 0.91\tilde{s}_i$.

Just as in the case of the network problem solved earlier, the solution is begun at the initial stage (4), and the work is carried on iteratively to the right, ending with the final stage (1). Thus,

$$f_1 \langle \tilde{s}_4 \rangle = \max_{0 \leq d_4 \leq 0.91\tilde{s}_4} \{0.715\tilde{s}_4 - 0.486d_4\} = 0.715\tilde{s}_4$$

since $d_4^* = 0$. Then

$$f_2 \langle \tilde{s}_3 \rangle = \max_{0 \leq d_3 \leq 0.91\tilde{s}_3} \{0.715\tilde{s}_3 - 0.486d_3 + 0.715(1.43\tilde{s}_3 - 0.572d_3)\}$$

$$= \max_{0 \leq d_3 \leq 0.91\tilde{s}_3} \{1.736\tilde{s}_3 - 0.894d_3\} = 1.736\tilde{s}_3$$

since $d_3^* = 0$. Continuing this process, one finds $f_3 \langle \tilde{s}_2 \rangle = 3.2\tilde{s}_2$ and $f_4 \langle \tilde{s}_1 \rangle = 5.28\tilde{s}_1$, generated by the optimal decisions $d_2^* = 0$ and $d_1^* = 0$. Since $\tilde{s}_1 \equiv \tilde{c}_1$, we have $f_4 \langle \tilde{c}_1 \rangle = 5.28\tilde{c}_1$ and, tracing back through the system, $s_1 = 1.43\tilde{c}_1, s_2 = 2.04\tilde{c}_1, s_3 = 2.92\tilde{c}_1$, and $s_4 = 4.17\tilde{c}_1$.

The interesting feature of this problem lies in the comparison of the optimal solution for the final-value problem, found previously, with that for the same problem treated earlier as an initial-value problem; namely, $d_1^* = 0$, $0 \leq d_2^* \leq s_2$, $d_3^* = s_3$, and $d_4^* = s_4$, for an optimal four-stage return of $f_4 \langle s_4 \rangle = 1.6585s_4$. Selecting $d_2^* = 0$, we find $\tilde{s}_1 = 0.5929s_4$, or $s_4 = 1.69\tilde{s}_1$, so that $f_4 \langle \tilde{s}_1 \rangle = 2.8\tilde{s}_1$, compared to the optimal return of $f_4 \langle \tilde{s}_1 \rangle = 5.28\tilde{s}_1$ for the final-value problem. (The choice $d_2^* = s_2$ in the initial-value problem yields only $f_4 \langle \tilde{s}_1 \rangle = 1.94\tilde{s}_1$.) This is an even more striking demonstration of the essential difference in character between initial and final-value problems.

The contrast between these two types of multistage decision problems may be seen clearly in the economic context of the industry allocation problem described earlier. If one begins with a fixed amount of capital (the state variable in this problem), then the optimal policy consists in first building up investment capital by investing in growth industry B in the early stages, and then in the later stages investing the accumulated capital in extractive industry A to produce the maximum total quantity of the commodity. If, however, the circumstances require that one must end with a fixed amount of capital, while being free to choose the amount of capital with which to begin, then the optimal policy will differ from that of the initial-value problem. For this final-value problem, there is no need to build up capital, since one can begin with the amount producing the maximum quantity of the commodity at each stage while finishing with the required capital (that is, invest in extractive industry A at every stage).

8-11 State Inversion: Dimensionality Considerations

Certain complications arise in state inversion when the states are vectors with different dimensionalities. Let the dimensionality of s_i and $\tilde{s}_i$ be M and N, respectively, and assume that the transformation T_i consists of N independent equations, each one expressing one of the components of $\tilde{s}_i$ as a function of s_i and d_i. If all N equations are not independent, we deal with the largest set of independent equations and make a corresponding adjustment in the dimensionality of the output state vector. There are three cases to be considered, $M = N$, $M > N$ and $M < N$.

1. If $M = N$, the M input state variables can be expressed in terms of the decision variables and N output state variables.
2. If $M > N$, N of the input state variables can be expressed in terms of the decision variables, N output state variables, and the remaining $M - N$ input state variables, which become *choice variables*.
3. If $M < N$, M of the equations of T_i can be used to express the M input variables in terms of the decisions and M of the output state variables; the remaining $M - N$ equations become constraints relating d_i and s_i.

Of course, the computational feasibility of state inversion is another question. Fortunately, when state inversion is not practical there is another way of formulating and decomposing the final-value problem.

8-12 Final-Value and Two-Point Boundary-Value Problems: Decision Inversion

Even when state inversion is impractical, the N-decision, one-state final-value problem can still be decomposed into N smaller problems. These subproblems each involve only one decision, but instead of a single state as in the initial-value case, each has *two* state variables. Since the effort needed to solve these two-state subproblems is considerably greater than for one-state functions, this approach should be used only for final-value serial problems when state inversion is either impossible or computationally infeasible. The main reason for studying this method is its applicability to two-point boundary-value problems arising in the optimization of systems with cycles and branches (Aris, Nemhauser, and Wilde). Moreover, the apparent doubling of the state dimensionality is not usually as disastrous as might appear at first glance, for one of the state variables can, under favorable circumstances, be treated as a choice variable to which direct search methods may be applied.

Suppose that

$$\tilde{s}_1 = T_1 \langle s_1, d_1 \rangle \tag{8-32}$$

can be solved for d_1 in terms of s_1 and $\tilde{s}_1$ to give

$$d_1 = \hat{T}_1 \langle s_1, \tilde{s}_1 \rangle \tag{8-33}$$

This mathematical interchange of the roles of d_1 and s_1 is called *decision inversion*, and Eq. (8–33) tells what decision is needed to transform s_1 to $\tilde{s}_1$. As with state inversion, decision inversion calls for care when there are several output and decision variables. If, for example, there are more decision variables than output state variables, then there is still some freedom of choice left among the decisions which would permit limited optimization at stage 1. Even when there are exactly as many decisions as outputs, and when decision inversion is possible, any constraints on the decision variables will be translated into complicated state constraints. But although decision inversion is in principle just as difficult as state inversion, only one decision inversion is needed to solve a final-value problem which would otherwise require N state inversions.

For the serial system of Fig. 8–3, the sum of returns from stages 1 through n can be expressed in terms of the $n - 1$ independent decisions $d_2, \ldots, d_n$ and the two states s_n and $\tilde{s}_1$ by applying decision inversion Eq. (8–33) to Eq. (8–9) to obtain

$$S_n = S_n \langle \tilde{s}_1, d_2, \ldots, d_n, s_n \rangle; \qquad n = 1, \ldots, N \tag{8-34:n}$$

Let the two-state n-stage maximum return function $f_n \langle \tilde{s}_1, s_n \rangle$ be defined by

$$f_n \langle \tilde{s}_1, s_n \rangle \equiv \max_{d_2, \ldots, d_n} \{ S_n \langle \tilde{s}_1, d_2, \ldots, d_n, s_n \rangle \}; \qquad n = 1, \ldots, N \tag{8-35:n}$$

When $n = 1$, the definition degenerates into an equation involving no maximization, since the right side of Eq. (8–35:n) would have no decision variables.

$$f_1 \langle \tilde{s}_1, s_1 \rangle = R_1 \langle \hat{T}_1 \langle s_1, \tilde{s}_1 \rangle, \tilde{s}_1 \rangle \tag{8-36}$$

Thus Eq. (8–36) gives the optimal (and only possible) one-stage return as a function of the input and output states.

As in the initial-value problem, knowing $f_n\langle \bar{s}_1, s_n \rangle$ allows one to determine the maximum $n + 1$ stage return $f_{n+1}\langle \bar{s}_1, s_{n+1} \rangle$ from the following relation:

$$f_{n+1}\langle \bar{s}_1, s_{n+1} \rangle = \max_{d_{n+1}} \{R_{n+1}\langle d_{n+1}, s_{n+1} \rangle + f_n\langle \bar{s}_1, T_{n+1}\langle d_{n+1}, s_{n+1} \rangle\rangle\};$$
$$n = 1, \ldots, N \qquad (8\text{-}37\text{: }n)$$

It is a one-decision, two-state optimization problem to find the two-state decision function $d^*_{n+1}\langle \bar{s}_1, s_{n+1} \rangle$ such that

$$R_{n+1}\langle d^*_{n+1}\langle \bar{s}_1, s_{n+1} \rangle, s_{n+1} \rangle + f_n\langle \bar{s}_1, T_{n+1}\langle d^*_{n+1}\langle \bar{s}_1, s_{n+1} \rangle, s_{n+1} \rangle\rangle$$
$$= f_{n+1}\langle \bar{s}_1, s_{n+1} \rangle; \qquad n = 1, \ldots, N - 1 \qquad (8\text{-}38\text{: }n)$$

From the way the final-value problem is formulated, the initial state (the "state" input to stage N) is free to take on its optimal value and is therefore a choice state, written c_N. Hence, the desired final-value maximum return function $R^*\langle \bar{s}_1 \rangle$ is obtained ultimately by a two-decision one-state optimization:

$$R^*\langle \bar{s}_1 \rangle = \max_{c_N, d_N} \{R_N\langle c_N, d_N \rangle + f_{N-1}\langle \bar{s}_1, T_N\langle d_N, c_N \rangle\rangle\} \qquad (8\text{-}39)$$

In all there is a decision inversion, only $N - 2$ one-decision, two-state optimizations, and a two-decision one-state optimization. If s_N were not a choice state, the problem would be a *two-point boundary-value problem* with the maximization in Eq. (8–39) being over d_N only. Boundary-value problems always require decision inversion; final-value problems can be solved by either state or decision inversion.

Notice that $\bar{s}_1$ appears as one of the states in every partial optimization. When a state such as $\bar{s}_1$ is repeated at successive stages and calculations are being done tabularly, its value should be fixed so that an ordinary one-state optimization by dynamic programming can be carried out. This completed, the maximum return and optimal policy for that value of $\bar{s}_1$ can be stored and the intermediate calculations discarded. The computations are then repeated for another value of $\bar{s}_1$, and so on. The advantage of multiple one-stage optimizations over a single two-state optimization is the former method's saving in storage. Moreover, if $\bar{s}_1$ itself is free to assume any value advantageous for maximizing the total return, then it can be treated as a choice state and directed by optimum-seeking methods.

8-13 Decision Inversion: Network Routing Problems

The difference between state inversion and decision inversion techniques is shown clearly in the final-value network problem of Figs. 8–11 and 8–12.

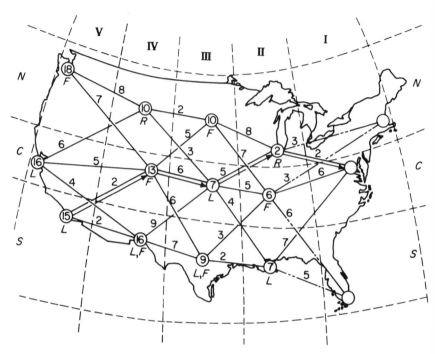

Figure 8-12. Solution of network routing problem by decision inversion.

It will be recalled that this problem, solved by state inversion in Fig. 8–11, has the given (fixed) final state $\bar{s}_1 \equiv C$. Using decision inversion, the solution procedure begins at stage 1 (the last stage). From Eq. (8–33) it can be seen that this is a decisionless stage, since, for given values of s_1 and $\bar{s}_1$, d_1 is uniquely determined. Thus, with $\bar{s}_1 \equiv C$, if $s_1 = N$, then $d_1 = R$; if $s_1 = C$, then $d_1 = F$; and if $s_1 = S$, then $d_1 = L$. The corresponding one-stage returns of Eq. (8–36) are 2, 6, and 7, respectively, as shown in Fig. 8–12. The solution now proceeds recursively to the left, just as though this were an initial-value problem; unlike the case in which state inversion is used, no more inversions are necessary. The process terminates at stage 4, having generated the optimal return, $f_4\langle s_4, C\rangle$, which is clearly seen to be maximized by the choice $s_4^* = S$, leading to an optimal return of 15, produced by the same policy (path) as that of Fig. 8–11. Notice from Fig. 8–1 that the initial-value problem, $s_4 = S$, achieves a better (smaller) cost of $f_4\langle s_4\rangle = 14$, with a resulting final value of $\bar{s}_1 = N$.

8-14 Decision Inversion: Continuous Variables

The analytic implications of the decision inversion method are best illustrated by problems in which d_i and s_i are continuous variables. To this end, consider the problem of maximizing $p = \sum\limits_{i=1}^{4} r_i$,

where
$$r_i = 0.5s_i - 0.2d_i;$$
$$\tilde{s}_i = 0.7s_i + 0.4d_i;$$
$$\tilde{s}_1 \equiv \tilde{c}_1;$$
$$0 \le d_i \le s_i, \quad i = 1, \ldots, 4.$$

This problem was solved previously using state inversion, with the result $f_4\langle \tilde{c}_1 \rangle = 5.28\tilde{c}_1$, generated by the optimal decisions $d_i^* = 0$, $i = 1, \ldots, 4$.

Using decision inversion, Eq. (8–33) becomes
$$d_1 = 2.5\tilde{s}_1 - 1.75s_1$$

and the optimal return at the decisionless stage 1 is, by Eq. (8–36),
$$f_1\langle \tilde{s}_1, s_1 \rangle = 0.85s_1 - 0.5\tilde{s}_1$$

where the restriction $0 \le d_1 \le s_1$ is translated into $0 \le 2.5\tilde{s}_1 - 1.75s_1 \le s_1$, or $0.909\tilde{c}_1 \le s_1 \le 1.43\tilde{c}_1$ by Eq. (8–33) and the requirement $\tilde{s}_1 \equiv \tilde{c}_1$.

Then for the last two stages,
$$f_2\langle s_2, \tilde{c}_1 \rangle = \max_{d_2} \{0.5s_2 - 0.2d_2 + 0.85(0.7s_2 + 0.4d_2) - 0.5\tilde{c}_1\}$$
$$= \max_{d_2} \{1.095s_2 + 0.14d_2 - 0.5\tilde{c}_1\}$$

where the decision variable is restricted by
$$0 \le d_2 \le s_2$$

and by
$$0.909\tilde{c}_1 \le 0.7s_2 + 0.4d_2 \le 1.43\tilde{c}_1$$

(from the stage 1 constraint, $0.909\tilde{c}_1 \le s_1 \le 1.43\tilde{c}_1$). This latter restriction is thus
$$2.27\tilde{c}_1 - 1.75s_2 \le d_2 \le 3.57\tilde{c}_1 - 1.75s_2$$

and the total restraints on d_2 are shown graphically in Fig. 8–13. Since the coefficient of d_2 in the expression for $f_2\langle s_2, \tilde{c}_1 \rangle$ is positive, the optimal decision at this stage is to make d_2 as large as possible, consistent with the constraints. The resulting value of d_2^* is given by the solid lines in Fig. 8–13, which place a limitation on the input, s_2; namely, $0.826\tilde{c}_1 \le s_2 \le 2.045\tilde{c}_1$. For $s_2 = 0.826\tilde{c}_1$, only one choice of decisions, $d_1^* = s_1$, $d_2^* = s_2$, will yield the required output, $\tilde{s}_1 = \tilde{c}_1$. Similarly, the input $s_2 = 2.045\tilde{c}_1$ requires the decisions, $d_1^* = 0$, $d_2^* = 0$ to produce the output, $\tilde{c}_1$. Between these two values of s_2, a true optimization problem exists, having the solution:
$$f_2\langle s_2, \tilde{c}_1 \rangle = \begin{cases} 0.850s_2, & 1.297\tilde{c}_1 \le s_2 \le 2.045\tilde{c}_1 \quad (d_2^* = 3.57\tilde{c}_1 - 1.75s_2) \\ 1.235s_2 - 0.5\tilde{c}_1, & 0.826\tilde{c}_1 \le s_2 \le 1.297\tilde{c}_1 \quad (d_2^* = s_2) \end{cases}$$

achieved by substituting the optimal values of d_2 into the expression $1.095s_2 + 0.14d_2 - 0.5\tilde{c}_1$.

Notice that, superficially, $d_2^* \ne 0$, apparently contradicting the result obtained by state inversion. This seeming paradox occurs because we are solving here a more general problem; with state inversion, the initial state of

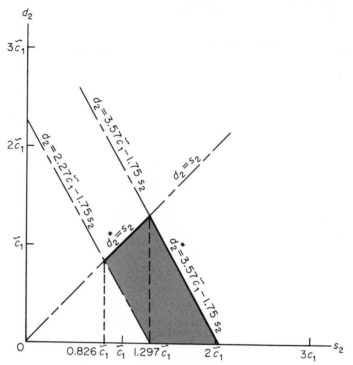

Figure 8-13. Optimal stage 2 decisions for linear problem solved by decision inversion.

the system is free to be directed to its optimal value; with decision inversion, we are effectively solving a problem with two fixed ends. This distinction will be made more precise after stages 3 and 4 are analyzed.

Continuing with the preceding type of analysis, one finds for the last three stages,

$$f_3\langle s_3, \tilde{c}_1\rangle = \max_{d_3}\{1.095s_3 + 0.14d_3\}, \quad \text{when} \quad 1.297\tilde{c}_1 \leq s_2 \leq 2.045\tilde{c}_1$$

and

$$f_3\langle s_3, \tilde{c}_1\rangle = \max_{d_3}\{1.365s_3 + 0.294d_3 - 0.5\tilde{c}_1\}, \quad \text{when} \quad 0.826\tilde{c}_1 \leq s_2 \leq 1.297\tilde{c}_1$$

where d_3 is restrained by the relations

$$0 \leq d_3 \leq s_3$$

and for $1.297\tilde{c}_1 \leq s_2 \leq 2.045\tilde{c}_1$,

$$3.243\tilde{c}_1 - 1.75s_3 \leq d_3 \leq 5.11\tilde{c}_1 - 1.75s_3$$

and for $0.826\tilde{c}_1 \leq s_2 \leq 1.297\tilde{c}_1$,

$$2.065\tilde{c}_1 - 1.75s_3 \leq d_3 \leq 3.243\tilde{c}_1 - 1.75s_3$$

as shown in Fig. 8–14. The optimal three-stage returns are then

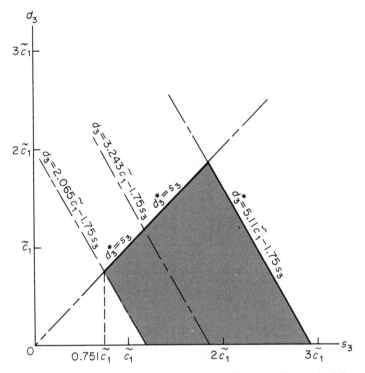

Figure 8-14. Optimal stage 3 decisions for linear problem solved by decision inversion.

$$f_3\langle s_3, \tilde{c}_1 \rangle = \begin{cases} 0.85s_3 + 0.715\tilde{c}_1, & 1.86\tilde{c}_1 \leq s_3 \leq 2.92\tilde{c}_1 & (d_3^* = 5.11\tilde{c}_1 - 1.75s_3) \\ 1.235s_3, & 1.18\tilde{c}_1 \leq s_3 \leq 1.86\tilde{c}_1 & (d_3^* = s_3) \\ 1.66s_3 - 0.5\tilde{c}_1, & 0.751\tilde{c}_1 \leq s_3 \leq 1.18\tilde{c}_1 & (d_3^* = s_3) \end{cases}$$

Continuing with this analysis, we arrive at the optimal four-stage returns:

$$f_4\langle s_4, \tilde{c}_1 \rangle = \begin{cases} 0.85s_4 + 1.736\tilde{c}_1, & 2.66\tilde{c}_1 \leq s_4 \leq 4.17\tilde{c}_1 & (d_4^* = 7.3\tilde{c}_1 - 1.75s_4) \\ 1.235s_4 + 0.715\tilde{c}_1, & 1.69\tilde{c}_1 \leq s_4 \leq 2.66\tilde{c}_1 & (d_4^* = s_4) \\ 1.659s_4, & 1.075\tilde{c}_1 \leq s_4 \leq 1.69\tilde{c}_1 & (d_4^* = s_4) \\ 2.126s_4 - 0.5\tilde{c}_1, & 0.685\tilde{c}_1 \leq s_4 \leq 1.075\tilde{c}_1 & (d_4^* = s_4) \end{cases}$$

where the limits on s_4 are obtained from the constraints on d_4, as shown in Fig. 8–15.

Notice how this solution differs from that obtained by state inversion. This points up the essential difference between the two inversion methods. In the case of state inversion, one finds, for fixed $\tilde{c}_1$, the optimal set $\{d_i^*\}$ which maximizes the total return as a function only of $\tilde{c}_1$; that is, one finds $f_N\langle \tilde{c}_1 \rangle$. Then this method *determines* s_N, which is treated as a free end in working the problem. In the case of decision inversion, the problem is

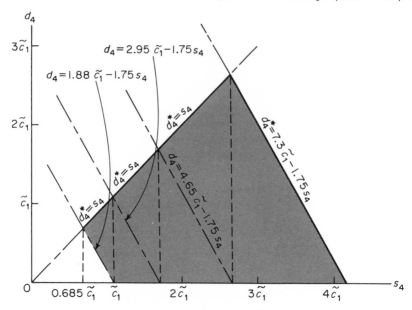

Figure 8-15. Optimal stage 4 decisions for linear problem solved by decision inversion.

worked with limits on each stage input s_i down the line, finally resulting in an optimal total return $f_N\langle s_N, \tilde{c}_1 \rangle$, a function of both input and output. This is necessary in solving problems containing loops or recycles since, then, the output is required to be a specified function of the input. Clearly, state inversion cannot be used to solve such problems, since s_N cannot be treated as a free end.

In order to solve the final-value problem using decision inversion, one computes $\max_{s_N} f_N\langle s_N, \tilde{c}_1 \rangle$, which is identical with the value $f_N\langle \tilde{c}_1 \rangle$, obtained by state inversion. In the present problem, it is easily seen that $\max_{s_4} f_4\langle s_4, \tilde{c}_1 \rangle$ $= 5.28\tilde{c}_1$, achieved by selecting $s_4^* = 4.17\tilde{c}_1$. Then tracing back through the stages from left to right, one finds (for $s_4 = 4.17\tilde{c}_1$) $d_i^* = 0, i = 1, \ldots, 4$, producing the stage inputs $s_3 = 2.92\tilde{c}_1, s_2 = 2.045\tilde{c}_1, s_1 = 1.43\tilde{c}_1$, and the individual stage returns of $r_4 = 2.09\tilde{c}_1, r_3 = 1.46\tilde{c}_1, r_2 = 1.02\tilde{c}_1$, and $r_1 = 0.71\tilde{c}_1$, for a total return of $f_4\langle \tilde{c}_1 \rangle = 5.28\tilde{c}_1$. This verifies the solution obtained for this problem using state inversion.

8-15 Decision Inversion: Nonlinear
Return Functions

As a final example of decision inversion, consider the nonlinear three-stage problem:

$$\text{maximize} \quad p = \sum_{i=1}^{3} r_i$$

where $r_i = 5d_i - id_i^2$, $\tilde{s}_i = s_i - 0.4d_i$, $0 \leq d_i \leq s_i$, and the final output state is fixed: $\tilde{s}_1 \equiv \tilde{c}_1$. This problem was solved earlier as an initial-value problem and it will be interesting to compare this solution with that obtained by treating it as a final-value problem.

At the last stage, the decision inversion gives $d_1 = 2.5s_1 - 2.5\tilde{c}_1$, so that, for given input and output, this becomes a decisionless stage and can be combined with stage 2. Then the total return from the last two stages is

$$S_2 = 12.5s_2 - 6.25s_2^2 + 5s_2d_2 - 5\tilde{c}_1d_2 - 3d_2^2 + 12.5\tilde{c}_1s_2 - 12.5\tilde{c}_1 - 6.25\tilde{c}_1^2$$

and setting $\partial S_2/\partial d_2 = 0$, $d_2^* = 0.83s_2 - 0.83\tilde{c}_1$, within the range of s_2 where this is a feasible solution. Since $0 \leq d_1 \leq s_1$, one has, through the inversion relation, $\tilde{c}_1 \leq s_1 \leq 1.67\tilde{c}_1$, and from $s_2 - 0.4d_2 = s_1$,

$$2.5s_2 - 4.18\tilde{c}_1 \leq d_2 \leq 2.5s_2 - 2.5\tilde{c}_1$$

in addition to the requirement: $0 \leq d_2 \leq s_2$. The situation is shown graphically in Fig. 8-16, which accounts for the two-valued nature of $f_2\langle s_2 \rangle$:

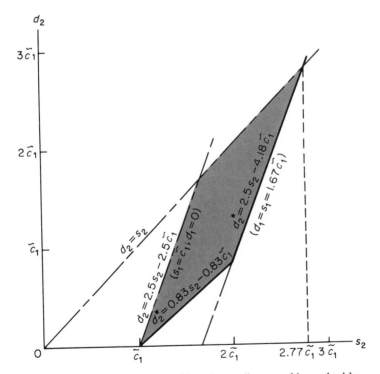

Figure 8-16. Optimal stage 2 decisions for nonlinear problem solved by decision inversion.

$f_2\langle s_2, \tilde{c}_1 \rangle =$

$$
\begin{cases}
12.5s_2 - 12.5s_2^2 + 41.8s_2\tilde{c}_1 - 37.77\tilde{c}_1^2 - 12.5\tilde{c}_1 \begin{cases} 2\tilde{c}_1 \leq s_2 \leq 2.77\tilde{c}_1 \\ (d_2^* = 2.5s_2 - 4.18\tilde{c}_1) \end{cases} \\[2ex]
12.5s_2 - 4.16s_2^2 + 8.33s_2\tilde{c}_1 - 4.17\tilde{c}_1^2 - 12.5\tilde{c}_1 \begin{cases} \tilde{c}_1 \leq s_2 \leq 2\tilde{c}_1 \\ (d_2^* = 0.83s_2 - 0.83\tilde{c}_1) \end{cases}
\end{cases}
$$

Continuing this analysis into the third stage, the solution to the problem is found to be

$$
f_3\langle s_3, \tilde{c}_1 \rangle =
\begin{cases}
12.5s_3 - 18.75s_3^2 + 103.875s_3\tilde{c}_1 - 161.76\tilde{c}_1^2 - 12.5\tilde{c}_1 \\
\qquad \begin{cases} 3.5\tilde{c}_1 \leq s_3 \leq 4.62\tilde{c}_1 \\ d_3^* = 2.5s_3 - 6.925\tilde{c}_1 \end{cases} \\[2ex]
12.5s_3 - 7.50s_3^2 + 25.04s_3\tilde{c}_1 - 23.76\tilde{c}_1^2 - 12.5\tilde{c}_1 \\
\qquad \begin{cases} 2.22\tilde{c}_1 \leq s_3 \leq 3.5\tilde{c}_1 \\ d_3^* = s_3 - 1.67\tilde{c}_1 \end{cases} \\[2ex]
12.5s_3 - 3.40s_3^2 + 6.82s_3\tilde{c}_1 - 3.41\tilde{c}_1^2 - 12.5\tilde{c}_1 \\
\qquad \begin{cases} \tilde{c}_1 \leq s_3 \leq 2.22\tilde{c}_1 \\ d_3^* = 0.455s_3 - 0.455\tilde{c}_1 \end{cases}
\end{cases}
$$

where the decision variable, d_3, is shown pictorially in Fig. 8–17. Again it can be seen that $f_3\langle s_3, \tilde{c}_1 \rangle$ is sectionally continuous.

From the solution to the initial-value problem, notice that an input of $s_3 = 3.33$ floods the system in the sense that each stage, i, achieves its individual optimum of $6.25/i$, with $d_i^* = 2.5/i$. The final output is then 1.50, and any further input is unused, serving only to increase the output. Therefore, the optimal solution to this problem when the input is $s_3 = 3.33 + K$, for K a nonnegative number, produces an output of $\tilde{s}_1 = 1.50 + K$ and a return of $f_3\langle 3.33 + K \rangle = 11.46$. Thus, from the final-value problem, we would like to have

$$
\frac{s_3}{\tilde{c}_1} = \frac{3.33 + K}{1.50 + K},
$$

which, for $K \geq 0$, lies in the range

$$
1 \leq \frac{3.33 + K}{1.50 + K} \leq 2.22,
$$

or $\tilde{c}_1 \leq s_3 \leq 2.22\tilde{c}_1$. For this range, we find

$$
f_3\langle s_3, \tilde{c}_1 \rangle = 12.5s_3 - 3.40s_3^2 + 6.82s_3\tilde{c}_1 - 3.41\tilde{c}_1^2 - 12.5\tilde{c}_1
$$

Now, $\qquad \dfrac{\partial}{\partial s_3} f_3\langle s_3, \tilde{c}_1 \rangle = 0$ implies $s_3^* = \tilde{c}_1 + 1.83$ $\left.\vphantom{\begin{matrix}1\\1\end{matrix}}\right\}$

$\qquad\qquad \dfrac{\partial}{\partial \tilde{c}_1} f_3\langle s_3, \tilde{c}_1 \rangle = 0$ implies $\tilde{c}_1^* = s_3 - 1.83$ $\qquad s_3 = \tilde{c}_1 + 1.83$

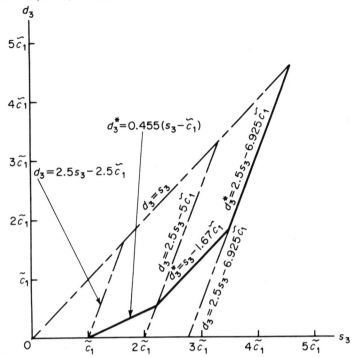

Figure 8-17. Optimal stage 3 decisions for nonlinear problem solved by decision inversion.

Then setting $s_3 = 3.33 + K$ results in

$$\tilde{c}_1 = 1.50 + K \quad \text{and} \quad f_3\langle 3.33 + K, 1.50 + K\rangle = 11.46.$$

8-16 Cyclic Optimization

Consider now an N-stage system similar to a serial one except that the "initial" state s_N and the "final" state $\tilde{s}_1$ are identical:

$$\tilde{s}_1 \equiv s_N \tag{8-40}$$

Such a system is said to be *cyclic* because its functional diagram, shown in Fig. 8-18, is a closed loop. Cycles arise in numerous industrial "recycle" or "feedback" technologies. Since removal of the *loop identity* converts a cyclic system into a serial one, the variable $\tilde{s}_1$ will be called a *cut state* and written $\tilde{c}_1$. The use of this symbol already given to choice states is intentional, for it will be shown that any cut state is also a choice state (although not vice versa). The functional diagram shows that there are only N degrees of freedom in a cyclic system, one less than for a serial one, the loop identity having eliminated the "input" variable s_N.

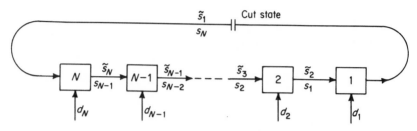

Figure 8-18. A cyclic system.

The *cyclic return function* Φ, depending on the cut state $\tilde{c}_1$ and the $N-1$ decisions $d_2, \ldots, d_N$ can be obtained from Eq. (8–34:n) by using Eq. (8–40) to eliminate s_N and writing $\tilde{c}_1$ for $\tilde{s}_1$.

$$\Phi\langle\tilde{c}_1, d_2, \ldots, d_N\rangle = S_N\langle\tilde{c}_1, d_2, \ldots, d_N\rangle \tag{8-41}$$

The maximum cyclic return Φ^* is defined by

$$\Phi^* \equiv \max_{\tilde{c}_1, d_2, \ldots, d_N} \{\Phi\langle\tilde{c}_1, d_2, \ldots, d_N\rangle\} \tag{8-42}$$

The *cyclic optimization problem* is to find an *optimal cyclic policy*, that is, a value $\tilde{c}_1^*$ of the cut state and a set of optimal decisions $d_2^*, \ldots, d_N^*$ such that

$$\Phi\langle\tilde{c}_1^*, d_2^*, \ldots, d_N^*\rangle = \Phi^* \tag{8-43}$$

This is an N-decision, no-state optimization problem.

To solve it, first select a particular value of $\tilde{c}_1$ and find the $N-1$ stage maximum return function $f_{N-1}\langle\tilde{c}_1, s_{N-1}\rangle$ by a decision inversion and $N-2$ one-decision, one-state optimizations as described in the preceding section. Then find $\Phi^*\langle\tilde{c}_1\rangle$ by the one-decision, no-state optimization:

$$\Phi^*\langle\tilde{c}_1\rangle = \max_{d_N} \{R_N\langle\tilde{c}_1, d_N\rangle + f_{N-1}\langle\tilde{c}_1, T_N\langle d_N, \tilde{c}_1\rangle\rangle\} \tag{8-44}$$

This return, together with the corresponding policy $d_2^*\langle\tilde{c}_1\rangle, \ldots, d_N^*\langle\tilde{c}_1\rangle$, is stored and the procedure repeated for a different choice of $\tilde{c}_1$, perhaps selected by a direct search technique. In this way a sequence of $N-1$ decision serial problems is solved until one finds the optimal cut state $\tilde{c}_1^*$.

$$\Phi^* = \max_{\tilde{c}_1} \{\Phi^*\langle\tilde{c}_1\rangle\} = \Phi\langle\tilde{c}_1^*\rangle \tag{8-45}$$

Since there are two fewer one-decision optimizations than there are stages, the decomposition just described is not worth performing when the loop has less than three stages. In a two-stage loop, for example, there are only two degrees of freedom anyway, so one might as well perform a two-decision, no-state optimization directly without bothering to make a preliminary decision inversion. Similar considerations hold for a single-stage cycle, sometimes called a *self-loop*. The important thing in optimizing a self-loop correctly is to express the return in terms of a single variable, using both the loop identity (8–40) and the sole transition function (8–2:1) to eliminate two out of the three original variables $\tilde{s}_1$, s_1, and d_1. Related problems involving different kinds of loop structures are discussed in the section following. Nemhauser also gives a full discussion of loop optimization, illustrated with good examples.

8-17 Cyclic Networks

Again consider the network problem of Fig. 8–1, where now we impose the additional constraint, $s_4 = \tilde{s}_1$. One may think of this network as a complete map of the earth, as shown in Fig. 8–19, which has the network of Fig. 8–1 folded back on itself so that New York now takes the place of both Seattle and Boston, Caracas that of San Francisco and Washington, and Santiago that of San Diego and Miami. The problem is to find the optimal (initial and final) state (New York, Caracas, or Santiago) and the optimal around-the-world path, taking into account the costs of the feasible paths.

One is tempted to solve loop problems as follows: first find the optimal solution to the unconstrained problem, and then impose the loop constraint. That is, find $f_N \langle s_N \rangle$, and then select as the optimal loop the path for which $s_N = \tilde{s}_1$ (or whatever equation, $s_N = g\langle \tilde{s}_1 \rangle$, forms the loop constraint). The present problem shows clearly the error in this approach. From the solutions to the initial-value problem given in Fig. 8–1, we have $f_4 \langle N \rangle = 18$, $\tilde{s}_1 = C$; $f_4 \langle C \rangle = 16$, $\tilde{s}_1 = C$; and $f_4 \langle S \rangle = 14$, $\tilde{s}_1 = N$. Now, imposing the loop constraint, we have $\Phi^* = 16$, $s_4 = C$, $\tilde{s}_1 = C$ (that is, begin and end in Caracas, following the path through London, Cairo, and Okhotsk). This is not the correct solution, however, since the constraint must be made a part of the problem from the outset.

To solve this problem correctly, one begins with a decision inversion at stage 1, for a given value of the output state, and proceeds as in a final-value problem, terminating with the return $f_N \langle s_N, \tilde{c}_1 \rangle$. Thus one has solved a problem with two fixed ends, and may now set $s_N = \tilde{c}_1$. Solving the problem either as an initial-value problem, or as a final-value problem using *state* inversion, implicitly assumes a *free* end, which does not exist when a loop is present. In Fig. 8–19, the solution is given for $\tilde{s}_1 \equiv S$, so that $f_4 \langle N, S \rangle = 20$, $f_4 \langle C, S \rangle = 18$, and $f_4 \langle S, S \rangle = 15$. By repeating this procedure for the output states $\tilde{s}_1 \equiv N$ and $\tilde{s}_1 \equiv C$, one finds $f_4 \langle N, N \rangle = 19$, and $f_4 \langle C, C \rangle = 16$. Therefore, the optimal solution to this simple loop problem is $\Phi^* = 15$, with $s_4 = \tilde{s}_1 = S$ as shown by the arrows in the figure. That is, the optimal loop path follows the route Santiago-Dakar-Madagascar-Melbourne-Santiago.

The fallacious reasoning (first optimize, *then* impose the constraints) discussed in connection with this simple loop problem has been advanced as a method of solution for optimization problems of many kinds. Usually, the

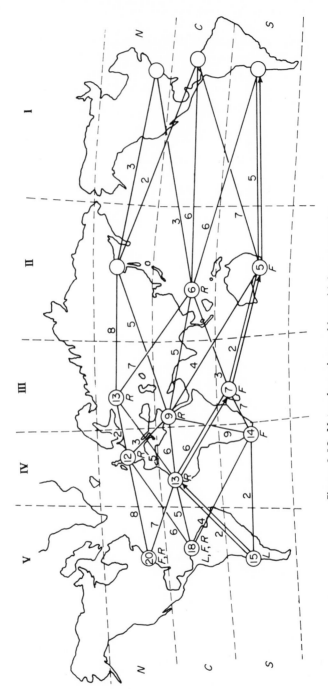

Figure 8-19. Network routing problem with loop constraint.

erroneous logic of this approach is not so apparent; consider, for example, the problem of finding nonnegative x_1, x_2, which *minimize* the function

$$y = 2x_1^2 - 4x_1x_2 + 4x_2^2 + x_1 - 3x_2$$

subject to the constraint

$$10x_1 + 5x_2 = 3$$

The geometric structure of this problem is shown in Fig. 8–20, in which several contours of the three-dimensional objective function have been drawn. In order to exhibit the fallacy of not taking the constraint into account at all times, let us solve the problem by first "optimizing out" x_1, obtaining the line $\partial y/\partial x_1 = 0$, and then imposing the constraint. Thus,

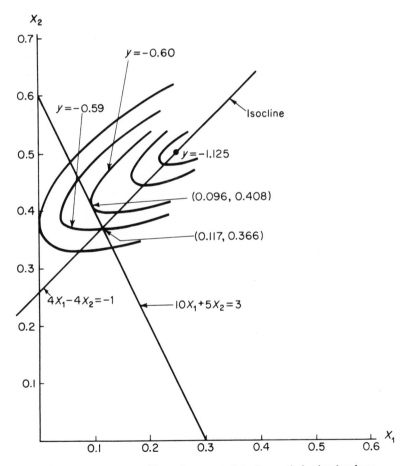

Figure 8-20. Fallacy of imposing constraint after optimization has been completed.

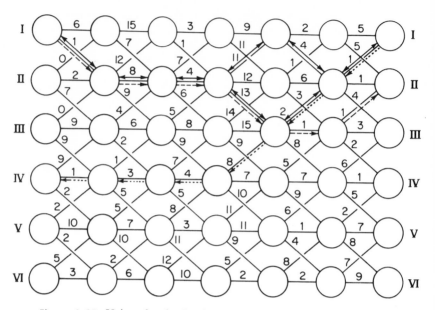

Figure 8-21. Union of optimal serial policies coinciding with optimal loop policy.

$$\frac{\partial y}{\partial x_1} = 4x_1 - 4x_2 + 1 = 0$$

which, when solved simultaneously with the line $10x_1 + 5x_2 = 3$, produces the point $(0.117, 0.366)$, as shown in Fig. 8–20. Substituting this value back into the objective function yields the false "optimal" value $\hat{y} = -0.589$.

From the figure, however, it can be seen that the true optimal solution to this problem lies at the point of tangency of the constraint line with the $y = -0.60$ contour, which is the point $(0.096, 0.408)$, so that the true optimal value is $y^* = -0.60$. The point is that one cannot superimpose the constraint conditions onto a solution obtained by an optimization which ignores the constraints, and obtain by this method the true constrained optimum.

An interesting relationship between initial-value, final-value, and loop problems seems apparent in Fig. 8–21. Here, the optimal path for the initial-value problem, $s_6 = $ I, is shown by the dashed arrows; the optimal path for the final-value problem, $\tilde{s}_1 = $ I, is shown by the dotted-line arrows. Since these paths cross (that is, they produce the same state, $s_3 = $ III, at stage 3), and the optimal loop path, I ⟷ I, given by the double-headed (solid line) arrows is formed from their union, one might be led to think that optimal loop paths could always be so constructed.

Figure 8–22 illustrates how complete is the difference in character between recycle problems (both ends fixed) and the serial problems, both initial

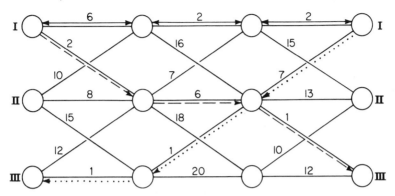

Figure 8-22. Counterexample: Union of optimal serial policies is not the optimal loop policy.

value and final value (one end free). Here the optimal path for the initial-value problem, $s_3 = \text{I}$, is shown by the dashed arrows, whereas the optimal solution to the final-value problem $\tilde{s}_1 = \text{I}$ is the path shown by the dotted arrows. These two paths intersect with $s_1 = \text{II}$, yet neither of them form any part of the optimal loop path, which is shown by the double-headed arrows. The fallacy in attempting to form an optimal solution to a loop problem from optimal initial- and final-value problem solutions is that the optimal decision for the loop problem may never generate, at any given stage, the same input state as that generated by the serial problems.

8-18 Cyclic Allocation

Here we consider the important class of problems in which the stage returns and transitions are *linear* in the continuous variables s_i and d_i. Specifically, suppose that we wish to maximize $\sum\limits_{i=1}^{P} r_i$, where $r_i = A_i s_i + B_i d_i$, $\tilde{s}_i = a_i s_i + b_i d_i$, and the stage decisions are constrained by $0 \leq d_i \leq s_i$. Here, A_i, B_i, a_i, and b_i are given constants, so that for a serial system,

$$f_1\langle s_1 \rangle = \max_{0 \leq d_1 \leq s_1} \{A_1 s_1 + B_1 d_1\} = k_1 s_1$$

where k_1 is a constant. Then by induction, we see that

$$f_n\langle s_n \rangle = \max_{0 \leq d_n \leq s_n} \{A_n s_n + B_n d_n + k_{n-1}(a_n s_n + b_n d_n)\} = k_n s_n, \quad n = 2, \ldots, P$$

$$(8\text{-}46)$$

where k_n is a constant. Thus, the optimal value of d_n is either s_n or zero, depending upon whether the term $B_n + k_{n-1} b_n$, the coefficient of d_n, is respectively positive or negative. Notice that this coefficient does *not* depend upon the input s_n.

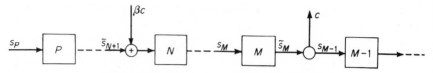

Figure 8-23. Quasi-loop imposed on serial system.

Now suppose that a *quasi-loop* is imposed on this serial system by adding a constant, βC, to the input to stage N, and subtracting a constant, C, from the output of stage M, as shown in Fig. 8-23. In the context of an allocation problem, one may think of βC as investment capital borrowed at time period N, and C as the sum repaid at time period M, including interest. [Thus, $\beta < 1$, and the effective annual interest rate is $(1 - \beta)/\beta(N - M)$.]

The effect of this quasi-loop on the serial structure is best seen by introducing the constants βC and C sequentially. Denote by single primes the optimal returns which result when βC is added to the system at stage N (and C is *not* subtracted from the output of stage M). Then by Eq. (8-46) and Fig. 8-23 it is clear that

$$f'_N = k_N(\tilde{s}_{N+1} + \beta C) \quad \text{and} \quad f'_{M-1} = k_{M-1}\left(\tilde{s}_M \frac{1 + \beta C}{\tilde{s}_{N+1}}\right)$$

Denote by double primes the stage inputs and optimal returns which result when C is subtracted from the output of stage M (and βC is *still* added to the input to stage N). Then owing to the linearity of the system, we find

$$s''_{M-1} = \tilde{s}_M \frac{1 + \beta C}{\tilde{s}_{N+1}}$$

from which it follows that the optimal return from all P stages of this quasi-loop system is

$$f''_P = f_P + f'_N - f_N + f''_{M-1} - f'_{M-1} = f_P + C(\beta k_N - k_{M-1})$$

where f_P is the optimal P-stage return for the original serial system. Accordingly, β must be at least k_{M-1}/k_N to make the investment loan profitable.

Furthermore, since the coefficient of the decision variable at each stage is not a function of the input to that stage, the *qualitative* policies for the two problems are the same (Beightler, Johnson, and Wilde):

$$\frac{d''_n}{s''_n} = \begin{cases} \dfrac{d_n}{s_n}, & \text{if } s_n \neq 0 \\[2mm] 0, & \text{if } s_n = 0 \end{cases} \tag{8-47}$$

This quasi-loop is the most degenerate case of a loop constraint, since the fixed amounts added to, and subtracted from, the two stages are *not* affected by the system *decisions*. We shall now consider real loop problems in which the quantities cycled are dependent upon the decisions employed at each stage, and in general the optimal loop policy will differ from the policy which is optimal when the loop constraint is removed.

As an example of a real loop constraint applied to a problem in continuous variables, consider the following: maximize $\sum_{i=1}^{4} r_i$, where $r_i = 0.5s_i - 0.2d_i$, $\bar{s}_i = 0.7s_i + 0.4d_i$, $\bar{s}_1 \equiv \bar{c}_1$, and $0 \leq d_i \leq s_i$, for $i = 1, \ldots, 4$. This problem was solved earlier by decision inversion, with the resulting expression for $f_4\langle s_4, \bar{c}_1 \rangle$ given in four ranges of values for s_4. If we now append the homogeneous loop constraint

$$\bar{c}_1 = \tfrac{1}{2}s_4$$

the corresponding serial solution is $f_4\langle s_4, \bar{c}_1 \rangle = 1.235s_4 + 0.715\bar{c}_1$, since this value applies in the range $1.69\bar{c}_1 \leq s_4 \leq 2.66\bar{c}_1$. Substituting the loop constraint into this solution results in $f_4\langle \bar{c}_1 \rangle = 3.185\bar{c}_1$. Beginning with the given value of $d_4^* = s_4 \equiv 2\bar{c}_1$, we find $s_3^* = 0.7(2\bar{c}_1) + 0.4(2\bar{c}_1) = 2.2\bar{c}_1$, so that from the optimal three-stage returns, we compute

$$d_3^* = 5.11\bar{c}_1 - 1.75(2.2\bar{c}_1) = 1.26\bar{c}_1$$

Using this value, it follows that

$$s_2^* = 0.7(2.2\bar{c}_1) + 0.4(1.26\bar{c}_1) = 2.044\bar{c}_1$$

and from the value of $f_2\langle s_2, \bar{c}_1 \rangle$, we have

$$d_2^* = 3.57\bar{c}_1 - 1.75(2.044\bar{c}_1) = 0$$

just as was the case in the serial problem. Then, $s_1^* = 0.7(2.044\bar{c}_1) = 1.43\bar{c}_1$, and by the decision inversion equation, $d_1^* = 2.5\bar{c}_1 - 1.75(1.43\bar{c}_1) = 0$. Using these values of the s_i^* and d_i^*, we may verify the value of $f_4\langle \bar{c}_1 \rangle$ found earlier:

$$\sum_{i=1}^{4} r_i = 0.5(1.43\bar{c}_1) + 0.5(2.044\bar{c}_1) + 0.5(2.2\bar{c}_1) - 0.2(1.26\bar{c}_1)$$

$$+ 0.5(2\bar{c}_1) - 0.2(2\bar{c}_1) = 3.185\bar{c}_1$$

In order to illustrate once again the fallacy of not taking a constraint into account at all times in an optimization problem, consider the previous example solved as an initial-value serial problem. The solution to this serial problem was obtained earlier: $d_4^* = s_4$, $d_3^* = 1.1s_4$, $0 \leq d_2^* \leq 1.21s_4$, and $d_1^* = 0$, producing an optimal four-stage return of $f_4\langle s_4 \rangle = 1.6585s_4$. To be specific, let us take $d_2^* = 0$. With this solution, we find $\bar{s}_1 = 0.5929s_4$. If the loop constraint, $s_4 = \bar{c}_1^2 - 0.313\bar{c}_1$, is now imposed on the preceding solution, then (with $\bar{s}_1 \equiv \bar{c}_1$), there results: $\bar{c}_1^* = 2$, $s_4^* = 3.374$, for a total return of $f_4\langle s_4^* \rangle = 1.6585 (3.374) = 5.596$.

The correct procedure for solving this problem, however, is to perform a decision inversion at stage 1, thus obtaining the solution in terms of both s_4 and $\bar{c}_1$. These calculations were carried out earlier, and combining those results with the loop constraint, we find the true optimal return for this loop problem to be $f_4\langle s_4^*, \bar{c}_1^* \rangle = 23.67$, where $\bar{c}_1^* = 4.483$, $s_4^* = 18.694$, and the optimal policy is $d_i^* = 0$, $i = 1, \ldots, 4$.

As a final example of a loop problem, we shall solve a problem in which the stage returns are nonlinear. We wish to maximize $\sum_{i=1}^{3} r_i$, where $r_i = 5d_i - id_i^2$, $\bar{s}_i = s_i - 0.4d_i$, $0 \leq d_i \leq s_i$, for $i = 1, 2, 3$, and $\bar{s}_1 \equiv \bar{c}_1$. This serial problem was solved in a previous example, using decision inversion, so that solution was obtained in the form $f_3\langle s_3, \bar{c}_1 \rangle$. We shall employ the preceding solution in solving the loop problem which results when the constraint $s_3 = 2\bar{c}_1$ is adjoined to this serial system.

Now consider the following context for this problem: let the input and output states be the capital (in, say, millions of dollars) available for investment in an enterprise which yields a return (in the amount of commodity K produced) of r_i during year i, when d_i millions of dollars are invested in the enterprise that year. An allocation of d_i also produces $s_i - 0.4d_i$ of new capital during the year, which results from the sale of by-products. It is desired to maximize the total production of this commodity over the next three years if one-half of the total capital invested now (s_3) must be available for repayment of part of the cost of obtaining the initial capital. Note that if the loop constraint were an inequality, say, $2\bar{c}_1 \geq s_3$, it could be converted into an equality by investing the extra money at stage 1 (that is, liquidate the excess capital at that stage). The form of the solution would not change, however, and we lose no generality in using an equality constraint in this example.

For this loop, the two-point boundary serial solution which is applicable is $f_3\langle s_3, \bar{c}_1 \rangle = 12.5s_3 - 3.4s_3^2 + 6.8s_3\bar{c}_1 - 3.4\bar{c}_1^2 - 12.5\bar{c}_1$, since it corresponds to the range $\bar{c}_1 \leq s_3 \leq 2.22\bar{c}_1$. Substituting the loop constraint into this solution results in $f_3\langle \bar{c}_1 \rangle = 12.5\bar{c}_1 - 3.4\bar{c}_1^2$, which is maximized by choosing $\bar{c}_1^* = 1.83$, so that the optimal initial capital to invest becomes $s_3^* = 3.66$, and the total return is $f_3\langle 1.83 \rangle = 11.5$. Tracing back through the system using the results found for the two-point boundary serial problem, we find $d_3^* = 0.833$, $d_2^* = 1.24$, and $d_1^* = 2.5$.

8-19 Diverging Branches

The methods described earlier for solving initial-value serial problems can be adapted to the optimization of systems with a diverging branch as in Fig. 8–24. In such systems one of the stages (say, k) of a subsystem has, in addition to its ordinary output state $\bar{s}_{k1}$, another output $\bar{s}_{k2}$ which is the initial state for a different sequence of M serial stages labeled $1'$ through M' and forming a *diverging branch*. The branch transition functions are

$$\bar{s}_i' = T_i'\langle d_i', s_i' \rangle; \qquad i = 1, \ldots, M \tag{8-48: i}$$

and the incidence identities are

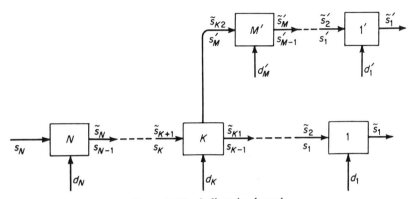

Figure 8-24. A diverging branch.

$$\tilde{s}'_{i+1} \equiv s'_i; \qquad i = 1, \ldots, M-1 \qquad (8\text{-}49\text{:}\,i)$$

Connection of the branch to the main system at stage k is represented by the additional transition function

$$\tilde{s}_{k2} = T_{k2}\langle d_k, s_k\rangle \qquad (8\text{-}50)$$

and incidence identity

$$s'_M \equiv \tilde{s}_{k2} \qquad (8\text{-}51)$$

As usual there are M return functions

$$r'_i = R'_i\langle d'_i, s'_i\rangle; \qquad i = 1', \ldots, M' \qquad (8\text{-}52\text{:}\,i)$$

and it is desired to optimize the sum of the returns from all $M + N$ stages.

Let $f'_M\langle s'_M\rangle$ be the *diverging branch maximum return function* defined by

$$f'_M\langle s'_M\rangle \equiv \max_{d'_1, \ldots, d'_M}\left\{\sum_{i=1}^{M} r'_i\right\} \qquad (8\text{-}53)$$

Finding this function is an initial-value problem solvable by the methods used for optimizing serial systems. By the connection Eq. (8–50) and identity (8–51) this branch return can be combined with the stage k return to give a new return function depending only on d_k and state s_k.

$$R'_k\langle d_k, s_k\rangle \equiv f'_M\langle T_{k2}\langle d_k, s_k\rangle\rangle + R_k\langle d_k, s_k\rangle \qquad (8\text{-}54)$$

This new function can be used in place of $R_k\langle d_k, s_k\rangle$ in the regular optimization plan for the main system, even when it is not serial, since nonserial systems can be optimized by serial methods, as shown in a preceding section. The replacement of $R_k\langle d_k, s_k\rangle$ by $R'_k\langle d_k, s_k\rangle$ is called *absorption of a diverging branch*.

In Section 8–20 it will be important to know how to handle a final-value version of the diverging branch problem. This would involve first finding the *two-state M-stage maximum return function* $f'_M\langle\tilde{s}'_1, s'_M\rangle$ of Eq. (8–35:M') by using Eq. (8–36) and iterating recursion relation (8–37:n') $M - 1$ times.

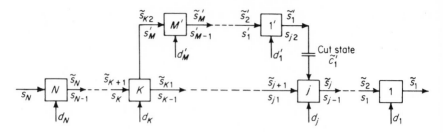

Figure 8-25. A feedforward loop.

This would take a decision inversion and $M - 1$ one-decision, two-state optimizations. Absorption of the branch requires that the three-variable function $R'_k\langle d_k, \tilde{s}'_1, s_k\rangle$ be substituted for $R_k\langle d_k, s_k\rangle$ in the main stem optimization scheme.

$$R'_k\langle d_k, \tilde{s}'_1, s_k\rangle \equiv R_k\langle d_k, s_k\rangle + f'_M\langle \tilde{s}'_1, T_{k2}\langle d_k, s_k\rangle\rangle \qquad (8\text{-}55)$$

Notice that the mathematical description of the single-loop optimization problem differs only slightly from that of the diverging branch problem. Such a loop is shown in Fig. 8–25 for $j < k$, making it a *feedforward* loop; for the case in which $j > k$, the loop would be described as *feedback*. Thus one need only add the incidence identity

$$s_{j2} \equiv \tilde{s}'_1 \qquad (8\text{-}56)$$

and replace Eqs. (8–1:j) and (8–2:j) for the junction stage j by the three-variable functions

$$r_j = R_j\langle d_j, s_{j1}, s_{j2}\rangle \qquad (8\text{-}57)$$

$$\tilde{s}_j = T_j\langle d_j, s_{j1}, s_{j2}\rangle \qquad (8\text{-}58)$$

To optimize such a system, feedback or feedforward, one treats $\tilde{s}'_1$ as a cut state, rewritten $\tilde{c}'_1$ or $\tilde{c}_{j2}$. When this cut state is fixed at a specific value, the system can be treated as a serial one with a diverging branch having a fixed output $\tilde{c}'_1$.

Applying decision inversion to stage $1'$, we find the diverging branch maximum return $f'_M\langle s'_M, \tilde{c}'_1\rangle$. When $\tilde{c}'_1$ is treated as a constant, the $M - 1$ optimizations are all one-state one-decision problems. Stages 1 through $j - 1$ are treated using the initial value model to obtain $f_{j-1}\langle s_{j-1}\rangle$. For the junction stage j the return and transition Eqs. (8–57) and (8–58) are used to obtain $f_j\langle s_j, \tilde{c}'_1\rangle$, again for the particular value of $\tilde{c}'_1$. Then $f_{k-1}\langle s_{k-1}, \tilde{c}'_1\rangle$ is determined by proceeding in this way through stage $k - 1$. At stage k, absorption Eq. (8–55) is applied to absorb $f'_M\langle s_M, \tilde{c}'_1\rangle$ into r_k. From a partial optimization at stage k, $f_k\langle s_k, \tilde{c}'_1\rangle$ is obtained, together with the decision functions $d'_i{}^*\langle s'_i, \tilde{c}'_1\rangle, i = 1', \ldots, M$; $d^*_i\langle s_i\rangle, i = 1, \ldots, j - 1$ and $d^*_i\langle s_i, \tilde{c}'_1\rangle$, $i = j, \ldots, k$. These functions are all stored and the process is then repeated for a new value of $\tilde{c}'_1$, possibly selected by a direct search method. Ultimately this gives the optimal value $\tilde{c}_1'^*$ and hence $f_k\langle s_k\rangle$. Stages $k + 1$ through N are then optimized, using the initial-value model, by applying Eq. (8–17:n). At $n = N$ we obtain the maximum total return $f_N\langle s_N\rangle = \Phi^*\langle s_N\rangle$.

$$\Phi^*\langle s_N\rangle \equiv \max_{\tilde{c}_1'} \{\Phi^*\langle \tilde{c}_1', s_N\rangle\} = \Phi^*\langle \tilde{c}_1'^*, s_N\rangle \tag{8-59}$$

This return "function" is a single value if the input state s_N is a constant k_N, and if it is a choice variable c_N, a direct search method can guide c_N simultaneously with $\tilde{c}_1'$ to find the single maximum return Φ^*.

$$\Phi^* \equiv \max_{\tilde{c}_1', c_N} \{\Phi^*\langle \tilde{c}_1', c_N\rangle\} \tag{8-60}$$

8-20 Diverging Networks

As an example of a diverging branch problem, consider the system shown in Fig. 8–26. Here three networks have been linked together to form a system having one diverging branch; this system is also represented by the functional diagram just below the network. This is an initial-value problem in which it is desired to find the shortest path from stage 12 to stages 1 and 13, taking into account the length (returns) of the individual links and the returns associated with the junction stage 7.

The optimal four-stage returns, $f_4'\langle s_{16}\rangle$, for the upper branch are found by the usual dynamic programming methods for serial systems. The input state, s_{16}, to this branch can take on any one of five values, I–V, corresponding to the five rows of this network, as indicated on the figure. The optimal returns for this branch are easily found to be $f_4'\langle I\rangle = 13$, $f_4'\langle II\rangle = 17$, $f_4'\langle III\rangle = 19$, $f_4'\langle IV\rangle = 14$, $f_4'\langle V\rangle = 20$.

The results from analysis of the six stages of the lower branch, also obtained by serial methods, are $f_6\langle 1\rangle = 23$, $f_6\langle 2\rangle = 17$, $f_6\langle 3\rangle = 24$, and $f_6\langle 4\rangle = 28$, where the values of the input state, s_6, correspond to the row numbering on Fig. 8–26. We now define the optimal (minimum) return from the 11-stage system consisting of stages 1–7 and 13–16 as

$$f_{11}\langle s_7\rangle = \min_{d_7} \{R_7\langle s_7, d_7\rangle + f_4'\langle s_{16}\rangle + f_6\langle s_6\rangle\}$$

where R_7, s_6, and s_{16} are functions of d_7 and s_7 as defined by the tables of Fig. 8–27. For each of the six possible values of the initial state, s_7, a decision, d_7, must be made as to which of the 20 available combinations of output states, s_6 and s_{16}, will minimize $f_{11}\langle s_7\rangle$. The tables in Fig. 8–27 are read as follows: If the value of the initial state at stage 7 is $s_7 = 5$, the return associated with the decision to go to output states $s_{16} = III$, $s_6 = 3$, is 6; to this must be added $f_4'\langle III\rangle = 19$ and $f_6\langle 3\rangle = 24$, to yield $M_{11}\langle 5; III, 3\rangle = 49$. The reader may verify that the optimal returns are $f_{11}\langle 1\rangle = 43$, $f_{11}\langle 2\rangle = 44$, $f_{11}\langle 3\rangle = 35$, $f_{11}\langle 4\rangle = 40$, $f_{11}\langle 5\rangle = 37$, and $f_{11}\langle 6\rangle = 33$. The optimal deci-

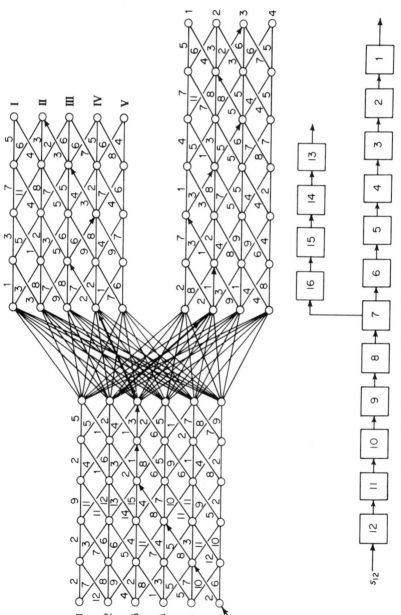

Figure 8-26. Example of diverging branch network problem.

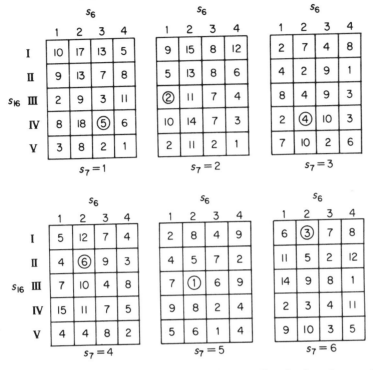

Figure 8-27. Tabular description of stage 7 in diverging branch network problem.

sions, d_7^*, are indicated by the circles in the tables describing stage 7 in Fig. 8-27.

The remaining stages of the system are analyzed in the usual recursive manner to find the optimal return from the process, $f_{16}\langle s_{12}\rangle$, for the given initial value s_{12}. If, for example, the initial state is specified as $s_{12} = 6$, the optimal return is found to be $f_{16}\langle 6\rangle = 57$, and the optimal decision at each stage is shown by the arrows which define the minimum path in Fig. 8-26.

8-21 Diverging Branches: Nonlinear Returns

Consider the system depicted by Fig. 8-28, in which the returns for stages 1, 2, 3, and 4 are $5d_i - id_i^2$, whereas those for stages I and II in the lower branch are $4d_i - id_i^2$. In addition, the transition functions are $s_I = s_{II} - 0.2d_{II}$, and $\bar{s}_i = s_i - 0.4d_i$, $i = 1, 2, 3, 4$. The problem

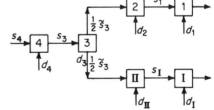

Figure 8-28. Nonlinear diverging branch example problem.

is to maximize the sum of all of the returns for a given system input, s_4.

Proceeding as in the nonlinear serial problem example solved earlier, one finds, for the upper branch,

$$f_2\langle \tilde{s}_3\rangle = \begin{cases} 9.375, & \begin{cases} 6 \leq \tilde{s}_3 \leq \infty \\ (d_2^* = 1.25) \end{cases} \\ 2.778\tilde{s}_3 - 0.232\tilde{s}_3^2 + 1.042, & \begin{cases} 1.706 \leq \tilde{s}_3 \leq 6 \\ (d_2^* = 0.93\tilde{s}_3 + 0.685) \end{cases} \\ 4\tilde{s}_3 - 0.59\tilde{s}_3^2, & \begin{cases} 0 \leq \tilde{s}_3 \leq 1.706 \\ (d_2^* = 0.5\tilde{s}_3) \end{cases} \end{cases}$$

and, for the lower branch,

$$f_{II}\langle \tilde{s}_3\rangle = \begin{cases} 6, & \begin{cases} 4.4 \leq \tilde{s}_3 \leq \infty \\ d_{II}^* = 1 \end{cases} \\ 2.157\tilde{s}_3 - 0.245\tilde{s}_3^2 + 1.255, & \begin{cases} 1.738 \leq \tilde{s}_3 \leq 4.4 \\ d_{II}^* = 0.049\tilde{s}_3 + 0.784 \end{cases} \\ 3.6\tilde{s}_3 - 0.66\tilde{s}_3^2, & \begin{cases} 0 \leq \tilde{s}_3 \leq 1.738 \\ d_{II}^* = 0.5\tilde{s}_3 \end{cases} \end{cases}$$

Then at stage 3, d_3 must be chosen so as to maximize the sum of the returns from both branches plus R_3, the return *at* stage 3. For example, in the range $1.706 \leq \tilde{s}_3 \leq 1.738$, this sum is

$$M_5\langle s_3, d_3\rangle = 2.45d_3 - 3.14d_3^2 + 6.38s_3 - 0.89s_3^2 + 0.714s_3d_3 + 1.04$$

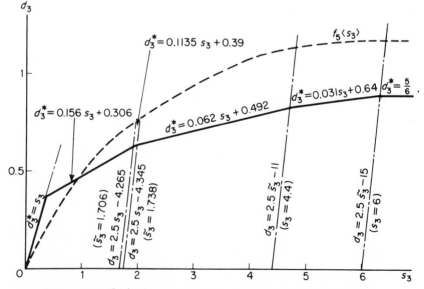

Figure 8-29. Optimal stage 3 decisions and returns for nonlinear diverging branch problem.

from which it follows by differentiation that

$$d_3^* = 0.1135s_3 + 0.3896$$

When this value of d_3 is substituted into the constraint

$$1.706 \leq s_3 - 0.4d_3 \leq 1.738$$

it is seen to be valid in the range $1.947 \leq s_3 \leq 1.984$. Continuing in this manner, the optimal values of d_3 for the appropriate ranges of the input s_3 are those described in Fig. 8–29. The optimal returns for the two branches follow:

$$f_5\langle s_3 \rangle = \begin{cases} 17.458, & \begin{cases} 6.333 \leq s_3 \leq \infty \\ d_3^* = \frac{5}{6} \end{cases} \\[2mm] 2.897s_3 - 0.230s_3^2 + 8.287, & \begin{cases} 4.714 \leq s_3 \leq 6.333 \\ d_3^* = 0.0306s_3 + 0.640 \end{cases} \\[2mm] 5.123s_3 - 0.465s_3^2 + 3.041, & \begin{cases} 1.984 \leq s_3 \leq 4.714 \\ d_3^* = 0.062s_3 + 0.492 \end{cases} \\[2mm] 6.656s_3 - 0.851s_3^2 + 1.519, & \begin{cases} 1.947 \leq s_3 \leq 1.984 \\ d_3^* = 0.1135s_3 + 0.3896 \end{cases} \\[2mm] 7.9063s_3 - 1.172s_3^2 + 0.300, & \begin{cases} 0.363 \leq s_3 \leq 1.947 \\ d_3^* = 0.156s_3 + 0.306 \end{cases} \\[2mm] 9.56s_3 - 3.45s_3^2, & \begin{cases} 0 \leq s_3 \leq 0.363 \\ d_3^* = s_3 \end{cases} \end{cases}$$

The remaining stage 4 is now included in the analysis by the usual serial methods of dynamic programming. The total solution to this diverging branch problem is then

$$f_6\langle s_4 \rangle = \begin{cases} 19.02, & \begin{cases} 6.58 \leq s_4 \leq \infty \\ d_4^* = 0.625 \end{cases} \\[2mm] 2.98s_4 - 0.23s_4^2 + 9.20, & \begin{cases} 4.95 \leq s_4 \leq 6.58 \\ d_4^* = 0.23s_4 + 0.47 \end{cases} \\[2mm] 5.26s_4 - 0.46s_4^2 + 3.58, & \begin{cases} 2.17 \leq s_4 \leq 4.95 \\ d_4^* = 0.05s_4 + 0.362 \end{cases} \\[2mm] 6.85s_4 - 0.83s_4^2 + 1.85, & \begin{cases} 2.13 \leq s_4 \leq 2.17 \\ d_4^* = 0.083s_4 + 0.28 \end{cases} \\[2mm] 8.11s_4 - 1.11s_4^2 + 0.50, & \begin{cases} 0.47 \leq s_4 \leq 2.13 \\ d_4^* = 0.112s_4 + 0.219 \end{cases} \\[2mm] 9.92s_4 - 3.03s_4^2 + 0.10, & \begin{cases} 0.185 \leq s_4 \leq 0.47 \\ d_4^* = 0.30s_4 + 0.13 \end{cases} \\[2mm] 10.73s_4 - 5.24s_4^2, & \begin{cases} 0 \leq s_4 \leq 0.185 \\ d_4^* = s_4 \end{cases} \end{cases}$$

8-22 Converging Branches

Figure 8–30 illustrates a system with an M-stage *converging* serial branch, that is, one whose output state $\tilde{s}'_1$ is an input to stage $k(\neq 1)$ of another N-stage system. Although the return, transition, and incidence Eqs. (8–48),

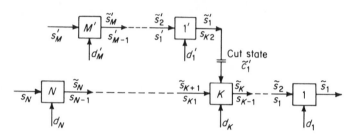

Figure 8-30. A converging branch.

(8–49), and (8–52) for a diverging branch hold also for a converging one, the mathematical description of connecting stage k is different. The diverging junction Eqs. (8–1:k), (8–2:k), (8–3:k), (8–50), and (8–51) must be replaced by the triple input functions

$$r_k = R_k \langle d_k, s_{k1}, s_{k2} \rangle \tag{8-61}$$

and

$$\tilde{s}_k = T_k \langle d_k, s_{k1}, s_{k2} \rangle \tag{8-62}$$

with the new incidence relations being

$$\tilde{s}_{k+1} \equiv s_{k1} \tag{8-63}$$

and

$$\tilde{s}'_1 \equiv s_{k2} \tag{8-64}$$

The problem is to maximize the sum of returns from all $M + N$ stages. To solve it, first find $f_{k-1}\langle s_{k-1} \rangle$, the optimal return function for stages 1 through $k - 1$, using dynamic programming Eqs. (8–10:1) and Eqs. (8–17:1)–(8–17:k-2). If s'_M must be considered a state variable, next choose a particular value $\tilde{c}'_1$ of the branch output $\tilde{s}'_1$, treated as a cut state, and determine the optimal branch return $f'_M\langle \tilde{c}'_1, s'_M \rangle$, a boundary-value serial problem. Simultaneous selection of a value of decision d_k and choice state $\tilde{c}'_1$ would, for a given value of state s_{k1}, determine a total return which is the maximand inside the braces in Eq. (8–65). Once this quantity has been stored, together with the corresponding policy, new values of $\tilde{c}'_1$ and d_k can be chosen by a direct search method. Repetition of this guided search eventually gives $\tilde{c}'^*_1\langle s_{k1} \rangle$ and $d^*_k\langle s_{k1} \rangle$, the optimal values of $\tilde{c}'_1$ and d_k for every value of state s_{k1}, as well as the optimal $M + k$ stage return function $f_{M+k}\langle s_{k1}, s'_M \rangle$, defined as

$$f_{M+k}\langle s_{k1}, s'_M \rangle \equiv \max_{\tilde{c}'_1, d_k} \{ R_k\langle \tilde{c}'_1, d_k, s_{k1} \rangle + f_{k-1}\langle T_k\langle \tilde{c}'_1, d_k, s_{k1} \rangle \rangle + f'_M\langle \tilde{c}'_1, s'_M \rangle \}$$

$$\tag{8-65}$$

This is not difficult to do if the branch input s'_M is a constant k'_M. When s'_M can be treated as a choice state c'_M the optimal branch return $f'_M\langle \tilde{c}'_1 \rangle$ can be found more easily by state inversion of the branch, followed by solution of M one-decision one-state problems. Furthermore, the optimization of Eq. (8-65) would then involve only one state variable (s_{k1}). On the other hand, if state inversion were not possible and decision inversion had to be used, we would determine $f'_M\langle \tilde{c}'_1, c'_M \rangle$, treating $\tilde{c}'_1$ as a cut state as given earlier, and then determine f_{M+k} by a three-decision one-state optimization using Eq. (8–66).

$$f_{M+k}\langle s_{k1} \rangle \equiv \max_{\tilde{c}'_1, c'_M, d_k} \{ R_k\langle \tilde{c}'_1, d_k, s_{k1} \rangle + f_{k-1}\langle T_k\langle \tilde{c}'_1, d_k, s_{k1} \rangle \rangle + f'_M\langle \tilde{c}'_1, c'_M \rangle \} \quad (8\text{-}66)$$

This illustrates the advantage of using state inversion whenever possible, since with state inversion the converging branch problem is only about as difficult as the diverging branch problem. Otherwise, even though there is no loop, its difficulty would be comparable to that of a single-loop problem. If s_N is a choice state but s'_M is not, stages $k + 1$ through N should be treated as the converging branch and stages $(1, \ldots, k, 1', \ldots, M')$ as the serial chain.

The rest of the main trunk is optimized by ordinary dynamic programming. It is important to carry out the double (or triple) decision optimization right at the junction stage k; otherwise, the states $\tilde{s}'_1$ and s'_M would have to be carried as state variables to be examined exhaustively during every partial optimization following.

8-23 A Converging Network

Consider the converging branch system described by the network of Fig. 8–31 and also represented schematically by the functional diagram just below the network. The problem is to find, for a given value of the input state s_8(s_{11} is a choice variable), the shortest path through the network (to stage 1). One begins at the free end, solving the last four stages serially to obtain the optimal returns $f_4\langle 1 \rangle = 20$, $f_4\langle 2 \rangle = 19$, and $f_4\langle 3 \rangle = 17$, where the values of s_4 correspond to the row numbering in Fig. 8–31. The upper branch is treated as a final-value problem, and is solved by state inversion. The minimum returns for each value of s_9 are now given, along with the corresponding optimal value s_{11}^*:

$$f'_3\langle 1 \rangle = 10; \qquad s_{11}^* = 1$$
$$f'_3\langle 2 \rangle = 11; \qquad s_{11}^* = 1$$
$$f'_3\langle 3 \rangle = 14; \qquad s_{11}^* = 1$$

The returns for stage 5 are given in tabular form in Fig. 8–32 for the two input states, $\tilde{s}_9$ and s_5, and the decision variable d_5. The values which d_5 can assume correspond to the values of three output state, $\tilde{s}_5$; in other words,

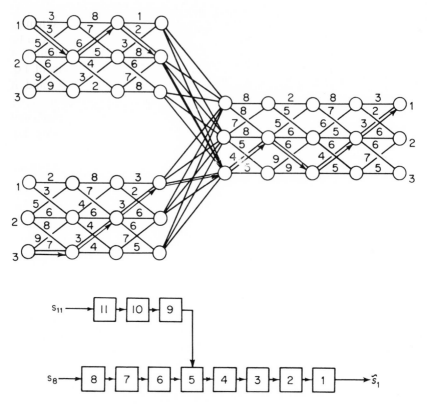

Figure 8-31. Converging branch network problem.

these choices select the input row to the common network made up of stages 1–4. For example, if the input states to stage 5 are $\bar{s}_9 = 3$ and $s_5 = 2$, the return associated with the decision to go to output state $\bar{s}_5 = 2$ (that is, $d_5 = 2$) is 3.

Now the two-variable optimization

$$f_8\langle s_5 \rangle = \min_{\bar{s}_9, d_5} \{ R_5\langle \bar{s}_9, s_5, d_5 \rangle + f'_3\langle T_4\langle \bar{s}_9, d_5 \rangle\rangle + f_4\langle T_5\langle s_5, d_5 \rangle\rangle \}$$

must be carried out at stage 5.

The results of this optimization are

$$f_8\langle 1 \rangle = 30; \quad \text{for} \quad \bar{s}_9^* = 2 \quad \text{and} \quad d_5 = 3$$
$$f_8\langle 2 \rangle = 31; \quad \text{for} \quad \bar{s}_9^* = 2 \quad \text{and} \quad d_5 = 2$$
$$f_8\langle 3 \rangle = 29; \quad \text{for} \quad \bar{s}_9^* = 1 \quad \text{and} \quad d_5 = 3$$

The remaining stages of the system are optimized using the conventional serial methods. If, for example, the initial state is given as $s_8 = 3$, the optimal

$s_5 = 1$

$\tilde{s}_9$ ╲ d_5	1	2	3
1	1	7	5
2	7	7	2
3	3	3	3

$s_5 = 2$

$\tilde{s}_9$ ╲ d_5	1	2	3
1	8	6	7
2	5	1	7
3	7	3	6

$s_5 = 3$

$\tilde{s}_9$ ╲ d_5	1	2	3
1	4	7	2
2	6	7	4
3	9	5	6

Figure 8-32. Tabular description of stage 5 in converging branch network problem.

return is $f_{11}\langle 3 \rangle = 43$, resulting in $s_{11}^* = 1$, $\tilde{s}_1^* = 1$, as shown by the corresponding optimal path described by the arrows in Fig. 8–31.

8-24 Converging Allocation : Superposition

From the theoretical development and example problems just given, it can be seen that, for general return and transition functions, diverging branch problems can be solved with no more effort than that needed for the same size serial problem, whereas the treatment required for converging branch problems is more complicated. In allocation problems where the returns and transition functions are linear, however, a system having n converging branches can be solved as n serial problems, and the resulting solutions superimposed to form the solution to the original branched problem (Beightler, Johnson, and Wilde). It suffices to demonstrate this principle for a system having just one branch, as in Fig. 8–33, and transition functions.

$$\tilde{s}_i = a_i s_i + b_i d_i; \qquad i = 1, \dots, N + P \qquad (8\text{-}67:\text{i})$$

Where the a_i, b_i, are given constants, and the incidence identities are

$$s_i \equiv \tilde{s}_{i+1}; \qquad i = 1, \dots, M-1, M+1, \dots, N-1, N+1, \dots, N+P$$

and

$$s_M \equiv \tilde{s}_{N+1} + \tilde{s}_{M+1}$$

We wish to maximize $\sum\limits_{i=1}^{N+P} r_i$

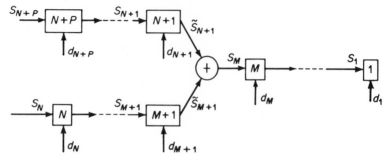

Figure 8-33. Superposition in linear converging branch problem.

where $\qquad\qquad r_i = A_i s_i + B_i d_i; \qquad i = 1, \ldots, N + P$ $\qquad$ (8-68: i)

the A_i and B_i being given constants, and the decision variables constrained by

$$0 \le d_i \le s_i; \qquad i = 1, \ldots, N + P \qquad\qquad (8\text{-}69\text{:}\,i)$$

Let d_i^* be the optimal policy, and s_i^* the resulting optimal states, $i = 1, \ldots, N + P$.

Now consider two *serial* systems derived from this branched system. Let serial problem I be

$$\max \sum_{i=1}^{N} r_i$$

where Eqs. (8-67), (8-68), and (8-69) hold for $i = 1, \ldots, N$, and the incidence identities are

$$s_i' \equiv \tilde{s}_{i+1}'; \qquad i = 1, \ldots, N - 1,$$

and let $d_i'^*$, $i = 1, \ldots, N$, be the optimal policy for this problem, and $\tilde{s}_i'^*$ the resulting optimal states.

Let serial problem II be

$$\max \sum_{i=1}^{M} r_i + \sum_{i=N+1}^{N+P} r_i$$

where Eqs. (8-67), (8-68), and (8-69) hold for $i = 1, \ldots, M, N + 1, \ldots, N + P$, and the incidence identities are

$$s_i'' \equiv \tilde{s}_{i+1}''; \qquad i = 1, \ldots, M - 1, N + 1, \ldots, N + P - 1$$

and $\qquad\qquad\qquad s_M'' \equiv \tilde{s}_{N+1}''$

and let $d_i''^*$, $i = 1, \ldots, M, N + 1, \ldots, N + P$, be the optimal policy for this problem, and $\tilde{s}_i''^*$, $i = 1, \ldots, M, N+1, \ldots, N+P$, the resulting optimal states.

SUPERPOSITION THEOREM:

(1) The *qualitative* policies for all three problems are the same:

$$\frac{d_i}{s_i} = \begin{cases} \dfrac{d_i'}{s_i'}, & \text{if } s_i' \neq 0 \\ 0, & \text{if } s_i' = 0 \end{cases} \qquad i = 1, \ldots, N \qquad (8\text{-}70')$$

and

$$\frac{d_i}{s_i} = \begin{cases} \dfrac{d_i''}{s_i''}, & \text{if } s_i'' \neq 0 \\ 0, & \text{if } s_i'' = 0 \end{cases} \qquad i = 1, \ldots, M, N+1, \ldots, N+P$$

$$(8\text{-}70'')$$

(2) Superposition of the *quantitative* policies for problems I and II gives the quantitative policy for the branch problem:

$$\left. \begin{aligned} s_i &= s_i' + s_i'' \\ d_i &= d_i' + d_i'' \end{aligned} \right\} \qquad i = 1, \ldots, M$$

$$\left. \begin{aligned} s_i &= s_i' \\ d_i &= d_i' \end{aligned} \right\} \qquad i = M+1, \ldots, N \qquad (8\text{-}71\text{:}i)$$

$$\left. \begin{aligned} s_i &= s_i'' \\ d_i &= d_i'' \end{aligned} \right\} \qquad i = N+1, \ldots, N+P$$

Proof: Let

$$f_i \langle s_i, s_{N+1}, d_{N+1} \rangle \equiv \max_{d_1, \ldots, d_i} \sum_{j=1}^{i} r_j; \qquad i = 1, \ldots, N$$

where r_j is defined by Eq. (8–68:j). Then (by induction on i), for the branch problem,

$$\begin{aligned} f_i \langle s_i, s_{N+1}, d_{N+1} \rangle &= \max_{0 \leq d_i \leq s_i} \{\mu_i s_i + \lambda_i d_i + \delta_i \tilde{s}_{N+1}\} \\ &= k_i s_i + \delta_i \tilde{s}_{N+1}, \qquad i = 1, \ldots, N \end{aligned} \qquad (8\text{-}72)$$

where $k_0 \equiv 0$,

$$\left. \begin{aligned} \lambda_i &\equiv B_i + k_{i-1} b_i \\ \mu_i &\equiv A_i + k_{i-1} a_i \\ k_i &\equiv \max \{\mu_i, \lambda_i + \mu_i\} \end{aligned} \right\} \qquad i = 1, \ldots, N$$

and

$$\delta_i \equiv \begin{cases} 0, & \text{for } i = 1, \ldots, M \\ k_M, & \text{for } i = M+1, \ldots, N \end{cases}$$

Then the optimal decisions, d_i^*, are given by

$$\frac{d_i^*}{s_i^*} = \begin{cases} 0, & \text{if } \lambda_i \leq 0 \\ 1, & \text{if } \lambda_i \geq 0 \end{cases}; \qquad i = 1, \ldots, N$$

where

$$s_N^* \equiv s_N$$

and

$$s_i^* = a_{i+1} s_{i+1}^* + b_{i+1} d_{i+1}^*,$$

for

$$i = 1, \ldots, M-1, M+1, \ldots, N-1$$

$$(8\text{-}73\text{:}i)$$

and

$$s_M^* = a_{M+1}s_{M+1}^* + b_{M+1}d_{M+1}^* + a_{N+1}s_{N+1}^* + b_{N+1}d_{N+1}^* \quad (8\text{-}73\text{: M})$$

This holds for all values of s_{N+1} and d_{N+1}, and in particular when $s_{N+1} = d_{N+1} = 0$, which is the case for serial problem I, the optimal decisions and states of which are $d_i'^*$ and $s_i'^*$, respectively. Therefore,

$$\frac{d_i'^*}{s_i'^*} = \frac{d_i^*}{s_i^*}$$

as asserted in Eq. (8–70′). A similar argument can be used to prove Eq. (8–70″).

Since $s_N \equiv s_N'$, Eq. (8–71: i) for $i = M + 1, \ldots, N$, can be proved inductively using Eqs. (8–70′) and (8–73: i). The proof for $i = N + 1, \ldots, N + P$ is similar, based on the identity of s_{N+P} and s_{N+P}''.

In serial problem I, $s_{N+1}' = d_{N+1}' \equiv 0$ and Eq. (8–73: i) becomes

$$s_i'^* = a_{i+1}s_{i+1}'^* + b_{i+1}d_{i+1}'^*; \qquad i = 1, \ldots, M \qquad (8\text{-}73'\text{: i})$$

Similarly for serial problem II, $s_{M+1}'' = d_{M+1}'' \equiv 0$, so that

$$s_M''^* = a_{N+1}s_{N+1}''^* + b_{N+1}d_{N+1}''^* \qquad (8\text{-}73''\text{: M})$$

and
$$s_i''^* = a_{i+1}s_{i+1}''^* + b_{i+1}d_{i+1}''^*; \qquad i = 1, \ldots, M - 1 \qquad (8\text{-}73''\text{: i})$$

Combination of Eqs. (8–73: i), (8–73: M), (8–73′: i), (8–73″: M) and (8–73″: i) with Eqs. (8–70′) and (8–70″) gives, by induction,

$$s_i^* = s_i'^* + s_i''^*; \qquad i = 1, \ldots, M \qquad (8\text{-}71\text{: i})$$

which completes the proof.

The superposition theorem also holds for more general systems. First, the transition functions may be written as inhomogeneous linear expressions containing a constant, K_i:

$$\tilde{s}_i = a_i s_i + b_i d_i + K_i$$

since adding a constant to the homogeneous linear transitions will not affect the *qualitative* policy. Second, the theorem is also valid for those systems in which the transition function at the branching junction has the more general form:

$$s_M = \gamma \tilde{s}_{N+1} + \varphi \tilde{s}_{M+1}$$

where γ and φ are any real constants. Third, the foregoing results generalize to large systems comprised of any number of linear branches, so that each branch may be analyzed independently of the others.

Generally, the method of superposition is applicable only to initial-value, linear converging branch problems or to final-value linear diverging branch problems (which are mathematically equivalent). If a nonlinear branch is adjoined to a linear system, the optimal qualitative decisions in the linear portion are unaffected by the introduction of the branch. This is clear from Eq. (8–72), which could just as well have been written

$$f_i\langle s_i, s_{N+1}, d_{N+1}\rangle = k_i s_i + \delta_i [\Phi\langle s_{N+1}, d_{N+1}\rangle]$$

where $\Phi\langle s_{N+1}, d_{N+1}\rangle$ is any analytic function, without affecting the subsequent analysis and proof.

These results have an economic interpretation. Consider a firm which has worked out an optimal policy for a linear allocation problem. Even if an unknown number of mergers at arbitrary future times were to add allocation capital to the system, the original qualitative plan would still be optimal— even if the merging firms were nonlinear. Moreover, the original *quantitative* plan remains optimal until the first merger takes place. Therefore long-range planners with linear allocation problems need never worry about their policies being upset by future mergers.

When the method of superposition is applied to linear diverging branch problems in which one is free to choose the branch inputs, the branching problem becomes a single serial system. Consider, for example, the system shown schematically in Fig. 8–34. The total return for stage $M + 1$ plus the returns for all stages to the right is

$$f_{M+P-N+1}\langle s_{M+1}\rangle = \max_{d_{M+1}} \{r_{M+1} + k_P s_P + k_M s_M\}$$

We lose no generality in assuming that

$$s_M + s_P = \tilde{s}_{M+1}$$

since a more general relationship between these variables could be achieved by inserting a decisionless stage for that purpose at the circled junction point in Fig. 8–34. Now since the branch inputs are decision variables in this problem, one simply chooses $s_M^* = 0$ when $k_P \geq k_M$, and $s_P^* = 0$ when $k_P < k_M$. Thus, in every case, one of the branches receives no input and is effectively removed from the system, producing a simple serial structure. Note that this is a special case of the linear diverging branch problem. In general the branch inputs may not be choice variables but might instead be determined by the expressions

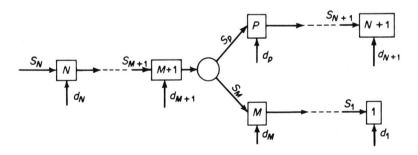

Figure 8-34. Superposition in linear diverging branch problem.

$$s_P = a_{M+1}s_{M+1} + b_{M+1}d_{M+1}$$
$$s_M = \tilde{a}_{M+1}s_{M+1} + \tilde{b}_{M+1}d_{M+1}$$

where $a_{M+1}, b_{M+1}, \tilde{a}_{M+1}$, and $\tilde{b}_{M+1}$ are given constants. It is left as an exercise for the reader to show that for this general case, the superposition principle does *not* hold.

8-25 Functional Diagrams and Optimization Plans

A real problem requires careful construction of a master optimization strategy for the particular system in question. Such a plan specifies what structure is to be exploited and what part ignored, the order of performing the partial optimizations, the preliminary transformations needed, and the variables to be manipulated. Having an optimization plan to guide him, an engineer can decide which procedures to use in optimizing the component parts effectively. This section, taken from Wilde, 1965, sets down precise principles for using functional diagrams to devise acceptable optimization strategies. It summarizes and integrates, in graphical form, most of the material of this chapter, showing when (and when *not*) to use partial optimization.

The principal difference between this section and the rest of the chapter is the extensive use here of graphic rather than analytic representation of the structures. In contrast to the earlier work, there are few equations and many diagrams here, and with good reason. The elegance and compactness of the conventional functional equation presentation depends heavily on careful identification of the state and decision variables, astute transformation of the pertinent equations, and clever numbering of the subunits or stages. But the structure of a system should be independent of how things are labelled, and diagrams often show clearly structures which would be hidden by an algebraic representation with its multitude of equations and symbols.

The process flow diagram is not adequate for developing an optimization plan because it is often information flow rather than material flow which must be depicted. With the addition of a few new symbols, the functional diagram appears best suited to exhibit the relationships needed to develop an optimization plan. Even when applied to fairly standard situations the functional diagrams produce surprises. For example, they show how to improve dynamic programming, even on ordinary serial systems. They also show that one should not use dynamic programming on loops with fewer than four decisions.

Besides extending and refining the functional diagram concept, we develop six rules for simplifying a system, breaking it down efficiently into subsystems, and making necessary mathematical transformations and rearrangements. Briefly, the rules involve removal of irrelevancies, order of optimization, combination of subunits, elimination of constraints, handling small loops, and location of cuts for optimizing large loops. Simple as they are individually, the rules interact powerfully to reduce a functional diagram to a workable and efficient optimization plan.

Note that we are now departing from the notation used for labeling states in the foregoing analytic sections. Figure 8–35 represents schematically the dependence of two variables y_1 and y_2 upon three independent variables x_1, x_2, and x_3. The rectangle stands for two functions (one for each output variable y_1 and y_2) of the three input variables x_1, x_2, and x_3. Half arrows directed into the rectangle represent inputs; outputs are shown as half arrows directed out of the rectangle. Such a collection of one or more functions, all depending on the same input variables, is called a stage.

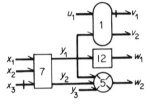

Figure 8-35. Stage functional diagram.   **Figure 8-36.** System functional diagram.

A *multistage problem* arises when outputs from one stage are also inputs to others, as shown in Fig. 8–36 in which v_1 and v_2 depend on u_1 and y_1, w_1 depends on y_1, and w_2 depends on y_1, y_2, and y_3. The set of all stages is called the *system*, and its diagram is called the system *functional diagram*. Variables which are both outputs from one stage and inputs to others are called *state variables* (y_1 and y_2 in Fig. 8–36). Variables behaving only as inputs are called *system inputs* or *decision variables* (x_1, x_2, x_3, u_1, and y_3), while those which are outputs only are called *system outputs* (v_1, v_2, w_1, and w_2). If any variable is to be held constant, its half arrow is crossed in the middle with a vertical line, as for x_3 and v_1 in Fig. 8–36. Stages may be numbered or lettered to distinguish them from each other, as in Fig. 8–36.

Assume that for at least one stage there is another dependent variable called the *return function* measuring the performance of the stage. A stage with a return function is symbolized by a rectangle (stages 7 and 12 in Fig 8–36) while one with zero return is represented by an oval (stages 1 and 5). The *system optimization problem* is to find the values of the variables making the total return (the sum of the return functions) optimum. Actually one need only find the optimum values of the decision variables, since all state and system output variables can be computed from these system inputs. The set of the values of the decision variables optimizing the total return is called the *optimal policy*.

Rule 1 (Irrelevant stages):

If a stage has no return function and if all its outputs are system outputs, then the stage and its decision variables may be eliminated.

Such a stage (stage 5, Fig. 8–36) is called *irrelevant* because it in no way affects the system objective function. Elimination of an irrelevant stage is shown on the functional diagram by crossing out the stage oval. Removal of irrelevant stages is worthwhile because it simplifies the problem, often removing decision variables (y_3 for example).

Consider stage 1 of the three-stage serial system of Fig. 8–37. When s_2 is given, one need not examine all possible values of d_1 to find the best one $d_1^* \langle s_2 \rangle$. One can in fact use direct search methods that rapidly concentrate the searching effort in the neighborhood of $d_1^* \langle s_2 \rangle$. However, one cannot use these techniques on the state variable s_2 because it connects stage 1 with the rest of the system. Hence $d_1^* \langle s_2 \rangle$ and $f_1 \langle s_2 \rangle$ must be found for all possible values of s_2. This *partial optimization* with respect to d_1 is indicated on the functional diagram by making the arrowheads into triangles, filled in solidly for the exhaustively searched state variables to distinguish them from the selectively searched decision variables, Fig. 8–38.

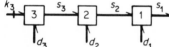

Figure 8-37. Initial value serial problem.   **Figure 8-38.** Standard dynamic programming.

Since state s_2 depends on both d_2 and s_3, i.e., $s_2 = T_2 \langle d_2, s_3 \rangle$, the one-stage maximum return $f_1 \langle s_2 \rangle$ may be written as a function of d_2 and s_3 and added to the stage 2 return $R_2 \langle d_2, s_3 \rangle$, which depends on the same variables. Partial optimization of this sum with respect to d_2 gives the optimal two-stage return $f_2 \langle s_3 \rangle$ as a function only of s_3

$$f_2 \langle s_3 \rangle = \max_{d_2} \left(R_2 \langle d_2, s_3 \rangle + f_1 \langle d_2, s_3 \rangle \right)$$

Here s_3 must be searched exhaustively, while direct search techniques can be used on d_2, as shown schematically in Fig. 8–38.

The same procedure can be repeated for stage 3, with one difference. Since k_3 is a constant, the optimal three-stage return f_3 is a constant rather than a function

$$f_3 = \max_{d_3} \left(R_3 \langle d_3 \rangle + f_2 \langle d_3 \rangle \right)$$

To indicate that the exhaustive search of k_3 involves only one value (k_3 itself), the k_3 arrow in Fig. 8–38 is not closed. The nature of partial optimization determines the rule following.

Rule 2 (Order of partial optimization):

Partial optimization must proceed in the direction opposite to that of the state arrows.

This is not a simplifying rule; it is instead intended to guide the choice of transformations which put an arbitrary nonserial system into the required form.

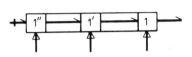

Figure 8-39. Simultaneous optimization.

Partial optimization takes advantage of the structure of a serial system to permit optimizing only one decision variable at a time. Consider an alternate approach called *simultaneous optimization* which ignores the system structure altogether. One expresses the total return as a function of the decision variables alone and then optimizes it with respect to all of them simultaneously.

$$f_3 = \max_{d_1, d_2, d_3} (R_1 + R_2 + R_3)$$

This is symbolized in Fig. 8–39 by connecting the corners of adjacent stage rectangles with solid lines to make a single stage with three decision inputs and one fixed input (k_3).

To compare the effort expended by the two procedures, an upper bound will be developed on the number of function evaluations needed to find an optimum by simultaneous optimization. Let D_i be the total number of values of d_i which might be examined. If the return is a unimodal function of d_i, then F_i ($i = 1, 2, \ldots, n$), the least number of evaluations needed to find the optimum by the Fibonacci technique of Section 6–10, is approximately:

$$F_i \approx \frac{\log 1.62\, D_i}{\log 1.62}$$

If the slightly less effective dichotomous method is used, the number G_i of evaluations needed is approximately:

$$G_i \approx \frac{2 \log D_i}{\log 2}$$

Suppose there are n decision variables and that the return is unimodal with respect to any particular decision variable whenever all the others are fixed. This property of rectangular unimodality makes possible the use of the multivariable dichotomous technique, for which an upper bound on the number of function evaluations N_n is, as given in Section 6–20,

$$N_n < \frac{\left[(F_1 + n - 1) \prod_{i=2}^{n} G_i \right]}{2^{n-1}} \qquad n = 1, 2, \ldots$$

One can readily prove, by induction on n, that

$$F_1 + n - 1 \leq 2^{n-1} F_1$$

and so

$$N_n < F_1 G_2 G_3 \ldots G_n$$

Although there are several search techniques which are probably more effective, the multivariable dichotomous procedure is the most efficient among those for which an upper bound is known. For purposes of comparison, $F_1 G_2 \ldots G_n$ is a suitably conservative upper bound.

Suppose now that the number of possibilities is the same for every state variable s_i and decision variable d_i. Then if S_i is the number of state values to be examined exhaustively,

$$S_i = D_i = K$$

where K is a constant. In an n-stage serial system with fixed initial value such as that shown in Fig. 8-37, the total number of function evaluations (assuming Fibonacci search on the decision variables) for partial optimization would be

$$F_n + \sum_{i=1}^{n-1} S_{i+1} F_i = (nK - K + 1) \left[\frac{\log 1.62\, K}{\log 1.62} \right]$$

If, on the other hand, simultaneous optimization were used, the upper bound on N_n would be

$$F_1 G_2 \ldots G_n = \left[\frac{2 \log K}{\log 2} \right]^{n-1} \left[\frac{\log 1.62\, K}{\log 1.62} \right]$$

The first quantity increases linearly with n; the second geometrically, which is why partial optimization is usually advantageous when n exceeds 2.

Suppose, however, that there are two state variables s_{n1} and s_{n2} connecting stages $n - 1$ and n as in Fig. 8-40. Partial optimization of stages $n - 1$ and n would require

$$S_{n1} S_{n2} F_{n-1} + F_n = (K^2 + 1) \left[\frac{\log 1.62\, K}{\log 1.62} \right]$$

function evaluations. Simultaneous optimization would need no more than

$$G_{n-1} F_n = \left[\frac{2 \log K}{\log 2} \right] \left[\frac{\log 1.62\, K}{\log 1.62} \right]$$

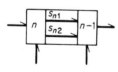

Figure 8-40. Stage combination.

which is considerably less, especially if K is large. For example, if $K = 100$, partial optimization would require 1010 evaluations; simultaneous optimization, no more than 140. Hence partial optimization has a clear advantage only for stages having more inputs than outputs.

If there are as many or more outputs as inputs, simultaneous optimization will be advantageous when the grid size is the same for all variables. In other cases, one should make comparisons of the sort described above to choose between partial and simultaneous optimization.

Rule 3 (Stage combination):

Elimination of outputs by stage combination should be considered for any stage having as many or more output than input variables.

Deserving of comment are two special applications of the combination rule: to stages with no decision variable and to stages with fixed input state. The decisionless stage simply transforms its input states into output states without partial optimization, Fig. 8–41(a). The combination rule will lead to combining the decisionless stage with an adjacent stage except in a situation like that shown in Fig. 8–41(b), where stage 3 has three inputs and two outputs to decisionless stage 2, which has only one output to stage 1. However, application of ordinary dynamic programming will in this case degenerate to combination of stages 2 and 3, for at stage 3 one seeks

$$f_3\langle s_{41}, s_{42}\rangle = \max_{d_3} [R_3\langle s_{41}, s_{42}, d_3\rangle + R_2\langle T_{31}\langle s_{41}, s_{42}, d_3\rangle, T_{32}\langle s_{41}, s_{42}, d_3\rangle\rangle$$
$$+ f_1\langle T_2\langle T_{31}\langle s_{41}, s_{42}, d_3\rangle, T_{32}\langle s_{41}, s_{42}, d_3\rangle\rangle\rangle]$$

Thus the states s_{31} and s_{32} are eliminated anyway, just as if the stages had been combined. This gives the following corollary to rule 3:

Corollary (Decisionless stages):

Any decisionless stages should be combined with an adjacent stage. Where several combinations are possible, the one eliminating the most state variables is preferable.

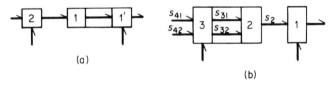

(a)

(b)

Figure 8-41. Decisionless stage combination.

When a stage has a single input state which is held constant, as for stage 3 in Fig. 8–37, rule 3 requires combination of the stage as in Fig. 8–42, since fixed inputs do not qualify as variables. This is remarkable because the simultaneous

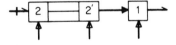

Figure 8-42. Improved dynamic programming.

optimization of d_2 and d_3 is at odds with present dynamic programming practice, which would instead use partial optimizations at every stage. But the optimization plan of Fig. 8–42 does require fewer function evaluations and less storage than either the dynamic programming scheme of Figure 8–38 or the simultaneous optimization plan of Fig. 8–39.

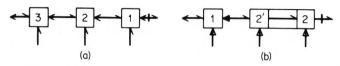

Figure 8-43. Final value serial problem: (a) state inversion; (b) optimization.

Rule 2 on optimization direction often makes it necessary to interchange the roles of various dependent and independent variables. Solution for an input state in terms of an output state is called *state inversion*. It is represented schematically by drawing full arrowheads on the functional diagram as shown in Fig. 8–43(a). Notice that Fig. 8–43(a) describes a serial optimization problem having fixed the final output s_1, rather than the initial input s_4. By state inversion one converts this final value problem into an initial value one which can be solved by improved dynamic programming as shown in Fig. 8–43(b). In the development of the optimization plan the original half arrows are considered to be superseded by the full arrows.

Solution for a decision variable instead of an input state is called *decision inversion*. Full arrows are used to represent decision inversion schematically as shown for stage 1 in Fig. 8–44(a). After decision inversion a stage may become decisionless as in Fig. 8–44(a); in such circumstances the stage should then be combined with another as in Fig. 8–44(b). The usual partial optimizations can then be applied to the rest of the serial system. The optimization plans of Figs. 8–43(b) and 8–44(b) both involve a one-decision, one-state optimization followed by a two-decision, no-state optimization.

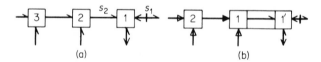

Figure 8-44. Final value serial problem: (a) decision inversion; (b) optimization.

Rule 4 (Fixed output constraints):

Any fixed output should be transformed into an input by either decision or state inversion.

Application of rule 4 results eventually in some decision inputs being transformed into dependent outputs, which of course reduces the apparent number of decision variables. Thus fixed points, if exploited properly by rule 4, actually simplify the optimization problem. After the inversions, each arrow still directed into the system represents a degree of freedom. On an optimization plan these are shown by empty triangles, and by counting them up, one obtains the total number of degrees of freedom [three in Figs. 8–42, 8–43(b), and 8–44(b)]. If one had simply counted free inputs in Figs. 8–43(a) and 8–44(a), one might have gained the mistaken impression that there were four, not three, degrees of freedom. In general, the number of degrees of freedom equals the number of independent variables (free system inputs) minus the number of equality constraints (fixed outputs).

The initial stage of a serial system is the one whose inputs, if any, are not outputs from any other stage, while the final stage of a serial system is the one whose outputs, if any, are not inputs to any other stage. In Fig. 8–37, stage 3 is the initial stage and stage 1 the final stage. By making the multiple final stage outputs from one serial system the initial stage inputs to several other serial systems, one can construct a *diverging* branched system as in Fig. 8–45(a), in which the outputs from stage 5 are the inputs to stages 2 and 4. Such systems may be optimized by a slight extension of ordinary dynamic programming, as shown in the optimization plan of Fig. 8–45(b).

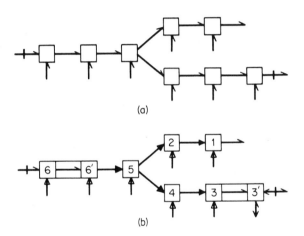

(a)

(b)

Figure 8-45. (a) Diverging branched system; (b) optimization plan.

A *converging* branched system occurs when the final outputs from several serial systems form the multiple inputs to another one as at stage 3 in Fig. 8–46(a). To make applicable rule 2 on optimization direction, all but one of the input branches must be inverted, state inversion usually being the easiest way to do this (see stages 2 and 3' in Fig. 8–46(b)). This generates a special situation for the original output state from the branch being inverted (s_3 in Fig. 8–46(b)) because after inversion such a state must act as an input not only to the junction stage, but also to the inverted branch. This is handled in the functional diagram by adding to the junction stage an input arrow, connected to the state in question by a dashed line as in Fig. 8–46(b), showing

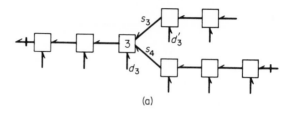

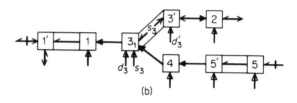

(a)

(b)

Figure 8-46. (a) Converging branched system; (b) optimization plan.

that a trivial transition function ($s_3 = T_3\langle d_3, s_3, s_4 \rangle \equiv s_3$) has been added to the others of the junction stage. Now that s_3 is a decision rather than a state variable, it would be unwise to perform a partial optimization of stage 3', originally the final stage for the inverted converging branch, for this would involve an unnecessary search of all values of s_3. Instead this stage should be combined with the junction stage as shown. Then the partial optimization of combined stages 3 and 3' would involve three decisions d_3, d_3', s_3 and one state variable s_4.

Consider the system in Fig. 8–47(a) in which the output c_1 from stage 1 is also the input to stage 3, so that the functional diagram forms a loop. To optimize such a cyclic system, one of the state variables (say c_1) is designated the *cut state*, a name suggested by the fact that the functional diagram for a loop can be made into a serial one by cutting it. For any fixed value of the cut state the problem of finding the optimal policy is a serial one with fixed input and output states, both equal to the chosen value of c_1 [Fig. 8–47(b)]. Thus, a sequence of such serial problems is solved, one for each different value of c_1. The value of c_1 giving the best result is then the optimum one. It is not always necessary to examine all

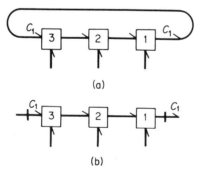

(a)

(b)

Figure 8-47. (a) Cyclic system; (b) serial equivalent for fixed c_1.

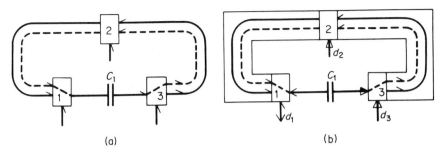

Figure 8-48. Cyclic optimization: (a) cutting the loop; (b) optimization.

possible values of c_1 because direct search methods may be used to direct it to its optimum value.

The process may be viewed as one in which a new transition function and state variable (the cut state) is added to each stage. This fictitious (and trivially simple) transformation is indicated schematically [Fig. 8–48(a)] by passing a dashed line through the stage rectangles from where the cut state enters the system (at stage 3) to where it leaves (at stage 1). The half arrowheads emphasize that c_1 must be treated as an input to each stage. The location of the cut is shown by two vertical lines, which recall that the cut state is fixed during each serial optimization.

In optimizing the system one starts at the cut and works in the direction opposite to that of the state arrows as required by rule 2. Since c_1 is considered fixed temporarily, decision inversion is needed at stage 1, as shown in Fig. 8–48(b). This makes stage 1 decisionless so that it must be combined with stage 2 by the corollary of rule 3. Moreover, rule 2 requires that stage 3 also be combined with stage 2, since there are as many outputs as inputs there. Thus in this case, the optimization plan reduces to a simultaneous optimization with c_1, d_2, and d_3 as the independent variables. This special character of the cut state, intermediate between that of a state variable and a decision variable, is indicated by filling in only half of its triangle.

Rule 5 (Small loops):

Any loop with less than four decision variables should be optimized with respect to all decisions simultaneously.

This rule is interesting because many practical loop problems in industry involve a small number of variables as, for example, a single chemical reactor with recycle of unreacted feed. In these cases, the rule precludes the dynamic programming approach as inefficient. There are still industrial situations, with many decisions in the loop, to which the cut state approach is efficient— such a five-decision loop with its optimization plan is shown in Fig. 8–49.

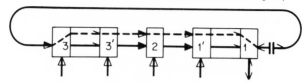

Figure 8-49. Five-decision loop with its optimization plan.

Combinations of loops and branches occur when branch output states are also inputs to other stages. Figure 8–50 shows one example, a feedforward or bypass loop. Such systems are optimized by choosing cut states that break the loops and form branched systems. The fact, already mentioned, that diverging branches are easier to optimize than converging ones leads to the next rule.

Rule 6 (Cut state location):

Cut states should always be inputs to multiple input stages.

This rule, illustrated in Figs. 8–50 and 8–51, breaks the loops into desirable diverging branched systems.

Although each rule by itself is simple and often obvious, the cumulative effect of all of them can be considerable. The simplifications stemming from one rule often make applicable some other rule, triggering further simplifications. The functional diagram, by exposing the structure underlying a set of macrosystem equations, helps the engineer decide how to group and order

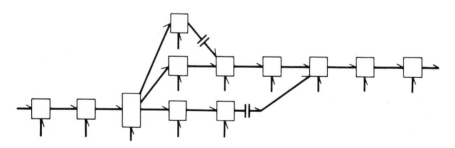

Figure 8-50. Feedforward or bypass loop.

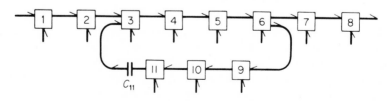

Figure 8-51. Recycle or feedback loop.

optimization calculations into an efficient plan. Inversions, cuts, eliminations, and partial optimizations can be shown directly on the functional diagram, resulting ultimately in a schematic representation of an optimization strategy. Six simple rules are available to transform the original functional diagram into the final optimization plan. Such methods promise to bring optimization theory to bear on systems of greater complexity than has been possible until now.

8-26 Concluding Summary

This chapter has shown how to optimize large systems partially, one stage at a time. The technique, first developed under the name *dynamic programming* for systems having the stages in series, can be extended in principle to loop and branch structures by cutting them up into serial pieces. Care must be exercised in reassembling the serial subsystems, and the extra computation at the junctions renders decomposition impractical when many stages are cross-connected.

The guiding strategies for partial optimization involve exploiting the information flow *between* stages, described abstractly by functional equations and diagrams. These overall strategies are the same no matter what mathematical form the stage transition and return functions take, although the partial optimization within a stage is certainly influenced by the stage's mathematical character. Furthermore, the way information is transmitted by a state variable depends on the form of the originating stage and, at the receiving stage, affects the maximand and hence the mode of partial optimization. Since such interactions are not easily grasped in an abstract discussion, detailed examples were given involving total enumeration, linear inequalities, and nonlinear differentiation for every system structure studied. Overall strategies are most easily grasped by studying the network examples, more subtle points concerning constraints and inversions being illustrated by the linear and nonlinear allocation problems.

The complexity of looped and branched decision processes facilitates mistakes. Optimization strategies of great plausibility which lead to inefficient or nonoptimal computations were illustrated with detailed examples so that the reader will recognize these fallacies and avoid them.

The mathematical parables of this chapter suggest guides to making intelligent decisions in complicated situations. In long range planning when present circumstances, but not future positions, are known, one should start the analysis as far into the future as possible, working backward in time to the present. Diverging branch decision problems, which occur when a raw material is made into several products and distributed to many consumer outlets, can be analyzed in much the same way as a serial problem by working backward from distributors to the original supply. Loop systems, which correspond to planning over a seasonal or business cycle, can be analyzed by passing once around the cycle, starting anywhere, but making sure the two ends of the cut match properly. General recycle (feedback) or bypass (feedforward) systems, arising often in manufacturing operations, can usually be reduced to diverging branch systems by careful location of the cut. Linear allocation problems lend themselves to additive superposition of decisions in converging branch systems. The most important thing to be learned from this chapter is that information flow, as represented by functional equations and diagrams, may differ in direction from the flow of time and materials. For effective optimization of large systems, one must understand information flow and know how to reverse it when expedient.

Although partial optimization has found many applications to serial systems, mainly involving planning over a succession of time periods, its extension to systems with more general structure has been too recent for widespread use. Because state variables carry information and must therefore be evaluated exhaustively, practical application is limited to systems with no more than two or three state variables at any stage, especially when loops or branches introduce extra cut states. The policy improvement procedures of the next chapter will show how to overcome this difficulty.

BIBLIOGRAPHY

Aris, R., *Discrete Dynamic Programming* (Blaisdell, New York, 1964).

———, G. L. Nemhauser, and D. J. Wilde, "Optimization of multistage cyclic and branching systems by serial procedures," *Amer. Inst. Chem. Engs. J.*, **10**, 6 (November, 1964), 913–919.

Beckwith, R. E., "Dynamic programming and network routing: an introduction to the technique of functional equations," *Proc. Dynamic Programming Workshop*, Purdue Univ., 1961, pp. 89–100.

Beightler, C. S., D. B. Johnson, and D. J. Wilde, "Superposition in branching allocation problems," *J. Math. Anal. Appl.*, **12**, 1 (1965), 65–70.

———, and L. G. Mitten, "Design of an optimal sequence of interrelated sampling plans," *J. Amer. Stat. Assoc.*, **59** (March, 1964), 96–104.

Bellman, R. E., *Dynamic Programming* (Princeton Univ., Princeton, N.J., 1957).

———, "Some problems in the theory of dynamic programming," *Econometrica*, **22** (January, 1954), 37–48.

————, "Equipment replacement policy," *J. Soc. Indust. Appl. Math.*, **3** (1955), 133–36.

————, and S. Dreyfus, *Applied Dynamic Programming* (Princeton Univ., Princeton, N.J., 1962).

Cartaino, T., and S. Dreyfus, "Application of dynamic programming to the airplane minimum time-to-climb problem," *Aero. Eng. Rev.*, **16** (1957), 74–77.

Mitten, L. G., "Composition principles for synthesis of optimal multistage processes," *Opns. Res.*, **12**, 4 (July, 1964), 610–19.

Nemhauser, G. L., *Introduction to Dynamic Programming* (Wiley, New York, 1966).

Wilde, D. J., "Strategies for optimizing macrosystems," *Chem. Engng. Prog.*, **61**, 3 (March, 1965), 86–93.

EXERCISES

8-1. (a) Find the shortest path from each western (W) node to an eastern node.

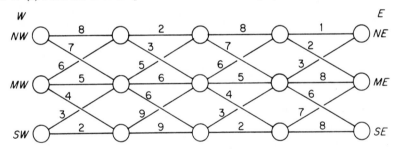

Exercise 8-1(a)

(b) Find the shortest path from each eastern (E) node to a western node.

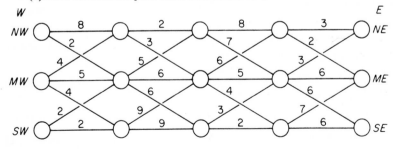

Exercise 8-1(b)

8-2. (a) Find the shortest path from each western node to an eastern node.

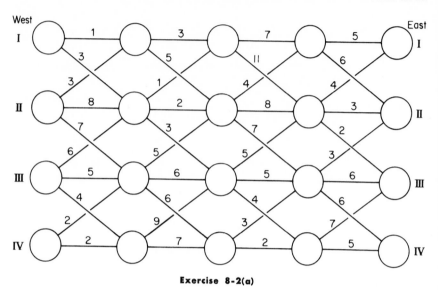

Exercise 8-2(a)

(b) Find the shortest path from each eastern node to a western node.

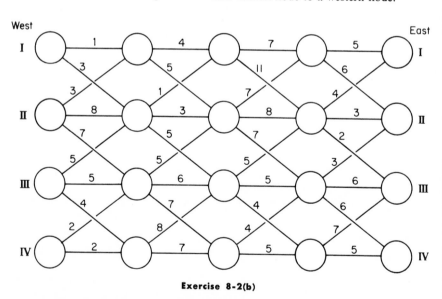

Exercise 8-2(b)

8-3. Find the shortest and longest paths from O to P, where no backward movement (toward O) is permitted.

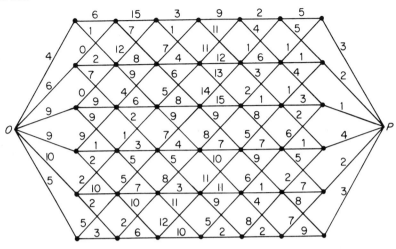

Exercise 8-3

8-4. Given a total resource of 7 units, and a return (profit) at stage i of $8x_i - ix_i^2$, where $x_i = 0, 1, 2, 3$ is the allocation made to the ith stage, find the optimal allocation policy to use to maximize the total return for a 4-stage system if all 7 units must be allocated. That is, maximize the function $p = \sum_{i=1}^{4} (8x_i - ix_i^2)$, subject to the constraints $\sum_{i=1}^{4} x_i = 7$, and $x_i = 0, 1, 2, 3$ for $i = 1, \ldots, 4$.

8-5. Three kinds of items are available for packing into a survival kit which has a maximum volumetric capacity of V. The table below gives the pertinent information on these items, where u_i and v_i are respectively the per-unit utility and volume of item i.

i	u_i	v_i
1	3	2
2	4	3
3	1	1

(a) Assuming that there is no limitation on the numbers of each item selected, find the optimal selection for values of V up to 10.
(b) From part (a), find the general solution for any value of V as a function of V.

8-6. A production process must be scheduled over five periods, I–V. Production during each period is restricted to integral numbers of units and the maximum production per period is four units. The following table gives the total cost of production (in hundreds of dollars) for the different numbers of units that may be produced per period. In addition to these production costs, there is an inventory cost of $100 per unit stored per period. The inventory cost may be taken into account for complete periods only.

Number produced	Period				
	I	II	III	IV	V
0	2	2	3	5	3
1	3	4	4	6	8
2	7	6	8	8	10
3	10	11	13	17	15
4	11	12	14	21	18

Find the optimal number of items to be produced during each period (to minimize the total cost) if the total production requirement is (a) 18 units; (b) 15 units; (c) 13 units; (d) 10 units.

8-7. Solve Exercise 8–4 for the case in which x_i is a continuous, nonnegative variable and compare the answers with those found in Exercise 8–4.

8-8. Solve the following initial-value problem:

$$\max \sum_{i=1}^{5} r_i$$

where
$$\left.\begin{array}{c} r_i = s_i + 3d_i; \\ s_{i-1} \equiv \bar{s}_i = 2s_i - 0.2d_i; \\ 0 \le d_i \le s_i \end{array}\right\} \quad i = 1, \ldots, 5$$

and the initial state is $s_5 = 100$.

8-9. (a) Solve the following problem using dynamic programming by writing it as a serial decision problem:

maximize $p = x_1 x_2 x_3 x_4 x_5$

subject to the constraints:

$$x_1 + x_2 + x_3 + x_4 + x_5 = 20, \quad x_j \ge 0, \quad j = 1, \ldots, 5.$$

(b) Generalize the method used to solve the problem in part (a) to provide a solution to

maximize $p = \prod_{j=1}^{n} x_j$

where

$$\sum_{j=1}^{n} x_j = k, \quad x_j \ge 0, \quad j = 1, \ldots, n$$

and from this solution show that for all $x_j \ge 0$,

$$\sqrt[n]{\prod_{j=1}^{n} x_j} \le \frac{1}{n} \sum_{j=1}^{n} x_j$$

8-10. Solve the six final-value problems, $\bar{c}_1 = I, \ldots, IV$, described by the network of Fig. 8–2, using state inversion. Compare the solution for $\bar{c}_1 = I$ with the initial value problem $s_6 = I$.

8-11. Solve the problem: maximize $p = \sum_{i=1}^{3} r_i$, where $r_i = 5d_i - id_i^2$, $\bar{s}_i = s_i - 0.4d_i$, $0 \le d_i \le s_i$ as a *final*-value problem, $\bar{s}_1 = \bar{c}_1$, using state inversion. Compare your answer with that given in the text where this problem is solved both as an initial-value and as a final-value problem using decision inversion.

8-12. Solve the following as a final-value problem, using state inversion: maximize $p = \sum_{i=1}^{5} r_i$, where $r_i = s_i + 3d_i$, $\bar{s}_i = 2s_i - 0.2d_i$, $\bar{s}_1 \equiv \bar{c}_1$, and the decisions are restricted by $0 \le d_i \le s_i$. This problem is the final-value version of Exercise 8-8; in that problem the optimal solution produced a value of $\bar{s}_1^* = 2332.8$. Setting $\bar{c}_1 = 2332.8$ in your solution, compare the resulting value of f_5 with that for the initial-value problem.

8-13. Solve Exercise 8-10 using *decision* inversion and notice the difference in the solution procedure and computational effort from that employed in state inversion for the same network.

8-14. Using decision inversion, solve the two-industry problem described in the text as a final-value problem. That is, for $0 \le d_i \le s_i$, $i = 1, \ldots, 5$,

$$\text{maximize } \sum_{j=1}^{5} (s_j + d_j)$$

where

$$\bar{s}_i = 1.9s_i - 0.4d_i, \quad i = 1, \ldots, 4$$
$$\bar{s}_5 = 0.9s_5 - 0.4d_5$$

and the final output is fixed at $\bar{s}_1 \equiv \bar{c}_1$

8-15. Find the shortest path from West to East under the loop constraint of beginning and ending at the same level (I, ..., IV).

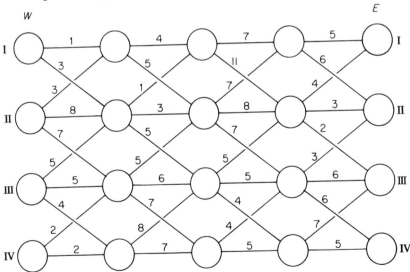

Exercise 8-15

8-16. (a) Solve the following initial-value problem: maximize $p = r_1 + r_2$, where $r_n = 0.8s_n - 0.2s_n d_n$, $\bar{s}_n = 0.7s_n + 0.5s_n d_n$, $0 \le d_n \le 1$, for $n = 1, 2$, and the system input is $s_2 = 100$.

(b) Consider the foregoing problem when augmented by the inhomogeneous loop constraint, $s_2 = 100 + \frac{1}{2}\bar{s}_1$.

  Show that the policy $\{d_1^* = 1, d_2^* = 1\}$ produces a larger value of p than does the policy which was optimal for the serial problem in part (a). [*Hint:* First derive the expression: $s_2 = 100/(1 - \frac{1}{2}K)$, where $K = (0.7 + 0.5d_2)(0.7 + 0.5d_1)$].

8–17. Solve Exercise 4–10 using partial optimization.

Optimal Control
by Policy Improvement: **9**
The Optimum Principle

For each value of every state variable, partial optimization must perform an optimization and store the results. Hence dynamic programming is usually impractical when there are more than two state variables per stage. Since most of the information generated by partial optimization is never used, it would seem reasonable to deal with selected values of the state variables rather than with all of them. A particularly attractive idea is to guess at a set of decisions, generate the values of the states resulting, and then decide how to adjust the decisions so as to improve the objective function. This successive improvement approach needs much less computer storage, although it may require a great many trials if the initial hunch is bad or the functions poorly behaved.

To adjust the trial decisions intelligently, one must know how the changes will affect the system objective function, at least to a first-order approximation. We have seen in other situations that these rates of change are conveniently measured by constrained derivatives. Thus it is profitable to formulate the serial optimization problem in terms of optimizing the objective function subject to the equality constraints which specify that the states and decisions satisfy the transition functions. The serial structure then makes it easy to find recursion relations for computing constrained derivatives measuring the ultimate effect of each state variable perturbation upon the objective function. From these constrained derivatives with respect to the states one can readily find other constrained derivatives needed to improve the policy, namely, those with respect to the decisions. This analysis gives necessary conditions which can in certain simple cases be solved explicitly to give the optimal policy in closed form. Most of the time, however, numerical solutions can be obtained only by successive approximation algorithms.

The results for staged serial systems, in which the transitions are described by recursion or difference equations, can by passage to the limit be generalized to the continuous case where differential equations define the system. Such problems arise in automatic control theory, and the formulation here involves the "state variable" approach. The continuous theory, closely related to the calculus of variations but usually easier to understand, is illustrated by deriving control schemes for minimizing quadratic measures of effectiveness, such as integral squared error, in dynamic systems described by linear differential equations. Extension to problems involving minimum time or minimum control effort is straightforward.

Two prices must be paid to replace dynamic programming by the more economical constrained derivative approach. First, one must require the return and transition functions to be piecewise continuously differentiable functions of the states and decisions; this rules out the network problems solved so easily by dynamic programming. Secondly, successive approximation can be time-consuming, and convergence is not always assured.

As elsewhere in this book, the constrained derivative approach is used here to show how it joins the various optimization techniques into a unified theory. The historical development of the subject is in the opposite direction. The continuous case was studied first, by the Russian mathematicians L. S. Pontryagin, V. G. Boltyanskii, R. V. Gramkrelidze, and E. F. Mischenko, who for their efforts were awarded the Lenin Prize for Science and Technology because their theory, called the *Maximum Principle*, contributed to the spectacular success of the Russian space program in the late 1950's. Their rigorous, topologically inspired proofs are stronger, but more difficult to understand, than those presented here.

Independently of the Russians, F. Horn developed the theory for the continuous case in his Ph.D. dissertation on optimal design of chemical reactors at the Technical University of Vienna. His point of view, subsequently developed in the German and then in the English literature, is very close to that used here. The Austrian theoretical physicist is now Professor of Chemical Engineering at Rice University in the United States.

The work of the English mathematician H. P. F. Swinnerton-Dyer on the same subject, which was also completely independent, went unrecognized at the time. The doctoral dissertation, subsequently published as a book, of the American electrical engineer, R. Howard, developed the "policy improvement" algorithm, the first after dynamic programming to address itself to staged serial optimization. His book earned the Lanchester Prize of the Operations Research Society of America.

By 1961 the Russian work was known in the United States, and S. S. L. Chang indicated how to extend a weakened version of the "Minimum Principle" to the staged case. Concurrently S. Katz gave a fuller treatment containing a subtle technical flaw, subsequently corrected by Butkovskii, and Horn and Jackson, after wide application of Katz's algorithm to chemical engineering problems by L. T. Fan and co-workers. Fortunately the error affected only statements concerning the generality of Fan's results rather than the validity of the specific numerical optima obtained.

9-01 Staged Serial Optimization

Consider an N-stage serial optimization problem with P input state variables and Q decision variables at every stage. No generality is lost in assuming that the number of state and decision variables is unchanged from stage to stage, since dummy variables can be added to any stage which is deficient. Each state variable s_{np} has a double subscript, the first identifying the stage number and the second the variable itself ($n = 1, \ldots, N; p = 1, \ldots, P$). The decisions d_{nq} are identified similarly ($q = 1, \ldots, Q$). On occasion the dummy indices i and j may be used in place of p and q, as in the following paragraph.

Let there be NP continuously differentiable transition functions $T_{np}\langle s_{ni}, d_{nj}\rangle$ giving the output states $s_{n+1,p}$ from stage n as a function of the input variables s_{ni} and d_{nj}, gathered into vectors $\mathbf{s}_n$ and $\mathbf{d}_n$.

$$s_{n+1,p} = T_{np}\langle s_{ni}, d_{nj}\rangle = T_{np}\langle \mathbf{s}_n, \mathbf{d}_n\rangle \tag{9-1}$$

Notice that the incidence identities ($\tilde{\mathbf{s}}_n \equiv \mathbf{s}_{n+1}$) of partial optimization have been incorporated into these transition functions directly, with the stages numbered in the direction of information flow, opposite to that of the preceding chapter. Let there also be N continuously differentiable return functions $R_n\langle \mathbf{s}_n, \mathbf{d}_n\rangle$ giving the economic value r_n generated at each stage by the input variables.

$$r_n = R_n\langle \mathbf{s}_n, \mathbf{d}_n\rangle \tag{9-2}$$

The objective is to optimize the sum of the returns from all stages.

$$y = \sum_{n=1}^{N} r_n \tag{9-3}$$

It is convenient to introduce N new state variables $s_{n+1,0}$, one for each stage. These *accounting variables* measure the sum of the returns from stages 1 through n.

$$s_{n+1,0} \equiv \sum_{k=1}^{n} r_k \tag{9-4}$$

This variable may be included with the other stage n outputs and a transition function T_{n0} written, giving the return for the first n stages in terms of the stage n inputs, including the new accounting variable s_{n0}.

$$s_{n+1,0} = \sum_{k=1}^{n-1} r_k + r_n = s_{n0} + R_n\langle \mathbf{s}_n, \mathbf{d}_n \rangle$$
$$\equiv T_{n0}\langle \mathbf{s}_n, \mathbf{d}_n \rangle \tag{9-5}$$

It is to be understood from now on that the indices i and p run from 0 to P, s_{n0} being considered a state variable like the others. The new problem is to optimize $s_{N+1,0}$

$$y = s_{N+1,0} \tag{9-6}$$

subject to the equality constraints (9–1) and (9–5). This form of the problem, in which one wants to optimize the final, or terminal, state of the serial system, is sometimes called the *terminal control* problem. All serial optimization problems can be cast into this form, including those in which the objective function also contains a contribution from the terminal states $s_{N+1,1}, \ldots, s_{N+1,P}$. If

$$y = \sum_{n=1}^{N} r_n + \varphi\langle s_{N+1,1}, \ldots, s_{N+1,P} \rangle$$

where $\varphi\langle \ldots \rangle$ is the contribution from the terminal states, write the transition function T_{N0} as

$$s_{N+1,0} = T_{N0}\langle \mathbf{s}_N, \mathbf{d}_N \rangle$$
$$= s_{N0} + R_N\langle \mathbf{s}_N, \mathbf{d}_N \rangle + \varphi\langle T_{N1}\langle \mathbf{s}_N, \mathbf{d}_N \rangle, \ldots, T_{NP}\langle \mathbf{s}_N, \mathbf{d}_N \rangle\rangle \tag{9-7}$$

Therefore all serial optimization problems can (and will) be formulated as terminal control problems.

9-02 Constrained Optimization

The serial optimization problem is then to find the NQ decisions $d_{11}, \ldots, d_{NQ}$ optimizing $s_{N+1,0}$

$$y^* = \operatorname*{opt}_{d_{11}, \ldots, d_{NQ}} (s_{N+1,0}) \tag{9-8}$$

subject to NP equality constraints based on the transition functions.

$$s_{n+1,p} - T_{np}\langle \mathbf{s}_n, \mathbf{d}_n \rangle = 0 \tag{9-9}$$

All these functions being assumed continuously differentiable, the solution of this constrained optimization problem must be at a stationary point of the Lagrangian function L defined by

$$L \equiv s_{N+1,0} - \sum_{n=1}^{N} \sum_{i=0}^{P} \lambda_{n+1,i}(s_{n+1,i} - T_{ni}\langle \mathbf{s}_n, \mathbf{d}_n \rangle) \qquad (9\text{-}10)$$

where the $\lambda_{n+1,i}$ are Lagrange multipliers, one for each constraint.

Before finding the stationary points, it is well to recall the theory of Chapter 2, where the equality constrained problem was first discussed, in order to interpret the multipliers as constrained derivatives. Suppose the optimum values of the decisions, states, and objective function have been found. Imagine that one of the output states $s_{n+1,i}$ from stage n is required to assume a value slightly different from $s_{n+1,i}^*$, its optimum value. This disturbance will force other states and decisions to adjust if the objective is to remain optimal. Of course the value of the optimal objective will usually change, and the rate of change of y^* with respect to the perturbation in $s_{n+1,i}$ has been called the *constrained derivative* $\delta y/\delta s_{n+1,i}$. In Chapter 2 this function was given the abbreviation $\lambda_{n+1,i}$ and called a *Lagrange multiplier*. In the serial optimization problem at hand, the interpretation of the undetermined multipliers as constrained derivatives with respect to the states will be emphasized by calling them *state derivatives*.

9-03 State Derivatives

At the stationary points of L, its first derivatives with respect to the state variables must vanish. Because of the special serial structure of the problem, the resulting equations will be easy to solve for the state derivatives $\lambda_{n+1,i}$.

First differentiate L with respect to $s_{N+1,0}$ to obtain

$$\frac{\partial L}{\partial s_{N+1,0}} = 1 - \lambda_{N+1,0} = 0$$

whence
$$\lambda_{N+1,0} = 1 \qquad (9\text{-}11)$$

Similarly, for $i \neq 0$,

$$\frac{\partial L}{\partial s_{N+1,i}} = -\lambda_{N+1,i} = 0$$

so that
$$\lambda_{N+1,i} = 0 \qquad (i \neq 0) \qquad (9\text{-}12)$$

These simple final values of the state derivatives are obtained whenever the final conditions on the state variables are unspecified. This question will be discussed further in Section 9–08 concerning more general boundary conditions.

The state derivatives with respect to the accounting variables s_{n0} are readily found to be unity for every stage.

$$\frac{\partial L}{\partial s_{n0}} = -\lambda_{n0} + \sum_{i=0}^{P} \lambda_{n+1,i}\left(\frac{\partial T_{ni}}{\partial s_{n0}}\right) = 0$$

But only T_{n0} depends on s_{n0}, so $\partial T_{ni}/\partial s_{n0} = 0$ for $i \neq 0$. Moreover, by Eq. (9-5), $\partial T_{n0}/\partial s_{n0} = 1$, so Eq. (9-11) implies

$$\lambda_{n0} = \lambda_{n+1,0} = \ldots = \lambda_{N+1,0} = 1 \tag{9-13}$$

This simple relation holds, no matter what boundary conditions on the states apply.

The rest of the state derivatives are found from

$$\frac{\partial L}{\partial s_{np}} = -\lambda_{np} + \sum_{i=0}^{P} \lambda_{n+1,i}\left(\frac{\partial T_{ni}}{\partial s_{np}}\right) = 0$$

whence, for $n = 2, \ldots, N$,

$$\lambda_{np} = \sum_{i=0}^{P} \lambda_{n+1,i}\left(\frac{\partial T_{ni}}{\partial s_{np}}\right) \qquad (p \neq 0) \tag{9-14}$$

This expression enables calculation of state derivatives for stage n from knowledge of those at stage $n+1$, provided that the values of the derivatives $\partial T_{ni}/\partial s_{np}$ are known. For a given policy, these derivatives can be evaluated, and finding the λ_{np} is a straightforward recursive computation, beginning with the terminal conditions of Eqs. (9-11) and (9-12) and running backwards from stage N to stage 1.

9-04 Decision Derivatives

If the NQ decision variables d_{nq} are not constrained, then the Lagrangian L must also be stationary with respect to the decisions. Although most practical problems involve constrained decisions, analysis of the unconstrained case first will build a foundation for studying the more general situation. When decisions are not constrained, the derivatives $\partial L/\partial d_{nq}$ must vanish.

$$\frac{\partial L}{\partial d_{nq}} = \sum_{i=0}^{P} \lambda_{n+1,i}\left(\frac{\partial T_{ni}}{\partial d_{nq}}\right) = 0 \tag{9-15}$$

For each stage n there are exactly Q of these equations, one for each of the unknown decisions at the stage. Notice that the equations for any stage do not involve decisions at any other stage. Because of the serial structure, the original optimization problem involving all NQ decisions simultaneously has been decomposed into N separate problems each involving only Q decisions.

It is instructive to write the multipliers as state derivatives in the sum in Eq. (9-15) and then apply the chain rule.

$$\sum_{i=0}^{P} \lambda_{n+1,\,i} \left(\frac{\partial T_{ni}}{\partial d_{nq}}\right) = \sum_{i=0}^{P} \left(\frac{\delta y}{\delta s_{n+1,\,i}}\right)\left(\frac{\partial T_{ni}}{\partial d_{nq}}\right) = \frac{\delta y}{\delta d_{nq}} \qquad (9\text{-}16)$$

The right member is in fact the constrained derivative called the *decision derivative* of the optimal value y^* of the objective function with respect to the decision d_{nq}. Equations (9–15) and (9–16) together show that the derivatives of the Lagrangian with respect to the decisions are the decision derivatives.

$$\frac{\delta y}{\delta d_{nq}} = \frac{\partial L}{\partial d_{nq}} \qquad (9\text{-}17)$$

9-05 The Discrete Optimum Principle

When the decisions are unconstrained, one sets the decision derivatives to zero to find the optimum. Suppose, however, that the decision variables must themselves satisfy certain inequality constraints. If each set of constraint functions involves only decisions from the same stage and is wholly independent of any state variables, one could write, for each stage, conditions on the decision derivatives that would resemble those of Kuhn and Tucker developed in Chapter 3. A more elegant procedure is to construct an optimization problem for each stage whose solution would satisfy the Kuhn-Tucker conditions for the original problem. This is readily accomplished by introducing a new function whose first partial derivatives with respect to the decisions are the decision derivatives. Define

$$H_n \equiv \sum_{i=0}^{P} \lambda_{n+1,\,i} T_{ni} \qquad (9\text{-}18)$$

This function is called the *stage n Hamiltonian* after the astronomer-physicist W. R. Hamilton, who first used such functions to unify mechanics and optics. By Eq. (9-16)

$$\frac{\partial H_n}{\partial d_{nq}} = \sum_{i=0}^{P} \lambda_{n+1,\,i}\left(\frac{\partial T_{ni}}{\partial d_{nq}}\right) = \frac{\delta y}{\delta d_{nq}} \qquad (9\text{-}19)$$

as required. The equivalent problem is to find *local* optima or stationary points for each Hamiltonian with respect to its constrained decision variables. Hence if one is maximizing y one wishes to find decisions $\mathbf{d}_n^*$ such that, for all decisions $\mathbf{d}_n$ *in the neighborhood of* $\mathbf{d}_n^*$,

$$H_n\langle \boldsymbol{\lambda}_{n+1}^*, \mathbf{s}_n^*, \mathbf{d}_n^* \rangle \geq H_n\langle \boldsymbol{\lambda}_{n+1}^*, \mathbf{s}_n^*, \mathbf{d}_n \rangle \qquad (9\text{-}20)$$

Notice that the decision derivatives $\boldsymbol{\lambda}_{n+1}^*$ and the state variables $\mathbf{s}_n^*$ must also be at their optimal values. It is understood that the optimization is only over the set of decisions satisfying the constraints.

This form of stating the necessary (although not sufficient) conditions for the solution is known as the *discrete optimum principle*, the word "discrete" referring to the staged character of the problem. It is based on a similar

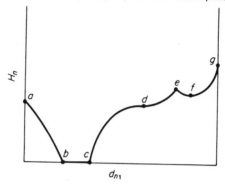

Figure 9-1. A pathological Hamiltonian.

idea for continuous cases to be developed later, known as the "maximum" or "minimum" principle of Pontryagin, and following Leibniz' example, we have included both possibilities by using the word "optimum." The adjective "digitized" was used instead of "discrete" by Chang, who first stated the principle correctly. It is very important to notice that, since only first derivatives are used, not only all local optima, but all stationary points, must be considered candidates for the solution to the original problem. Figure 9-1, inspired by a particularly striking example of Butkovskii, shows a pathological Hamiltonian for a maximization problem in which the solution may be at the local maxima a, e, and g, at the local minimum f, at the stationary point of inflection d, or on any point on the horizontal line between b and c where every point is a global minimum. Fortunately, many practical cases have only one local optimum and no other stationary points per Hamiltonian. Hamiltonians also have the interesting property that their derivatives with respect to the state variables give the state derivatives, for by Eq. (9–14),

$$\frac{\partial H_n}{\partial s_{np}} = \sum_{i=0}^{P} \lambda_{n+1,i} \left(\frac{\partial T_{ni}}{\partial s_{np}} \right) = \lambda_{np} \qquad (9\text{-}21)$$

9-06 Linear Allocation Example

Using the discrete optimum principle on the four-stage linear allocation problem solved previously by dynamic programming will not only show how closely the two approaches are related, but also give insight into the meanings of the Hamiltonians and state derivatives. It will also give practice in converting into the terminal control problem form. In the original problem of Chapter 8, one wished to maximize the total dividend from four successive investments of an initial capital of $100, given that the returns and transition functions are, respectively,

$$r_n = 0.5s_n - 0.2d_n$$

$$s_{n+1} = 0.7s_n + 0.4d_n; \qquad n = 1, \ldots, 4$$

The constraints

$$0 \le d_n \le s_n \qquad (9\text{-}22)$$

involving both states and decisions, are not in the proper form for application of the optimum principle, but the change of variable

$$d_{n1} \equiv \frac{d_n}{s_n} \qquad (9\text{-}23)$$

removes the explicit dependence on the state variable.

$$0 \le d_{n1} \le 1 \qquad (9\text{-}24)$$

Substituting this new variable into the transition functions and affixing a second subscript 1 to the state variable to conform to the practice of this chapter gives

$$s_{n+1,1} = T_{n1}\langle s_{n1}, d_{n1} \rangle = 0.7s_{n1} + 0.4s_{n1}d_{n1} \qquad (9\text{-}25)$$

The accounting variable s_{nc} is now introduced through Eq. (9–5).

$$s_{n+1,0} = s_{n0} + 0.5s_{n1} - 0.2s_{n1}d_{n1}$$
$$= T_{n0}\langle s_{n0}, s_{n1}, d_{n1} \rangle \qquad (9\text{-}26)$$

The equivalent terminal control problem is therefore to maximize s_{50} with respect to $d_{11}, \ldots, d_{41}$, subject to the constraints (9–25) and (9–26) and given the initial conditions $s_{10} = 0$ and $s_{11} = 100$.

Since the state derivatives $\lambda_{50} (= 1)$ and $\lambda_{51} (= 0)$ are the only ones known, the analysis should start with the final stage 4, just as in partial optimization. Knowing the state derivatives, one can immediately write the Hamiltonian for stage 4 by Eq. (9–18).

$$H_4 = \lambda_{50}T_{40} + \lambda_{51}T_{41} = s_{40} + s_{41}(0.5 - 0.2d_{41})$$

For any positive s_{40} and s_{41}, this expression is maximized globally when

$$d_{41}^* = 0$$

As in all linear cases, this decision is the only one to be considered, since no others can give interior stationary points or local maxima.

Hence $\qquad H_4^* = s_{40}^* + 0.5s_{41}^* = s_{40}^* + f_1\langle s_{41}^* \rangle = s_{50}^*$

where $f_1\langle s_{41} \rangle$ is the optimal one-stage return of dynamic programming. In this linear homogeneous case the Hamiltonian H_4 is simply the objective function expressed in terms of the inputs to stage 4. Since s_{40}, the return from stages 1, 2, and 3, cannot be affected by d_{41}, maximizing H_4 is equivalent to maximizing $R_4\langle s_{41}, d_{41} \rangle$, the return from stage 4 alone.

To extend the analysis to stage 3, the optimal state derivatives λ_{40}^* and λ_{41}^* must be found from Eqs. (9–13) and (9–14).

$$\lambda_{40}^* = 1$$

$$\lambda_{41} = \lambda_{50} \left(\frac{\partial T_{40}}{\partial s_{41}} \right) + \lambda_{51} \left(\frac{\partial T_{41}}{\partial s_{41}} \right)$$

$$= \frac{\partial T_{40}}{\partial s_{41}} = 0.5 - 0.2 d_{41}$$

whence
$$\lambda_{41}^* = 0.5 - 0.2 d_{41}^* = 0.5$$

Notice that λ_{41}^* is the coefficient of $f_1 \langle s_4 \rangle$ in the solution by partial optimization, verifying that $\lambda_{41}^* = \delta y / \delta s_{41}$.

The Hamiltonian for stage 3 is

$$H_3 = \lambda_{40} T_{30} + \lambda_{41}^* T_{31}$$

$$= s_{30} + s_{31}(0.5 - 0.2 d_{31}) + 0.5 s_{31}(0.7 + 0.4 d_{31})$$

$$= s_{30} + 0.85 s_{31}$$

This function does not depend on d_{31}, so any allowable value may be assigned to it.

$$0 \le d_{31}^* \le 1$$

The optimal state derivatives for stage 3, needed to extend the analysis to stage 2, are

$$\lambda_{30}^* = 1$$

and
$$\lambda_{31}^* = 0.5 - 0.2 d_{31}^* + 0.5(0.7 + 0.4 d_{31}^*)$$

$$= 0.85$$

Notice that this state derivative also happens to be independent of the decision d_{31}. (Completion of the optimization for stages 2 and 1 is left to the reader as an exercise.)

The foregoing example was intended to emphasize similarities between partial optimization and the optimum principle, but one should not jump to the conclusion that the two approaches are almost identical. In the terminal control formulation of the linear allocation problem, the optimal decisions happen to be independent of the state variable, which is not the case in general. This independence permitted knowledge of the optimal values of state derivatives at every stage, a fortuitous circumstance rarely found in practice. More often, one must estimate these state derivatives and set up a successive approximation scheme.

The linearity and homogeneity of this special problem has made the Hamiltonians equal to the objective function at every stage, but this would not be true in nonlinear situations. In any case, however, the first derivatives of the Hamiltonians with respect to the decisions would match the decision derivatives.

9-07 Final Conditions

The preceding analysis holds for situations where the initial and terminal states are free to assume any value optimizing the objective function. In the absence of initial conditions, one can treat all the stage 1 inputs (except the accounting variable s_{10}) as decision variables in optimizing the stage 1 Hamiltonian. They would in fact be "choice variables" in the parlance of partial optimization. Initial conditions can therefore be regarded merely as constraints on the choices available for optimizing H_1.

Final conditions must be treated differently. The strategy used here will be to introduce them into the objective function with Lagrange multipliers and, by finding stationary points of this new Lagrangian, to derive additional conditions on the final state derivatives $\lambda_{N+1,1}, \ldots, \lambda_{N+1,P}$.

Suppose that the final state variables $s_{N+1,1}, \ldots, s_{N+1,P}$ must satisfy the following R equations, in which $R \leq P$, and the functions h_r ($r = 1, \ldots, R$) are continuously differentiable.

$$h_r\langle s_{N+1,1}, \ldots, s_{N+1,P}\rangle = 0 \tag{9-27}$$

Let μ_r be Lagrange multipliers corresponding to these constraints. Then the Lagrangian for the serial optimization problem with these final conditions imposed is

$$L = s_{N+1,0} - \sum_{n=1}^{N} \sum_{i=0}^{P} \lambda_{n+1,i}[s_{n+1,i} - T_{ni}\langle \mathbf{s}_n, \mathbf{d}_n\rangle] - \sum_{r=1}^{R} \mu_r h_r\langle s_{N+1,p}\rangle \tag{9-28}$$

Differentiation with respect to the $s_{N+1,p}$ gives

$$\frac{\partial L}{\partial s_{N+1,p}} = -\lambda_{N+1,p} - \sum_{r=1}^{R} \mu_r \frac{\partial h_r}{\partial s_{N+1,p}} = 0 \tag{9-29}$$

Contrast this with the initial value situation described by Eq. (9–12), where the state derivatives $\lambda_{N+1,p}$ turn out to be zero.

Since $P \geq R$, any R of these equations can be solved for the μ_r in terms of R of the state derivatives, say $\lambda_{N+1,1}, \ldots, \lambda_{N+1,R}$. By Cramer's rule the solution may be given in terms of Jacobian determinants as

$$\mu_r =$$
$$-\sum_{p=1}^{R} \frac{\lambda_{N+1,p}\, \partial(h_{r+1}, \ldots, h_R, h_1, \ldots, h_{r-1})/\partial(s_{N+1,p+1}, \ldots, s_{N+1,R}, s_{N+1,1}, \ldots, s_{N+1,p-1})}{\partial(h_1, \ldots, h_R)/\partial(s_{N+1,1}, \ldots, s_{N+1,R})} \tag{9-30}$$

This can be expressed more compactly by defining, in terms of these Jacobians, the constrained derivatives $\delta s_{N+1,p}/\delta h_r$ of the final states with respect to the terminal constraint slack variables.

$$\frac{\delta s_{N+1,p}}{\delta h_r} \equiv$$

$$-\frac{\partial(h_{r+1}, \ldots, h_R, h_1, \ldots, h_{r-1})/\partial(s_{N+1, p+1}, \ldots, s_{N+1, R}, s_{N+1, 1}, \ldots, s_{N+1, p-1})}{\partial(h_1, \ldots, h_R)/\partial(s_{N+1, 1}, \ldots, s_{N+1, R})}$$

(9-31)

Equations (9–30) and (9–31) give

$$\mu_r = \sum_{p=1}^{R} \lambda_{N+1, p} \left(\frac{\delta s_{N+1, p}}{\delta h_r} \right)$$

(9-32)

To see that this is consistent with the interpretation of the Lagrange multiplier μ_r as the constrained derivative of the objective function with respect to the constraint, substitute $\lambda_{N+1, p} \equiv \delta y / \delta s_{N+1, p}$ into (9–32).

$$\mu_r = \sum_{p=1}^{R} \left(\frac{\delta y}{\delta s_{N+1, p}} \right) \left(\frac{\delta s_{N+1, p}}{\delta h_r} \right) \equiv \frac{\delta y}{\delta h_r}$$

(9-33)

The remaining $P - R$ state derivatives can now be expressed in terms of the first R by combining Eqs. (9–29) and (9–32).

$$\lambda_{N+1, i} = - \sum_{r=1}^{R} \sum_{p=1}^{R} \lambda_{N+1, p} \left(\frac{\delta s_{N+1, p}}{\delta h_r} \right) \left(\frac{\partial h_r}{\partial s_{N+1, i}} \right); \qquad i = R+1, \ldots, P$$

(9-34)

Equations (9–18) and (9–34) give

$$H_N = T_{N0} + \sum_{p=1}^{R} \lambda_{N+1, p} T_{Np} - \sum_{i=R+1}^{P} \sum_{r=1}^{R} \sum_{p=1}^{R} \lambda_{N+1, p} \left(\frac{\delta s_{N+1, p}}{\delta h_r} \right) \left(\frac{\partial h_r}{\partial s_{N+1, i}} \right) T_{Ni}$$

$$= T_{N0} + \sum_{p=1}^{R} \lambda_{N+1, p} \left[T_{Np} - \sum_{i=R+1}^{P} \sum_{r=1}^{R} \left(\frac{\delta s_{N+1, p}}{\delta h_r} \right) \left(\frac{\partial h_r}{\partial s_{N+1, i}} \right) T_{Ni} \right]$$

(9-35)

The state derivatives λ_{Np} are given by an expression derived similarly.

$$\lambda_{Np} = \frac{\partial T_{N0}}{\partial s_{Np}} + \sum_{k=1}^{R} \lambda_{N+1, k} \left[\frac{\partial T_{Nk}}{\partial s_{Np}} - \sum_{i=R+1}^{P} \sum_{r=1}^{R} \left(\frac{\delta s_{N+1, k}}{\delta h_r} \right) \left(\frac{\partial h_r}{\partial s_{N+1, i}} \right) \left(\frac{\partial T_{Ni}}{\partial s_{Np}} \right) \right]$$

(9-36)

All other equations are unchanged. Noticeably absent are any expressions for the terminal state derivatives $\lambda_{N+1, 1}, \ldots, \lambda_{N+1, R}$ needed to start the calculations. Every condition imposed on the final state removes knowledge about the terminal state derivatives.

This phenomenon displays itself most clearly when, as is often the case in practice, each terminal constraint merely assigns a number to one of the final states, that is,

$$h_r = s_{N+1, r} - k_r = 0$$

(9-37)

where k_r is a constant. In this case only the state derivatives for the free states $s_{N+1, R+1}, \ldots, s_{N+1, P}$ remain zero

$$\lambda_{N+1, i} = 0 \qquad (i = R+1, \ldots, P)$$

(9-38)

whereas $\lambda_{N+1, 1}, \ldots, \lambda_{N+1, R}$ are undetermined. Equations (9–35) and (9–36) simplify to

$$H_N = \sum_{p=0}^{R} \lambda_{N+1, p} T_{Np}$$

(9-39)

and
$$\lambda_{Np} = \sum_{i=0}^{R} \lambda_{N+1, i} \left(\frac{\partial T_{Ni}}{\partial s_{Np}}\right) \tag{9-40}$$

Since there are R unknown parameters, this is still an unsatisfactory state of affairs. After interpreting these conditions in geometric terms, we shall show how the state and decision inversion techniques of partial optimization can be used to circumvent this problem.

9-08 The Transversality Conditions

Rozenoer stated the preceding conditions in geometric terms by visualizing all solutions of the terminal constraints as forming a $(P - R)$-dimensional surface in the P-dimensional space of all possible terminal states $s_{N+1, 1}$, $\ldots, s_{N+1, P}$. This surface contains all terminal states satisfying the final conditions. Let $\mathbf{s}'_{N+1} \equiv (s'_{N+1, 1}, \ldots, s'_{N+1, P})$ be any point in the $(P - R)$-dimensional hyperplane tangent to the surface at $\mathbf{s}'_{N+1}$. Such points must satisfy the R linear equations

$$\sum_{p=1}^{P} \left(\frac{\partial h_r}{\partial s_{N+1, p}}\right)(s_{N+1, p} - s'_{N+1, p}) = 0 \tag{9-41}$$

The points $\boldsymbol{\lambda}_{N+1} \equiv (\lambda_{N+1, 1}, \ldots, \lambda_{N+1, P})$, being P-dimensional themselves, can also be considered as vectors in this space with their tails at the origin. To measure the angle between the vectors $\boldsymbol{\lambda}_{N+1}$ and the points in the tangent plane, take the scalar product and apply Eqs. (9–29) and (9–41).

$$\boldsymbol{\lambda}_{N+1}(\mathbf{s}_{N+1} - \mathbf{s}'_{N+1}) = \sum_{p=1}^{P} \lambda_{N+1, p}(s_{N+1, p} - s'_{N+1, p})$$
$$= -\sum_{p=1}^{P} \sum_{r=1}^{R} \mu_r \left(\frac{\partial h_r}{\partial s_{N+1, p}}\right)(s_{N+1, p} - s'_{N+1, p}) \tag{9-42}$$
$$= 0$$

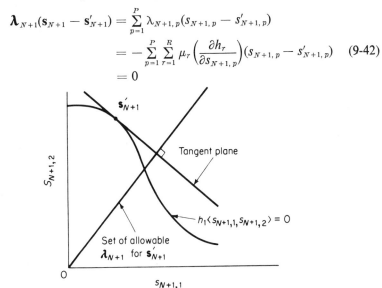

Figure 9-2. The transversality conditions.

Hence $\boldsymbol{\lambda}_{N+1}$ is orthogonal (perpendicular) to the tangent plane at s'_{N+1}. The value of $\boldsymbol{\lambda}_{N+1}$, of course, changes as s'_{N+1} moves. Figure 9–2 illustrates these *transversality conditions*, a term borrowed from the calculus of variations, (see Gelfand and Fomin), for a problem with two state variables. This geometric formulation is the one usually given in the literature.

9-09 Inversion

As in partial optimization, the easiest way to solve a final-value problem is to use state inversion. One solves transition functions for the input state variables s_n in terms of the outputs s_{n+1} and the decisions d_n, in this way converting the problem to an initial-value one. Since this procedure was described in Section 8–07, state inversion is not discussed further here. The subject will be reopened during the later development of detailed algorithms in Section 9–11.

State inversions become difficult when the transition functions are nonlinear or dependent on many variables. An alternate tactic is decision inversion, in which one solves the final stage transition functions T_{Nj} for the decisions d_{Nq} as functions of the input and output states s_{Np} and $s_{N+1,p}$. Assume there are at least as many decisions d_{Nq} as terminal constraints $h_r\langle s_{N+1,p}\rangle = 0$ $(r = 1, \ldots, R \leq Q)$. Were this untrue, a composite stage satisfying this requirement could be built by the stage combination tactics described in Section 8–25. Decision inversion is possible if the terminal constraint functions, expressed in terms of the stage N input states s_{Np} and decisions d_{Nq} by substituting the transition functions T_{Nj} for the output states $s_{N+1,p}$, can be solved explicitly for R of the decisions, say, $d_{N1}, \ldots, d_{NR}$. That is, one must be able to solve the R simultaneous equations $(j = 1, \ldots, R; i = R+1, \ldots, P)$

$$h_r\langle T_{Nj}\langle s_N, d_{Nq}\rangle, s_{N+1,i}, d_{Nq}\rangle = 0$$

The solutions are R functions

$$d_{Nj} = \hat{T}_{Nj}\langle s_N, s_{N+1}, d_{N,R+1}, \ldots, d_{NQ}\rangle$$

These functions can be used to eliminate the first R decisions from the accounting variable transition function T_{N0}.

$$\begin{aligned}
s_{N+1,0} &= T_{N0}\langle s_{Np}, \hat{T}_{N1}, \ldots, \hat{T}_{NR}, d_{N,R+1}, \ldots, d_{NQ}\rangle \\
&= \hat{T}_{N0}\langle s_{Np}, s_{N+1,i}, d_{N,R+1}, \ldots, d_{NQ}\rangle
\end{aligned} \tag{9-43}$$

Since this procedure removes the transition functions $T_{N1}, \ldots, T_{NR}$ from the problem, one can forget about the state derivatives $\lambda_{N+1,1}, \ldots, \lambda_{N+1,R}$. To verify this statement, write the Lagrangian for this new problem and observe that $\lambda_{N+1,1}, \ldots, \lambda_{N+1,R}$ do not appear in it. Setting the first partial derivatives of the Lagrangian to zero as before gives

$$\lambda_{N+1,R+1} = \ldots = \lambda_{N+1,P} = 0 \qquad (9\text{-}44)$$

$$H_N = \hat{T}_{N0}\langle s_{Np}, s_{N+1,r}, d_{N,R+1}, \ldots, d_{NQ}\rangle \qquad (9\text{-}45)$$

and $$\lambda_{Np} = \frac{\partial \hat{T}_{N0}}{\partial s_{Np}}; \qquad p = 1, \ldots, P \qquad (9\text{-}46)$$

The state derivatives and Hamiltonians for the remaining stages are computed in the usual way.

Direct inversion methods, requiring the explicit solution of simultaneous equations which may be nonlinear, are often impossible to apply to practical problems. How to circumvent this difficulty is revealed in the following sections, which deal with numerical algorithms.

9-10 Katz's Initial Value Algorithm

S. Katz has proposed an algorithm for initial-value problems which has been applied extensively by L. T. Fan and co-workers. One first guesses a set of decisions $d_{nq}^{(j)}$ (the superscript indicating that the jth iteration is under discussion). Computing recursively starting with the known initial conditions, one uses the transition functions to generate the corresponding values $s_{np}^{(j)}$ of the state variables.

$$s_{n+1,p}^{(j)} = T_{np}\langle \mathbf{s}_n^{(j)}, \mathbf{d}_n^{(j)}\rangle \qquad (9\text{-}47)$$

With all states and decisions known, calculation of the state derivatives proceeds recursively, starting with $\lambda_{N+1,0}^{(j)} = 1$ and $\lambda_{N+1,1}^{(j)} \ldots = \lambda_{N+1,P}^{(j)} = 0$, and using an analog of Eq. (9–14),

$$\lambda_{np}^{(j)} = \sum_{i=0}^{P} \lambda_{n+1,i}^{(j)} \left(\frac{\partial T_{ni}}{\partial s_{np}}\right)^{(j)} \qquad (9\text{-}48)$$

The superscript on the derivative indicates that it is evaluated at $\mathbf{s}_n^{(j)}$ and $\mathbf{d}_n^{(j)}$. Then all the Hamiltonians can be written and optimized (or made stationary) with respect to the decisions, either stage by stage or all at once. This procedure does not always converge (see Exercise 9–5), and one might prefer adjusting the decisions only slightly in the direction of the apparent optimum, using a direct search method. No matter which approach is favored, the decisions generated, $d_{nq}^{(j+1)}$, are used in the next iteration. The algorithm terminates when potential improvement of the Hamiltonians is no longer significant.

9-11 Horn's Final Value Algorithm

Horn has suggested solving final-value problems by what amounts to indirect state inversion. He selects a provisional set of decisions $\mathbf{d}_n^{(j)}$ as before, but this time the corresponding state variables are calculated recursively from the given final states $s_{N+1,p}$ $(p \neq 0)$ by solving the transition functions for the input states. That is, at stage n one must find the numerical value of the input states $\mathbf{s}_n^{(j)}$ such that

$$T_{ni}\langle \mathbf{s}_n^{(j)}, \mathbf{d}_n^{(j)} \rangle = s_{n+1,i}^{(j)} \tag{9-49}$$

where the $s_{n+1,i}^{(j)}$ are known from the stage $n+1$ computation.

Horn recommends using the Newton-Raphson procedure to solve the equations because certain by-product information is generated which turns out to be useful later in calculating the state derivatives. A second superscript k is needed to describe the process of finding the solutions, since the Newton-Raphson method is also iterative. Let $s_{np}^{(jk)}$ be the kth estimate of $s_{np}^{(j)}$. Using Taylor's expansion in the neighborhood of this trial, and neglecting second- and higher-order terms, one would estimate the new value of the transition function from

$$T_{ni}\langle s_{np}^{(j,k+1)}, d_{nm}^{(j)} \rangle = T_{ni}\langle s_{np}^{(jk)}, d_{nm}^{(j)} \rangle + \sum_{p=1}^{P} (s_{np}^{(j,k+1)} - s_{np}^{(jk)})\left(\frac{\partial T_{ni}}{\partial s_{np}}\right)^{(jk)}$$

Therefore the new estimates $s_{np}^{(j,k+1)}$ are chosen to make the left member equal the known desired value $s_{n+1,i}^{(j)}$ by solving the following P linear equations in the P unknown estimates on the left:

$$\sum_{p=1}^{P} s_{np}^{(j,k+1)} \left(\frac{\partial T_{ni}}{\partial s_{np}}\right)^{(jk)} = s_{n+1,i}^{(j)} - T_{ni}\langle s_{np}^{(jk)}, d_{nm}^{(j)} \rangle + \sum_{p=1}^{P} s_{np}^{(jk)} \left(\frac{\partial T_{ni}}{\partial s_{np}}\right)^{(jk)} \tag{9-50}$$

Suppose that the $(K+1)$th estimate is considered close enough to terminate the search. If Gauss elimination (see Section 3–17) was used to solve Eq. (9–50) on the last iteration, then finding the inverse of the matrix of the derivatives $(\partial T_{ni}/\partial s_{np})^{(jK)}$ involves little additional effort. The elements of this inverse matrix, written $(\partial s_{np}/\partial T_{nl})^{(j)}$ to emphasize that they are derivatives measuring changes in input states resulting from output perturbations, satisfy

$$\sum_{p=1}^{P} \left(\frac{\partial T_{ni}}{\partial s_{np}}\right)\left(\frac{\partial s_{np}}{\partial T_{nl}}\right) = \delta_{il} \tag{9-51}$$

Here δ_{il} is the Kronecker delta, unity when $i = l$ but zero otherwise.

The numerical values of the inverse derivatives $(\partial s_{np}/\partial T_{nl})^{(j)}$ prove useful in evaluating the state derivatives from Eq. (9–48). This time, in contrast to the initial-value case, the state derivatives are unknown at terminal stage N. But since the initial states $s_{11}, \ldots, s_{1P}$ are unconstrained and can be chosen freely for optimization, their corresponding state derivatives must vanish.

$$\lambda_{11} = \ldots = \lambda_{1P} = 0 \tag{9-52}$$

Hence Eq. (9–48) must be used recursively *forward*, starting with stage 1 and finding the λ_{ni} from the $\lambda_{n-1,p}$. Ordinarily this would require solution of P linear equations, but knowledge of the inverse derivatives makes this unnecessary. Multiply Eq. (9-48) by each of the P inverse derivatives $(\partial s_{np}/\partial T_{nl})^{(j)}$ and sum over the index p to obtain

$$\sum_{p=1}^{P} \lambda_{n-1,p}^{(j)} \left(\frac{\partial s_{np}}{\partial T_{nl}}\right)^{(j)} = \sum_{p=1}^{P} \left(\frac{\partial T_{n0}}{\partial s_{np}}\right)^{(j)} \left(\frac{\partial s_{np}}{\partial T_{nl}}\right)^{(j)} + \sum_{i=1}^{P} \lambda_{ni}^{(j)} \sum_{p=1}^{P} \left(\frac{\partial T_{ni}}{\partial s_{np}}\right)^{(j)} \left(\frac{\partial s_{np}}{\partial T_{nl}}\right)^{(j)}$$

which by virtue of Eq. (9-51) reduces upon rearrangement to

$$\lambda_{nl}^{(j)} = \sum_{p=1}^{P} \left[\lambda_{n-1,p}^{(j)} - \left(\frac{\partial T_{n0}}{\partial s_{np}}\right)^{(j)}\right]\left(\frac{\partial s_{np}}{\partial T_{nl}}\right)^{(j)} \qquad (9\text{-}53)$$

Calculation of the $\lambda_{nl}^{(j)}$ for $l = 1, \ldots, P$ is straightforward because all quantities on the right side are known from the recursion at the preceding stage.

When all state derivatives have been found, the Hamiltonians can be formed and the decisions adjusted to improve them, just as in Katz's algorithm. Horn's procedure may be considered an extension of state inversion to the case where the inversions cannot be accomplished explicitly.

9-12 Indirect Decision Inversion

Section 9-09 described how to solve final-value problems by direct decision inversion requiring closed form solution of the terminal stage transition functions for the decisions. When explicit solution is impractical, indirect methods based on the Newton-Raphson method can be used. In one of the two variants of this approach, the original N-stage problem is converted to an unconstrained $N-1$ stage problem, just as in Section 9-09. The other variant uses the results of the Newton-Raphson calculation to compute the final-state derivatives $\delta y/\delta s_{N+1,i}$.

As in Section 9-09, suppose there are R terminal constraints $h_r = 0$, and Q decisions d_{Nq}, with $R \le Q$. Let the initial states be given, and select values $d_{nq}^{(j)}$ for the first $QN - R$ decision variables. Recursive calculation forward from stage 1 through stage $N-1$, using the initial conditions and the first $Q(N-1)$ decisions, gives the values $s_n^{(j)}$ for $n = 1, \ldots, N$. Knowing the stage N input states $s_N^{(j)}$ and the last $Q - R$ decisions $d_{N,R+1}^{(j)}, \ldots, d_{NQ}^{(j)}$ one finds the correct decisions $d_{N1}^{(j)}, \ldots, d_{NR}^{(j)}$ by solving the R terminal constraints, into which the stage N transition functions have been substituted where necessary as in Eq. (9-43).

$$h_r \langle \mathbf{T}_N \langle s_N^{(j)}, d_{N1}^{(j)}, \ldots, d_{NR}^{(j)}, d_{N,R+1}^{(j)}, \ldots, d_{NQ}^{(j)} \rangle s_{N+1}^{(j)}, d_{N1}^{(j)}, \ldots, d_{NQ}^{(j)} \rangle = 0 \qquad (9\text{-}54)$$

This accomplished, the stage combination tactics of Section 8-25 will give an equivalent system with only $N-1$ stages, in which the state derivatives $\lambda_{N+1,1}, \ldots, \lambda_{N+1,R}$ do not appear and the rest $(\lambda_{N+1,R+1}, \ldots, \lambda_{N+1,P})$ are zero. Equations (9-45) and (9-46) give the Hamiltonian H_N and the state derivatives $\boldsymbol{\lambda}_{N-1}$ for decision inversion; the remaining state derivatives are computed backwards as in Katz's algorithm [Eq. (9-48)]. New decisions $d_{1,1}^{(j+1)}, \ldots,$

$d_{N-1,Q}^{(j+1)}, d_{N,R+1}^{(j+1)}, \ldots, d_{NQ}^{(j+1)}$ are found by improving the Hamiltonians, of which $H_1, \ldots, H_{N-1}$ take the usual form (9–18). The iteration is repeated with these new decisions.

If Eq. (9–54) is solved by the Newton-Raphson procedure, the results can be used to compute terminal state derivatives λ_{N+1} for the original N-stage problem. This gives a symmetric formulation in which Katz's algorithm can be used at all stages, including the Nth one. Let $(\partial h_r/\partial d_{Nm})^{(jk)}$ for $m = 1, \ldots, R$ be the numerical values of the derivatives of the substituted constraint functions with respect to the R unknown decisions at the kth estimate on iteration j. The $(k+1)$th estimates $d_{Nm}^{(j,k+1)}$ are the solutions to the R equations

$$\sum_{m=1}^{R} d_{Nm}^{(j,k+1)} \left(\frac{\partial h_r}{\partial d_{Nm}}\right)^{(jk)} = -h_r\langle \mathbf{T}_N\langle \mathbf{s}_N^{(j)}, d_{Nm}^{(jk)}, d_{N,R+1}^{(j)}, \ldots, d_{NQ}^{(j)}\rangle, \mathbf{s}_{N+1}^{(j)}, d_{Nm}^{(jk)},$$
$$d_{N,R+1}^{(j)}, \ldots, d_{NQ}^{(j)}\rangle + \sum_{m=1}^{R} d_{Nm}^{(jk)} \left(\frac{\partial h_r}{\partial d_{Nm}}\right)^{(jk)} \qquad (9\text{-}55)$$

Suppose the search is terminated on the $(K+1)$th estimate. The matrix of the R^2 derivatives $(\partial h_r/\partial d_{Nm})^{(jK)}$ can be inverted with little additional work if Gauss elimination has been used, giving the R^2 inverse derivatives $(\partial d_{Nm}/\partial h_r)^{(j)}$. The definition of the terminal state derivatives $\lambda_{N+1,p}$ and the inverse derivatives from the Newton-Raphson calculation can be combined by the chain rule to give

$$\lambda_{N+1,p} \equiv \frac{\delta y}{\delta s_{N+1,p}} = \sum_{m=1}^{R} \sum_{r=1}^{R} \left(\frac{\partial T_{N0}}{\partial d_{Nm}}\right)\left(\frac{\partial d_{Nm}}{\partial h_r}\right)\left(\frac{\partial h_r}{\partial s_{N+1,p}}\right) \qquad (9\text{-}56)$$

The analog of this relation needed for the algorithm is

$$\lambda_{N+1,p}^{(j)} = \sum_{m=1}^{R} \sum_{r=1}^{R} \left(\frac{\partial T_{N0}}{\partial d_{Nm}}\right)^{(j)}\left(\frac{\partial d_{Nm}}{\partial h_r}\right)^{(j)}\left(\frac{\partial h_r}{\partial s_{N+1,p}}\right)^{(j)} \qquad (9\text{-}57)$$

This enables computation of the $\lambda_{N+1,p}^{(j)}$, and the other state derivatives can be calculated recursively backwards from stage N through stage 1. The decisions are then adjusted to improve the ordinary Hamiltonians of Eq. (9–18), and the procedure iterated.

Since this method requires the solution of only as many simultaneous equations as there are terminal constraints, it appears to require less computation than Horn's method. It proves especially useful for solving two-point boundary value problems of the sort arising in the cyclic and branching optimization problems discussed in the following section.

9-13 Nonserial Structures

The serial methods presented in this chapter can be extended to handle cyclic and branching systems just as in Chapter 8 on partial optimization. There it was shown that nonserial systems can be built up from serial ones simply by adding constraints expressing the connections between serial subsystems. Policy improvement algorithms can be developed by introducing these new constraints into the Lagrangian functions with appropriate state derivatives, or Lagrange multipliers, as Jackson has suggested. Only cyclic systems will be discussed here, since the formulations of Chapter 8 can be adapted readily to policy improvement once cyclic systems are understood. The rule developed there concerning cutting a loop system so as to make its branches diverge rather than converge is still valid when policy improvement is used.

Suppose then that the serial problem described by Eqs. (9-1)–(9-9) is made cyclic by appending a *loop constraint*.

$$s_{1i} - G_{1i}\langle s_{N+1,p}\rangle = 0 \tag{9-58}$$

Let $\lambda_{1i} \equiv \delta y/\delta s_{1i}$ $(i = 1, \ldots, P)$ be the corresponding state derivatives used to introduce these constraints into the Lagrangian function, which becomes

$$L = s_{N+1,0} - \sum_{n=1}^{N}\sum_{i=0}^{P} \lambda_{n+1,i}[s_{n+1,i} - T_{ni}\langle \mathbf{s}_n, \mathbf{d}_n\rangle] - \sum_{i=1}^{P} \lambda_{1i}[s_{1i} - G_{1i}\langle \mathbf{s}_{N+1}\rangle] \tag{9-59}$$

Setting to zero the first derivatives of L with respect to state variables s_{1p} through s_{Np} gives the usual state derivative recursion equation for $n = 1, \ldots, N$,

$$\lambda_{np} = \sum_{i=0}^{P} \lambda_{n+1,i}\left(\frac{\partial T_{ni}}{\partial s_{np}}\right) \qquad (p \neq 0) \tag{9-14}$$

But differentiation with respect to the $s_{N+1,p}$ gives

$$\lambda_{N+1,p} = \sum_{i=1}^{P} \lambda_{1i}\left(\frac{\partial G_{1i}}{\partial s_{N+1,p}}\right) \tag{9-60}$$

As usual, $\lambda_{n0} = 1$, but the simple terminal conditions $\lambda_{N+1,p} = 0$ $(p \neq 0)$ are replaced by Eq. (9-60), which gives the final state derivatives in terms of the unknown initial ones. The Hamiltonians are as in Eq. (9-18).

To solve this cyclic problem by policy improvement, one could initiate the cut state procedure by choosing numerical values $s_{N+1,p}^{(j)}$ for the terminal state variables (the "cut" states). This choice defines a two-point boundary-value problem solvable by decision inversion, either directly as in Section 9-09, or indirectly by either method given in Section 9-12. The solution, which in general would involve iteration, would be a set of states satisfying the loop constraint and a set of state derivatives satisfying Eq. (9-57) for the $\lambda_{N+1,p}$ and the recursion Eqs. (9-14), but Eq. (9-60) relating the initial to final state derivatives may not be satisfied if the cut states are not optimum themselves. In the latter event, new cut states $s_{N+1,p}^{(j+1)}$ should be chosen to improve the objective function. The state derivatives $\lambda_{N+1,p}^{(j)}$ computed on the jth iteration can guide the choice, since each of them measures $\delta y/\delta s_{N+1,p}$. The process ends if all Hamiltonians are optimized or stationary and all state derivatives satisfy Eq. (9-60) as well as (9-14).

There is, however, no real need to hold the cut states constant while iterating on the decisions. Instead one could choose cut states $s_{N+1, p}^{(j)}$ and decisions $\mathbf{d}_n^{(j)}$ which, by decision inversion, are made consistent with the loop constraint (9–58). Then one computes $\lambda_{N+1, p}^{(j)}$ from Eq. (9–57) and the remaining state derivatives by backward recursion of Eq. (9–14), enabling the formation of Hamiltonians. The $QN - R$ free decisions are then adjusted and Eq. (9–60) checked to see whether the loop condition on the state derivatives is satisfied. If not, the cut states are adjusted in directions appearing favorable according to the state derivatives $(\delta y / \delta s_{N+1, p})^{(j)}$ found on the jth iteration. These new cut states, together with the new decisions $d_{11}^{(j+1)}, \ldots, d_{N-1, Q}^{(j+1)}$; $d_{N, R+1}^{(j+1)}, \ldots, d_{NQ}^{(j+1)}$, generate the remaining decisions and state derivatives for the next iteration.

9-14 Continuous Systems

In many problems involving automatic control, it is convenient to regard each stage as a process transforming input into output states during a fixed amount of time, say Δt. If t represents the total time elapsed from the beginning of the serial process to the end of the nth stage, then

$$t = n \, \Delta t$$

and the process terminates at time T, given by

$$T \equiv N \, \Delta t \tag{9-61}$$

Each state variable can be identified by elapsed time rather than stage number in the following manner:

$$s_{n+1, p} \equiv s_p \langle t \rangle \equiv T_{np} \langle \mathbf{s}_n, \mathbf{d}_n \rangle \equiv T_p \langle \mathbf{s} \langle t - \Delta t \rangle, \mathbf{d} \langle t - \Delta t \rangle, t - \Delta t \rangle \tag{9-62}$$

where p runs from 0 to P, $s_0 \langle t \rangle$ representing the accounting variable for the terminal control form of the problem. The *continuous* serial optimization problem is obtained from the discrete one formulated here by letting the number of stages N increase without limit while Δt approaches zero in such a manner that the product $N \, \Delta t$ remains equal to T.

Since upon passage to the limit all changes become differential rather than finite, the transitions of the state variables between one instant and the next are expressed more conveniently by differential equations. For abbreviation the symbol $\dot{s}_p \langle t \rangle$ will represent the first derivative of s_p with respect to time, evaluated at time t. These derivatives are related to the finite transition functions as follows:

$$\dot{s}_p \langle t \rangle \equiv \lim_{\Delta t \to 0} \left[\frac{s_p \langle t \rangle - s_p \langle t - \Delta t \rangle}{\Delta t} \right] \equiv \lim_{\Delta t \to 0} \left[\frac{s_p \langle t + \Delta t \rangle - s_p \langle t \rangle}{\Delta t} \right]$$

$$\equiv \lim_{\Delta t \to 0} \left[\frac{s_p \langle t + \Delta t \rangle - T_p \langle \mathbf{s} \langle t - \Delta t \rangle, \mathbf{d} \langle t - \Delta t \rangle, t - \Delta t \rangle}{\Delta t} \right] \tag{9-63}$$

$$\equiv \mathscr{T}_p \langle \mathbf{s} \langle t \rangle, \mathbf{d} \langle t \rangle, t \rangle$$

The function $\mathcal{T}_p\langle \mathbf{s}\langle t\rangle, \mathbf{d}\langle t\rangle, t\rangle$, related to the finite transition function T_p through Eq. (9–63), is called the *continuous transition function*. Equation (9–63) is mainly of academic interest, since $\mathcal{T}_p$ is usually known without recourse to the finite case. Essentially it was derived to emphasize the difference between the continuous transition functions and the discrete ones used until now.

In the limit the state and decision variables become functions of time, and the transition functions are continuous functions of time as well as of the states and decisions upon which they depend. The *continuous* serial optimization problem is to find the decision functions optimizing $s_0\langle T\rangle$, subject to the given boundary conditions, the differential equality constraints,

$$\dot{s}_p = \mathcal{T}_p\langle \mathbf{s}\langle t\rangle, \mathbf{d}\langle t\rangle, t\rangle \qquad (9\text{-}64)$$

and whatever inequality constraints bind the decision variables

$$a_k\langle t\rangle \leq f_k\langle \mathbf{d}\langle t\rangle, t\rangle \leq b_k\langle t\rangle \qquad (9\text{-}65)$$

Here $a_k\langle t\rangle$ and $b_k\langle t\rangle$ are functions of time and the f_k are continuous functions of the decisions. Notice that additional constraints on the state variables, or constraints involving decisions at different times, or constraints depending on states as well as decisions, are not allowed.

The boundary conditions most often given in control problems are that the terminal states (except $s_0\langle T\rangle$) all be constant (often zero)

$$s_p\langle T\rangle = B_p \qquad (p \neq 0) \qquad (9\text{-}66)$$

and that initial conditions be given for all states.

$$s_0\langle 0\rangle = 0 \qquad (9\text{-}67)$$

$$s_p\langle 0\rangle = A_p \qquad (p \neq 0) \qquad (9\text{-}68)$$

Here the A_p and B_p are constants, and the accounting variable s_0 is naturally set to zero at the beginning of the operation.

Notice that the objective function can also be expressed as a definite integral depending on the state and decision functions chosen.

$$y \equiv s_0\langle T\rangle = \int_0^T \dot{s}_0\langle t\rangle \, \partial t = \int_0^T \mathcal{T}_0\langle \mathbf{s}\langle t\rangle, \mathbf{d}\langle t\rangle, t\rangle \, \partial t \qquad (9\text{-}69)$$

Choosing a function that optimizes an integral is a problem in the classical *calculus of variations*. When differential equation constraints must also be satisfied, a "problem of Lagrange" arises, and the further specification of inequality constraints on the decision variables generates a "bounded control problem."

9-15 Equivalent Problems

When the continuous transition functions $\mathcal{T}_p$ depend explicitly on time, the system of differential equations (9–64) is said to be *nonautonomous*. On the other hand, an *autonomous* system is one where the transition functions depend only on the states and decisions at time t, in which case the differential equations are

$$\dot{s}_p\langle t \rangle = \mathcal{T}_p\langle \mathbf{s}\langle t \rangle, \mathbf{d}\langle t \rangle\rangle \tag{9-70}$$

Nonautonomous systems can always be expressed in the simpler autonomous form by introducing a new state variable $s_{P+1}\langle t \rangle$ which is simply the time itself.

$$s_{P+1}\langle t \rangle \equiv t \tag{9-71}$$

$$\dot{s}_{P+1} = 1 \tag{9-72}$$

Thus the theory for autonomous systems extends easily to include the non-autonomous case merely by letting the range of the state index p run from 0 through $P + 1$ instead of P. In the development to follow only the autonomous case will be studied, Eq. (9–70) replacing Eq. (9–64) in the problem statement. Whenever the terminal time is specified in advance as T, the time variable should be introduced, even when the system is autonomous in the first place, and the final condition

$$s_{P+1}\langle T \rangle = T \tag{9-73}$$

must be appended to those of Eq. (9–66). If the terminal time is immaterial or unknown in advance, Eq. (9–73) is omitted. The initial condition on the time variable is, of course,

$$s_{P+1}\langle 0 \rangle = 0 \tag{9-74}$$

The *minimum-time* problem, in which one wishes to pass from some initial to final state in the least possible time, can be expressed in autonomous form by letting the accounting variable be the time

$$s_0\langle t \rangle \equiv t \tag{9-75}$$

so that

$$\dot{s}_0\langle t \rangle = 1 \tag{9-76}$$

with

$$s_0\langle 0 \rangle = 0 \tag{9-77}$$

In this case the additional time variable s_{P+1} need not be appended, even when the system is nonautonomous, for s_0 can fulfill all the roles of s_{P+1} in converting to the autonomous form.

9-16 The Continuous Optimum Principle

Necessary conditions for an optimum in continuous autonomous systems can be derived heuristically by approximating the process by infinitesimal stages and passing to the limit. The result not only resembles the discrete optimum principle but is in fact stronger, since not all interior stationary points of the Hamiltonians need be considered as candidates for the optimal policy. The continuous optimum principle was stated by Pontryagin *et al.*, before the discrete version, and their proofs are rigorous, although much more complicated than the demonstrations given here.

If Δt is regarded as an increment of time, then the constraint Eqs. (9–70) can be written

$$s_p\langle t\rangle - s_p\langle t - \Delta t\rangle - \mathcal{T}_p\langle \mathbf{s}\langle t - \Delta t\rangle, \mathbf{d}\langle t - \Delta t\rangle\rangle \Delta t = 0 \qquad (9\text{-}78)$$

or, in terms of the stage numbers n,

$$s_p\langle n\,\Delta t\rangle - s_p\langle (n-1)\,\Delta t\rangle - \mathcal{T}_p\langle \mathbf{s}\langle (n-1)\,\Delta t\rangle, \mathbf{d}\langle (n-1)\,\Delta t\rangle\rangle \Delta t = 0$$
$$(9\text{-}79)$$

There are N of these constraints, and by introducing $N(P+2)$ Lagrange multipliers $\lambda_p\langle t\rangle$ one can form the Lagrangian function

$$L \equiv s_0\langle N\,\Delta t\rangle - \sum_{n=1}^{N}\sum_{p=0}^{P+1} \lambda_p\langle n\,\Delta t\rangle (s_p\langle n\,\Delta t\rangle - s_p\langle (n-1)\,\Delta t\rangle \qquad (9\text{-}80)$$
$$- \mathcal{T}_p\langle \mathbf{s}\langle (n-1)\,\Delta t\rangle, \mathbf{d}\langle (n-1)\,\Delta t\rangle\rangle \Delta t)$$

This Lagrangian must be stationary with respect to the unrestricted state variables for the optimum policy, so $\partial L/\partial s_0\langle N\,\Delta t\rangle = 1 - \lambda_0\langle N\,\Delta t\rangle = 0$

whence
$$\lambda_0\langle T\rangle = 1 \qquad (9\text{-}81)$$

If any of the state variables $s_p\langle T\rangle$ are unconstrained, then

$$\frac{\partial L}{\partial s_p\langle N\,\Delta t\rangle} = -\lambda_p\langle N\,\Delta t\rangle = 0$$

so that
$$\lambda_p\langle T\rangle = 0 \qquad (p \neq 0) \qquad (9\text{-}82)$$

This is not true for variables with equality terminal conditions, for then their terminal multipliers $\lambda_p\langle T\rangle$ are not zero and must be determined by other methods, as will be seen in the examples.

Differentiation with respect to $s_p\langle n\,\Delta t\rangle$ gives

$$\frac{\partial L}{\partial s_p\langle n\,\Delta t\rangle} = -\lambda_p\langle n\,\Delta t\rangle + \lambda_p\langle (n+1)\,\Delta t\rangle$$
$$+ \sum_{i=0}^{P+1}\left(\lambda_i\langle (n+1)\,\Delta t\rangle \frac{\partial \mathcal{T}_i\langle n\,\Delta t\rangle}{\partial s_p\langle n\,\Delta t\rangle}\right)\Delta t = 0$$

Division of this equation by Δt, followed by transposition of the sum and allowing Δt to approach zero gives, in the limit [see Eq. (9–63)],

$$\dot{\lambda}_p\langle t\rangle = -\sum_{i=0}^{P+1} \lambda_i\langle t\rangle \frac{\partial \mathcal{T}_i}{\partial s_p\langle t\rangle} \qquad (9\text{-}83)$$

where $\dot{\lambda}_p\langle t\rangle$ is the first derivative of λ_p with respect to time, evaluated at time t, whereas $\partial \mathcal{T}_i/\partial s_p\langle t\rangle$ represents the first partial derivative of $\mathcal{T}_i$ at time t with respect to $s_p\langle t\rangle$.

Hence the multipliers $\lambda_p\langle t\rangle$ become functions of time. Since each of them can be regarded as a constrained derivative of the objective function with respect to a transition function, they will be called *state derivatives*.

$$\lambda_p \langle t \rangle = \frac{\delta s_0 \langle T \rangle}{\delta \mathcal{T}_p \langle t \rangle} = \frac{\delta y}{\delta \dot{s}_p \langle t \rangle} \qquad (9\text{-}84)$$

To obtain $\delta y / \delta d_m \langle t \rangle$, the constrained derivatives of the objective function with respect to the decision variables, evaluated at time t, one can invoke the chain rule and Eq. (9–84).

$$\frac{\delta y}{\delta d_m \langle t \rangle} = \sum_{p=0}^{P+1} \lambda_p \langle t \rangle \left(\frac{\partial \mathcal{T}_p}{\partial d_m \langle t \rangle} \right) \qquad (9\text{-}85)$$

As in the discrete case, this may be expressed in terms of a Hamiltonian function $\mathcal{H} \langle t \rangle$ defined by

$$\mathcal{H} \langle \boldsymbol{\lambda} \langle t \rangle, \mathbf{s} \langle t \rangle, \mathbf{d} \langle t \rangle \rangle \equiv \sum_{p=0}^{P+1} \lambda_p \langle t \rangle \mathcal{T}_p \langle \mathbf{s} \langle t \rangle, \mathbf{d} \langle t \rangle \rangle \qquad (9\text{-}86)$$

so that

$$\frac{\delta y}{\delta d_m \langle t \rangle} = \frac{\partial \mathcal{H} \langle t \rangle}{\partial d_m \langle t \rangle} \qquad (9\text{-}87)$$

Since the first-order behavior of the Hamiltonian with respect to the decisions is the same as that of the objective function itself, an optimal policy must optimize the Hamiltonian with respect to the decisions at every instant of time. In contrast to the discrete case, this continuous "optimum principle" excludes all interior nonoptimal stationary points and subsidiary local optima of the Hamiltonians from consideration—only the global optimum need be sought. Proof of this stronger result is beyond the scope of this book (see Pontryagin).

The state derivatives $\lambda_p \langle t \rangle$ are also known as "Green's functions" (Denn and Aris) or "influence functions" (Bliss, Kelley) as in the discrete case. Their differential equations (9–83) can, in view of definition (9–86), be written in terms of the Hamiltonians as

$$\dot{\lambda}_p \langle t \rangle = - \frac{\partial \mathcal{H} \langle t \rangle}{\partial s_p \langle t \rangle} \qquad (9\text{-}88)$$

The *optimum principle* is that the set of functions $\boldsymbol{\lambda}^* \langle t \rangle$, $\mathbf{s}^* \langle t \rangle$ and $\mathbf{d}^* \langle t \rangle$ which optimize y $(\equiv s_0 \langle T \rangle)$ subject to the side conditions (9–64)–(9–68) must also optimize the Hamiltonians subject to Eq. (9–88).

$$\mathcal{H} \langle \boldsymbol{\lambda}^* \langle t \rangle, \mathbf{s}^* \langle t \rangle, \mathbf{d}^* \langle t \rangle \rangle = \operatorname*{opt}_{\mathbf{d} \langle t \rangle} \{ \mathcal{H} \langle \boldsymbol{\lambda}^* \langle t \rangle, \mathbf{s}^* \langle t \rangle, \mathbf{d} \langle t \rangle \rangle \} \qquad (9\text{-}89)$$

It is understood that the decisions are to be chosen from among those satisfying constraint Eq. (9–65).

When, often the case in practice, digital computers must be used to solve continuous problems, they must be broken down into finite stages for application of the discrete algorithms described earlier in this chapter. Still there are many interesting problems in automatic control capable of closed form solution by the continuous optimum principle, as the examples to follow will show. For descriptions of situations in which the "strong" optimum principle—the one applicable in the continuous case—can be used with confidence even for discrete problems, see the work of Halkin and Holtz-man. Most important, when differential equations are approximated by finite difference methods on a digital computer, only the global optimum of the Hamiltonian need be sought.

9-17 The Continuous Hamiltonian

Canonical equations involving the continuous Hamiltonian can be derived resembling those for the staged case.

$$\frac{\partial \mathcal{H}}{\partial \lambda_p} = \mathcal{T}_p = \dot{s}_p \tag{9-90}$$

$$\frac{\partial \mathcal{H}}{\partial s_p} = \sum_{j=0}^{P+1} \lambda_j \left(\frac{\partial \mathcal{T}_j}{\partial s_p} \right) = -\dot{\lambda}_p \tag{9-91}$$

Moreover, the continuity of the time parameter permits statements about the continuous Hamiltonian which do not hold for staged systems. Consider the time derivative

$$\dot{\mathcal{H}} = \sum_{p=0}^{P+1} \left[\left(\frac{\partial \mathcal{H}}{\partial \lambda_p} \right) \dot{\lambda}_p + \left(\frac{\partial \mathcal{H}}{\partial s_p} \right) \dot{s}_p \right] + \sum_{m=1}^{Q} \left(\frac{\partial \mathcal{H}}{\partial d_m} \right) \dot{d}_m$$

Substitution of the canonical equations into this expression causes the first sum to vanish identically so that

$$\dot{\mathcal{H}} = \sum_{m=1}^{Q} \left(\frac{\partial \mathcal{H}}{\partial d_m} \right) \dot{d}_m \tag{9-92}$$

If the decisions are unconstrained, then when the Hamiltonian is optimum, $\partial \mathcal{H} / \partial d_m = 0$ for every decision, and

$$\dot{\mathcal{H}} = 0 \tag{9-93}$$

This relation also holds when the decision constraints are constants independent of time, for then if the Hamiltonian is at a constraint, $\dot{d}_m = 0$, whereas, if it is not, $\partial \mathcal{H} / \partial d_m = 0$. Thus one can assert that along the optimal trajectory, constancy of the decision constraints implies constancy of the continuous Hamiltonian. This is not true in the discrete case except in such special circumstances as those of the allocation example, where the autonomous transition functions happen to be linear in the state variables.

Constancy of the continuous Hamiltonian leads to another interesting property. Let Δt in Eq. (9–80) approach zero to give in the limit

$$L = \int_0^T \sum_{p=0}^{P+1} \lambda_p \mathcal{T}_p \, \partial t = \int_0^T \mathcal{H} \langle t \rangle \, \partial t = \mathcal{H} T$$

Hence $\mathcal{H}$ may be interpreted as the derivative of the Lagrangian L with respect to the terminal time T.

$$\mathcal{H} = \frac{\partial L}{\partial T} \tag{9-94}$$

It follows that when T may be chosen to optimize the objective,

$$\mathscr{H} = 0 \qquad (9\text{-}95)$$

since L in this case must be stationary with respect to the free variable T.

When the terminal time is fixed, the value of the optimal Hamiltonian is not zero, and it may be interpreted as the derivative of the objective function with respect to the terminal time along the optimal trajectory. The proof follows:

$$\frac{\partial L}{\partial T} = \frac{\partial s_0 \langle T \rangle}{\partial T} + \frac{\partial}{\partial T} \int_0^T \sum_{p=0}^{P+1} \lambda_p \mathscr{T}_p \, \partial t = \frac{\partial y^*}{\partial T} + \sum_{p=0}^{P+1} \lambda_p \langle T \rangle \mathscr{T}_p \langle T \rangle$$

$$= \frac{\partial y^*}{\partial T} + \sum_{p=0}^{P+1} \lambda_p \langle T \rangle \frac{\partial s_p \langle T \rangle}{\partial t} \qquad (9\text{-}96)$$

But the transversality condition for the continuous case, resembling that in the discrete case [see Eq. (9–42)], is

$$\sum_{p=0}^{P+1} \lambda_p \langle T \rangle \, \partial s_p \langle T \rangle = 0 \qquad (9\text{-}97)$$

for any perturbations $\partial s_p \langle T \rangle$ satisfying the final conditions. Hence Eqs. (9–94), (9–96), and (9–97) give

$$\mathscr{H} = \frac{\partial y^*}{\partial T} \qquad (9\text{-}98)$$

9-18 Minimum Time Control

In many situations it is time, rather than control energy, which is expensive, and one therefore wishes to minimize the time required to drive an object to the desired state. Intuition would suggest trading cheap control energy for valuable time, so one would expect bounds on the decision variables to become important in the analysis. The form of the optimal decision function in this case turns out to be quite different from the kind generated by conventional industrial automatic controllers.

Imagine a group of mining and exploration colonies on the moon. Because of obvious obstacles to agriculture in a lunar climate, all fresh food is grown on a central farm inside a controlled weather enclosure and then shipped by automatic rocket to the outlying villages. Since at this early stage of lunar history all machinery must come from Earth, there is only one vehicle to do the job, so its time is valuable. The rocket uses little fuel, and the thrust is fully and instantaneously reversible for stopping the vehicle. Deliveries are made by launching the vehicle in a low trajectory, just clearing the mountains, and landing it at its destination. For simplicity consider the path to be frictionless and horizontal, so that gravitational effects can be neglected. Given an initial distance x_0 from the destination, one wants to find the thrust program

$d*\langle t \rangle$ causing the vehicle to make the run in the least time, starting and ending with zero velocity. Mathematically, the problem is to find $d*\langle t \rangle$ such that

$$T\langle d* \rangle = \min_{d\langle t \rangle} T\langle d \rangle \qquad (9\text{-}99)$$

Subject to the thrust constraint

$$|d\langle t \rangle| \leq D \quad \text{(a constant)} \qquad (9\text{-}100)$$

and the equation of motion

$$M\ddot{x}\langle t \rangle = d\langle t \rangle \qquad (9\text{-}101)$$

where M is the mass of the rocket in appropriate units. The boundary conditions are

$$x\langle 0 \rangle = x_0$$
$$x\langle T \rangle = 0$$
$$\dot{x}\langle 0 \rangle = \dot{x}\langle T \rangle = 0$$

Expression of the second-order equation of motion in terms of the first derivatives only is accomplished by solving for the highest derivative $\ddot{x}$ in Eq. (9–101) and designating it as $\dot{s}_2\langle t \rangle$, the time derivative of a second state variable.

$$\dot{s}_2 \equiv \ddot{x} = \frac{d}{M} \qquad (9\text{-}102)$$

Hence
$$s_2 = \dot{x} \qquad (9\text{-}103)$$

and s_2 can be interpreted physically as the velocity at time t. But this velocity is the first derivative of the distance x, which is therefore selected as the other state variable s_1.

$$\dot{s}_1 \equiv \dot{x} = s_2 \qquad (9\text{-}104)$$

Equations (9–102) and (9–104) are completely equivalent to the original equation of motion (9–101).

This transformation of a Pth-order differential equation in a single variable into P simultaneous first-order equations in P variables can always be accomplished in the manner illustrated. The number P used throughout the derivation of the optimum principle can therefore be interpreted as the order of the system of differential equations describing the motion. In the discrete case, P represents the order of the recursion or difference equations describing the system.

If the accounting variable s_0 is taken to be the elapsed time after launch, then the equivalent problem is to minimize $y = s_0\langle T \rangle$ subject to

$$\dot{s}_0 = 1 = \mathscr{T}_0 \qquad (9\text{-}105)$$

$$\dot{s}_1 = s_2 = \mathscr{T}_1 \qquad (9\text{-}106)$$

$$\dot{s}_2 = \frac{d}{M} = \mathscr{T}_2 \qquad (9\text{-}107)$$

with
$$|d| \leq D \tag{9-108}$$

and
$$s_1\langle T \rangle = s_0\langle 0 \rangle = s_2\langle 0 \rangle = s_2\langle T \rangle = 0 \tag{9-109}$$

$$s_1\langle 0 \rangle = x_0 \tag{9-110}$$

The state derivative functions $\lambda_0\langle t \rangle$, $\lambda_1\langle t \rangle$, and $\lambda_2\langle t \rangle$ are obtained from Eq. (9–83). First

$$\dot{\lambda}_0 = -\lambda_0 \frac{\partial \mathcal{T}_0}{\partial s_0} - \lambda_1 \frac{\partial \mathcal{T}_1}{\partial s_0} - \lambda_2 \frac{\partial \mathcal{T}_2}{\partial s_0}$$
$$= 0$$

since none of the continuous transition functions depend on s_0. It follows that λ_0 is constant, and by Eq. (9–81),

$$\lambda_0\langle t \rangle = 1 \tag{9-111}$$

for all $0 \leq t \leq T$. Next

$$\dot{\lambda}_1 = -\lambda_0 \frac{\partial \mathcal{T}_0}{\partial s_1} - \lambda_1 \frac{\partial \mathcal{T}_1}{\partial s_1} - \lambda_2 \frac{\partial \mathcal{T}_2}{\partial s_1}$$
$$= 0$$

since s_1 does not appear explicitly in any of the transition functions. Hence $\lambda_1\langle t \rangle$ is also a constant, as yet unknown.

$$\lambda_1\langle t \rangle = \lambda_1\langle T \rangle \tag{9-112}$$

Finally,
$$\dot{\lambda}_2 = -\lambda_0 \frac{\partial \mathcal{T}_0}{\partial s_2} - \lambda_1 \frac{\partial \mathcal{T}_1}{\partial s_2} - \lambda_2 \frac{\partial \mathcal{T}_2}{\partial s_2}$$
$$= -\lambda_1\langle T \rangle$$

Integration gives

$$\lambda_2\langle t \rangle = \lambda_2\langle 0 \rangle + \int_0^t \dot{\lambda}_2 \, \partial t' = \lambda_2\langle 0 \rangle - \lambda_1\langle T \rangle t \tag{9-113}$$

To find the optimal policy, form the Hamiltonian $\mathcal{H}\langle t \rangle$, using Eqs. (9–86), (9–105)–(9–107), and (9–111)–(9–113).

$$\mathcal{H} = 1 + \lambda_1\langle T \rangle s_2 + (\lambda_2\langle 0 \rangle - \lambda_1\langle T \rangle t) \frac{d}{M} \tag{9-114}$$

Hence the decision derivative is

$$\frac{\delta y}{\delta d} = \frac{\partial \mathcal{H}}{\partial d} = \frac{\lambda_2\langle 0 \rangle - \lambda_1\langle T \rangle t}{M} \tag{9-115}$$

At any given time t, this derivative is constant, and so the Hamiltonian is minimized when $d\langle t \rangle$ assumes one of its extreme values. When $\delta y/\delta d$ is positive, d should be as small as possible; when $\delta y/\delta d$ is negative, d should be as large as possible. Hence the optimal thrust program $d^*\langle t \rangle$ is

$$d^*\langle t \rangle = -D \operatorname{sgn}(\lambda_2\langle 0 \rangle - \lambda_1\langle T \rangle t) \tag{9-116}$$

where $\operatorname{sgn}(w)$ (read "signum w") is $+1$ when $w > 0$, -1 when $w < 0$, and zero when $w = 0$.

Since the function $\lambda_2\langle 0\rangle - \lambda_1\langle T\rangle t$ depends linearly on time, it can change sign no more than once. It follows that the rocket engine is always producing maximum thrust, merely reversing its direction once during the run. This mode of control is nonlinear, having a discontinuity when the thrust is switched from one extreme to the other. It is called *contactor* or *switching* control in the literature, although the breezier term *bang-bang* control is also in vogue.

The optimal trajectory has two distinct parts, one in which $d = +D$ and the other in which $d = -D$. The equations of motion must be integrated for each part and matched with the boundary conditions to specify the thrust program precisely. Let t_s be the time elapsed when the thrust switches, and for simplicity assume $x_0 > 0$ so that

$$d\langle t\rangle = \begin{cases} -D & \text{for } 0 \leq t \leq t_s \\ D & \text{for } t_s \leq t \leq T \end{cases} \tag{9-117}$$

Then

$$s_1\langle t\rangle = \begin{cases} x_0 - \dfrac{Dt^2}{2M} & \text{for } 0 \leq t \leq t_s \\ \dfrac{D(T-t)^2}{2M} & \text{for } t_s \leq t \leq T \end{cases} \tag{9-118}$$

and

$$s_2\langle t\rangle = \begin{cases} \dfrac{-Dt}{M} & \text{for } 0 \leq t \leq t_s \\ \dfrac{-D(T-t)}{M} & \text{for } t_s \leq t \leq T \end{cases} \tag{9-119}$$

When the switch occurs, the position and velocity given by each branch of the preceding functions must be identical, so

$$s_2\langle t_s\rangle = \frac{-Dt_s}{M} = \frac{-D(T-t_s)}{M}$$

which implies, as one would expect,

$$t_s = \frac{T}{2} \tag{9-120}$$

Similarly, using this relation,

$$s_1\langle t_s\rangle = x_0 - \frac{Dt_s^2}{2M} = \frac{Dt_s^2}{2M}$$

whence

$$T = 2\sqrt{\frac{Mx_0}{D}} \tag{9-121}$$

The switching position and velocity are

$$s_1\langle t_s\rangle \equiv x\langle t_s\rangle = \frac{x_0}{2} \tag{9-122}$$

and

$$s_2\langle t_s\rangle \equiv \dot{x}\langle t_s\rangle = -\sqrt{\frac{Dx_0}{M}} \tag{9-123}$$

This is sufficient information to specify the thrust program precisely in terms of the position.

$$d\langle t \rangle = \begin{cases} -D & \text{when } x \geq \dfrac{x_0}{2} \\[2mm] D & \text{when } x \leq \dfrac{x_0}{2} \end{cases} \tag{9-124}$$

The constants $\lambda_1\langle T \rangle$ and $\lambda_2\langle 0 \rangle$ are not needed in this case, since once the form of the trajectory was found, the switching time was computed by straight-forward mechanics. They are, however, easily found by considering the instant of switching, when by Eqs. (9–116), (9–120), and (9–121),

$$\lambda_2\langle 0 \rangle - \lambda_1\langle T \rangle t_s = \lambda_2\langle 0 \rangle - \lambda_1\langle T \rangle \sqrt{\frac{Mx_0}{D}} = 0 \tag{9-125}$$

Since this is a minimum time problem, the Hamiltonian is identically zero, and when the control is switched, Eqs. (9–95) and (9–114) give

$$\mathscr{H} = 0 = 1 + \lambda_1\langle T \rangle \left(-\sqrt{\frac{Dx_0}{M}} \right)$$

which implies

$$\lambda_1\langle T \rangle = \sqrt{\frac{M}{Dx_0}}$$

and by Eq. (9–125),

$$\lambda_2\langle 0 \rangle = \frac{M}{D}$$

Bushaw's original work with switching control, including the analysis of a system similar to that considered here, is formulated in terms of the optimum principle in Pontryagin *et al.*

9-19 Minimum Fuel Control

In the previous example, time was considered all-important, and fuel costs were neglected. It is instructive to study the reverse situation, which will be seen to lead to a smooth decision function quite different from the switching action found in the minimum-time problem. Thus the form of the controller depends heavily on the measure of effectiveness chosen.

Suppose then that the moon colony obtains another rocket truck, reducing the usage on each vehicle to the point where transit time is no longer critical. Instead, an economy drive to pay for the second unit is under way, and the transportation manager now wants to minimize fuel costs. Assume the fuel consumption rate $\dot{m}$ to be proportional to d^2, the square of the thrust, k being the proportionality constant in consistent units.

$$\dot{m} = kd^2 \tag{9-126}$$

The total fuel consumption during the time of flight T being

$$y = \int_0^T \dot{m}\, \partial t = k \int_0^T d^2\, \partial t \tag{9-127}$$

the accounting variable s_0 is chosen as the total fuel consumed at time t so that

$$s_0\langle 0 \rangle = 0 \tag{9-128}$$

and

$$\dot{s}_0\langle t \rangle = kd^2\langle t \rangle \tag{9-129}$$

The equations of motion and boundary conditions are the same as in the minimum-time problem, namely, Eqs. (9–106), (9–107), (9–109), and (9–110). It is now assumed that the thrust available is unbounded, since the quadratic dependence of fuel consumption on thrust will prevent large thrusts from being required.

A moment's reflection would show that, in this case, the transit time had better be specified in advance, for otherwise the optimum policy would be to take as long as possible, since this would require only a little bit of fuel to get the vehicle started and a corresponding amount to stop it. Therefore let a finite terminal time T be specified in advance, say, the most that the consumers (or the produce) will tolerate before becoming unpleasant. The problem is to minimize $s_0\langle T \rangle$ subject to the equations of motion and boundary conditions of the minimum-time problem.

The state derivatives are found, by the same reasoning as in the preceding section, to be $\lambda_0\langle t \rangle = 1$; $\lambda_1\langle t \rangle = \lambda_1\langle T \rangle$; and $\lambda_2\langle t \rangle = \lambda_2\langle 0 \rangle - \lambda_1\langle T \rangle t$. Thus the Hamiltonian is

$$\mathcal{H} = kd^2 + \lambda_1\langle T \rangle s_2 + (\lambda_2\langle 0 \rangle - \lambda_1\langle T \rangle t)\frac{d}{M} \tag{9-130}$$

Its derivative with respect to the decision can be equated to zero, since d is unconstrained, to obtain the optimum thrust program, which in this case is a linear function of time.

$$d^*\langle t \rangle = \frac{\lambda_1\langle T \rangle t - \lambda_2\langle 0 \rangle}{2kM} \tag{9-131}$$

The second derivative of $\mathcal{H}$ is clearly positive as required. Next the constants $\lambda_1\langle T \rangle$ and $\lambda_2\langle 0 \rangle$ are obtained by integrating the equations of motion and matching boundary conditions.

$$s_2 = \frac{\lambda_1\langle T \rangle t^2 - 2\lambda_2\langle 0 \rangle t}{4kM^2} \tag{9-132}$$

$$s_1 = x_0 + \frac{\lambda_1\langle T \rangle t^3 - 3\lambda_2\langle 0 \rangle t^2}{12kM^2} \tag{9-133}$$

Setting $t = T$ gives the simultaneous equations

$$s_2\langle T \rangle = 0 = \frac{\lambda_1\langle T \rangle T^2 - 2\lambda_2\langle 0 \rangle T}{4kM^2} \qquad (9\text{-}134)$$

$$s_1\langle T \rangle = 0 = x_0 + \frac{\lambda_1\langle T \rangle T^3 - 3\lambda_2\langle 0 \rangle T^2}{12kM^2} \qquad (9\text{-}135)$$

whose solutions are

$$\lambda_1\langle T \rangle = \frac{24kM^2 x_0}{T^3} \qquad (9\text{-}136)$$

and

$$\lambda_2\langle 0 \rangle = \frac{12kM^2 x_0}{T^2} \qquad (9\text{-}137)$$

Hence
$$d^*\langle t \rangle = \frac{6Mx_0(2t - T)}{T^3} \qquad (9\text{-}138)$$

The negative starting thrust has the same magnitude as the positive final thrust, the variation from beginning to end being linear with time. The minimum fuel consumption is

$$y^* = k \int_0^T (d^*)^2 \, \partial t = \frac{12kM^2 x_0^2}{T^3} \qquad (9\text{-}139)$$

Notice that, in verification of Eq. (9-98),

$$\mathcal{H} = \frac{-36kM^2 x_0^2}{T^4} = \frac{\partial y^*}{\partial T}$$

9-20 A Feedback Regulator

The control systems studied so far, which seek to drive a variable from one state to another, are called *servomechanisms*. Another type of system of interest is the *regulator*, which strives to hold the state as nearly constant as possible. Usually the state variable is an error signal one wants to keep near zero, and often the regulator's effectiveness is measured in part by the time integral of the squared error resulting from a disturbance. When the objective function also has a term proportional to a quadratic function of the control effort, the decision variable can be made a linear function of the state variables alone, independent of time. Such a scheme, known as a *linear feedback* system in control jargon, is desirable because it can usually be implemented by standard analog controllers, which are simple and inexpensive compared to the nonlinear special purpose computers needed in the examples already considered. Moreover, feedback (or "closed loop") systems perform better than the feedforward or open loop schemes discussed previously when such design information as mass, thrust, or initial position is not known with perfect accuracy.

The advantages of feedback systems, which are thoroughly discussed in most control theory texts (Shilling), will not be elaborated here. Instead, an important special case of Kalman's state variable synthesis technique will be illustrated by showing how it gives the optimal linear feedback scheme for regulating the position of the inertial object studied in the two previous examples.

Consider then an oceanographic ship of mass M drilling a hole in the ocean bottom. To avoid breaking the drill stem, the ship's position must be held constant in the face of wind, wave, and mechanical vibration. For simplicity consider only the problem of regulating the north-south displacement; a similar controller would be needed for east-west disturbances. Let s_1 be the northerly position error, which is to be corrected by manipulating the reversible thrust d of a set of screw propellers whose fuel consumption rate is proportional to d^2. Mainly for mathematical convenience, the measure of control effectiveness chosen is a weighted sum of the integral squared error and the total fuel consumption, k now being a weighting coefficient.

$$y = \int_0^T (s_1^2 + kd^2)\, \partial t \tag{9-140}$$

The terminal time is now free to take its optimal value, since the squared error term will prevent the trivial case $d = 0$ from occurring. This time the accounting variable derivative is

$$\dot{s}_0 = s_1^2 + kd^2 \tag{9-141}$$

and Eqs. (9-104) and (9-102) describe the motion as before ($\dot{s}_1 = s_2$; $\dot{s}_2 = d/M$).

The state derivatives, Hamiltonian, and optimal decisions are

$$\dot{\lambda}_0 = 0 \tag{9-142}$$

$$\dot{\lambda}_1 = -2s_1 \tag{9-143}$$

$$\dot{\lambda}_2 = -\lambda_1 \tag{9-144}$$

$$\mathscr{H} = s_1^2 + kd^2 + \lambda_1 s_2 + \frac{\lambda_2 d}{M} \tag{9-145}$$

$$d^* = -\frac{\lambda_2}{2kM} \tag{9-146}$$

Notice that none of the differential equations has been integrated; it isn't necessary when this method is applicable. Kalman showed that the state derivatives are in this case linear functions of the state variables. Thus there are constants c_{11}, c_{12}, c_{21}, and c_{22} such that

$$\lambda_1 = c_{11}s_1 + c_{12}s_2 \tag{9-147}$$

$$\lambda_2 = c_{21}s_1 + c_{22}s_2 \tag{9-148}$$

These may be combined with Eqs. (9-102), (9-104), (9-143), (9-144), and (9-146) to give

$$\dot{\lambda}_1 = c_{11}\dot{s}_1 + c_{12}\dot{s}_2 = c_{11}s_2 - \frac{c_{12}\lambda_2}{2kM^2}$$

$$= c_{11}s_2 - \frac{c_{12}(c_{21}s_1 + c_{22}s_2)}{2kM^2} = -2s_1 \tag{9-149}$$

$$\dot{\lambda}_2 = c_{21}\dot{s}_1 + c_{22}\dot{s}_2$$

$$= c_{21}s_2 - \frac{c_{22}(c_{21}s_1 + c_{22}s_2)}{2kM^2} = -c_{11}s_1 - c_{12}s_2 \tag{9-150}$$

Four simultaneous quadratic equations in the four unknown coefficients are obtained by equating corresponding coefficients of the state variables in these two equations. Hence Eq. (9–149) gives

$$\frac{-c_{12}c_{21}}{2kM^2} = -2$$

$$c_{11} - \frac{c_{12}c_{22}}{2kM^2} = 0$$

$$\frac{-c_{21}c_{22}}{2kM^2} = -c_{11}$$

$$c_{21} - \frac{c_{22}^2}{2kM^2} = -c_{12}$$

The solutions are

$$c_{11} = \sqrt{8}\,(kM^2)^{1/4} \tag{9-151}$$

$$c_{12} = c_{21} = 2M\sqrt{k} \tag{9-152}$$

$$c_{22} = \sqrt{8}\,(kM^2)^{3/4} \tag{9-153}$$

Equations (9–146), (9–148), (9–152), and (9–153) give the optimal linear feedback control.

$$d^* = -\frac{s_1}{\sqrt{k}} - \frac{\sqrt{2M}\,s_2}{k^{1/4}} \tag{9-154}$$

A conventional "proportional-derivative" controller would have the equation

$$d = -K(x + T_d\dot{x})$$

where K is the *controller gain*, T_d the *derivative time*, $x\,(\equiv s_1)$ the error, and $(\dot{x}\equiv s_2)$ the error velocity. In this case the gain is $1/\sqrt{k}$ and the derivative time is $\sqrt{2M}\,k^{1/4}$. In practice one would also add a control action known as "integral mode" (Shilling).

If desired, the optimal feedforward control functions, expressed parametrically in terms of time, could be found by the methods used on the previous examples. This time, however, the state and the state derivative Eqs. (9–102), (9–104), (9–143), and (9–144) would have to be solved simultaneously.

Kalman also proved that if the objective function integrand is positive definite, then the optimal control obtained in this way will always be stable, eventually driving the error to zero asymptotically no matter what the initial perturbation. Notice that the method works only when the objective is quadratic in both the state and decision variables. If it had been linear in, or independent of, the decision, a switching control would be optimal; whereas if it had been linear in, or independent of, all the states, the coefficients c_{11}, etc. would all vanish, indicating the impossibility of a linear feedback implementation of the optimal control. As in the previous example, however, an optimal nonlinear time-varying feedforward control is realizable. When the system is not autonomous, a linear time-varying feedback control can be constructed when the objective is quadratic in states and decisions. One must then solve a quadratic *Riccati* differential equation of first order in the coefficients c_{11}, etc.

9-21 Conclusions

This chapter, the last to concern itself with the mathematics of optimization, shows how to improve entire policies rather than individual decisions. Unlike the partial optimization approach of Chapter 8, policy improvement can be applied even when there are many state variables. The procedure is iterative, however, and not much is yet known about its stability or rate of convergence.

The principal applications of policy improvement have been in such time-dependent processes as long-range planning and automatic control, although it can be used for any serial system. Cyclic and branching systems can also be optimized by combining these serial methods with the cut state concept of Chapter 8. By extending the constrained derivative idea to constraints which are differential rather than algebraic, the theory shows how to assess a decision's long-range consequences. In quantitative language, it demonstrates that "coming events cast their shadows before them."

BIBLIOGRAPHY

Aris, R., R. Bellman, and R. Kalaba, "Some optimization problems in chemical engineering," *Chem. Eng. Prog. Symp. Ser.*, **56**, 31 (1960), 95.

Aris, R., G. L. Nemhauser, and D. J. Wilde, "Optimization of multistage cyclic and branching systems by serial procedures," *A. I. Ch. E. J.*, **10**, 6 (November, 1964), 913–19.

Bateman, H., in *A Collection of Papers in Memory of Sir William Rowan Hamilton* (Scripta Mathematica, New York, 1945).

Bliss, G. A. "Differential equations containing arbitrary functions," *Trans. Amer. Math. Soc.*, **21** (1920), 79–92.

———, "The use of adjoint systems in the problems of differential corrections for trajectories," *J. U. S. Artillery*, **51** (1919), 296–311.

———, "Functions of lines in ballistics," *Trans. Amer. Math. Soc.*, **21** (1920), 93–106.

Bryson, A. E., W. F. Denham, and S. E. Dreyfus, "Optimal programming problems with inequality constraints I: necessary conditions for extremal solutions," *AIAA J.* **1** (1963), 2544.

Bushaw, D. W., Ph.D. thesis, Princeton University Department of Mathematics (Princeton, N.J., 1952).

Butkovskii, A. G., "The necessary and sufficient conditions for optimality of discrete control systems," *Avtomatika i Telemekhanika* (USSR), **24**, 8 (August, 1963), 1956–64.

Chang, S. S. L., *Inst. Radio Engrs. Conv. Rec.*, **9**, 4 (1961), 48.

Denham, W. F., and A. E. Bryson, "Optimal programming problems with inequality constraints II: solution by steepest-ascent," *AIAA J.*, **2** (1964), 25.

Denn, M. M., and R. Aris, "Green's functions and optimal systems," *Ind. Engng. Chem. Fund.*, **4**, 1 (February, 1965), 7–16.

———, and ———, "An elementary derivation of the maximum principle," *Amer. Inst. Chem. Engrs. J.*, **11**, 2 (March, 1965), 367–68.

Douglas, J. M., and M. M. Denn, "Optimal design and control by variational methods," *Ind. Engng. Chem.*, **57**, 11 (November, 1965), 18–30.

Dunn, J. C., "Green's functions for space trajectory perturbation analysis," *J. Astronaut. Sci.*, **8** (1961), 95–103.

Fan, L. T., and C. S. Wang, *The Discrete Maximum Principle* (Wiley, New York, 1964).

———, *The Continuous Maximum Principle* (Wiley, New York, 1966).

Gelfand, I. M., and S. V. Fomin, *Calculus of Variations* (R. A. Silverman, trans.) (Prentice-Hall, Inc., Englewood Cliffs, N.J., 1963).

Halkin, H., "Optimal control for systems described by difference equations" (See C. T. Leondes, pp. 173–96).

Hamilton, W. R., *Roy. Soc. London Trans.* (1834), 247–308.

———, *Roy. Soc. London Trans.* (1835), 95–144.

Happel, J., *Chemical Process Economics* (Wiley, New York, 1958).

Holtzman, J. M., "Convexity and the maximum principle for discrete systems," *IEEE Trans. Auto. Contr.*, **AC-11**, 1 (January, 1966).

———, and H. Halkin, "Directional convexity and the maximum principle for discrete systems," *SIAM J. Contr.*, **4**, 2 (May, 1966), 263–75.

Horn, F., *Optimalprobleme bei kontinuierlichen chemischen Prozessen*, Ph.D. dissertation, Technische Hochschule (Vienna, 1958).

———, *Chem. Engng. Sci.*, **15** (1961), 176.

———, and R. Jackson, "Discrete maximum principle," *Ind. Engng. Chem. Fund. Quart.*, **4**, 1 (February, 1965), 110–12.

———, and U. Troltenier, "Zur Berechnung von Ruhrkesselkaskaden mit Hilfe eines programmgesteuerten Rechnenautomaten," *Chem. Ing. Techn.* (W. Germany) **35** (1963), 11.

Howard, R. A., *Dynamic Programming and Markov Processes* (Technology Press, M.I.T. and Wiley, New York, 1960).

Jackson, R., "Some algebraic properties of optimization problems in complex chemical plants," *Chem. Engng. Sci.*, **9** (1964), 19–31.

Kalman, R. E., "Contributions to the theory of automatic control," *Bol. Soc. Mex. Mat.* (1960), pp. 102–19.

Katz, S., *Ann. N. Y. Acad. Sci.*, **80** (1960), 441.

———, "Best operating points for staged systems," *Ind. Engng. Chem. Fund. Quart.*, **1**, 4 (November, 1962), 226–40.

———, *J. Electron. Contr.*, **16** (1964), 189.

Kelley, H. J., "Gradient theory of optimal flight paths," *Amer. Rocket Soc. J.*, **30** (1960), 947–54.

Lasdon, L., Paper, Natl. Meeting A. I. Ch. E. (Las Vegas, Nev., September, 1964), *Case Inst. Tech. Report.*

Leitman, G. (ed.), *Optimization Techniques* (Academic Press, New York, 1962).

Leondes, C. T. (ed.), *Advances in Control Systems: Theory and Applications* (Academic Press, New York, 1966).

MacFarlane, A. G. J., "An eigenvector solution of the optimal linear regulator problem," *J. Electr. Contr.*, **14**, 1 (1963), 643–53.

Pontryagin, L. S., V. G. Boltyanski, R. V. Gamkrelidze, and E. F. Mischenko, *The Mathematical Theory of Optimal Processes* (K. N. Trirogoff, trans.) (Interscience, New York, 1962).

Rozenoer, L. I., "L. S. Pontryagin maximum principle in the theory of optimum systems—II," *Avtomatika i Telemekhanika* (USSR), **20**, 12 (1960).

Shilling, G. D., *Process Dynamics and Control* (Holt, Rinehart & Winston, New York, 1963).

Swinnerton-Dyer, H. P. F., *Proc. Lond. Math. Soc.*, **7** (1957), 568.

EXERCISES

9–1. Solve the following three-stage, two-state, two-decision problem:

$$\max s_{40}$$

subject to

$$s_{n+1,0} = s_{n0} + 5s_{n1} - 2s_{n1}d_{n1} + s_{n2} + 3s_{n2}d_{n2}$$

$$s_{n+1,1} = 7s_{n1}s_{n2} + 4s_{n1}d_{n1}$$

$$s_{n+1,2} = 10s_{n1}s_{n2} - s_{n2}d_{n2} \qquad n = 1, 2, 3$$

$$0 \leq d_{n1} \leq 1; \qquad 0 \leq d_{n2} \leq 1$$

and the initial conditions $s_{10} = 0$, $s_{11} = 1$, $s_{12} = 10$.

9-2. Use Katz's algorithm on the following problem:

$$\max s_{30}$$

subject to

$$s_{n+1,0} = s_{n0} + s_{n1} + 3s_{n1}d_{n1}$$

$$s_{n+1,1} = 10s_{n1} - s_{n1}d_{n1} \qquad n = 1, 2$$

$$0 \leq d_{n1} \leq 1$$

with $s_{10} = 0$, $s_{11} = 1$. Start with $d_{11}^{(1)} = 1$, $d_{21}^{(1)} = 0$. It should converge to the solution on the third iteration.

9-3. A frictionless milk rocket runs in an essentially horizontal trajectory from lunar station New Chicago to lunar station Nova Kiev, a distance of 100 kilometers. The thrust f is unbounded, but the adjustable rate of change of thrust can be varied instantaneously anywhere between R and $-R$, where R is a constant (kilograms force per second):

$$\left| \frac{\partial f}{\partial t} \right| \leq R$$

Find the thrust program $f\langle t \rangle$ minimizing the total flight time T. Sketch $f^*\langle t \rangle$ for $0 \leq t \leq T$, giving times and values of maximum, minimum, and zero thrust.

9-4. (Happel; Aris, Bellman, and Kalaba; Fan and Wang) An ideal gas is compressed from an initial pressure p_0 to a final pressure p_N by N isentropic compressors in series. After each adiabatic compression, the gas is cooled at constant pressure to the initial temperature. Hence the energy consumption at stage n is

$$E_n = mRT\left[\left(\frac{p_n}{p_{n-1}} \right)^{(\gamma-1)/\gamma} - 1 \right] \left(\frac{\gamma}{\gamma - 1} \right)$$

where m = number of mols of gas compressed;
$\quad R$ = gas constant;
$\quad T$ = initial temperature of gas;
$\quad \gamma = c_p/c_v$; ratio of heat capacity at constant pressure to that at constant volume;
$\quad p_n$ = pressure leaving nth stage.

Find the set of pressures p_n minimizing the total energy consumption.

9-5. The return and transition functions for a three-stage allocation problem are respectively

$$r_n = 8d_n - nd_n^2$$

$$s_{n+1} = s_n - d_n \qquad n = 1, 2, 3$$

The initial capital is

$$s_1 = 6$$

and the investment decisions are constrained by

$$0 \leq d_n \leq s_n$$

Maximize the total three stage return:
(a) analytically, using the discrete optimum principle;
(b) using Katz's algorithm, starting with $d_{11}^{(1)} = \frac{1}{2}$, $d_{21}^{(1)} = \frac{1}{3}$, $d_{31}^{(1)} = \frac{1}{2}$. Terminate the algorithm when it starts to diverge.
(c) Modify the step size in part (b) to make the procedure converge.

Choice and the Goddess 10

> *"Decide not rashly. The decision made*
> *Can never be recalled. The gods implore not,*
> *Plead not, solicit not; they only offer*
> *Choice and occasion, which once being passed*
> *Return no more. Dost thou accept the gift?"*
>
> HENRY WADSWORTH LONGFELLOW
> "Masque of Pandora," *Tower of*
> *Prometheus on Mount Caucasus*

It is now time to disengage from the details of optimization theory and try to see in perspective its relation to rational decision making. This final chapter discusses first the quantitative, then the qualitative, implications of optimization theory, summarizing the principles developed in the preceding chapters. It ends by tracing the root of Leibniz's word "optimum" back to pre-Roman times to show how much the ancients shared our contemporary enthusiasm for the fruits of optimization.

Optimization is only the last of three steps needed to reach a rational decision. The first two, description of the system and adoption of a measure of effectiveness, are absolute prerequisites for the third. Therefore in taking the time to apply optimization theory, one cannot neglect more conventional engineering and economic phases of a problem without risking ultimate failure. Optimization theory should be regarded not as an isolated specialty to be applied only by detached consultants, but rather as a valuable addition to the existing professional knowledge of the practicing economist, operations analyst, engineer, or administrator. In most industrial problems the work expended on defining the decision problem mathematically, gathering reliable data, and agreeing on objectives far exceeds the effort needed for mathematical optimization. True, a decision without optimization is as unfinished as an arch without a keystone. But optimization, like a keystone, is only a small part of the total structure and consequently cannot compensate for shoddy workmanship or faulty materials elsewhere in the project.

Surprisingly, the main justification for attempting to optimize a complicated decision, say an engineering design, may be that it motivates good modeling and accurate economic estimates. Unless a project is to be optimized, there is little advantage in describing the system carefully. But as soon as optimization enters the picture, everybody must become quantitative, and consequently more meticulous, rigorous, and scientific. A good way to rekindle an engineer's waning interest in the scientific basis of his profession is to teach him optimization theory, for getting his optimization plans to work usually forces him to examine closely the hypotheses and assumptions that go into the system description. Even after the optimization has been completed, one can use sensitivity analysis to assess in economic terms the value of reducing uncertainties in the model. This could help managers decide where to expend further research effort. Thus the precise mathematical nature of optimization theory imposes on a project a certain discipline which focuses effort into the channels most valuable economically.

Although current interest in optimization theory depends on its applicability to mathematical decision problems, its most permanent contribution may well be qualitative rather than quantitative. Often one can identify the structure of a problem without going into the numerical details, and this done, discern the character of the decision to be made.

Let us summarize the sort of qualitative conclusions to be drawn from the preceding chapters. Chapter 2 showed that optima occur, in the absence of side conditions, where the objective function is insensitive to changes in the independent variables. Equality side conditions, although hurting the value of the optimum, make the decision problem easier by reducing the number of factors to be considered. The difficulty of a problem depends on the number of degrees of freedom—the difference between the number of variables and the number of constraint equations—rather than on either quantity alone. This fact leads to the useful distinction between decision and state variables and to definition of the decision derivatives. Through the decision derivatives one can apply the theory for unconstrained problems to ones with equality side conditions. Chapter 2 teaches how to discern the true complexity, or dimensionality, of an equality constrained problem and solve it indirectly by setting decision derivatives to zero.

The next three chapters study problems constrained by algebraic inequalities, treatment of the most general nonlinear situation being confined to Chapter 3. The concept of slack variables bridges the gap between this case and the equality situation of Chapter 2. Definition of a full set of constrained derivatives—generalizations of the decision derivatives—permits either identification of an optimum or improvement of a nonoptimal situation. One must proceed by short jumps, following various sets of tight constraints and using equality constraint theory. The main principles of Chapter 3, difficult to express verbally, are known technically as the "nonnegativity and complementary slackness conditions." Convexity, when it is present, leads to important simplifications.

Chapter 4 develops striking qualitative principles for analyzing problems involving generalized polynomials. One looks for the distribution of the unknown optimum cost among the various components of a system, *before* optimizing the cost itself. In such problems a key characteristic is the number of degrees of difficulty—roughly the difference between the number of terms and the number of variables. When there are no degrees of difficulty, the distribution does not depend on such transient economic conditions as prices, but rather on invariant physical, geometric, and technological considerations. The minimum system cost can be estimated easily, even when there are many degrees of difficulty. This makes possible a check on the economic feasibility of a project before going ahead with detailed policy or design computations. Profit maximization, involving both positive and negative contributions, does not lend itself to bounding procedures, but it can still be transformed into a dual problem with linear equality constraints, often easier to solve than the highly nonlinear original problem. All the other important features of geometric programming, previously developed exclusively for cost minimization, are extended in Chapter 4 to the more general profit maximization case. Negative signs of the terms, be they in the objective function or in the constraints, no longer prevent the application of geometric programming. The key lesson of Chapter 4 is one long known to engineering estimators—designs may change, but cost ratios often remain relatively constant.

Chapter 5 focuses on the fully linear case. Linearity permits mild extrapolation and large moves, making the computation and sensitivity analysis easiest of all. At a linear optimum, all decision variables must be zero, so that complementary slackness holds automatically. This leads to fast rules for spotting a nonoptimal condition, as when an oil refiner mixes five materials to meet only four specification constraints. Sensitivity analysis shows how much the value of something depends on where it is to be used and how much is available. Scarcity can greatly enhance the value of a relatively humble commodity. The slack and decision derivatives, which measure such changes in worth quantitatively, are easy to calculate in the linear case. As more of a commodity becomes available, its imputed value decreases in accord with the economic law of diminishing returns.

The direct methods of Chapters 6 and 7 can be used not only when the objective function is complicated, but even when it is unavailable in mathematical form and must be measured physically. Chapter 6 shows how to cut down the region known to contain the optimum by elimination techniques. To develop optimization procedures which are themselves optimal, one employs decision rules of fair generality. For example, the minimax philosophy—a sort of controlled pessimism—teaches how to find the best by avoiding the worst. One also learns how much more effective it is to keep plans flexible so that decisions may be guided by the freshest information. At the same time, one should be farsighted enough to avoid last-minute "crash" programs which lose the advantage of looking at results one at a time. Chapter 6 also shows the cost in lost opportunity due to uncertainty in measurement.

Study of the climbing methods of Chapter 7 develops a feeling for multidimensional geometry and multivariable situations. Acceleration techniques stop wasteful oscillation and point the search along the crest of a ridge leading to the peak. The least information required is the slope, whereas more complicated procedures employ curvature estimates. Preparation of the problem is important; where possible one should eliminate interaction between the variables, choose symmetric scales of measurement, and select representations approximated well by low-order expansions. Like chess, direct climbing problems have three phases: opening the search by gathering information, using it to push for advantages, and finally capturing the goal by surrounding it.

The technique of breaking a structured system down in order to suboptimize the components was first demonstrated in Chapter 5 for the linear case. By a system of quantitative subsidies or penalties, the component decisions were made mutually compatible so that they would interact in a manner optimal for the entire system. This decomposition strategy is carried much further in Chapter 8, where it is applied to nonlinear and discrete systems. The distinction between state and decision variables is particularly useful here. The state variables cannot be adjusted directly because they carry information from one subsystem to another. Consequently their optimal values can be found only by exhaustive enumeration. In contrast, the decisions can be chosen freely by efficient optimization procedures. When the components are connected in series, the order of the partial optimizations is reversed from that of the information flow, which suggests that planners should start their analyses in the distant future and work backward to the present. Systems with cycles and branches should be decomposed into serial groupings in a manner made clear by graphing the information flow in a functional diagram. Partial optimization exploits structure in much the same way an experienced engineer or executive would cut a problem down into manageable pieces.

When there are more than one or two state variables per component, partial optimization of the stages in sequence becomes impractical because of the information to be stored. In such circumstances the techniques of Chapter 9 show how to adjust all decisions simultaneously to improve a given nonoptimal policy. One trades time for computer space because, although each iteration requires little storage, many iterations may be needed. The constrained derivatives play an important role here, since they guide the successive policy improvements. In applying the theory to control problems one finds that switching, or contactor, control is appropriate for linear systems, whereas quadratic problems require the slightly more sophisticated proportional (linear) action. Study of problems constrained by difference or differential equations teaches how to estimate the long-range effects of present decisions.

Thus a comprehension of optimization theory in idealized, quantitative situations gives insight into the underlying structure of rational decisions. This understanding not only guides the fact-finding phase of a study, but also helps one decide wisely even when time does not permit gathering all the information needed. For in the words of Syrus, "The opportunity is often lost by deliberating."

Although the mathematics of optimization rarely goes back further than the Age of Reason, wanting the best is an ancient desire. Leibniz based his coined word "optimum" on the Latin *optimus*, meaning "best." *Optimus* contains the name of Ops, the Sabine goddess of agricultural abundance introduced into Rome in the eighth century B.C. (Varro, Duruy). From her name come the English words "opulence" and "copious," reflecting her later status as the Roman divinity of wealth. In Imperial times her temple in the Forum contained the Roman treasury. Wealth became the symbol of power, the rich aristocracy of Rome being known as the *optimates*, a name still used at Oxford University as a title for outstanding scholars. Thus "most" came to mean "best," and Jupiter took the surname *Optimus Maximus*.

Let us not forget the sources of plenty. Earlier Latin words deriving from Ops were *opus* (work) and *opera* (works), from which the English words "operations" and "operator" are descended. The fruits of Ops are not gathered without labor.

Famines at the dawn of the Christian era caused the Emperor Augustus to intensify the worship of Ops (Le Bonniec). On August 25 the *Opiconsivia* was celebrated when the grain was harvested and stored (Laing), and the granaries were opened on December 17 at the festival of *Opalia* (Howe and Harper). Optimization theorists should find it fitting that Ops was the wife of Saturn, old Father Time, and that she was honored with him when the *Saturnalia* closed the old year. About the *Saturnalia* Keightley writes:

> The utmost liberty prevailed at that time; all was mirth and festivity; friends made presents to one another; schools were closed; the senate did not sit; no war was proclaimed; no criminal executed; slaves were

permitted to jest with their masters, and were even waited on at table by them.

Figure 10-1. Ops (Cybele), Goddess of abundance.

If this sounds familiar, it is because many of these pleasant customs grace contemporary celebrations of the Christmas holidays.

Lacking a picture of the Sabine Ops herself, our opus concludes with one of Cybele, a Middle Eastern goddess later identified in Rome with Ops and the Greek Rhea. Bryant shows her on a coin from Damascus, holding the *cornucopia* (horn of plenty) and the scales of justice. Where there is wealth, there is measurement and decision.

May Ops, and optimization, bring you the best of everything in the best of all possible worlds!

BIBLIOGRAPHY

Bryant, Jacob, *A New System, or an Analysis of Ancient Mythology II* (London, 1775), plate VIII.

Duruy, V., *History of Rome and of the Roman People*, I, W. J. Clarke, trans. (Estes and Lauriat, 1894) pp. 145–46.

Grimal, P., *Dictionnaire de la Mythologie Greque et Romaine* (Presses Universitaires de France, Paris, 1963), p. 329.

Howe, G., and G. A. Harper, *A Handbook of Classical Mythology* (Crofts, New York, 1931), p. 194.

Keightley, T., *The Mythology of Ancient Greece and Italy* (Bell, London, 1877), 4th ed., p. 466.

Laing, G. J., *Survivals of Roman Religion* (Longmans, Green, New York, 1931), p. 53.

Le Bonniec, H., *Le culte de Cérés à Rome* (C. Klincksieck, Paris, 1958), pp. 194, 467.

Longfellow, Henry Wadsworth, "Masque of Pandora," *Tower of Prometheus on Mount Caucasus.*

Syrus, *Maxims*, cited in *Hoyt's Quotations.*

Varro, Marcus Terentius (116–27 B.C.), *De Lingua Latina* (Kent, London, 1938), pp. 64, 74.

Index